QUANTITATIVE APTITUDE
For Competitive Examinations
(Fully Solved)

For

- ¤ Bank P.O.
- ¤ Insurance (A.A.O.) – L.I.C., G.I.C.
- ¤ Excise & Income Tax (Inspectors)
- ¤ M.B.A., Hotel Management
- ¤ C.B.I. (Sub-Inspectors); C.D.S.
- ¤ Assistant Grade; Teachers' Examination
- ¤ U.D.C. & Other competitive examinations

R. S. AGGARWAL

1997

S. CHAND & COMPANY LTD.
RAM NAGAR NEW DELHI - 110 055

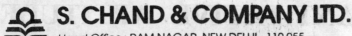

S. CHAND & COMPANY LTD.

Head Office : RAM NAGAR, NEW DELHI - 110 055
Phones : 7772080-81-82; Fax : 91-11-7777446

Branches :

No. 6, Ahuja Chambers, 1st Cross, Kumara Krupa Road, **Bangalore**-560 001. Ph : 2268048
285/J, Bipin Bihari Ganguli Street, **Calcutta**-700 012. Ph : 267459, 273914
S.C.O. 6, 7 & 8 Sector-9 D, **Chandigarh**-160 017. Ph : 43678, 692680
152, Anna Salai, **Chennai**-600 002. Ph : 8522026
Pan Bazar, **Guwahati**-781 001. Ph : 522155
Sultan Bazar, **Hyderabad**-500 195. Ph : 4651135
613-7, M.G. Road, Ernakulam, **Kochi**-682 035. Ph : 381740
Mahabeer Market, 25 Gwynne Road, **Lucknow**-226 001. Ph : 226801
Blackie House, 103/5, Walchand Hirachand Marg , Opp. G.P.O.,
Mumbai-400 001. Ph : 2690881, 2610885
3, Gandhi Sagar East, **Nagpur**-440 002. Ph : 723901
104, Citicentre Ashok, Govind Mitra Road, **Patna**-800 004. Ph : 651366

First Edition 1989
Sixth Revised Edition 1995, Reprints 1996
Reprint with corrections 1996
Reprint 1997

ISBN : 81-219-0632-6

Published by S. Chand & Company Ltd. Ram Nagar, New Delhi-110 055,
and Printed at Rajendra Ravindra Printers (Pvt.) Ltd.,
Ram Nagar, New Delhi-110055.

Preface

The tremendous response to the fifth edition of the book has encouraged me to bring out the sixth thoroughly revised edition.

This book on *Quantitative Aptitude* in its revised form is really an asset to those who plan to appear in a competitive examination for an executive post.

This book caters to the needs of candidates appearing for *Bank P.O.; Insurance A.A.O.; Assistant Grade; Excise & Income Tax Inspectors; C.B.I. Sub-Inspectors; Teachers' Exam.; C.D.S.; Railways; Hotel Management; M.B.A* and all other competitive examinations containing this as syllabus.

Most of the books in the market carry a very small number of objective type questions with their answers. But, how to get these answers is not given therein. More-over, how to solve a question is not significant in such examinations.

The most important aspect is to solve a question in a fraction of a minute, using short cut method.

This book contains a huge accumulation of objective type questions with their solutions, by short cut methods.

Latest questions asked in various examinations have been given on memory basis.

It is very much hoped that the subject matter will create a confidence among the candidates and the book will help them like an ideal teacher.

I convey my gratitude to Shri R. K. Gupta, Director and Shri T. N. Goel, Manager S. Chand & Co. Ltd. Delhi for taking all pains in the completion of this project.

For good Laser Type Setting I am thankful to Mr. Mukesh Maheshwari, Director of Brilliant Computers, Meerut.

Constructive suggestions for improvement of the book will be highly appreciated.

R. S. Aggarwal

Veenalaya
F–80, Shastri Nagar
Meerut - 250004

Contents

Contents

1. Numbers

GENERAL CONCEPTS

Place Value or Local Value Of a Digit in a Numeral :

In the numeral 68974532, we have :

Place value of 2 is 2 units = 2 ;

Place value of 3 is 3 tens = 30 ;

Place value of 5 is 5 hundreds = 500 ;

Place value of 4 is 4 thousands = 4000 and so on.

Face Value : *The face value of a digit in a numeral is the value of the digit itself at whatever place it may be.*

In the above numeral, the face value of 2 is 2; the face value of 3 is 3 and so on.

Natural Numbers : *Counting numbers 1, 2, 3, 4, ... are known as natural numbers.*

Unit's Digit in a Product :

Ex. 1 *Find the unit's digit in the product* $(256 \times 27 \times 159 \times 182)$.

Sol. Product of unit's digits in given numbers $= (6 \times 7 \times 9 \times 2) = 756$.

∴ Unit digit in the given product is 6.

Ex. 2. *Find the unit's digit in the product* $\left(3^{67} \times 6^{39} \times 7^{53}\right)$.

Sol. Clearly, unit digit in 3^4 is 1.

∴ Unit digit in 3^{64} is 1.

∴ **Unit digit in 3^{67} is 7.**   [∵ *Unit digit in* $1 \times 3 \times 3 \times 3$ *is* 7]

Clearly, unit digit in every power of 6 is 6.

∴ **Unit digit in 6^{39} is 6.**

Clearly, unit digit in 7^4 is 1.

∴ Unit digit in 7^{52} is 1.

∴ **Unit digit in 7^{53} is 7.**   [∵ *Unit digit in* 1×7 *is* 7]

∴ Unit digit in given product = Unit digit in $(7 \times 6 \times 7) = 4$.

Even Numbers : *A number divisible by 2 is called an even number.*
e.g. 2, 4, 6, 8, 10 etc.

Odd Numbers : *A number not divisible by 2 is called an odd number.*
e.g. 1, 3, 5, 7, 9, 11, 13, 15, 17 etc.

Prime Numbers : *Every number larger than 1 having exactly two factors is called a prime number.*

Ex. 3. *Prime numbers less than 100 are :*

2, 3, 5, 7, 11, 13, 17, 19, 23, 29, 31, 37, 41, 43, 47, 53, 59, 61, 67, 71, 73, 79, 83, 89, 97.

Prime Numbers Larger Than 100 :

Test : Let p be a given number. Find a whole number nearly greater than the square root of p.

Let $k > \sqrt{p}$.

Test whether p is divisible by any prime number less than k. If yes, then p is not prime. Otherwise, p is prime.

Ex. 4. *Which of the following are prime numbers ?*

            (i) 191   **(ii) 241**   **(iii) 337**   **(iv) 391**

Sol. (i) Clearly, $14 > \sqrt{191}$.

      Prime numbers less than 14 are 2, 3, 5, 7, 11, 13.

      191 is not divisible by any of them.

      So, 191 is a prime number.

    (ii) Clearly, $16 > \sqrt{241}$.

      Prime numbers less than 16 are 2, 3, 5, 7, 11, 13.

      241 is not divisible by any of them.

      ∴ 241 is a prime number.

    (iii) Clearly, $19 > \sqrt{337}$.

      Prime numbers less than 19 are 2, 3, 5, 7, 11, 13, 17.

      337 is not divisible by any of them.

      ∴ 337 is a prime number.

    (iv) Clearly, $20 > \sqrt{391}$.

      Prime numbers less than 20 are 2, 3, 5, 7, 11, 13, 17, 19.

      We find that 391 is divisible by 17.

      ∴ 391 is not prime.

TESTS OF DIVISIBILITY :

Divisibility By 2 : *A number is divisible by 2, if its unit digit is any of 0, 2, 4, 6, 8.*

Divisibility By 3 : *A number is divisible by 3, if the sum of its digits is divisible by 3.*

Ex. 5. Which of the following numbers is not divisible by 2 ?

        3567516, 9130525, 7870832 & 1371594

Sol. Clearly, the unit's digit of 9130525 is 5, which is not divisible by 2.

    So, 9130525 is not divisible by 2.

    Each one of the other numbers has a unit digit divisible by 2.

    So, each one other than 9130525 is divisible by 2.

Ex. 6. *Which of the following numbers is divisible by 3 ?*

      (i) 541326   **(ii) 5967013**

Sol. (i) Sum of digits in 541326 is 21, which is divisible by 3.

        So, 541326 is divisible by 3.

    (ii) Sum of digits in 5967013 is 31, which is not divisible by 3.

        Hence, 5967013 is not divisible by 3.

Divisibility By 9 : *A number is divisible by 9, if the sum of its digits is divisible by 9.*

Ex. 7. *Which of the following numbers is divisible by 9 ?*
> (*i*) **19725462**   (*ii*) **36870521**

Sol. (*i*) Sum of digits in 19725462 is 36, which is divisible by 9.
> So, the given number is divisible by 9.

(*ii*) Sum of digits in 36870521 is 32, which is not divisible by 9.
> So, the given number is not divisible by 9.

Divisibility By 4 : *A number is divisible by 4, if the number formed by the last two digits is divisible by 4.*

Ex. 8. *Which of the following numbers is divisible by 4 ?*
> (*i*) **67920594**   (*ii*) **618703572**

Sol. (*i*) The number formed by the last 2 digits in the given number is 94, which is not divisible by 4.
> $\therefore$ 67920594 is not divisible by 4.

(*ii*) The number formed by the last 2 digits in the given number is 72, which is divisible by 4.
> $\therefore$ 618703572 is divisible by 4.

Divisibility By 8 : *A number is divisible by 8, if the number formed by the last 3 digits of the given number is divisible by 8.*

Ex. 9. *Which of the following numbers is divisible by 8 ?*
> (*i*) **98016542**   (*ii*) **106598304**

Sol. (*i*) The number formed by the last 3 digits of the given number is 542, which is not divisible by 8.
> $\therefore$ 98016542 is not divisible by 8.

(*ii*) The number formed by the last 3 digits of the given number is 304, which is divisible by 8.
> $\therefore$ 106598304 is divisible by 8.

Divisibility By 11 : *A number is divisible by 11, if the difference of the sum of its digits at odd places and the sum of its digits at even places, is either 0 or a number divisible by 11.*

Ex. 10. *Show that 4832718 is divisible by 11.*

Sol. (Sum of digits at odd places) $-$ (Sum of digits at even places)
= [(8 + 7 + 3 + 4) $-$ (1 + 2 + 8)] = 11, which is divisible by 11.
$\therefore$ 4832718 is divisible by 11.

Co–Prime : *Two numbers are said to be co–prime, if their H.C.F. is 1. e.g. (2, 3), (4, 5), (7, 9), (8, 11) etc. are co primes.*

An Important Note : *A number is divisible by ab only when that number is divisible by each one of a and b, where a and b are co–prime.*

Ex. 11. *If a number is divisible by both 4 and 6, is it always divisible by 24 ? Why ? Give an example.*

Sol. No, since 6 and 4 are not co–prime.
36 is divisible by 6 as well as 4 but it is not divisible by 24.

Ex. 12. *Without actual division show that 52563744 is divisible by 24.*

Sol. 24 = 3 × 8, where 3 and 8 are co–prime.

The sum of the digits in given number is 36, which is divisible by 3.
So, the given number is divisible by 3.
The number formed by the last 3-digits of the given number is 744, which is divisible by 8.
So, the given number is divisible by 8.
Thus, the given number is divisible by both 3 and 8, where 3 and 8 are co–prime.
So, it is divisible by 3×8, *i.e.* 24.

FORMULAE :

$(i)\ (a+b)^2 = a^2 + b^2 + 2ab$ $\qquad (ii)\ (a-b)^2 = a^2 + b^2 - 2ab$

$(iii)\ (a+b)^2 - (a-b)^2 = 4ab$ $\qquad (iv)\ (a+b)^2 + (a-b)^2 = 2(a^2 + b^2)$

$(v)\ (a^2 - b^2) = (a+b)(a-b)$ $\qquad (vi)\ (a^3 + b^3) = (a+b)(a^2 - ab + b^2)$

$(vii)\ (a^3 - b^3) = (a-b)(a^2 + ab + b^2)$

$(viii)\ a\ .\ (b+c) = ab + ac\ \&\ a\ .\ (b-c) = ab - ac$ **(Distributive Laws)**

Ex. 13. *Multiply 5793405 by 99999 by short cut method.*

Sol. $5793405 \times 99999 = 5793405 \times (100000 - 1)$
$$= (579340500000 - 5793405)$$
$$= 579334706595.$$

Ex. 14. *Evaluate :*

$(i)\ \mathbf{986 \times 137 + 986 \times 863}$ $\qquad (ii)\ \mathbf{983 \times 207 - 983 \times 107}$

Sol. $(i)\ 986 \times 137 + 986 \times 863 = 986\,(137 + 863)$
$$= 986 \times 1000 = 986000\ .$$

$(ii)\ 983 \times 207 - 983 \times 107 = 983\,(207 - 107)$
$$= 983 \times 100 = 98300.$$

Ex. 15. *Evaluate :*

$$(i)\ \frac{527 \times 527 \times 527 + 183 \times 183 \times 183}{527 \times 527 - 527 \times 183 + 183 \times 183}$$

$$(ii)\ \frac{458 \times 458 \times 458 - 239 \times 239 \times 239}{458 \times 458 + 458 \times 239 + 239 \times 239}$$

$$(iii)\ \frac{(614 + 168)^2 - (614 - 168)^2}{614 \times 168}$$

$$(iv)\ \frac{(832 + 278)^2 + (832 - 278)^2}{832 \times 832 + 278 \times 278}$$

Sol. (i) Given Expression $= \dfrac{(527)^3 + (183)^3}{(527)^2 - 527 \times 183 + (183)^2}$

$$= \frac{a^3 + b^3}{a^2 - ab + b^2} = (a+b) = (527 + 183) = 710.$$

(ii) Given Expression $= \dfrac{(458)^3 - (239)^3}{(458)^2 + 458 \times 239 + (239)^2}$

$$= \frac{a^3 - b^3}{a^2 + ab + b^2} = (a - b) = (458 - 239) = 219.$$

(*iii*) Given Expression $= \dfrac{(a+b)^2 - (a-b)^2}{ab} = \dfrac{4ab}{4} = 4.$

(*iv*) Given Expression $= \dfrac{(a+b)^2 + (a-b)^2}{(a^2 + b^2)} = \dfrac{2(a^2 + b^2)}{(a^2 + b^2)} = 2.$

Ex. 16. *Simplify :*

(*i*) **1605 × 1605 = ?**   (*ii*) **1398 × 1398 = ?**

Sol. (*i*) $1605 \times 1605 = (1605)^2$

$$= (1600 + 5)^2$$
$$= (1600)^2 + 5^2 + 2 \times 1600 \times 5$$
$$= 2560000 + 25 + 16000 = 2576025.$$

(*ii*) $1398 \times 1398 = (1398)^2$

$$= (1400 - 2)^2$$
$$= (1400)^2 + 2^2 - 2 \times 1400 \times 2$$
$$= 1960000 + 4 - 5600 = 1954404.$$

Ex. 17. *Simplify :*

(*i*) **896 × 896 − 204 × 204 = ?**

(*ii*) **57 × 57 + 43 × 43 + 2 × 57 × 43 = ?**

(*iii*) **81 × 81 + 68 × 68 − 2 × 81 × 68 = ?**

Sol. (*i*) Given Exp. $= (896)^2 - (204)^2$

$$= (896 + 204)(896 - 204)$$
$$= 1100 \times 692 = 761200.$$

(*ii*) Given Exp. $= (57)^2 + (43)^2 + 2 \times 57 \times 43$

$$= a^2 + b^2 + 2ab, \text{ where } a = 57, b = 43$$
$$= (a + b)^2 = (57 + 43)^2 = (100)^2$$
$$= 10000.$$

(*iii*) Given Exp. $= (81)^2 + (68)^2 - 2 \times 81 \times 68$

$$= a^2 + b^2 - 2ab, \text{ where } a = 81 \text{ \& } b = 68$$
$$= (a - b)^2 = (81 - 68)^2 = (13)^2 = 169.$$

Ex. 18. *Evaluate :* $(313 \times 313 + 287 \times 287).$

Sol. $(a^2 + b^2) = \dfrac{1}{2}[(a + b)^2 + (a - b)^2]$

$$\therefore (313)^2 + (287)^2 = \frac{1}{2}[(313 + 287)^2 + (313 - 287)^2]$$

$$= \frac{1}{2}[(600)^2 + (26)^2]$$

$$= \frac{1}{2}(360000 + 676) = 180338.$$

RESULTS ON DIVISION

An important Result : *If we divide a given number by another number, then :*

Dividend = (Divisor × Quotient) + Remainder

Ex. 19. *On dividing 15968 by a certain number, the quotient is 89 and the remainder is 37. Find the divisor.*

Sol. $\text{Divisor} = \dfrac{(\text{Dividend} - \text{Remainder})}{\text{Quotient}} = \dfrac{(15968 - 37)}{89} = 179.$

Ex. 20. *What least number must be subtracted from 2000 to get a number exactly divisible by 17 ?*

Sol. On dividing 2000 by 17, we get 11 as remainder.

∴ Required number to be subtracted = 11.

Ex. 21. *What least number must be added to 3000 to obtain a number exactly divisible by 19 ?*

Sol. On dividing 3000 by 19, we get 17 as remainder.

∴ Number to be added = (19 − 17) = 2.

Ex. 22. *Find the number which is nearest to 3105 and exactly divisible by 21.*

Sol. On dividing 3105 by 21, we get 18 as remainder.

∴ Number to be added to 3105 is (21 − 18) = 3.

∴ 3108 is the required number.

Ex. 23. *A number when divided by 342 gives a remainder 47. When the same number is divided by 19, what would be the remainder ?*

Sol. On dividing the given number by 342, let k be the quotient and 47 as remainder.

Then, number = 342k + 47

$$= (19 \times 18k + 19 \times 2 + 9) = 19(18k + 2) + 9$$

∴ The given number when divided by 19, gives (18k + 2) as quotient and 9 as remainder.

Ex. 24. (*i*) **? ÷ 147 = 29**   (*ii*) **? × 144 = 12528**

Sol. (*i*) Let $\dfrac{x}{147} = 29$. Then, $x = (147 \times 29) = 4263.$

∴ Missing number is 4263.

(*ii*) Let $x \times 144 = 12528$. Then, $x = \dfrac{12528}{144} = 87.$

PROGRESSION

Progression : *A succession of numbers formed and arranged in a definite order according to certain definite rule, is called a progression.*

Arithmetic Progression (A.P.) : *If each term of a progression differs from its preceding term by a constant, then such a progression is called an arithmetical progression. This constant difference is called the common difference of the A.P.*

An A.P. with first term a and common difference d is given by $a, (a + d), (a + 2d), (a + 3d)$, ...

The **nth term of this A.P. is given by** $T_n = a + (n - 1)\, d$.

The sum of n terms of this A.P.

$$S_n = \frac{n}{2} [\, 2a + (n - 1)\, d\,] = \frac{n}{2} \text{ (first term + last term)}.$$

Ex. 25. *How many numbers between 11 and 90 are divisible by 7?*

Sol. The required numbers are 14, 21, 28, 35, ..., 77, 84.

This is an A.P. with $a = 14$ and $d = (21 - 14) = 7$.

Let it contain n terms.

Then, $T_n = 84 \Rightarrow a + (n - 1)\, d = 84$

$$\Rightarrow 14 + (n - 1) \times 7 = 84 \ \text{ or } \ n = 11 .$$

$\therefore$ Required number of terms = 11 .

Ex. 26. *Find the sum of all odd numbers upto 100.*

Sol. The given numbers are 1, 3, 5, 7, ..., 99.

This is an A.P. with $a = 1$ and $d = 2$.

Let it contain n terms. Then,

$$1 + (n - 1) \times 2 = 99 \ \text{ or } \ n = 50 .$$

$\therefore$ Required sum $= \dfrac{n}{2}$ (first term + last term)

$$= \frac{50}{2} \times (1 + 99) = 2500 .$$

Ex. 27. *Find the sum of all 2 digit numbers divisible by 3.*

Sol. All 2 digit numbers divisible by 3 are :

12, 15, 18, 21, ..., 99.

This is an A.P. with $a = 12$ and $d = 3$.

Let it contain n terms. Then,

$$12 + (n - 1) \times 3 = 99 \ \text{ or } \ n = 30 .$$

$\therefore$ Required sum $= \dfrac{30}{2} \times (12 + 99) = 1665 .$

Some Important Results

(i) $(1 + 2 + 3 + ... + n) = \dfrac{n\,(n + 1)}{2}$.

(ii) $(1^2 + 2^2 + 3^2 + ... + n^2) = \dfrac{n\,(n + 1)\,(2n + 1)}{6}$.

(iii) $(1^3 + 2^3 + 3^3 + ... + n^3) = \dfrac{n^2\,(n + 1)^2}{4}$.

Geometrical Progression (G.P.) : *A progression of numbers in which every term bears a constant ratio with its preceding term, is called a geometrical progression.*

The constant ratio is called the common ratio of the G.P.

A G.P. with first term a and common ratio r is :

$$a, ar, ar^2, ar^3, ...$$

In this G.P., $T_n = a\, r^{n-1}$.

Sum of the n terms, $S_n = \dfrac{a\,(1 - r^n)}{(1 - r)}$.

Ex. 28. *How many terms are there in 2, 4, 8, 16, ..., 1024 ?*

Sol. Clearly 2, 4, 8, 16, ..., 1024 form a G.P. with $a = 2$ and $r = \dfrac{4}{2} = 2$.

Let the number of terms be n. Then,

$2 \times 2^{n-1} = 1024$ or $2^{n-1} = 512 = 2^9$.

$\therefore$ $n - 1 = 9$ or $n = 10$.

Ex. 29. $2 + 2^2 + 2^3 + ... + 2^8 = ?$

Sol. Given series is a G.P. with $a = 2$, $r = 2$ & $n = 8$.

$\therefore$ Sum $= \dfrac{a\,(r^n - 1)}{(r - 1)} = \dfrac{2 \times (2^8 - 1)}{(2 - 1)} = (2 \times 255) = 510$.

EXERCISE 1

Mark ($\sqrt{}$) against the correct answer :

1. The difference between the local value and the face value of 7 in the numeral 657903 is :
    (a) 0   (b) 7896   (c) 6993   (d) 903

2. The difference between the place values of 7 in the numeral 574873 is :   **(Central Excise & I.Tax. 1992)**
    (a) 69930   (b) 59930   (c) 96390   (d) 69305

3. $6581 - (38 + 286 + 1593 + 3074) = (...?...)$
    (a) 1391   (b) 1590   (c) 2070   (d) 1940

4. $(3500731) - (...?...) = 1735618$
    (a) 1865113   (b) 1775123   (c) 1765113   (d) 1765123

5. $(...?...) - (1936248) = (1635773)$
    (a) 3572021   (b) 3561231   (c) 3562121   (d) 3536021

6. $35999 - 17102 - 8799 = (...?...)$
    (a) 27696   (b) 10098   (c) 20318   (d) None of these

7. $12846 \times 593 + 12846 \times 407 = (...?...)$
    (a) 24064000   (b) 12846000   (c) 24038606   (d) 14203706

8. $987 \times 999 = (...?...)$
    (a) 897013   (b) 988013   (c) 986013   (d) 967013

9. $469157 \times 9999 = (...?...)$
    (*a*) 4586970843   (*b*) 4686970743 (*c*) 4691100843   (*d*) 584649125

10. $935421 \times 625 = (...?...)$
    (*a*) 575648125   (*b*) 584638125 (*c*) 585628125 (*d*) 584649125

11. $(387 \times 387 + 114 \times 114 + 2 \times 387 \times 114) = (...?...)$
    (*a*) 250001   (*b*) 251001   (*c*) 260110   (*d*) 261001

12. $1014 \times 986 = (...?...)$
    (*a*) 998904   (*b*) 999804   (*c*) 998814   (*d*) 998804

13. $1299 \times 1299 = (...?...)$
    (*a*) 1585301   (*b*) 1684701   (*c*) 1685401   (*d*) 1687401

14. $106 \times 106 + 94 \times 94 = (...?...)$
    (*a*) 21032   (*b*) 20032   (*c*) 23032   (*d*) 20072

15. $(475 + 425)^2 - 4 \times 475 \times 425$ is equal to :
    (*a*) 3600   (*b*) 3500   (*c*) 2500   (*d*) 3160

16. $5358 \times 51 = (...?...)$
    (*a*) 273358   (*b*) 273258   (*c*) 273348   (*d*) 273268

17. $1307 \times 1307 = (...?...)$
    (*a*) 1601249   (*b*) 1607249   (*c*) 1701249   (*d*) 1708249

18 The unit's digit in the product $(274 \times 318 \times 577 \times 313)$ is :
    (*a*) 2   (*b*) 3   (*c*) 4   (*d*) 5
                                                    (U.D.C. 1993)

19. The unit's digit in the product $(3127)^{173}$ is :   **(Assistant Grade 1994)**
    (*a*) 1   (*b*) 3   (*c*) 7   (*d*) 9

20. If the unit digit in the product $(459 \times 46 \times 28 * \times 484)$ is 2, the digit in
    place of * is :   **(Hotel Management 1993)**
    (*a*) 3   (*b*) 5   (*c*) 7   (*d*) None

21. The unit's digit in the product $(7^{71} \times 6^{59} \times 3^{65})$ is :
    (*a*) 6   (*b*) 4   (*c*) 1   (*d*) 2

22. The unit's digit in the product $(2467)^{153} \times (341)^{72}$ is :   **(C.B.I. 1993)**
    (*a*) 1   (*b*) 3   (*c*) 7   (*d*) 9

23. The digit in the unit place of the number represented by $(7^{95} - 3^{58})$ is :
    (*a*) 7   (*b*) 0   (*c*) 6   (*d*) 4
                                   (Central Excise & I. Tax 1991)

24. The total number of prime factors in the expression
    $(4)^{11} \times (7)^5 \times (11)^2$ is :   **(C.B.I. 1993)**
    (*a*) 7   (*b*) 18   (*c*) 29   (*d*) 110

25. The least prime number is :
    (*a*) 0   (*b*) 1   (*c*) 2   (*d*) 3

26. What is the total number of prime numbers less than 70 ?
    (*a*) 17   (*b*) 18   (*c*) 19   (*d*) 20

27. The sum of all prime numbers between 60 and 90 is :

    (*a*) 373   (*b*) 460   (*c*) 523   (*d*) 610

28. Which one of the following is a prime number ?

    (*a*) 161   (*b*) 221   (*c*) 373   (*d*) 437

29. Which one of the following numbers is not a square of any natural number ?

    (*a*) 17956   (*b*) 18225   (*c*) 53361   (*d*) 63592

30. If $\dfrac{a}{b} = \dfrac{4}{3}$, then $\dfrac{3a + 2b}{3a - 2b} = ?$

                                                    (C.B.I. 1990)

    (*a*) – 1   (*b*) 3   (*c*) 5   (*d*) 6

31. If $\dfrac{x}{y} = \dfrac{3}{5}$, then $\left(\dfrac{6}{7} - \dfrac{2y - x}{2y + x}\right)$ is equal to :

    (*a*) $\dfrac{9}{35}$ (*b*) $\dfrac{11}{28}$ (*c*) $\dfrac{29}{91}$ (*d*) $\dfrac{18}{13}$

32. If $a^3 b = abc = 180$ and a, b, c are positive integers, then the value of c is :   **(Hotel Management 1993)**

    (*a*) 110   (*b*) 25   (*c*) 15   (*d*) None

33. $\left(1 - \dfrac{1}{3}\right)\left(1 - \dfrac{1}{4}\right)\left(1 - \dfrac{1}{5}\right) \cdots \left(1 - \dfrac{1}{n}\right)$ is equal to :

                                                           (I. Tax 1988)

    (*a*) $\dfrac{1}{n}$ (*b*) $\dfrac{2}{n}$ (*c*) $\dfrac{2}{n(n+1)}$ (*d*) $\dfrac{2(n-1)}{n}$

34. When simplified, the product   **(C.B.I. 1990)**

$\left(2 - \dfrac{1}{3}\right)\left(2 - \dfrac{3}{5}\right)\left(2 - \dfrac{5}{7}\right) \cdots \left(2 - \dfrac{997}{999}\right)$ is equal to :

    (*a*) $\dfrac{5}{999}$ (*b*) $\dfrac{1001}{999}$ (*c*) $\dfrac{1001}{3}$ (*d*) None of these

35. $(256)^{.18} \times (256)^{.07}$ is equal to :

    (*a*) 4   (*b*) 6   (*c*) 8   (*d*) 64

36. $(5)^{.25} \times (125)^{.25}$ is equal to :

    (*a*) $\sqrt{5}$ (*b*) 5   (*c*) $5\sqrt{5}$ (*d*) 25

37. Given that $(1^2 + 2^2 + 3^2 + \ldots + 10^2) = 385$, then the value of $(2^2 + 4^2 + 6^2 + \ldots + 20^2)$ is equal to :   **(Central Excise & I. Tax 1992)**

    (*a*) 770   (*b*) 1540   (*c*) 1155   (*d*) $(385)^2$

38. If $(64)^2 - (36)^2 = 20\,z$, the value of z is :   **(Hotel Management 1993)**

    (*a*) 70   (*b*) 180   (*c*) 120   (*d*) None

39. If $x * y = (x + 2)^2 \cdot (y - 2)$, then the value of $(7 * 5)$ is :

    (*a*) 175   (*b*) 205   (*c*) 213   (*d*) 243

                                                   (Assistant Grade 1993)

40. If $2^{x-1} + 2^{x+1} = 320$, then the value of x is :

(a) 4   (b) 5   (c) 6   (d) 7

41. The sum of first 45 natural numbers is :   **(Teacher's Exam. 1991)**
    (a) 2070   (b) 1035   (c) 1280   (d) 2140

42. $(51 + 52 + 53 + ... + 100)$ is equal to :
    (a) 2525   (b) 2975   (c) 3225   (d) 3775

43. The remainder obtained when 2^{31} is divided by 5, is :
    (a) 2   (b) 3   (c) 4   (d) 1

44. What least value must be given to * so that the number 451 * 603 is exactly divisible by 9 ?
    (a) 2   (b) 5   (c) 8   (d) 7

45. What least value must be assigned to * so that the number 63576*2 is divisible by 8 ?
    (a) 1   (b) 2   (c) 3   (d) 4

46. What least value must be assigned to * so that 86325*6 is divisible by 11 ?
    (a) 1   (b) 2   (c) 3   (d) 5

47. Which of the following numbers is exactly divisible by 99 ?
    (a) 114345   (b) 135792   (c) 3572404   (d) 913464

48. If the number 42573 * is completely divisible by 72, then which of the following number should replace the asterisk ? **(Assistant Grade 1994)**
    (a) 4   (b) 5   (c) 6   (d) 7

49. 5 * 2 is a three digit number with * as a missing digit. If the number is divisible by 6, the missing digit is :   **(C.B.I. 1993)**
    (a) 3   (b) 6   (c) 7   (d) 2

50. There is one number which is formed by writing one digit 6 times (e.g. 111111, 444444 etc.). Such number is always divisible by :
    (a) 7   (b) 11   (c) 13   (d) All of these
                                                        (Assistant Grade 1994)

51. Which of the following numbers should be added to 11158 to make it exactly divisible by 77 ?   **(Bank P.O. 1993)**
    (a) 9   (b) 8   (c) 7   (d) 5

52. The number nearest to 99547 which is exactly divisible by 687 is :
    (a) 100166   (b) 98928   (c) 99479   (d) 99615
                                                        (Teacher's Exam. 1991)

53. What least number must be subtracted from 13294 so that the remainder is exactly divisible by 97 ?
    (a) 3   (b) 5   (c) 1   (d) 4

54. What largest number of five digits is divisible by 99 ?
    (a) 99999   (b) 99981   (c) 99909   (d) 99990

55. What smallest number of six digits is divisible by 111 ?
    (a) 111111   (b) 110011   (c) 100011   (d) None of these

56. What number should replace both the asterisks in $\left(\dfrac{*}{21} \times \dfrac{*}{181}\right) = 1$?

    (*a*) 21   (*b*) 63   (*c*) 147   (*d*) 3969

                                                  (C.B.I. 1991)

57. When a certain number is multiplied by 13, the product consists entirely of fives. The smallest such number is :

    (*a*) 41625   (*b*) 42515   (*c*) 42735   (*d*) 42135

58. A four digit number divisible by 7 becomes divisible by 3, when 10 is added to it. The largest such number is :   **(Central Excise & I. Tax 1992)**

    (*a*) 9987   (*b*) 9989   (*c*) 9996   (*d*) 9947

59. Which of the following numbers is exactly divisible by all prime numbers between 1 and 17 ?

    (*a*) 515513   (*b*) 440440   (*c*) 345345   (*d*) 510510

60. A number when divided by 119 leaves 19 as remainder. If the same number is divided by 17, the remainder obtained is :

    (*a*) 10   (*b*) 7   (*c*) 3   (*d*) 2

                                      (Assistant Grade 1993)

61. How many numbers between 200 and 600 are divisible by 4, 5 and 6 ?   **(Assistant Grade 1993)**

    (*a*) 5   (*b*) 6   (*c*) 7   (*d*) 8

62. How many three digit numbers are divisible by 6 in all ?

    (*a*) 149   (*b*) 150   (*c*) 151   (*d*) 166

                                      (Assistant Grade 1993)

63. The largest natural number which exactly divides the product of any four consecutive natural numbers is :   **(Assistant Grade 1993)**

    (*a*) 6   (*b*) 12   (*c*) 24   (*d*) 120

64. The largest natural number by which the product of three consecutive even natural numbers is always divisible, is :   **(Central Excise & I. Tax 1989)**

    (*a*) 16   (*b*) 24   (*c*) 48   (*d*) 96

65. If x and y are positive integers such that $(3x + 7y)$ is a multiple of 11, then which of the following will also be divisible by 11 ?

    (*a*) $4x + 6y$ (*b*) $x + y + 4$ (*c*) $9x + 4y$ (*d*) $4x - 9y$

                                      (C.B.I. 1993)

66. In a division sum, the divisor is 10 times the quotient and 5 times the remainder. If the remainder is 46, the dividend is :   **(C.B.I. 1993)**

    (*a*) 4236   (*b*) 4306   (*c*) 4336   (*d*) 5336

67. The number $(10^n - 1)$ is divisible by 11 for :

    (*a*) all values of n (*b*) odd values of n

    (*c*) even values of n (*d*) n = multiples of 11

68. If $\sqrt{3^n} = 81$, then $n = ?$ **(Assistant Grade 1990)**

    (*a*) 2   (*b*) 4   (*c*) 6   (*d*) 8

69. $\dfrac{392}{\sqrt{?}} = 28$

    (a) 144   (b) 196   (c) 24   (d) 48

70. Which of the following can be a product of two 3-digit numbers **3 and ** 8 ?

    (a) 1010024   (b) 991014   (c) 9124   (d) None

71. If $(1 \times 2 \times 3 \times 4 \times \ldots \times n) = n\,!$, then $(14\,! - 13\,! - 12\,!)$ is equal to :

    (a) $14 \times 12 \times (12\,!)$ (b) $14 \times 12 \times (13\,!)$

    (c) $14 \times 13 \times (13\,!)$ (d) $13 \times 12 \times (12\,!)$

                                    (Central Excise & I. Tax 1992)

72. How many of the following numbers are divisible by 132 ?

    264, 396, 462, 792, 968, 2178, 5184, 6336. **(Hotel Management 1993)**

    (a) 4   (b) 5   (c) 6   (d) 7

73. A 3-digit number $4a3$ is added to another 3-digit number 984 to give the four digit number $13b7$, which is divisible by 11. Then, $(a + b)$ is :   **(C.B.I. 1993)**

    (a) 10   (b) 11   (c) 12   (d) 15

74. If x and y are the two digits of the number $653\,xy$ such that this number is divisible by 80, then $x + y$ is equal to :   **(Assistant Grade 1993)**

    (a) 2   (b) 3   (c) 4   (d) 6

75. If n is any positive integer, then $(3^{4n} - 4^{3n})$ is always divisible by :

    (a) 7   (b) 17   (c) 112   (d) 145

                                      (Central Excise & I. Tax 1992)

76. The least number by which 72 must be multiplied in order to produce a multiple of 112, is :

    (a) 6   (b) 12   (c) 14   (d) 18

77. On dividing a number by 999, the quotient is 366 and the remainder is 103. The number is :

    (a) 364724   (b) 365387   (c) 365737   (d) 366757

78. If $-1 \le x \le 2$ and $1 \le y \le 3$, then least possible value of $(2y - 3x)$ is :

    (a) 0   (b) -3 (c) -4 (d) -5

79. The least square number which is divisible by 2, 3, 4, 5, 6 is :

    (a) 400   (b) 900   (c) 1600   (d) 3600

80. The smallest number which when added to the sum of the squares of 9 and 10, gives a perfect square, is :

    (a) 0   (b) 3   (c) 8   (d) 15

81. $8756 \times 99999 = ?$

    (a) 815491244   (b) 796491244   (c) 875591244   (d) None of these

82. $9787 \times 123 + 9787 \times 77 = ?$

    (a) 1867400   (b) 1957400   (c) 1967600   (d) 1887400

83. $1399 \times 1399 = ?$

    (a) 1687401   (b) 1901541   (c) 1943211   (d) 1957201

84. $397 \times 397 + 104 \times 104 + 2 \times 397 \times 104 = ?$

(a) 250001   (b) 251001   (c) 260101   (d) 261001

85. $\left(\dfrac{973 \times 973 \times 973 + 127 \times 127 \times 127}{973 \times 973 + 127 \times 127 - 973 \times 127}\right)$ is equal to :

(a) 1000   (b) 1100   (c) 846   (d) None of these

86. $\left(\dfrac{714 \times 714 \times 714 - 97 \times 97 \times 97}{714 \times 714 + 714 \times 97 + 97 \times 97}\right)$ is equal to :

(a) 617   (b) 811   (c) $\dfrac{703}{27}$ (d) 653

87. $\dfrac{(856 + 167)^2 + (856 - 167)^2}{856 \times 856 + 167 \times 167}$ is equal to :

(a) 1   (b) 2   (c) 689   (d) 1023

88. $\dfrac{(469 + 174)^2 - (469 - 174)^2}{469 \times 174}$ is equal to :

(a) 2   (b) 4   (c) 643   (d) 295

89. $(186 \times 186 + 159 \times 159 - 2 \times 186 \times 159)$ is equal to :

(a) 7029   (b) 1039   (c) 2019   (d) 729

90. $\left(\dfrac{147 \times 147 + 147 \times 143 + 143 \times 143}{147 \times 147 \times 147 - 143 \times 143 \times 143}\right)$ is equal to :

(a) 4   (b) $\dfrac{1}{4}$ (c) 290   (d) $\dfrac{1}{290}$

91. The value of :

$$\left(1 + \frac{1}{1 \times 2} + \frac{1}{1 \times 2 \times 4} + \frac{1}{1 \times 2 \times 4 \times 8} + \frac{1}{1 \times 2 \times 4 \times 8 \times 16}\right) \text{upto four}$$

places of decimal is :   **(Central Excise & I. Tax 1993)**

(a) 1.6414   (b) 1.6415   (c) 1.6416   (d) 1.6428

92. The product of two numbers is $\dfrac{y}{x}$. If one of the numbers is $\dfrac{x}{2}$, then the

other one is :   **(Central Excise & I. Tax 1994)**

(a) $\dfrac{y^3}{x^2}$ (b) $\dfrac{y^2}{x^3}$ (c) $\dfrac{x^2}{y}$ (d) $\dfrac{x}{y^2}$

93. $(64)^{-2/3} \times \left(\dfrac{1}{4}\right)^{-2}$ is equal to :

          (Central Excise & I. Tax 1994)

(a) 1   (b) $\dfrac{1}{4}$ (c) 4   (d) 16

94. The value of $\left(\dfrac{2^n + 2^{n-1}}{2^{n+1} - 2^n}\right)$ is :

(a) $\dfrac{1}{2}$　　　　(b) $\dfrac{3}{2}$　　　　(c) $2^{\frac{n-1}{n+1}}$　　　　(d) None of these

95. The expression $\left[\dfrac{1}{1.2}+\dfrac{1}{2.3}+\dfrac{1}{3.4}+\ldots+\dfrac{1}{n\,(n+1)}\right]$ for any natural number n, is :
    (a) always greater than 1　　　　(b) always less than 1
    (c) always equal to 1　　　　(d) not definite

96. The smallest integer by which 3750 should be divided so that the quotient is a perfect square number, is :
    (a) 2　　　　(b) 3　　　　(c) 5　　　　(d) 6

97. On dividing 4150 by a certain number, the quotient is 55 and the remainder is 25. The divisor is :
    (a) 65　　　　(b) 70　　　　(c) 75　　　　(d) 80

98. When n is divided by 4, the remainder is 3. What is the remainder when $2n$ is divided by 4 ?
    (a) 1　　　　(b) 2　　　　(c) 3　　　　(d) 6

99. $217 \times 217 + 183 \times 183 = ?$
    (a) 79698　　　　(b) 80578　　　　(c) 81268　　　　(d) 80698

ANSWERS

1. (c)	2. (a)	3. (b)	4. (c)	5. (a)	6. (b)	7. (b)	8. (c)	9. (c)
10. (b)	11. (b)	12. (b)	13. (d)	14. (d)	15. (c)	16. (b)	17. (d)	18. (a)
19. (c)	20 .(c)	21 .(b)	22 .(c)	23 .(d)	24 .(c)	25. (c)	26. (c)	27. (c)
28. (c)	29. (d)	30. (b)	31. (c)	32. (d)	33. (b)	34. (c)	35. (a)	36. (b)
37. (b)	38. (d)	39. (d)	40. (d)	41. (b)	42. (d)	43. (b)	44. (c)	45. (c)
46. (c)	47. (a)	48. (c)	49. (d)	50. (d)	51. (c)	52. (d)	53. (b)	54. (d)
55. (c)	56. (b)	57. (c)	58. (b)	59. (d)	60. (d)	61. (b)	62. (b)	63. (c)
64. (c)	65. (d)	66. (d)	67. (c)	68. (d)	69. (b)	70. (b)	71. (a)	72. (a)
73. (a)	74. (a)	75. (b)	76. (c)	77. (c)	78. (c)	79. (b)	80. (d)	81. (c)
82. (b)	83. (d)	84. (b)	85. (b)	86. (a)	87. (b)	88. (b)	89. (d)	90. (b)
91. (c)	92. (a)	93. (a)	94. (b)	95. (b)	96. (d)	97. (c)	98. (b)	99. (b)

SOLUTIONS

1. Required difference = $(7000 - 7) = 6993$.
2. Required difference = $(70000 - 70) = 69930$.
3. Required number = $(6581 - 4991) = 1590$.
4. Let $3500731 - x = 1735618$.
   Then, $x = (3500731 - 1735618) = 1765113$.
5. Let $x - 1936248 = 1635773$ or $x = (1635773 + 1936248) = 3572021$.
6. Required number = $35999 - (17102 + 8799)$
   $\qquad\qquad\qquad = 35999 - 25901 = 10098$.

7. $12846 \times 593 + 12846 \times 407$
   $= 12846 \times (593 + 407)$
   $= 12846 \times 1000 = 12846000$.
8. $987 \times 999 = 987 \times (1000 - 1) = (987 \times 1000) - (987 \times 1)$
   $\qquad\qquad\qquad = (987000 - 987) = 986013$.
9. $469157 \times 9999 = 4691570000 - 469157 = 4691100843$.
10. $935421 \times 625 = 935421 \times 25 \times 25$
    $$= 935421 \times \frac{100}{4} \times \frac{100}{4} = \frac{9354210000}{16} = 584638125 \ .$$

11. Use the formula, $(a^2 + b^2 + 2ab) = (a + b)^2$.
    $387 \times 387 + 114 \times 114 + 2 \times 387 \times 114$
    $= (387)^2 + (114)^2 + 2 \times 387 \times 114$
    $= (387 + 114)^2 = (501)^2 = (500 + 1)^2$
    $= (500)^2 + (1)^2 + 2 \times 500 \times 1$
    $= 250000 + 1 + 1000 = 251001$.
12. $1014 \times 986 = (1000 + 14) \times (1000 - 14)$
    $\qquad\qquad = (1000)^2 - (14)^2 \qquad$ [Use, $(a + b)(a - b) = (a^2 - b^2)$]
    $\qquad\qquad = (1000000 - 196) = 999804$.
13. $1299 \times 1299 = (1299)^2 = (1300 - 1)^2$
    $\qquad\qquad\qquad = (1300)^2 + (1)^2 - 2 \times 1300 \times 1$
    $\qquad\qquad\qquad = 1690000 + 1 - 2600 = 1687401.$
14. $2(a^2 + b^2) = (a + b)^2 + (a - b)^2$
    $\therefore \ 2[(106)^2 + (94)^2] = [(106 + 94)^2 + (106 - 94)^2]$
    $\qquad\qquad\qquad\qquad = [(200)^2 + (12)^2] = 40000 + 144 = 40144$.
    So, $[(106)^2 + (94)^2] = 20072$.
15. Given expression = $(a + b)^2 - 4ab = (a - b)^2$
    $\qquad\qquad\qquad = (475 - 425)^2 = (50)^2 = 2500$.
16. $5358 \times 51 = 5358 \times (50 + 1)$

$$= (5358 \times 50) + (5358 \times 1)$$
$$= 267900 + 5358 = 273258 .$$

17. $1307 \times 1307 = (1307)^2 = (1300 + 7)^2$
$$= (1300)^2 + (7)^2 + 2 \times 1300 \times 7$$
$$= 1690000 + 49 + 18200 = 1708249.$$

18. Required digit = unit digit in the product $(4 \times 8 \times 7 \times 3) = 2.$

19. Unit digit in $(3127)^{173} =$ Unit digit in $(7)^{173}$

Now, 7^4 gives unit digit 1.

$\therefore \ 7^{172} = (7^4)^{43}$ gives unit digit 1.

$\therefore \ 7^{173}$ gives unit digit $= (1 \times 7) = 7.$

20. $9 \times 6 \times 4 = 216.$ In order to obtain 2 at the unit place it must be multiplied by a number whose unit digit is 7.

So, * must be replaced by 7.

21. Unit digit in 7^4 is 1.

$\therefore$ Unit digit in 7^{68} is 1.

$\therefore$ *Unit digit in 7^{71} is 3.*   [*1 × 7 × 7 × 7 gives unit digit 3*]

Again, every power of 6 will give unit digit 6.

$\therefore$ *Unit digit in 6^{59} is 6.*

Clearly, unit digit in 3^4 is 1.

So, unit digit in 3^{64} is 1.

$\therefore$ *Unit digit in 3^{65} is 3.*

$\therefore$ Unit digit in $(7^{71} \times 6^{59} \times 3^{65})$ is 4.   [*3 × 6 × 3 gives unit digit 4*]

22 Unit digit in the given product = unit digit in $7^{153} \times 1^{72}.$

Now 7^4 gives unit digit 1.

$\therefore \ 7^{152}$ gives unit digit 1.

$\therefore \ 7^{153}$ gives unit digit $(1 \times 7) = 7.$

Also 1^{72} gives unit digit 1.

$\therefore$ Unit digit in the product $= (7 \times 1) = 7.$

23. Unit digit in 7^4 is 1.

So, unit digit in 7^{92} is 1.

$\therefore$ *Unit digit in 7^{95} is 3.*   [$\because$ *Unit digit in $1 \times 7 \times 7 \times 7$ is 3*]

Unit digit in 3^4 is 1.

$\therefore$ Unit digit in 3^{56} is 1.

$\therefore$ *Unit digit in 3^{58} is 9*   [$\because$ *Unit digit in $1 \times 3 \times 3$ is 9*]

$\therefore$ Unit digit in $(7^{95} - 3^{58})$ is 4.

[Subtracting unit digit 9 from unit digit 3]

24. $4^{11} \times 7^5 \times 11^2 = (2 \times 2)^{11} \times 7^5 \times 11^2$

$= 2^{11} \times 2^{11} \times 7^5 \times 11^2 = 2^{22} \times 7^5 \times 11^2$.

$\therefore$ Total number of prime factors is $(22 + 5 + 2) = 29$.

25. The least prime number is 2.

26. Prime numbers less than 70 are :

2, 3, 5, 7, 11, 13, 17, 19, 23, 29, 31, 37, 41, 43, 47, 53, 59, 61 & 67.

Their number is 19.

27. Sum of all prime numbers between 60 and 90

$= (61 + 67 + 71 + 73 + 79 + 83 + 89) = 523$.

28. 161 is divisible by 7. So, it is not prime.

221 is divisible by 13. So, it is not prime.

Clearly, $20 > \sqrt{373}$.

Prime numbers less than 20 are 2, 3, 5, 7, 11, 13, 17 & 19.

Clearly, 373 is not divisible by any of them.

So, 373 is prime.

Since 437 is divisible by 19, so it is not prime.

29. A perfect square number can not have 2 as its unit digit. So, the required number is 63592.

30. $\dfrac{3a + 2b}{3a - 2b} = \dfrac{3\left(\dfrac{a}{b}\right) + 2}{3\left(\dfrac{a}{b}\right) - 2} = \dfrac{3 \times \dfrac{4}{3} + 2}{3 \times \dfrac{4}{3} - 2} = \dfrac{6}{2} = 3$.

[Dividing Nr & Dr by b]

31. $\left(\dfrac{6}{7} - \dfrac{2y - x}{2y + x}\right) = \left(\dfrac{6}{7} - \dfrac{2 - \dfrac{x}{y}}{2 + \dfrac{x}{y}}\right)$

$= \left(\dfrac{6}{7} - \dfrac{2 - \dfrac{3}{5}}{2 + \dfrac{3}{5}}\right) = \left(\dfrac{6}{7} - \dfrac{7}{13}\right) = \dfrac{29}{91}$.

32. Since a, b, c are positive integers and 180 is not divisible by any of $2^3, 3^3, 4^3$ and 5^3.

So, $a^3 b = 180$ is possible only when $a^3 = 1$ and $b = 180$.

$\therefore a = 1$ and $b = 180$.

Now $a^3 b = abc \Rightarrow c = a^2 = 1$.

33. Given Exp. $= \left[\dfrac{2}{3} \times \dfrac{3}{4} \times \dfrac{4}{5} \times \dots \times \dfrac{(n-1)}{n}\right] = \dfrac{2}{n}$.

34. Given Exp. $= \left(\dfrac{5}{3} \times \dfrac{7}{5} \times \dfrac{9}{7} \times \dots \times \dfrac{1001}{999}\right) = \dfrac{1001}{3}$.

35. $(256)^{.18} \times (256)^{.07} = (256)^{.18 + .07} = (256)^{.25} = (256)^{1/4}$

$$= (4^4)^{1/4} = 4^{\left(4 \times \frac{1}{4}\right)} = 4^1 = 4.$$

36. $(5)^{.25} \times (125)^{.25} = (5)^{.25} \times (5^3)^{.25} = (5)^{.25} \times (5)^{.75}$

$$= 5^{(.25 + .75)} = 5^1 = 5.$$

37. $2^2 + 4^2 + 6^2 + \dots + 20^2$

$= (2 \times 1)^2 + (2 \times 2)^2 + (2 \times 3)^2 + \dots + (2 \times 10)^2$

$= 2^2 \times 1^2 + 2^2 \times 2^2 + 2^2 \times 3^2 + \dots + 2^2 \times 10^2$

$= 2^2 \times (1^2 + 2^2 + 3^2 + \dots + 10^2) = (4 \times 385) = 1540.$

38. $20z = (64 + 36)(64 - 36)$ or $z = \left(\dfrac{100 \times 28}{20}\right) = 140.$

39. Putting $x = 7$ and $y = 5$ in $(x * y) = (x + 2)^2 \cdot (y - 2)$, we get :

$7 * 5 = (7 + 2)^2 \cdot (5 - 2) = 81 \times 3 = 243.$

40. $2^{x-1} + 2^{x+1} = 320 \Rightarrow 2^{x-1}(1 + 2^2) = 320 \Rightarrow 2^{x-1} = 64 = 2^6.$

$\therefore \ x - 1 = 6$ or $x = 7.$

41. We know that : $(1 + 2 + 3 + \dots + n) = \dfrac{n(n+1)}{2}.$

$\therefore \ (1 + 2 + 3 + \dots + 45) = \left(\dfrac{45 \times 46}{2}\right) = 1035.$

42. $(51 + 52 + 53 + \dots + 100)$

$= (1 + 2 + 3 + \dots + 100) - (1 + 2 + 3 + \dots + 50)$

$= \left(\dfrac{100 \times 101}{2} - \dfrac{50 \times 51}{2}\right) = (5050 - 1275) = 3775.$

43. $2^{10} = 1024.$

Unit digit of $2^{10} \times 2^{10} \times 2^{10}$ is 4 [as $4 \times 4 \times 4$ gives unit digit 4]

$\therefore$ Unit digit of 2^{31} is 8.

Now, 8 when divided by 5, gives 3 as remainder.

44. The sum of the digits must be divisible by 9.

Sum of the digits $= (19 + x)$, where x is in place of *.

The least value of x for which $19 + x$ is divisible by 9 is $x = 8$.

45. 6 * 2 must be divisible by 8.

So, * must be replaced by 3.

46. (Sum of digits at odd places) − (Sum of digits at even places)

$$= (6 + 5 + 3 + 8) - (x + 2 + 6) = 14 - x.$$

Clearly, $x = 3$.

47. A number divisible by 99 must be divisible by 9 as well as 11.
    Clearly, 114345 is divisible by both 9 and 11.
    So, it is divisible by 99.

48. The given number should be divisible by both 9 and 8.
    Clearly, * must be replaced by 6.

49. The given number must be divisible by 2 as well as 3. Whatever may be the value of *, given number is divisible by 2.
    Now $5 + x + 2 = 7 + x$ must be divisible by 3.
    So, $x = 2$.

50. Since 111111 is divisible by each one of 7, 11 and 13, so each one of such numbers is divisible by all the numbers 7, 11 and 13, since we may write, $222222 = 2 \times (111111)$, $333333 = 3 \times (111111)$ etc.

51. On dividing 11158 by 77, the remainder is 70.
    $\therefore$ Number to be added $= (77 - 70) = 7$.

52. On dividing 99547 by 687, the remainder is 619, which is more than half of 687.
    So, we must add $(687 - 619) = 68$ to the given number.
    $\therefore$ Required number $= (99547 + 68) = 99615$.

53. On dividing 13294 by 97, we get 5 as remainder.
    So, the number to be subtracted is 5.

54. Largest number of 5 digits is 99999.
    On dividing 99999 by 99, we get 9 as remainder.
    $\therefore$ Required number $= (99999 - 9) = 99990$.

55. Smallest number of 6 digits is 100000.
    On dividing 100000 by 111, we get 100 as remainder.
    $\therefore$ Number to be added $= (111 - 100) = 11$.
    $\therefore$ Required number $= 100011$.

56. Let $\dfrac{x}{21} \times \dfrac{x}{189} = 1$. Then $x^2 = 21 \times 189 = 21 \times 21 \times 3 \times 3$.
    $\therefore \ x = \sqrt{21 \times 21 \times 3 \times 3} = (21 \times 3) = 63$.

57. By hit and trial, we find that a number exactly divisible by 13 and consisting entirely of fives is 555555. On dividing 555555 by 13, we get 42735 as quotient.
    $\therefore$ Required number $= 42735$.

58. Largest number of four digits is 9999.
    On dividing 9999 by 7, we get 3 as remainder.
    $\therefore$ Largest number of four digits divisible by 7 is 9996.
    Let $9996 - x + 10$ be divisible by 3.
    By hit and trial, we find that $x = 7$.
    $\therefore$ Required number $= (9996 - 7) = 9989$.

59. None of the numbers in (*a*) & (*c*) is divisible by 2.

Number in (*b*) is not divisible by 3.

Clearly, 510510 is divisible by each prime number between 1 and 17.

60. Let the given number when divided by 119 give k as quotient and 19 as remainder. Then,

Given number $= 119k + 19$

$$= 17 \times 7k + 17 + 2 = 17\,(7k+1) + 2.$$

So, the given number when divided by 17 gives $(7k+1)$ as quotient and 2 as remainder.

61. Every such number must be divisible by l.c.m. of 4, 5, 6.

i.e. 60.

Such numbers are 240, 300, 360, 420, 480, 540.

Their number is 6.

62. Required numbers are 102, 108, 114, ..., 996.

This is an A.P. with $a = 102$ & $d = 6$.

Let the number of its terms be n.

$a + (n-1)\,d = 996 \Leftrightarrow 102 + (n-1) \times 6 = 996 \Leftrightarrow n = 150.$

63. Required number $= 1 \times 2 \times 3 \times 4 = 24$.

64. Required number $= 2 \times 4 \times 6 = 48$.

65. Keeping $y = 1$, for $x = 5$, we have $3x + 7y = 22$, which is divisible by 11.

Now, substitute $x = 5$ and $y = 1$ in each alternative and find out which expression becomes a multiple of 11.

Now, $4x + 6y = 4 \times 5 + 6 = 26$,

$x + y + 4 = 5 + 1 + 4 = 10$,

$9x + 4y = 9 \times 5 + 4 = 49$,

$4x - 9y = 4 \times 5 - 9 = 20 - 9 = 11$, which is divisible by 11.

$\therefore 4x - 9y$ is the answer.

66. Let, quotient $= Q$ and remainder $= R$.

Divisor $= 10\,Q = 5R$.

Now, $R = 46 \Rightarrow 10Q = 5 \times 46$ or $Q = 23$.

Now, $Q = 23$, $R = 46$ & Divisor $= 5 \times 46 = 230$.

$\therefore$ Number $= 230 \times 23 + 46 = 5290 + 46 = 5336$.

67. For even values of n, the number $(10^n - 1)$ consists of even number of nines and hence it will be divisible by 11.

68. $\sqrt{3^n} = 81 \Leftrightarrow 3^n = 81 \times 81 = 3^4 \times 3^4 = 3^8 \Leftrightarrow n = 8.$

69. Let $\dfrac{392}{\sqrt{x}} = 28$. Then, $\sqrt{x} = \dfrac{392}{28} = 14$ or $x = 14 \times 14 = 196$.

70. When two 3-digit numbers are multiplied, the product must consist of 5 or 6 digits only.

Product can not contain 4 or 7 digits.

So, the required number can be 991014.

71. $(14 ! - 13 ! - 12 !) = 14 \times 13 \times 12 ! - 13 \times 12 ! - 12 !$
$$= (14 \times 13 - 13 - 1)(12 !) = 168 \times 12 ! = 14 \times 12 \times 12 !.$$

72. A number is divisible by 132 if it is divisible by each one of 11, 3 and 4.
Clearly, 968 is not divisible by 3.
None of 462 and 2178 is divisible by 4.
Also 5184 is not divisible by 11.
∴ Required type of numbers are 4.

73. $a + 8 = b \Rightarrow b - a = 8$.
Also 13b7 is divisible by 11, so $(7 + 3) - (b + 1) = 0$ or $b = 9$.
Now, $b - a = 8$ and $b = 9$. So, $a = 1$.
∴ $a + b = (1 + 9) = 10$.

74. Since $653xy$ is divisible by 5 as well as 2, so $y = 0$.
Now $653x0$ must be divisible by 8, so $3x 0$ must be divisible by 8.
By hit & trial, we get $x = 2$.
∴ $x + y = 2 + 0 = 2$.

75. When $n = 1$, $(3^{4n} - 4^{3n}) = (3^4 - 4^3) = (81 - 64) = 17$, which is
divisible by 17.

76. Required number is divisible by 72 as well as 112, if it is divisible by
their l.c.m., which is 1008.
Now 1008 when divided by 72, gives quotient = 14.
∴ Required number = 14.

77. Required number = $366 \times 999 + 103$
$$= 366 \times (1000 - 1) + 103$$
$$= 366000 - 366 + 103 = 365737.$$

78. For $(2y - 3x)$ to be minimum, take the least value of y and the greatest
value of x.
∴ Required value $= (2 \times 1 - 3 \times 2) = -4$.

79. Least number divisible by 2, 3, 4, 5, 6 is their l.c.m. which is 60.
Now, $60 = 5 \times 2 \times 2 \times 3$.
To make it a perfect square, it must be multiplied with 5×3.
∴ Required number = $60 \times 15 = 900$.

80. $(9)^2 + (10)^2 = 181$.
Clearly, $(13)^2 < 181 < (14)^2$
∴ Required number to be added = $(14)^2 - 181 = 15$.

81. $8756 \times 99999 = 8756 \times (100000 - 1) = (875600000 - 8756)$
$$= 875591244.$$

82. Using distributive law, we get :

$$9787 \times 123 + 9787 \times 77 = 9787 \times (123 + 77) = 9787 \times 200$$
$$= 1957400.$$

83. $1399 \times 1399 = (1399)^2 = (1400 - 1)^2$

$$= (1400)^2 + 1^2 - 2 \times 1400 \times 1$$
$$= (1960000 + 1 - 2800) = 1957201.$$

84. Given Expression $= a^2 + b^2 + 2ab$, where $a = 397$ & $b = 104$

$$= (a + b)^2 = (397 + 104)^2 = (501)^2$$
$$= (500 + 1)^2 = (250000 + 1 + 1000) = 251001.$$

85. Given Exp. $= \left(\dfrac{a^3 + b^3}{a^2 + b^2 - ab} \right) = (a + b) = (973 + 127) = 1100.$

86. Given Exp. $= \left(\dfrac{a^3 - b^3}{a^2 + ab + b^2} \right) = (a - b) = (714 - 97) = 617.$

87. Given Exp. $= \dfrac{(a + b)^2 + (a - b)^2}{(a^2 + b^2)} = \dfrac{2\,(a^2 + b^2)}{(a^2 + b^2)} = 2.$

88. Given Exp. $= \dfrac{(a + b)^2 - (a - b)^2}{ab} = \dfrac{4ab}{ab} = 4.$

89. Given Exp. $= a^2 + b^2 - 2ab = (a - b)^2 = (186 - 159)^2 = (27)^2 = 729.$

90. Given Exp. $= \left(\dfrac{a^2 + ab + b^2}{a^3 - b^3} \right) = \left(\dfrac{1}{a - b} \right) = \dfrac{1}{(147 - 143)} = \dfrac{1}{4}.$

91. Given Exp. $= \left(1 + \dfrac{4 \times 8 \times 16 + 8 \times 16 + 16 + 1}{1 \times 2 \times 4 \times 8 \times 16} \right) = 1 + \dfrac{657}{1024} = 1.6416.$

92. Let the other number be z.

Then, $z \times \dfrac{x}{y^2} = \dfrac{y}{x}$. So, $z = \dfrac{y}{x} \times \dfrac{y^2}{x} = \dfrac{y^3}{x^2}.$

93. $(64)^{-2/3} \times \left(\dfrac{1}{4} \right)^{-2} = (4^3)^{-2/3} \times \left(\dfrac{1}{4} \right)^{-2} = 4^{3 \times \left(-\frac{2}{3} \right)} \times \left(\dfrac{1}{4} \right)^{-2}$

$$= \left(4^{-2} \times \dfrac{1}{4^{-2}} \right) = 1.$$

94. Given Exp. $= \dfrac{2^{n-1}\,(2 + 1)}{2^n\,(2 - 1)} = \dfrac{3}{2}.$

95. Given Exp. $= \left(1 - \frac{1}{2}\right) + \left(\frac{1}{2} - \frac{1}{3}\right) + \left(\frac{1}{3} - \frac{1}{4}\right) + \dots + \left(\frac{1}{n} - \frac{1}{n+1}\right)$

$= 1 - \frac{1}{2} + \frac{1}{2} - \frac{1}{3} + \frac{1}{3} - \frac{1}{4} + \dots + \frac{1}{n} - \frac{1}{n+1}$

$= \left(1 - \frac{1}{n+1}\right) = \frac{n}{n+1} < 1.$

96. $3750 = 5 \times 5 \times 5 \times 5 \times 2 \times 3.$

$\therefore$ Required number by which 3750 must be divided $= 2 \times 3 = 6.$

97. Divisor $= \left(\dfrac{\text{Dividend} - \text{Remainder}}{\text{Quotient}}\right) = \left(\dfrac{4150 - 25}{55}\right) = 75.$

98. When n is divided by 4, let Q be the quotient and 3 be the remainder.
Then, $n = 4Q + 3.$

$\therefore 2n = 8Q + 6 = (8Q + 4) + 2 = 4(2Q + 1) + 2.$

So, remainder $= 2.$

99. $217 \times 217 + 183 \times 183$

$= (217)^2 + (183)^2$

$= \frac{1}{2}[(217 + 183)^2 + (217 - 183)^2]$

$= \frac{1}{2}[(400)^2 + (34)^2] = \frac{1}{2}(160000 + 1156) = 80578.$

---

2. H.C.F. & L.C.M. of Numbers

Factors & Multiples : *If a number a divides another number b exactly, we say that a is a factor of b and we write, a/b. In this case, b is called a multiple of a.*

Highest Common Factor or Greatest Common Measure :

(H.C.F. or G.C.D. or G.C.M.)

The H.C.F. of two or more than two numbers is the greatest number that divides each one of them exactly.

H.C.F. By Factorization : *Express each one of the given numbers as the product of prime factors. The product of least powers of common prime factors gives H.C.F.*

Ex. 1. *What is the H.C.F. of*
$$2^3 \times 3^2 \times 5 \times 7^4, 2^2 \times 3^5 \times 5^2 \times 7^3, 2^3 \times 5^3 \times 7^2 \text{ ?}$$

Sol. The prime numbers common to given numbers are 2, 5 & 7.

$\therefore$ H.C.F. $= 2^2 \times 5 \times 7^2 = 980.$

Ex. 2. *Find the H.C.F. of 108, 288 and 360.*

Sol. $108 = 2^2 \times 3^3, 288 = 2^5 \times 3^2$ and $360 = 2^3 \times 5 \times 3^2.$

$\therefore$ H.C.F. $= 2^2 \times 3^2 = 36.$

Ex. 3. *Find the H.C.F. of 1056, 1584 and 2178.*

Sol. $1056 = 2^5 \times 3 \times 11, 1584 = 2^4 \times 3^2 \times 11$ and $2178 = 2 \times 3^2 \times 11^2.$

$\therefore$ H.C.F. $= (2 \times 3 \times 11) = 66.$

H.C.F. By Division Method : *Suppose we have to find the H.C.F. of two given numbers. Divide the larger number by the smaller one. Now, divide the divisor by the remainder. Repeat the process of dividing the preceding divisor by the remainder last obtained till zero is obtained as remainder. The last divisor is the required H.C.F.*

Suppose we have to find the H.C.F of three numbers. Then, H.C.F. of [(H.C.F. of any two) & (the third number)] gives the H.C.F. of three given numbers.

Similarly, the H.C.F. of more than three numbers may be obtained.

Ex. 4. *Find the H.C.F. of 513, 1134 and 1215.*

Sol.

```
        1134) 1215  (1
              1134
               81)  1134  (14
                      81
                     324
                     324
                       ×
```

∴ H.C.F. of 1134 and 1215 is 81.

∴ Required H.C.F. = H.C.F. of 513 and 81.

$$81) \quad 513 \quad (6$$
$$\underline{486}$$
$$27) \quad 81 \quad (3$$
$$\underline{81}$$
$$\times$$

∴ H.C.F. of given numbers = 27.

Lowest Common Multiple (L.C.M.) : *The least number which is exactly divisible by each one of the given numbers is called their L.C.M.*

Product of Two Numbers = Product of their H.C.F. & L.C.M.

L.C.M. By Factorization : *Resolve each one of the given numbers into a product of prime factors. Then, L.C.M. is the product of highest powers of all the factors.*

Ex. 5. Find the L.C.M. of $2^2 \times 3^3 \times 5 \times 7^2, 2^3 \times 3^2 \times 5^2 \times 7^4,$ $2 \times 3 \times 5^3 \times 7 \times 11.$

Sol. L.C.M. = Product of highest powers of 2, 3, 5, 7 and 11.

$$= 2^3 \times 3^3 \times 5^3 \times 7^4 \times 11.$$

Ex. 6. Find the L.C.M. of 72, 108 and 2100.

Sol. $72 = 2^3 \times 3^2, 108 = 3^3 \times 2^2, 2100 = 2^2 \times 5^2 \times 3 \times 7.$

∴ L.C.M. $= 2^3 \times 3^3 \times 5^2 \times 7 = 37800.$

Ex. 7. Find L.C.M. of 852 and 1491.

Sol. H.C.F. of 852 and 1491 is 213.

∴ L.C.M. $= \dfrac{\text{Product of numbers}}{\text{Their H.C.F.}} = \dfrac{852 \times 1491}{213} = 5964.$

Ex. 8. (Short Cut Method) : *Find the L.C.M. of 16, 24, 36 & 54.*

Sol.

2	16	—	24	—	36	—	54
3	8	—	12	—	18	—	27
3	8	—	4	—	6	—	9
2	8	—	4	—	2	—	3
2	4	—	2	—	1	—	3
	2	—	1	—	1	—	3

∴ L.C.M. $= 2 \times 3 \times 3 \times 2 \times 2 \times 2 \times 3 = 432.$

H.C.F. & L.C.M. of Fractions :

(i) H.C.F. $= \dfrac{\text{H.C.F. of numerators}}{\text{L.C.M. of denominators}}$

(ii) L.C.M. $= \dfrac{\text{L.C.M. of numerators}}{\text{H.C.F. of denominators}}$

Ex. 9. Find the H.C.F. and L.C.M. of $\dfrac{2}{3}, \dfrac{8}{9}, \dfrac{16}{81}$ **&** $\dfrac{10}{27}.$

Sol. H.C.F. of given fractions $= \dfrac{\text{H.C.F. of } 2, 8, 16, 10}{\text{L.C.M. of } 3, 9, 81, 27} = \dfrac{2}{81}$.

L.C.M. of given fractions $= \dfrac{\text{L.C.M. of } 2, 8, 16, 10}{\text{H.C.F. of } 3, 9, 81, 27} = \dfrac{80}{3}$.

Some More Solved Problems

Ex. 10. *Reduce* $\dfrac{391}{667}$ *to lowest terms.*

Sol. H.C.F. of 391 & 667 is 23.

On dividing the numerator and denominator by 23, we get :

$\dfrac{391}{667} = \dfrac{391 \div 23}{667 \div 23} = \dfrac{17}{29}$.

Ex. 11. *The H.C.F. of two numbers is 11 and their L.C.M. is 693. If one of the numbers is 77, find the other.*

Sol. The other number $= \left(\dfrac{11 \times 693}{77} \right) = 99$.

Ex. 12. *Find the largest number that can exactly divide 513, 783 and 1107.*

Sol. Required number = H.C.F. of 513, 783 and 1107.

Now, $513 = 3^3 \times 19$, $783 = 3^3 \times 29$, $1107 = 3^3 \times 41$.

$\therefore$ H.C.F. $= 3^3 = 27$.

Hence, the required number is 27.

Ex. 13. *Find the least number exactly divisible by 12, 15, 20 and 27.*

Sol. Required number = L.C.M. of 12, 15, 20, 27.

3	12	—	15	—	20	—	27
4	4	—	5	—	20	—	9
5	1	—	5	—	5	—	9
	1	—	1	—	1	—	9

$\therefore$ L.C.M. $= 3 \times 4 \times 5 \times 9 = 540$.

$\therefore$ Required number $= 540$.

Ex. 14. *Find the least number which when divided by 6, 7, 8, 9 and 12 leaves the same remainder 1 in each case.*

Sol. Required number = (L.C.M. of 6, 7, 8, 9, 12) + 1.

3	6	—	7	—	8	—	9	—	12
2	2	—	7	—	8	—	3	—	4
2	1	—	7	—	4	—	3	—	2
	1	—	7	—	2	—	3	—	1

$\therefore$ L.C.M. $= 3 \times 2 \times 2 \times 7 \times 2 \times 3 = 504$.

Hence, required number $= (504 + 1) = 505$.

Ex. 15. *Find the greatest number which can divide 284, 698 and 1618 leaving the same remainder 8 in each case.*

Sol. Required number = H.C.F. of $(284-8)$, $(698-8)$ & $(1618-8)$
$$= \text{H.C.F. of } 276, 690 \text{ and } 1610.$$

Now, $276 = 2^2 \times 3 \times 23$, $690 = 2 \times 3 \times 5 \times 23$, $1610 = 2 \times 5 \times 7 \times 23$

∴ H.C.F. of 276, 690 & 1610 is 23.

Hence, the required number is 23.

Ex. 16. *Find the largest number which divides 62, 132 and 237 to leave the same remainder in each case.*

Sol. Required number = H.C.F. of $(132-62)$, $(237-132)$ & $(237-62)$
$$= \text{H.C.F. of } 70, 105 \text{ & } 175 = 35.$$

Ex. 17. *Find the largest number of four digits exactly divisible by 12, 15, 18 and 27.*

Sol. The largest number of four digits is 9999.

Required number must be divisible by l.c.m. of 12, 15, 18, 27 i.e. by 540.

On dividing 9999 by 540, we get 279 as remainder.

∴ Required number = $(9999-279) = 9720$.

Ex. 18. *Find the smallest number of five digits exactly divisible by 16, 24, 36 and 54.*

Sol. Smallest number of five digits is 10000.

Required number must be divisible by l.c.m. of 16, 24, 36, 54 i.e. 432.

On dividing 10000 by 432, we get 64 as remainder.

∴ Required number = $10000 + (432-64) = 10368$.

EXERCISE 2

Mark (√) against the correct answer :

1. $\dfrac{444}{629}$ when expressed in lowest terms is :

   (a) $\dfrac{13}{37}$ (b) $\dfrac{11}{17}$ (c) $\dfrac{11}{19}$ (d) $\dfrac{12}{17}$

2. The H.C.F. of $2^2 \times 3^3 \times 5^5$, $2^3 \times 3^2 \times 5^2 \times 7$ and $2^4 \times 3^4 \times 5 \times 7^2 \times 11$ is :

   (a) $2^2 \times 3^2 \times 5 \times 7 \times 11$ (b) $2^4 \times 3^4 \times 5^5$

   (c) $2^4 \times 3^4 \times 5^5 \times 7 \times 11$ (d) $2^2 \times 3^2 \times 5$

3. The H.C.F. of $2^4 \times 3^2 \times 5^3 \times 7$, $2^3 \times 3^3 \times 5^2 \times 7^2$ and $3 \times 5 \times 7 \times 11$ is :

   (a) 105   (b) 27720   (c) 1155   (d) 2310

4. The H.C.F. of 1095 and 1168 is :

   (a) 37   (b) 73   (c) 43   (d) 83

5. The H.C.F. of 2923 and 3239 is :

   (a) 37   (b) 47   (c) 73   (d) 79

6. The H.C.F. of 3556 and 3444 is :

   (a) 25   (b) 26   (c) 28   (d) 23

7. The H.C.F. of 210, 385 and 735 is :
   (a) 7   (b) 14   (c) 21   (d) 35

8. Which of the following is a pair of co-primes ?
   (a) (21, 35)   (b) (23, 92)   (c) (18, 25)   (d) (16, 62)

9. The H.C.F. of $\dfrac{2}{3}, \dfrac{8}{9}, \dfrac{64}{81}$ and $\dfrac{10}{27}$ is :

   (a) $\dfrac{2}{3}$ (b) $\dfrac{2}{81}$ (c) $\dfrac{160}{3}$ (d) $\dfrac{160}{81}$

10. The H.C.F. of $\dfrac{9}{10}, \dfrac{12}{25}, \dfrac{18}{35}$ and $\dfrac{21}{40}$ is :

   (a) $\dfrac{3}{5}$ (b) $\dfrac{252}{5}$ (c) $\dfrac{3}{2800}$ (d) $\dfrac{63}{700}$

11. The L.C.M. of 26, 56, 104 and 182 is :
   (a) 546   (b) 1274   (c) 728   (d) 784

12. The L.C.M. of 148 and 185 is :
   (a) 680   (b) 740   (c) 3700   (d) 2960

13. The L.C.M. of $2^3 \times 3^2 \times 5 \times 11, 2^4 \times 3^4 \times 5^2 \times 7$ and $2^5 \times 3^3 \times 5^3 \times 7^2 \times 11$
   is :

   (a) $2^5 \times 3^4 \times 5^3$ (b) $2^5 \times 3^4 \times 5^3 \times 7^2 \times 11$

   (c) $2^3 \times 3^2 \times 5 \times 7 \times 11$ (d) $2^3 \times 3^2 \times 5$

14. The L.C.M. of $\dfrac{1}{3}, \dfrac{5}{6}, \dfrac{2}{9}, \dfrac{4}{27}$ is :

   (a) $\dfrac{1}{54}$ (b) $\dfrac{10}{27}$ (c) $\dfrac{20}{3}$ (d) None of these

15. The L.C.M. of $\dfrac{2}{3}, \dfrac{3}{5}, \dfrac{4}{7}, \dfrac{9}{13}$ is :

   (a) 36   (b) $\dfrac{1}{36}$ (c) $\dfrac{1}{1365}$ (d) $\dfrac{12}{455}$

16. Two numbers are in the ratio of 15 : 11. If their H.C.F. is 13, then the
   numbers are :   **(Central Excise & I. Tax 1993)**
   (a) 75, 55   (b) 105, 77   (c) 15, 11   (d) 195, 143

17. Three numbers are in the ratio 1 : 2 : 3 and their H.C.F. is 12. The
   numbers are :   **(C.B.I. 1991)**
   (a) 12, 24, 36   (b) 10, 20, 30   (c) 5, 10, 15   (d) 4, 8, 12

18. The sum of two numbers is 216 and their H.C.F. is 27. The numbers
   are :   **(C.B.I. 1993)**
   (a) 27, 189   (b) 154, 162   (c) 108, 108   (d) 81, 189

19. The sum of two numbers is 528 and their H.C.F. is 33. The number of
   pairs of such numbers satisfying the above condition is :
   (a) 6   (b) 12   (c) 8   (d) 4
                                          (Central Excise & I. Tax 1992)

20. The product of two 2-digit numbers is 2028 and their G.C.M. is 13. The numbers are :

    (*a*) 26, 78   (*b*) 39, 52   (*c*) 13, 156   (*d*) 36, 68

21. The H.C.F. of two numbers is 12 and their difference is 12. The numbers are :

    (*a*) 66, 78   (*b*) 70, 82   (*c*) 94, 106   (*d*) 84, 96

22. The H.C.F. of two numbers is 11 and their L.C.M. is 7700. If one of these numbers is 275, then the other one is :   **(Assistant Grade 1993)**

    (*a*) 279   (*b*) 283   (*c*) 308   (*d*) 318

23. The L.C.M. of two numbers is 45 times their H.C.F. If one of the numbers is 125 and the sum of H.C.F. and L.C.M. is 1150, the other number is :   **(C.B.I. 1993)**

    (*a*) 215   (*b*) 220   (*c*) 225   (*d*) 235

24. About the number of pairs which have 16 as their H.C.F. and 136 as their L.C.M., we can definitely say that :   **(C.B.I. 1990)**

    (*a*) only one such pair exists   (*b*) only two such pairs exist

    (*c*) many such pairs exist   (*d*) no such pair exists

25. The L.C.M. of three different numbers is 120. Which of the following can not be their H.C.F. ?   **(Central Excise & I. Tax 1992)**

    (*a*) 8   (*b*) 12   (*c*) 24   (*d*) 35

26. The H.C.F. and L.C.M. of two numbers are 50 and 250 respectively. If the first number is divided by 2, the quotient is 50. The second number is :   **(C.B.I. 1993)**

    (*a*) 50   (*b*) 100   (*c*) 125   (*d*) 250

27. The product of two numbers is 1320 and their H.C.F. is 6. The L.C.M. of the numbers is :

    (*a*) 7920   (*b*) 220   (*c*) 1314   (*d*) 1326

28. The greatest number which exactly divides 105, 1001 & 2436 is :

    (*a*) 3   (*b*) 7   (*c*) 11   (*d*) 21

29. The largest number which divides 25, 73 and 97 to leave the same remainder in each case is :   **(Assistant Grade 1994)**

    (*a*) 24   (*b*) 23   (*c*) 21   (*d*) 6

30. The greatest number that will divide 187, 233 and 279 leaving the same remainder in each case is :   **(Central Excise & I. Tax 1992)**

    (*a*) 30   (*b*) 36   (*c*) 46   (*d*) 56

31. The greatest number which can divide 1356, 1868 and 2764 leaving the same remainder 12 in each case, is :

    (*a*) 64   (*b*) 124   (*c*) 156   (*d*) 260

32. The greatest number by which if 1657 and 2037 are divided to give remainders 6 and 5 respectively, is :

    (*a*) 127   (*b*) 123   (*c*) 235   (*d*) 305

33. The greatest possible length which can be used to measure exactly the lengths 4 m 95 cm, 9 m and 16 m 65 cm is :
    (*a*) 15 cm   (*b*) 25 cm   (*c*) 35 cm   (*d*) 45 cm

34. Three different containers contain 496 litres, 403 litres and 713 litres of mixtures of milk and water respectively. What biggest measure can measure all the different quantities exactly ?
    (*a*) 1 litre   (*b*) 7 litres   (*c*) 31 litres   (*d*) 41 litres

35. The least number which is a perfect square and is divisible by each of the numbers 16, 20 and 24, is :
    (*a*) 1600   (*b*) 3600   (*c*) 6400   (*d*) 14400

36. What is the least number which when divided by 8, 9, 12 and 15 leaves the same remainder 1 in each case ?   **(C.B.I. 1993)**
    (*a*) 179   (*b*) 181   (*c*) 359   (*d*) 361

37. What is the greatest number of three digits which when divided by 6, 9 and 12 leaves a remainder of 3 in each case ?   **(C.B.I. 1993)**
    (*a*) 975   (*b*) 996   (*c*) 939   (*d*) 903

38. The least number of five digits which is exactly divisible by 12, 15 and 18 is :   **(Teacher's Exam 1991)**
    (*a*) 10010   (*b*) 10015   (*c*) 10020   (*d*) 10080

39. The smallest number which when diminished by 3 is divisible by 21, 28, 36 and 45 is :
    (*a*) 423   (*b*) 1257   (*c*) 1263   (*d*) 1260

40. The smallest number which when increased by 5 is divisible by each one of 24, 32, 36 and 54, is :
    (*a*) 869   (*b*) 859   (*c*) 4320   (*d*) 427

41. The least multiple of 7, which leaves a remainder of 4, when divided by 6, 9, 15 and 18, is :
    (*a*) 74   (*b*) 94   (*c*) 184   (*d*) 364

42. The least number which when divided by 18, 27 and 36 leaves the remainders 5, 14 and 23 respectively, is
    (*a*) 95   (*b*) 113   (*c*) 149   (*d*) 77

43. The least number which when divided by 20, 25, 35 and 40 leaves the remainder 14, 19, 29 and 34 respectively, is :
    (*a*) 1664   (*b*) 1406   (*c*) 1404   (*d*) 1394

44. The least number which when divided by 5, 6, 7 and 8 leaves a remainder 3, but when divided by 9 leaves no remainder, is :
    (*a*) 1677   (*b*) 1683   (*c*) 2523   (*d*) 3363

45. The least number which when divided by 5, 6, 8, 9 and 12 leaves a remainder 1 in each case, but when divided by 13 leaves no remainder, is :
    (*a*) 361   (*b*) 721   (*c*) 1801   (*d*) 3601

46. An electronic device makes a beep after every 60 sec. Another device makes a beep after every 62 sec. They beeped together at 10 a.m. The time when they will next make a beep together at the earliest, is :

(a) 10.30 a.m.   (b) 10.31 a.m.   (c) 10.59 a.m.   (d) 11 a.m.

(C.B.I. 1993)

47. Six bells commence tolling together and toll at intervals of 2, 4, 6, 8, 10 and 12 seconds respectively. In 30 minutes, how many times do they toll together ?

(C.B.I. 1991)

(a) 4   (b) 10   (c) 15   (d) 16

48. The traffic lights at three different road crossings change after every 48 sec, 72 sec and 108 sec respectively. If they all change simultaneously at 8 : 20 : 00 hours, then they will again change simultaneously at :

(a) 8 : 27 : 12 hrs   (b) 8 : 27 : 24 hrs
(c) 8 : 27 : 36 hrs   (d) 8 : 27 : 48 hrs

(C.B.I. 1992)

ANSWERS

1. (d)   **2.** (d)   **3.** (a)   **4.** (b)   **5.** (d)   **6.** (c)   **7.** (d)   **8.** (c)   **9.** (b)
10. (c)   **11.** (c)   **12.** (b)   **13.** (b)   **14.** (c)   **15.** (a)   **16.** (d)   **17.** (a)   **18.** (a)
19. (d)   **20.** (b)   **21.** (d)   **22.** (c)   **23.** (c)   **24.** (d)   **25.** (d)   **26.** (c)   **27.** (b)
28. (b)   **29.** (a)   **30.** (c)   **31.** (a)   **32.** (a)   **33.** (d)   **34.** (c)   **35.** (b)   **36.** (d)
37. (a)   **38.** (d)   **39.** (c)   **40.** (b)   **41.** (d)   **42.** (a)   **43.** (d)   **44.** (b)   **45.** (d)
46. (b)   **47.** (d)   **48.** (a)

SOLUTIONS

1. H.C.F. of 444 and 629 is 37.

On dividing Nr & Dr by 37, we get $\frac{444}{629} = \frac{12}{17}$.

2. H.C.F. = product of lowest powers of common factors
$$= 2^2 \times 3^2 \times 5.$$

3. H.C.F. = product of lowest powers of common factors
$$= 3 \times 5 \times 7 = 105.$$

4.

```
1095)  1168  (1
       1095
        73)  1095  (15
              73
             365
             365
              ×
```

∴ H.C.F. = 73.

5.

$$
\begin{array}{r}
2923)\ \ 3239\ \ (1 \\
\underline{2923} \\
316)\ \ 2923\ \ (9 \\
\underline{2844} \\
79)\ \ 316\ \ (4 \\
\underline{316} \\
\times
\end{array}
$$

∴ H.C.F. = 79.

6.

$$
\begin{array}{r}
3444)\ \ 3556\ \ (1 \\
\underline{3444} \\
112)\ \ 3444\ \ (30 \\
\underline{3360} \\
84)\ \ 112\ \ (1 \\
\underline{84} \\
28)\ \ 84\ \ (3 \\
\underline{84} \\
\times
\end{array}
$$

7. $210 = 2 \times 3 \times 5 \times 7$, $385 = 5 \times 7 \times 11$ & $735 = 3 \times 5 \times 7^2$.

∴ H.C.F. = $5 \times 7 = 35$.

8. H.C.F. of 18 and 25 is 1. So, they are co–primes.

9. H.C.F. = $\dfrac{\text{H.C.F. of 2, 8, 64, 10}}{\text{L.C.M. of 3, 9, 81, 27}} = \dfrac{2}{81}$.

10. H.C.F. = $\dfrac{\text{H.C.F. of 9, 12, 18, 21}}{\text{L.C.M. of 10, 25, 35, 40}} = \dfrac{3}{2800}$.

11.

13	26	—	56	—	104	—	182
7	2	—	56	—	8	—	14
2	2	—	8	—	8	—	2
4	1	—	4	—	4	—	1
	1	—	1	—	1	—	1

∴ L.C.M. = $(13 \times 7 \times 2 \times 4) = 728$.

12. H.C.F. of 148 and 185 is 37.

∴ L.C.M. = $\left(\dfrac{148 \times 185}{37} \right) = 740$.

13. L.C.M. = product of highest powers of prime factors

$$= 2^5 \times 3^4 \times 5^3 \times 7^2 \times 11.$$

14. L.C.M. = $\dfrac{\text{L.C.M. of 1, 5, 2, 4}}{\text{H.C.F. of 3, 6, 9, 27}} = \dfrac{20}{3}$.

15. L.C.M. = $\dfrac{\text{L.C.M. of 2, 3, 4, 9}}{\text{H.C.F. of 3, 5, 7, 13}} = \dfrac{36}{1} = 36$.

16. Let the required numbers be $15x$ and $11x$.
Then, their H.C.F. is x. so, $x = 13$.

∴ The numbers are $(15 \times 13 \ \& \ 11 \times 13)$ *i.e.* 195 & 143.

17. Let the required numbers be $x, 2x$ and $3x$.
Then, their H.C.F. $= x$. So, $x = 12$.
∴ The numbers are 12, 24 and 36.

18. Let the required numbers be $27a$ and $27b$.
Then, $27a + 27b = 216 \Rightarrow a + b = 8$.
Now, co–primes with sum 8 are (1, 7) & (3, 5).
∴ Required numbers are $(27 \times 1, 27 \times 7)$ & $(27 \times 3, 27 \times 5)$
i.e. (27, 189) & (81, 135).
Out of these, the given one in the answer is the pair (27, 189).

19. Let the required numbers be $33a$ and $33b$. Then,
$33a + 33b = 528$ or $a + b = 16$.
Now, two co–primes with sum 16 are :
(1, 15), (3, 13), (5, 11) & (7, 9)
∴ Numbers with sum 528 and H.C.F. 33 are :
$(33 \times 1, 33 \times 15), (33 \times 3, 33 \times 13), (33 \times 5, 33 \times 11), (33 \times 7, 33 \times 9)$.
The number of such pairs is 4.

20. Let the numbers be $13a$ and $13b$. Then,
$13a \times 13b = 2028 \Rightarrow ab = 12$.
Now, co–primes with product 12 are (1, 12) and (3, 4).
So, the numbers with H.C.F. 13 and product 2028 are :
$(13 \times 1, 13 \times 12)$ and $(13 \times 3, 13 \times 4)$.
∴ Required 2–digit numbers are 39 & 52.

21. Out of the given numbers, the two with H.C.F. 12 and difference 12 are 84 and 96.

22. Other number $= \left(\dfrac{11 \times 7700}{275} \right) = 308$.

23. Let H.C.F. be h and L.C.M. be l. Then, $l = 45h$ and $l + h = 1150$.
∴ $45h + h = 1150$ or $h = 25$. So, $l = (1150 - 25) = 1125$.
∴ Other number $= \left(\dfrac{25 \times 1125}{125} \right) = 225$.

24. H.C.F. of two numbers divides their L.C.M. exactly.
Since 16 is not a factor of 136, it follows that there does not exist any pair of numbers with H.C.F. 16 and L.C.M. 136.

25. Since H.C.F. is always a factor of L.C.M., so we can not have three numbers with H.C.F. 35 and L.C.M. 120.

26. First number $= (50 \times 2) = 100$.
Second number $= \left(\dfrac{50 \times 250}{100} \right) = 125$.

27. L.C.M. $= \dfrac{\text{Product of numbers}}{\text{Their H.C.F.}} = \dfrac{1320}{6} = 220$.

28. H.C.F. of 2436 & 1001 is 7.

Also, H.C.F of 105 & 7 is 7.

∴ H.C.F. of 105, 1001 & 2436 is 7.

29. Required number = H.C.F. of $(73 - 25)$, $(97 - 73)$ & $(97 - 25)$
= H.C.F of 48, 24 & 72 = 24.

30. Required number = H.C.F. of $(233 - 187)$, $(279 - 233)$ & $(279 - 187)$
= H.C.F. of 46, 46 & 92 = 46.

31. Required number = H.C.F. of $(1356 - 12)$, $(1868 - 12)$ & $(2764 - 12)$
= H.C.F. of 1344, 1856 & 2752 = 64.

32. Required number = H.C.F. of $(1657 - 6)$ & $(2037 - 5)$
= H.C.F. of 1651 & 2032 = 127.

33. Required length = H.C.F. of 900 cm, 495 cm & 1665 cm = 45 cm.

34. Required measurement = H.C.F. of 496, 403 & 713 litres = 31 litres.

35. The least number divisible by 16, 20, 24
= l.c.m. of 16, 20, 24 = 240 = $2 \times 2 \times 2 \times 2 \times 3 \times 5$
To make it a perfect square, it must be multiplied by 3×5.
∴ Required number = $240 \times 3 \times 5 = 3600$.

36. ∴ Required number = (l.c.m. of 8, 9, 12, 15) + 1 = 361.

37. Greatest number of 3 digits is 999.
L.C.M. of 6, 9 and 12 = 36.
On dividing 999 by 36, remainder obtained is 27.
∴ Greatest number of 3 digits divisible by 6, 9, 12 = $(999 - 27) = 972$.
∴ Required number = $(972 + 3) = 975$.

38. Least number of 5 digits is 10000.
L.C.M. of 12, 15, 18 is 180.
On dividing 10000 by 180, the remainder is 100.
∴ Required number = $10000 + (180 - 100) = 10080$.

39. Required number = (l.c.m. of 21, 28, 36, 45) + 3 = 1263.

40. Required number = (l.c.m. of 24, 32, 36, 54) − 5 = 859.

41. L.C.M. of 6, 9, 15, 18 is 90.
Let required number be $90k + 4$, which is a multiple of 7.
Least value of k for which $(90k + 4)$ is divisible by 7 is $k = 4$.
∴ Required number = $90 \times 4 + 4 = 364$.

42. Here $(18 - 5) = 13$, $(27 - 14) = 13$ & $(36 - 23) = 13$.
∴ Required number = (l.c.m. of 18, 27, 36) − 13 = 95.

43. Here $(20 - 14) = 6$, $(25 - 19) = 6$, $(35 - 29) = 6$ & $(40 - 34) = 6$.
∴ Required number = (l.c.m. of 20, 25, 35, 40) − 6 = 1394.

44. L.C.M. of 5, 6, 7, 8 = 840.
∴ Required number is of the from $840k + 3$.
Least value of k for which $(840k + 3)$ is divisible by 9 is $k = 2$.
∴ Required number = $(840 \times 2 + 3) = 1683$.

45. L.C.M. of 5, 6, 8, 9, 12 = 360.
∴ Required number is of the form $360k + 1$.
Least value of k for which $360k + 1$ is divisible by 13 is $k = 10$.

∴ Required number $= (360 \times 10 + 1) = 3601.$

46. L.C.M. of 60 and 62 seconds is 1860 sec = 31 min.

∴ They will beep together at 10.31 a.m.

47. L.C.M. of 2, 4, 6, 8, 10, 12 is 120.

So, the bells will toll together after every 120 seconds i.e. 2 minutes.

In 30 minutes, they will toll together in $\left(\dfrac{30}{2}\right) + 1 = 16$ times.

48. Interval of change = (l.c.m. of 48, 72, 108) sec. = 432 sec.

∴ The lights will change simultaneously after every 432 seconds, i.e. 7 min. 12 sec.

∴ Next simultaneous change will take place at 8 : 27 : 12 hrs.

---

3. Decimal Fractions

Decimal Fractions : *Fractions in which denominators are powers of 10, are known as decimal fractions.*

$\frac{1}{10} = 1$ tenth, $\frac{1}{100} = 1$ hundredth, $\frac{1}{1000} = 1$ thousandth etc

$\frac{1}{10} = 1$ tenth $= .1, \frac{2}{10} = 2$ tenths $= .2, \frac{3}{10} = 3$ tenths $= .3$ etc.

$\frac{1}{100} = 1$ hundredth $= .01, \frac{2}{100} = 2$ hundredths $= .02;$

$\frac{13}{100} = 13$ hundredths $= .13 ; \frac{99}{100} = 99$ hundredths $= .99;$

$\frac{1}{1000} = 1$ thousandth $= .001, \frac{9}{1000} = 9$ thousandths $= .009;$

$\frac{97}{1000} = 97$ thousandths $= .097; \frac{999}{1000} = 999$ thousandths $= .999.$

Ex. $69.374 = 60 + 9 + .3 + .07 + .004$.

Rule For Converting a Decimal Into Vulgar Fraction : *Put 1 in the denominator under the decimal point and annex with it as many zeros as is the number of digits after the decimal point. Now, remove the decimal point and reduce the fraction to its lowest terms.*

Ex. 1. *Convert the following into vulgar fractions :*

(i) **0.75**   (ii) **3.004**   (iii) **.0056**

Sol.   (i) $.075 = \frac{75}{100} = \frac{3}{4}.$

(ii) $3.004 = \frac{3004}{1000} = \frac{751}{250}.$

(iii) $\frac{.0056}{10000} = \frac{7}{1250}.$

Remark 1 : *Annexing zeros to the extreme right of a decimal fraction does not change its value.*

Thus, $0.8 = 0.80 = 0.800$ etc.

Remark 2 : *If numerator and denominator of a fraction contain the same number of decimal places, then we remove the decimal sign.*

Ex. 2. *Simplify :*   (i) $\frac{1.84}{2.99}$ (ii) $\frac{.365}{.584}$

Sol.   (i) $\frac{1.84}{2.99} = \frac{184}{299} = \frac{8}{13}.$

(ii) $\frac{.365}{.584} = \frac{365}{584} = \frac{5}{8}.$

Addition & Subtraction of Decimal Fractions :

Rule : *The given numbers are so placed under each other that the decimal points lie in one column. The numbers so arranged can now be added or subtracted in a usual way.*

Ex. 3. *Evaluate :*

(*i*) $617 + 6.017 + .617 + 6.0017 = ?$

(*ii*) $5.064 + 3.98 + .7036 + 7.6 + .3 + 2 = ?$

(*iii*) $31.004 - 17.2386 = ?$

(*iv*) $13 - 5.1967 = ?$

Sol.   (*i*)   617.0   (*ii*)   5.064

                       6.017   3.98

                       0.617   0.7036

                   + 6.0017   7.6

                   629.6357   0.3

                                             + 2.0

                                       19.6476

     (*iii*)   31.004   (*iv*)   13.0000

                −17.2386   −5.1967

                 13.7654   7.8033

Ex. 4. (*i*) $67.32 + ? = 431.146$ (*ii*) $107.07 - ? = 63.932$.

Sol. (*i*) Let $67.32 + x = 431.146$.

Then, $x = (431.146 - 67.32) = 363.826$.

(*ii*) Let $107.07 - x = 63.932$.

Then, $x = (107.07 - 63.932) = 43.138$.

Multiplication of a Decimal Fraction By a Power of 10 :

Rule : *Shift the decimal point to the right by as many places of decimal as is the power of 10.*

Ex. 5. *Find the products :*

(*i*) 6.3204×100 (*ii*) 0.5791×1000 (*iii*) $.069 \times 10000$

Sol. (*i*) $6.3204 \times 100 = 632.04$.

(*ii*) $0.5791 \times 1000 = 579.1$.

(*iii*) $0.069 \times 10000 = .0690 \times 10000 = 690$.

Multiplication of Decimal Fractions :

Rule : *Multiply the given numbers considering them without the decimal point. Now, in the product, the decimal point is marked off to obtain as many places of decimal as is the sum of the number of decimal places in the given numbers.*

Ex. 6. *Find the products :*

(*i*) 2.61×1.3 (*ii*) 2.1693×1.4 (*iii*) $.4 \times .04 \times .004 \times 40$

Sol. (*i*) $261 \times 13 = 3393$.

The sum of decimal places of given numbers $= (2 + 1) = 3$.

∴ $2.61 \times 1.3 = 3.393$.

(*ii*) $21693 \times 14 = 303702$.

Sum of decimal places $= (4 + 1) = 5$.

$\therefore$ $2.1693 \times 1.4 = 3.03702$.

(*iii*) $4 \times 4 \times 4 \times 40 = 2560$.

Sum of decimal places $= (1 + 2 + 3) = 6$.

$\therefore$ $.4 \times .04 \times .004 \times 40 = .002560$.

Ex. 7. *Given that* $268 \times 74 = 19832$, *find* $2.68 \times .74$.

Sol. Sum of decimal places $= (2 + 2) = 4$.

$\therefore$ $268 \times 74 = 1.9832$.

Dividing a Decimal Fraction By a Counting Number :

Rule : *Divide the given number without considering the decimal point by the given counting number. Now, in the quotient, put the decimal point to give as many places of decimal as are there in the dividend.*

Ex. 8. *Divide* :

      (*i*) **0.63 by 9**   (*ii*) **0.0204 by 17**   (*iii*) **3.1603 by 13**

Sol. (*i*) $63 \div 9 = 7$.

Dividend contains 2 places of decimal.

$\therefore$ $0.63 \div 9 = .07$.

(*ii*) $204 \div 17 = 12$.

Dividend contains 4 places of decimal.

$\therefore$ $0.0204 \div 17 = .0012$.

(*iii*) $31603 \div 13 = 2431$.

Dividend contains 4 places of decimal.

$\therefore$ $3.1603 \div 13 = .2431$.

Dividing a Decimal Fraction By a Decimal Fraction :

Rule : *Multiply both the dividend and the divisor by a suitable power of 10 to make divisor a whole number. Now, proceed as above.*

Ex. 9. *Evaluate* :

(*i*) **35 ÷ .07**   (*ii*) **.00066 ÷ 0.11**   (*iii*) **5.6 ÷ 0.008**

Sol. (*i*) $\dfrac{35}{.07} = \dfrac{35 \times 100}{.07 \times 100} = \dfrac{3500}{7} = 500$.

(*ii*) $\dfrac{0.00066}{0.11} = \dfrac{0.00066 \times 100}{0.11 \times 100} = \dfrac{.066}{11} = .006$.

(*iii*) $\dfrac{5.6}{0.008} = \dfrac{5.6 \times 1000}{0.008 \times 1000} = \dfrac{5600}{8} = 700$.

Ex. 10. (*i*) **0.006 ÷ ? = 0.6**   (*ii*) **? ÷ .025 = 80**

Sol. (*i*) $\dfrac{0.006}{x} = 0.6$ or $x = \dfrac{0.006}{0.6} = \dfrac{0.006 \times 10}{0.6 \times 10} = \dfrac{0.06}{6} = .01$.

(*ii*) $x \div .025 = 80$ or $\dfrac{x}{.025} = 80$.

$\therefore$ $x = 80 \times .025 = 2$.

H.C.F. & L.C.M. of Decimal Fractions :

Rule : *In given numbers, make the same number of decimal places by annexing zeros in some numbers, if necessary. Considering these numbers without decimal point, find H.C.F. or L.C.M. as the case may be. Now, in the result, mark off as many decimal places as are there in each of the given numbers.*

Ex. 11. *Find the H.C.F. and L.C.M. of .63, 1.05 and 2.1.*

Sol. Making the same number of decimal places, the given numbers are 0.63, 1.05 and 2.10.

Without decimal places, these numbers are 63, 105 and 210.

Now, H.C.F. of 63, 105 and 210 is 21.

∴ H.C.F. of .63, 1.05 and 2.1 is 0.21.

L.C.M. of 63, 105 & 210 is 630.

∴ L.C.M. of .63, 1.05 and 2.1 is 6.30.

Comparison of Fractions : *Suppose some fractions are to be arranged in ascending or descending order of magnitude.*

Rule : *Convert each one of the given fractions in the decimal form. Now, arrange them in ascending order, as per requirements.*

Ex. 12. *Arrange the fractions* $\dfrac{5}{8}, \dfrac{7}{12}, \dfrac{13}{16}, \dfrac{16}{29}$ *and* $\dfrac{3}{4}$ *in ascending order of magnitude.*

Sol. Converting each of the given fractions into decimal form, we get :

$\dfrac{5}{8} = 0.625, \dfrac{7}{12} = 0.5833, \dfrac{13}{16} = 0.8125, \dfrac{16}{29} = 0.5517 \& \dfrac{3}{4} = 0.75.$

Now $0.5517 < 0.5833 < 0.625 < 0.75 < 0.8125$

∴ $\dfrac{16}{29} < \dfrac{7}{12} < \dfrac{5}{8} < \dfrac{3}{4} < \dfrac{13}{16}.$

Recurring Decimal : *If in a decimal fraction, a figure or a set of figures is repeated continuously, then such a number is called a recurring decimal.*

In a recurring decimal, if a single figure is repeated, then it is expressed by putting a dot on it. If a set of figures is repeated, it is expressed by putting a bar on the set.

Thus, we have :

(*i*) $\dfrac{1}{3} = 0.333 \ldots = 0.\dot{3}.$ (*ii*) $\dfrac{22}{7} = 3.142857\,142857 \ldots = 3.\overline{142857}.$

Pure Recurring Decimal : *A decimal fraction in which all the figures after the decimal point are repeated, is called a pure recurring decimal e.g.*

$\dfrac{2}{3} = 0.666 \ldots = 0.\dot{6}.$

Converting a Pure Recurring Decimal Into Vulgar Fraction :

Rule : *Write the repeated figures only once in the numerator and take as many nines in the denominator as is the number of repeating figures.*

Ex. 13. *Express the following as vulgar fractions :*

$$(i)\ 0.\dot{6} \qquad (ii)\ 0.\overline{37} \qquad (iii)\ 0.\overline{053} \qquad (iv)\ 3.\overline{142857}$$

Sol. $(i)\ 0.\dot{6} = \dfrac{6}{9} = \dfrac{2}{3}.$ $\qquad (ii)\ 0.\overline{37} = \dfrac{37}{99}.$ $\qquad (iii)\ 0.\overline{053} = \dfrac{53}{999}.$

$$(iv)\ 3.\overline{142857} = 3 + 0.\overline{142857} = 3 + \frac{142857}{999999} = 3\frac{142857}{999999}.$$

Mixed Recurring Decimal : *A decimal fraction in which some figures do not repeat and some of them are repeated, is called a mixed recurring decimal. e.g.* $0.173333 \ldots = 0.17\overline{3}.$

Converting a Mixed Recurring Decimal Into Vulgar Fraction :

Rule : *In the numerator, take the difference between the number formed by all the digits after decimal point (taking repeated digits only once) and that formed by the digits which are not repeated. In the denominator, take the number formed by as many nines as there are repeating digits followed by as many zeros as is the number of non-repeating digits.*

Ex. 14. *Express the following as vulgar fractions :*

$$(i)\ 0.1\overline{7} \qquad (ii)\ 0.12\overline{54} \qquad (iii)\ 2.53\overline{6}$$

Sol. $(i)\ 0.1\overline{7} = \dfrac{17-1}{90} = \dfrac{16}{90} = \dfrac{8}{45}.$

$(ii)\ 0.12\overline{54} = \dfrac{1254-12}{9900} = \dfrac{1242}{9900} = \dfrac{69}{550}.$

$(iii)\ 2.53\overline{6} = 2 + 0.53\overline{6} = 2 + \dfrac{536-53}{900} = 2 + \dfrac{483}{900} = 2 + \dfrac{161}{300} = 2\dfrac{161}{300}.$

EXERCISE 3

Mark ($\sqrt{}$) against the correct answer :

1. $0.7683 + 0.369 + 0.05 + 0.8 = ?$
   (a) 0.8065 (b) 1.9873 (c) 0.8110 (d) None

2. $3.1469 + 6.837 + ? = 15$
   (a) 24.9839 (b) 5.7634 (c) 5.0161 (d) None

3. $1.086 - .3983 - .669 = ?$
   (a) .6208 (b) 1.3948 (c) .0048 (d) .0187

4. $14.3 + 16.78 - ? = 9.009$
   (a) 40.089 (b) 22.071 (c) 21.810 (d) None
   (Bank P.O. 1994)

5. $852.2109 + 106.78 - 59.157 = ?$
   (a) 899.8339 (b) 889.8339 (c) 899.9833 (d) 804.5879
   (Hotel Management 1993)

6. $5463 + 546.3 - 54.63 \div ? = 5999.3$
   (a) .05463 (b) .5463 (c) 5.463 (d) None

7. Which of the following sets of fractions is in descending order ?
   (a) $\dfrac{3}{5}, \dfrac{7}{9}, \dfrac{6}{7}$ (b) $\dfrac{7}{9}, \dfrac{3}{5}, \dfrac{6}{7}$ (c) $\dfrac{7}{9}, \dfrac{6}{7}, \dfrac{3}{5}$ (d) $\dfrac{6}{7}, \dfrac{7}{9}, \dfrac{3}{5}$
   (Bank P.O. 1993)

8. Which of the following sets of fractions is in ascending order ?

(a) $\dfrac{5}{6}, \dfrac{6}{8}, \dfrac{7}{9}, \dfrac{11}{13}$

(b) $\dfrac{6}{8}, \dfrac{7}{9}, \dfrac{5}{6}, \dfrac{11}{13}$

(c) $\dfrac{11}{13}, \dfrac{5}{6}, \dfrac{7}{9}, \dfrac{6}{8}$

(d) $\dfrac{11}{13}, \dfrac{7}{9}, \dfrac{6}{8}, \dfrac{5}{6}$

(C.B.I. 1993)

9. Which part contains the fractions in ascending order ?

(a) $\dfrac{11}{14}, \dfrac{16}{19}, \dfrac{19}{21}$

(b) $\dfrac{16}{19}, \dfrac{11}{14}, \dfrac{19}{21}$

(c) $\dfrac{19}{21}, \dfrac{11}{14}, \dfrac{16}{19}$

(d) $\dfrac{16}{19}, \dfrac{19}{21}, \dfrac{11}{14}$

10. Which of the following fractions is the smallest ?   **(C.B.I. 1990)**

(a) $\dfrac{13}{16}$

(b) $\dfrac{15}{19}$

(c) $\dfrac{17}{21}$

(d) $\dfrac{7}{8}$

11. 0.000006723 when expressed in scientific notation, is :

(a) 6723×10^{-5} (b) 67.23×10^{-7} (c) 6.723×10^{-6} (d) None

12. What decimal of an hour is a second ?

(a) .0025   (b) .0256   (c) .00027   (d) .000126

13. If $1.125 \times 10^{k} = 0.001125$, then the value of k is :

(a) -4 (b) -3 (c) -2 (d) -1

(Central Excise & I.Tax 1993)

14. Which of the following fractions is less than $\dfrac{7}{8}$ and greater than $\dfrac{1}{3}$?

(a) $\dfrac{1}{4}$

(b) $\dfrac{23}{24}$

(c) $\dfrac{11}{12}$

(d) $\dfrac{17}{24}$

(Central Excise & I.Tax 1993)

15. A metre is taken to be equal to 39.3701 inches. If the value is approximated to $39\dfrac{7}{20}$ inches, the relative percentage error is :

(a) 5%   (b) 0.5%   (c) .05%   (d) 0.005%

(Central Excise & I.Tax 1993)

16. 0.393939... is equivalent to the fraction :   **(C.D.S. 1993)**

(a) $\dfrac{39}{100}$

(b) $\dfrac{39}{99}$

(c) $\dfrac{93}{100}$

(d) None

17. The fraction for 0.535353... is :

(a) $\dfrac{26}{53}$

(b) $\dfrac{27}{53}$

(c) $\dfrac{28}{53}$

(d) $\dfrac{53}{99}$

18. $0.\overline{8}$ expressed as a fraction is :

(a) $\dfrac{8}{10}$

(b) $\dfrac{88}{100}$

(c) $\dfrac{88}{99}$

(d) $\dfrac{8}{9}$

19. $1.\overline{6}$ expressed as a fraction is :

    (a) $\dfrac{16}{10}$ (b) $\dfrac{16}{9}$ (c) $\dfrac{5}{3}$ (d) None

20. The value of $0.5\overline{7}$ is :   **(Assistant Grade 1993)**

    (a) $\dfrac{57}{10}$ (b) $\dfrac{57}{99}$ (c) $\dfrac{26}{45}$ (d) $\dfrac{52}{9}$

21. Let $F = 0.84\overline{181}$. When F is written as a fraction in lowest terms, the denominator exceeds the numerator by :   **(C.B.I. 1993)**

    (a) 13   (b) 14   (c) 29   (d) 87

22. $1.\overline{34}$ expressed as a fraction is :

    (a) $\dfrac{134}{100}$ (b) $\dfrac{134}{99}$ (c) $\dfrac{133}{99}$ (d) None

23. The value of $4.1\overline{2}$ is :

    (a) $4\dfrac{11}{90}$ (b) $4\dfrac{11}{99}$ (c) $\dfrac{371}{900}$ (d) None

24. The value of $2.1\overline{36}$ is :

    (a) $\dfrac{47}{220}$ (b) $\dfrac{68}{495}$ (c) $2\dfrac{3}{22}$ (d) None

25. The simplification of $(.\overline{6} + .\overline{7} + .\overline{8} + .\overline{3})$ yields the result :

    (a) $2\dfrac{3}{10}$ (b) $2\dfrac{2}{3}$ (c) $2.\overline{35}$ (d) $5\dfrac{3}{10}$

    (Central Excise & I.Tax 1991)

26. The value of $(3.\overline{87} - 2.\overline{59})$ equals :   **(I.Tax 1990)**

    (a) 1.20   (b) $1.\overline{2}$ (c) $1.\overline{27}$ (d) $1.\overline{28}$

27. $(0.\overline{63} + 0.\overline{37})$ is equal to :

    (a) 1   (b) $1.0\overline{1}$ (c) $0.\overline{101}$ (d) 1.01

28. $(0.34\overline{67} + 0.13\overline{33})$ is equal to :

    (a) 0.48   (b) $0.48\overline{01}$ (c) $0.\overline{48}$ (d) 0.48

29. The sum of $\overline{2}.75$ and $\overline{3}.78$ is :   **(Assistant Grade 1993)**

    (a) $\overline{5}.53$ (b) $\overline{4}.53$ (c) $\overline{1}.53$ (d) $\overline{1}.03$

30. $18.2 \times 0.013 \times 5.21$ is equal to :   **(Teacher's Exam 1991)**

    (a) 12.32686   (b) 123.2686   (c) 1.232686   (d) 0.1232686

31. $(7.5 \times 0.9 \times 14.4)$ is equal to :   **(Bank P.O. 1993)**

    (a) 48.6   (b) 91.44   (c) 97.2   (d) 94.95

32. $(.08 \times .007)$ is equal to :

    (a) .056   (b) .0056   (c) .00056   (d) .56

33. $3 \times 0.3 \times 0.03 \times 0.003 \times 30 = ?$ **(Bank P.O. 1991)**

    (a) 0.0000243   (b) 0.000243   (c) 0.00243   (d) 0.0243

34. On simplification $\dfrac{1}{0.04}$ is equal to :   **(I.Tax 1992)**

(a) 2.5   (b) 25   (c) $\frac{2}{5}$ (d) $\frac{1}{40}$

35. $(25.025 \div 0.025)$ is equal to :

(a) 10.01   (b) 100.1   (c) 1001   (d) .1001

36. $(32 \div .0008)$ is equal to :

(a) 40   (b) 400   (c) 4000   (d) None

37. $(.000044 \div .11)$ is equal to :

(a) .004   (b) .04   (c) .0004   (d) .4

38. $.8 \times ? = .0004$

(a) .005   (b) .0005   (c) .5   (d) 5

39. $.009 \div ? = .01$

(a) 9   (b) .9   (c) .09   (d) 0.0009

40. $\frac{86.04}{4000}$ is equal to :

(a) .10215   (b) .02151   (c) .15201   (d) .21015

41. $4.8438 \div .069 = ?$

                                                      (Assistant Grade 1994)

(a) 60.2   (b) 70.2   (c) 69.2   (d) 71.2

42. $.666666 \div .011$ is equal to :

(a) 60.606   (b) 66.06   (c) .60606   (d) None

43. $.973 \times .564 + .973 \times .436 = ?$

(a) 1   (b) 973   (c) .973   (d) 9.73

44. The value of $(3.75 \times 3.75 - 2 \times 3.75 \times 2.75 + 2.75 \times 2.75)$ is :

(a) 1   (b) 1.75   (c) 4.75   (d) 6.50

                                                      (Assistant Grade 1993)

45. The expression $(11.98 \times 11.98 + 11.98 \times x + .02 \times .02)$ will be a perfect square for x equal to :   **(Assistant Grade 1993)**

(a) .02   (b) .2   (c) .04   (d) 0.4

46. The value of $\left(\dfrac{2.75 \times 2.75 \times 2.75 - 2.25 \times 2.25 \times 2.25}{2.75 \times 2.75 + 2.75 \times 2.25 + 2.25 \times 2.25} \right)$ is :

(a) 0.30   (b) 0.50   (c) 3   (d) 5

                                                      (C.B.I. 1993)

47. The value of $\left(\dfrac{8.94 \times 8.94 \times 8.94 - 3.56 \times 3.56 \times 3.56}{8.94 \times 8.94 + 8.94 \times 3.56 + 3.56 \times 3.56} \right)$ is :

(a) .538   (b) 5.38   (c) .0538   (d) 53.8

48. The value of $\dfrac{(0.0347)^3 + (0.9653)^3}{(0.0347)^2 - 0.0347 \times 0.9653 + (0.9653)^2}$ is :

(a) 1   (b) 10   (c) 30   (d) None

49. The value of $\dfrac{(2.3)^3 + .027}{(2.3)^2 - .69 + .09}$ is :

(a) 2.6   (b) 2   (c) 2.33   (d) 2.27

50. The value of $\dfrac{(0.06)^2 + (0.47)^2 + (0.079)^2}{(0.006)^2 + (0.047)^2 + (0.0079)^2}$ is :

   (*a*) 0.1   (*b*) 10   (*c*) 100   (*d*) 1000

51. The value of $\left(\dfrac{.953 \times .953 - .953 \times .047 + .047 \times .047}{.953 \times .953 \times .953 + .047 \times .047 \times .047}\right)$ is :

   (*a*) .886   (*b*) 1.1286   (*c*) .32   (*d*) None

52. The value of $\left(\dfrac{8.6 \times 5.3 + 8.6 \times 4.7}{4.3 \times 9.7 - 4.3 \times 8.7}\right)$ is :

   (*a*) 13.9   (*b*) 3.3   (*c*) 6.847   (*d*) 20

53. The value of $\left(\dfrac{.896 \times .763 + .896 \times .237}{.7 \times .064 + .7 \times .936}\right)$ is :

   (*a*) .976   (*b*) 9.76   (*c*) 12.8   (*d*) 1.28

54. The value of $(25.732)^2 - (15.732)^2$ is :   **(Teacher's Exam 1991)**

   (*a*) 414.64   (*b*) 41.464   (*c*) 4146.4   (*d*) 4.1464

55. The value of $\left(\dfrac{.625 \times .0729 \times 28.9}{.0017 \times .025 \times 8.1}\right)$ is :

   (*a*) .3825   (*b*) 3.825   (*c*) 38.25   (*d*) 3825

56. $\dfrac{(0.6)^4 - (0.5)^4}{(0.6)^2 + (0.5)^2}$ is equal to :

   (*a*) 1.1   (*b*) 0.1   (*c*) 11   (*d*) .11

57. The value of $\dfrac{(2.697 - .498)^2 + (2.697 + .498)^2}{2.697 \times 2.697 + .498 \times .498}$ is :

   (*a*) 2.199   (*b*) 3.195   (*c*) 2   (*d*) $\dfrac{1}{2}$

58. The value of $\dfrac{(0.137 + 0.098)^2 - (0.137 - 0.098)^2}{0.137 \times 0.098}$ is :

   (*a*) 4   (*b*) 0.25   (*c*) .039   (*d*) .235

59. If $12276 \div 1.55 = 7920$, the value of $122.76 \div 15.5$ is :

   (*a*) 7.092   (*b*) 7.92   (*c*) 79.02   (*d*) 79.2

60. If $2805 \div 2.55 = 1100$, then $280.5 \div 25.5$ is equal to :

   (*a*) 1.01   (*b*) 1.1   (*c*) .11   (*d*) 11

61. If $\dfrac{1}{3.718} = .2689$, then the value of $\dfrac{1}{.0003718}$ is :

   (*a*) 2689   (*b*) 2.689   (*c*) 26890   (*d*) .2689

62. If $168 \times 54 = 9072$, then $.9072 \div 16.8$ is equal to :

   (*a*) 5.4   (*b*) .54   (*c*) .054   (*d*) .0054

63. The H.C.F. of 1.75, 5.6 and 7 is :

   (*a*) .07   (*b*) .7   (*c*) 3.5   (*d*) .35

64. The G.C.D. of 1.08, .36 and .9 is :

   (*a*) .03   (*b*) .9   (*c*) .18   (*d*) .108

65. The H.C.F. of 0.54, 1.8 and 7.2 is :
   (a) 1.8   (b) .18   (c) .018   (d) 18

66. The L.C.M. of 3, 2.7 and .09 is :
   (a) 2.7   (b) .27   (c) .027   (d) 27

67. .253 × .154 is the same as :   **(L.I.C. 1991)**
   (a) 2.53 × .00154   (b) 25.3 × 1.54
   (c) 253 × .0154   (d) 2.53 × .0154

68. If $\sqrt{15} = 3.88$, the value of $\sqrt{\dfrac{5}{3}}$ is :
   (a) 0.43   (b) 1.89   (c) 1.29   (d) 1.63

69. If $\sqrt{4096} = 64$, then the value of :
$\sqrt{40.96} + \sqrt{0.4096} + \sqrt{0.004096} + \sqrt{0.00004096}$ is :
   (a) 7.09   (b) 7.1014   (c) 7.1104   (d) 7.12

70. If $\sqrt{5} = 2.24$, then the value of $\dfrac{3\sqrt{5}}{2\sqrt{5} - 0.48}$ is :
   (a) 0.168   (b) 1.68   (c) 16.8   (d) 168

71. If $1.5x = 0.04y$, then the value of $\left(\dfrac{y-x}{y+x}\right)$ is :
                                          (L.I.C. 1991)
   (a) $\dfrac{730}{77}$ (b) $\dfrac{73}{77}$ (c) $\dfrac{7.3}{77}$ (d) None

72. 1 litre of water weighs 1 kg. How many cubic milliletres of water will weigh 0.1 gm ?
   (a) 0.1   (b) 1   (c) 10   (d) 100

73. If $\sqrt{.05 \times .5 \times a} = .5 \times .05 \times \sqrt{b}$, then $\dfrac{a}{b}$ is equal to :
   (a) .0025   (b) .025   (c) .25   (d) None

ANSWERS

1. (b)	**2.** (c)	**3.** (d)	**4.** (b)	**5.** (a)	**6.** (c)	**7.** (d)	**8.** (b)	**9.** (a)
10. (b)	**11.** (c)	**12.** (c)	**13.** (b)	**14.** (d)	**15.** (c)	**16.** (b)	**17.** (d)	**18.** (d)
19. (c)	**20.** (c)	**21.** (d)	**22.** (c)	**23.** (a)	**24.** (c)	**25.** (b)	**26.** (d)	**27.** (b)
28. (b)	**29.** (b)	**30.** (c)	**31.** (c)	**32.** (c)	**33.** (c)	**34.** (b)	**35.** (c)	**36.** (d)
37. (c)	**38.** (b)	**39.** (b)	**40.** (b)	**41.** (b)	**42.** (a)	**43.** (c)	**44.** (a)	**45.** (c)
46. (b)	**47.** (b)	**48.** (a)	**49.** (a)	**50.** (c)	**51.** (d)	**52.** (d)	**53.** (d)	**54.** (a)
55. (d)	**56.** (d)	**57.** (c)	**58.** (a)	**59.** (b)	**60.** (d)	**61.** (a)	**62.** (c)	**63.** (d)
64. (c)	**65.** (b)	**66.** (d)	**67.** (a)	**68.** (c)	**69.** (c)	**70.** (b)	**71.** (b)	**72** (d)
73. (b)								

SOLUTIONS

1.
$$0.7683$$
$$0.369$$
$$0.05$$
$$+ \ 0.8$$
$$\overline{1.9873}$$

2. Let $3.1469 + 6.837 + x = 15$.
Then, $9.9839 + x = 15$
or $x = (15 - 9.9839) = 5.0161$.

3. $1.086 - .3983 - .669 = 1.086 - (.3983 + .669)$
$$= 1.086 - 1.0673 = 0.0187.$$

4. Let $14.3 + 16.78 - x = 9.009$. Then, $31.08 - x = 9.009$.
$\therefore \ x = (31.08 - 9.009) = 22.071$.

5. $852.2109 + 106.78 - 59.157 = 985.9909 - 59.157 = 899.8339$.

6. Let $5463 + 546.3 - 54.63 \div x = 5999.3$.

Then, $5463 + \overset{\text{.}}{5}46.3 - \dfrac{54.63}{x} = 5999.3$

or $6009.3 - \dfrac{54.63}{x} = 5999.3$ or $\dfrac{54.63}{x} = 6009.3 - 5999.3$

or $\dfrac{54.63}{x} = 10$ or $x = \dfrac{54.63}{10} = 5.463$.

7. Converting each one of the given fractions in decimal form, we get :
$$\frac{3}{5} = 0.6, \frac{7}{9} = 0.777 \text{ and } \frac{6}{7} = 0.857$$

Clearly, $0.857 > 0.777 > 0.6$. So, $\dfrac{6}{7} > \dfrac{7}{9} > \dfrac{3}{5}$.

8. Converting each into decimal form, we get :
$$\frac{5}{6} = 0.833, \frac{6}{8} = 0.75, \frac{7}{9} = 0.777, \frac{11}{13} = 0.846.$$

Clearly, $0.75 < 0.777 < 0.833 < 0.846$ or $\dfrac{6}{8} < \dfrac{7}{9} < \dfrac{5}{6} < \dfrac{11}{13}$.

9. Converting each into decimal form, we get :
$$\frac{11}{14} = 0.785, \frac{16}{19} = 0.842 \ \& \ \frac{19}{21} = 0.904.$$

Clearly, $0.785 < 0.842 < 0.904$ or $\dfrac{11}{14} < \dfrac{16}{19} < \dfrac{19}{21}$.

10. We have : $\dfrac{13}{16} = 0.8125, \dfrac{15}{19} = 0.7894, \dfrac{17}{21} = 0.8095 \ \& \ \dfrac{7}{8} = 0.875$.

The smallest of these is $\dfrac{15}{19}$.

11. $0.000006723 = \dfrac{0.000006723 \times 10^6}{10^6} = \dfrac{6.723}{10^6} = 6.723 \times 10^{-6}$.

12. Required decimal $= \dfrac{1}{60 \times 60} = \dfrac{1}{3600} = .00027$.

13. $10^k = \dfrac{0.001125}{1.125} = \dfrac{1.125}{1125} = \dfrac{1.125 \times 10^3}{1125 \times 10^3} = \dfrac{1}{10^3} = 10^{-3}$.

$\therefore$ $k = -3$.

14. $\dfrac{7}{8} = 0.875$, $\dfrac{1}{3} = .333$, $\dfrac{1}{4} = 0.25$, $\dfrac{23}{24} = 0.958$, $\dfrac{11}{12} = 0.916$, $\dfrac{17}{24} = 0.708$

Clearly, 0.708 lies between 0.333 & 0.875.

$\therefore$ Required fraction is $\dfrac{17}{24}$.

15. Exact value = 39.3701 inches.

Approximate value $= 39 + \dfrac{7}{20} = 39 + 0.35 = 39.35$.

Error % $= \left[\dfrac{(39.3701 - 39.35)}{39.3701} \times 100\right]\% = \left(\dfrac{.0201}{39.3701} \times 100\right)\%$

$= \left(\dfrac{20100}{393701}\right)\% = 0.05\%$.

16. $0.393939\ldots = 0.\overline{39} = \dfrac{39}{99}$.

17. $0.5353\ldots = 0.\overline{53} = \dfrac{53}{99}$.

18. $0.\overline{8} = \dfrac{8}{9}$.

19. $1.\overline{6} = 1 + 0.\overline{6} = 1 + \dfrac{6}{9} = 1 + \dfrac{2}{3} = \dfrac{5}{3}$.

20. $0.5\overline{7} = \dfrac{57 - 5}{90} = \dfrac{52}{90} = \dfrac{26}{45}$.

21. $0.84\overline{181} = \dfrac{84181 - 841}{99000} = \dfrac{83340}{99000} = \dfrac{463}{550}$.

$\therefore$ Required difference = (550 − 463) = 87.

22. $1.\overline{34} = 1 + 0.\overline{34} = 1 + \dfrac{34}{99} = \dfrac{99 + 34}{99} = \dfrac{133}{99}$.

23. $4.1\overline{2} = 4 + 0.1\overline{2} = 4 + \dfrac{12 - 1}{90} = 4\dfrac{11}{90}$.

24. $2.1\overline{36} = 2 + 0.1\overline{36} = 2 + \dfrac{136 - 1}{990} = 2 + \dfrac{3}{22} = 2\dfrac{3}{22}$.

25. $0.\overline{6} + 0.\overline{7} + 0.\overline{8} + 0.\overline{3} = \left(\dfrac{6}{9} + \dfrac{7}{9} + \dfrac{8}{9} + \dfrac{3}{9}\right) = \dfrac{24}{9} = \dfrac{8}{3} = 2\dfrac{2}{3}$.

26. $3.\overline{87} - 2.\overline{59} = (3 + 0.\overline{87}) - (2 + 0.\overline{59})$

$$= \left(3 + \frac{87}{99}\right) - \left(2 + \frac{59}{99}\right) = 1 + \left(\frac{87}{99} - \frac{59}{99}\right).$$

$$= 1 + \frac{28}{99} = 1.\overline{28}.$$

27. $0.\overline{63} + 0.\overline{37} = \frac{63}{99} + \frac{37}{99} = \frac{63 + 37}{99} = \frac{100}{99} = 1\frac{1}{99} = 1 + 0.\overline{01} = 1.\overline{01}.$

28. $0.3\overline{467} + 0.1\overline{333} = \frac{3467 - 34}{9900} + \frac{1333 - 13}{9900} = \frac{3433 + 1320}{9900} = \frac{4753}{9900}.$

$$= \frac{4801 - 48}{9900} = 0.48\overline{01}.$$

29. $\overline{2}.75 + \overline{3}.78 = (-2 + 0.75) + (-3 + 0.78)$
$$= -5 + (0.75 + 0.78) = -5 + 1.53 = -5 + 1 + 0.53$$
$$= -4 + 0.53 = \overline{4}.53.$$

30. $182 \times 13 \times 521 = 1232686.$
    Sum of decimal places = 6.
    $\therefore 18.2 \times 0.013 \times 5.21 = 1.232686.$

31. $7.5 \times 0.9 \times 14.4 = \frac{75 \times 9 \times 144}{1000} = \frac{3 \times 9 \times 36}{10} = \frac{972}{10} = 97.2.$

32. Since $8 \times 7 = 56$ and sum of decimal places = 5.
    $\therefore .8 \times .007 = .00056.$

33. $3 \times 3 \times 3 \times 3 \times 30 = 2430.$
    Sum of decimal places = 6.
    $\therefore 3 \times 0.3 \times 0.03 \times 0.003 \times 30 = .002430 = 0.00243.$

34. $\frac{1}{0.04} = \frac{100}{4} = 25.$

35. $\frac{25.025}{0.025} = \frac{25025}{25} = 1001.$

36. $\frac{32}{.0008} = \frac{32 \times 10000}{8} = 40000.$

37. $\frac{.000044}{.11} = \frac{.0044}{11} = .0004.$

38. Let $.8 \times x = .0004.$ Then, $x = \frac{.0004}{.8} = \frac{.004}{8} = .0005.$

39. Let $\frac{.009}{x} = .01.$ Then $x = \frac{.009}{.01} = \frac{.9}{1} = .9.$

40. $\frac{86.04}{4000} = \frac{8604}{400000} = 0.02151.$

41. $\frac{4.8438}{0.069} = \frac{4.8438}{0.0690} = \frac{48438}{690} = 70.2.$

42. $\frac{.666666}{.011} = \frac{666.666}{11} = 60.606.$

43. Given Expression $= .973 \times (.564 + .436) = .973 \times 1 = .973.$

44. Given Exp. $= (3.75)^2 - 2 \times 3.75 \times 2.75 + (2.75)^2$

$= (a^2 - 2ab + b^2) = (a - b)^2 = (3.75 - 2.75)^2 = 1^2 = 1.$

45. Given Exp. $= (11.98)^2 + (.02)^2 + 11.98 \times x$

For the given expression to be a perfect square, we must have

$11.98 \times x = 2 \times 11.98 \times .02$ or $x = .04.$

46. Given Exp. $= \dfrac{(2.75)^3 - (2.25)^3}{(2.75)^2 + 2.75 \times 2.25 + (2.25)^2}$

$= \left(\dfrac{a^3 - b^3}{a^2 + ab + b^2} \right) = (a - b) = (2.75 - 2.25) = 0.50.$

47. Given Exp. $= \dfrac{(8.94)^3 - (3.56)^3}{(8.94)^2 + 8.94 \times 3.56 + (3.56)^2}$

$= \left(\dfrac{a^3 - b^3}{a^2 + ab + b^2} \right) = (a - b) = (8.94 - 3.56) = 5.38.$

48. Given Exp. $= \left(\dfrac{a^3 + b^3}{a^2 - ab + b^2} \right) = (a + b)$

$= (0.0347 + 0.9653) = 1.$

49. Given Exp. $= \dfrac{(2.3)^3 + (0.3)^3}{(2.3)^2 - 2.3 \times 0.3 + (0.3)^2}$

$= \left(\dfrac{a^3 + b^3}{a^2 - ab + b^2} \right) = (a + b) = (2.3 + 0.3) = 2.6.$

50. Given Exp. $= \dfrac{a^2 + b^2 + c^2}{\left(\dfrac{a}{10} \right)^2 + \left(\dfrac{b}{10} \right)^2 + \left(\dfrac{c}{10} \right)^2}$, where $a = .06, b = .47$ & $c = .079$

$= \dfrac{100 \, (a^2 + b^2 + c^2)}{(a^2 + b^2 + c^2)} = 100.$

51. Given Exp. $= \dfrac{(.953)^2 - (.953 \times .047) + (.047)^2}{(.953)^3 + (.047)^3}$

$= \left(\dfrac{a^2 - ab + b^2}{a^3 + b^3} \right) = \dfrac{1}{a + b} = \dfrac{1}{.953 + .047} = 1.$

52. Given Exp. $= \dfrac{8.6 \times (5.3 + 4.7)}{4.3 \times (9.7 - 8.7)} = \dfrac{8.6 \times 10}{4.3 \times 1} = 20.$

53. Given Exp. $= \dfrac{.896 \times (.763 + .237)}{.7 \times (.064 + .936)} = \dfrac{.896 \times 1}{.7 \times 1} = \dfrac{8.96}{7} = 1.28.$

54. Given Exp. $= (a^2 - b^2) = (a + b)(a - b)$
$$= (25.732 + 15.732)(25.732 - 15.732)$$
$$= 41.464 \times 10 = 414.64.$$

55. The sum of decimal places in the numerator and the denominator being the same, we may remove the decimal point.

$$\therefore \text{ Given Exp.} = \frac{625 \times 729 \times 289}{17 \times 25 \times 81} = 3825.$$

56. Given Exp. $= \dfrac{[(0.6)^2]^2 - [(0.5)^2]^2}{(.6)^2 + (0.5)^2} = \dfrac{[(0.6)^2 + (0.5)^2][(0.6)^2 - (0.5)^2]}{(0.6)^2 + (0.5)^2}$
$$= (0.6)^2 - (0.5)^2 = (0.6 + 0.5)(0.6 - 0.5)$$
$$= (1.1 \times 0.1) = .11.$$

57. Given Exp. $= \dfrac{(a - b)^2 + (a + b)^2}{a^2 + b^2} = \dfrac{2(a^2 + b^2)}{(a^2 + b^2)} = 2.$

58. Given Exp. $= \dfrac{(a + b)^2 - (a - b)^2}{ab} = \dfrac{4ab}{ab} = 4.$

59. Given, $\dfrac{12276}{1.55} = 7920.$

$$\therefore \frac{122.76}{15.5} = \frac{12.276}{1.55} = \frac{12276}{1.55} \times \frac{1}{1000} = \frac{7920}{1000} = 7.92.$$

60. Given, $\dfrac{2805}{2.55} = 1100.$

$$\therefore \frac{280.5}{25.5} = \frac{28.05}{2.55} = \frac{2805}{2.55} \times \frac{1}{100} = \frac{1100}{100} = 11.$$

61. $\dfrac{1}{.0003718} = \dfrac{10000}{3.718} = \left(10000 \times \dfrac{1}{3.718}\right) = 10000 \times .2689 = 2689.$

62. Given, $\dfrac{9072}{168} = 54.$

$$\therefore \frac{.9072}{16.8} = \frac{9.072}{168} = \frac{9072}{168} \times \frac{1}{1000} = \frac{54}{1000} = .054.$$

63. Given numbers with two decimal places are :
1.75, 5.60 and 7.00
Without decimal places, these numbers are :
175, 560 and 700, whose H.C.F. is 35.
$\therefore$ H.C.F. of given numbers = 0.35.

64. Given numbers are 1.08, .36 and .90.
H.C.F. of 108, 36 and 90 is 18.
$\therefore$ H.C.F. of given numbers = .18.

65. Given numbers are 0.54, 1.80 and 7.20.

H.C.F. of 54, 180 and 720 is 18.

∴ H.C.F. of given numbers = .18

66. Given numbers are 3.00, 2.70 and .09.

L.C.M. of 300, 270 and 9 is 2700.

∴ L.C.M. of given numbers = 27.00 = 27.

67. Sum of decimal places in given product = 5

Sum of decimal places in $253 \times .00154$ is 5.

∴ $2.53 \times .154 = 253 \times .00154$.

68. $\sqrt{\dfrac{5}{3}} = \sqrt{\dfrac{5 \times 3}{3 \times 3}} = \dfrac{\sqrt{15}}{3} = \dfrac{3.88}{3} = 1.29$.

69. $\sqrt{40.96} + \sqrt{0.4096} + \sqrt{0.004096} + \sqrt{0.00004096}$

$= \sqrt{\dfrac{4096}{100}} + \sqrt{\dfrac{4096}{10000}} + \sqrt{\dfrac{4096}{1000000}} + \sqrt{\dfrac{4096}{100000000}}$

$= \left(\dfrac{64}{10} + \dfrac{64}{100} + \dfrac{64}{1000} + \dfrac{64}{10000} \right)$

$= (6.4 + .64 + .064 + .0064) = 7.1104$.

70. $\dfrac{3\sqrt{5}}{2\sqrt{5} - 0.48} = \dfrac{3 \times 2.24}{2 \times 2.24 - 0.48} = \dfrac{6.72}{4.48 - 0.48} = \dfrac{6.72}{4} = 1.68$.

71. $\dfrac{x}{y} = \dfrac{0.04}{1.5} = \dfrac{4}{150} = \dfrac{2}{75}$.

∴ $\dfrac{y - x}{y + x} = \dfrac{1 - \dfrac{x}{y}}{1 + \dfrac{x}{y}} = \dfrac{1 - \dfrac{2}{75}}{1 + \dfrac{2}{75}} = \dfrac{73}{77}$.

72. 1000 gm is the weight of 1000 cu.mm.

1 gm is the weight of 1 cu. cm = 1000 cu.cm.

$\dfrac{1}{10}$ gm is the weight of $\left(\dfrac{1000}{10} \right)$ cu.mm = 100 cu.mm.

73. $\sqrt{.05 \times .5 \times a} = .5 \times .05 \times \sqrt{b}$.

∴ $\dfrac{\sqrt{a}}{\sqrt{b}} = \dfrac{.5 \times .05}{\sqrt{.5 \times .05}} = \sqrt{.5 \times .05}$

∴ $\dfrac{a}{b} = .5 \times .05 = .025$.

4. Simplification

In simplifying an expression, first of all bar must be removed. After removing the bar, the brackets must be removed, strictly in the order ( ), { } and [ ].

After removing the brackets, we must use the following operations strictly in the order :

(i) of (ii) Division (iii) Multiplication (iv) Addition (v) Subtraction.

Remark : Remember the word, 'BODMAS', where B, O, D, M, A and S stand for bracket, of, division, multiplication, addition and subtraction respectively.

Ex. 1. *Simplify :* $108 \div 36 \text{ of } \dfrac{1}{4} + \dfrac{2}{5} \times 3\dfrac{1}{4}$.

Sol. Given Expression $= 108 \div 9 + \dfrac{2}{5} \times \dfrac{13}{4}$

$$= \dfrac{108}{9} + \dfrac{13}{10} = \left(12 + \dfrac{13}{10}\right) = \dfrac{133}{10} = 13\dfrac{3}{10}.$$

Ex. 2. *Simplify :* $\dfrac{1}{3} \div \dfrac{5}{3} + \dfrac{1}{4} \times \dfrac{3}{5} - \dfrac{2}{5} \text{ of } \dfrac{5}{7}$.

Sol. Given Expression $= \dfrac{1}{3} \div \dfrac{5}{3} + \dfrac{1}{4} \times \dfrac{3}{5} - \dfrac{2}{5} \text{ of } \dfrac{5}{7}$

$$= \dfrac{1}{3} \div \dfrac{5}{3} + \dfrac{1}{4} \times \dfrac{3}{5} - \dfrac{2}{7} = \dfrac{1}{3} \times \dfrac{3}{5} + \dfrac{3}{20} - \dfrac{2}{7}$$

$$= \dfrac{1}{5} + \dfrac{3}{20} - \dfrac{2}{7} = \dfrac{4+3}{20} - \dfrac{2}{7} = \dfrac{7}{20} - \dfrac{2}{7}$$

$$= \left(\dfrac{49-40}{140}\right) = \dfrac{9}{140}.$$

Ex. 3. *Simplify :* $3.5 \div 0.7 \text{ of } 7 + 0.5 \times 0.3 - 0.1$

Sol. Given Expression $= 3.5 \div 4.9 + 0.5 \times 0.3 - 0.1$

$$= \dfrac{3.5}{4.9} + 0.15 - 0.1 = \dfrac{5}{7} + \dfrac{15}{100} - \dfrac{1}{10}$$

$$= \dfrac{5}{7} + \dfrac{15-10}{100} = \dfrac{5}{7} + \dfrac{5}{100} = \dfrac{5}{7} + \dfrac{1}{20}$$

$$= \left(\dfrac{100+7}{140}\right) = \dfrac{107}{140} = 0.764.$$

Ex. 4. *Simplify :* $2 - [\,3 - \{\,6 - \{\,(5 - \overline{4 - 3})\,\}\,\}\,]$

Sol. Given Expression $= 2 - [\,3 - \{\,6 - (5 - 1)\,\}\,]$

$$= 2 - [\,3 - \{6 - 4\}\,] = 2 - [\,3 - 2\,] = (2 - 1) = 1.$$

Ex. 5. *Simplify :* $\left[3\frac{1}{4} \div \left\{1\frac{1}{4} - \frac{1}{2}\left(2\frac{1}{2} - \overline{\frac{1}{4} - \frac{1}{6}}\right)\right\}\right]$

Sol. Given Exp. $= \left[\frac{13}{4} \div \left\{\frac{5}{4} - \frac{1}{2}\left(\frac{5}{2} - \frac{3-2}{12}\right)\right\}\right]$

$= \left[\frac{13}{4} \div \left\{\frac{5}{4} - \frac{1}{2}\left(\frac{5}{2} - \frac{1}{12}\right)\right\}\right]$

$= \left[\frac{13}{4} \div \left\{\frac{5}{4} - \frac{1}{2}\left(\frac{30-1}{12}\right)\right\}\right]$

$= \left[\frac{13}{4} \div \left\{\frac{5}{4} - \frac{29}{24}\right\}\right]$

$= \left[\frac{13}{4} \div \left\{\frac{30-29}{24}\right\}\right]$

$= \left[\frac{13}{4} \div \frac{1}{24}\right] = \left[\frac{13}{4} \times 24\right] = 78$.

Ex. 6. *If* $617 \div 24.68 + x = 90$, *find the value of* x .

Sol. Let $617 \div 24.68 + x = 90$. Then,

$\frac{617}{24.68} + x = 90$ or $25 + x = 90$ or $x = (90 - 25) = 65$.

Ex. 7. *Simplify :* $1 + \dfrac{1}{1 + \dfrac{1}{1 + \dfrac{1}{5}}}$

Sol. Given Expression $= 1 + \dfrac{1}{1 + \dfrac{1}{(6/5)}} = 1 + \dfrac{1}{1 + \dfrac{5}{6}} = 1 + \dfrac{1}{(11/6)}$

$= \left(1 + \dfrac{6}{11}\right) = 1\dfrac{6}{11}$.

Ex. 8. *Simplify :* $1 - \dfrac{5}{7 + \dfrac{1}{4 + \dfrac{1}{2 + \dfrac{1}{3}}}}$

Sol. Given Expression $= 1 - \dfrac{5}{7 + \dfrac{1}{4 + \dfrac{1}{(7/3)}}} = 1 - \dfrac{5}{7 + \dfrac{1}{\left(4 + \dfrac{3}{7}\right)}}$

$= 1 - \dfrac{5}{7 + \dfrac{1}{(31/7)}} = 1 - \dfrac{5}{7 + \dfrac{7}{31}} = 1 - \dfrac{5}{(224/31)}$

$$= \left(1 - \frac{5 \times 31}{224}\right) = \left(\frac{224 - 155}{224}\right) = \frac{69}{224}.$$

Ex. 9. *A boy was asked to multiply a certain number by 53. He multiplied it by 35 and got his answer less than the correct one by 1206. Find the number to be multiplied.*

Sol. Let the required number be x. Then,

$$53x - 35x = 1206 \quad \text{or} \quad 18x = 1206 \quad \text{or} \quad x = 67.$$

$\therefore$ Required number $= 67$.

Ex. 10. *In a college, $\frac{1}{5}$ th of the girls and $\frac{1}{8}$ th of the boys took part in a social comp. What of the total number of students in the college took part in the camp ?*

Sol. Out of 5 girls 1 took part in the camp.

Out of 8 boys 1 took part in the camp.

$\therefore$ Out of 13 students, 2 took part in the camp.

$\therefore \frac{2}{13}$ of the total strength took part in the camp.

Ex. 11. *The highest score in an inning was $\frac{3}{11}$ of the total and the next highest was $\frac{3}{11}$ of the remainder. If the scores differed by 9, find the total score.*

Sol. Let, total score be x. The, highest score $= \frac{3x}{11}$.

Remainder $= \left(x - \frac{3x}{11}\right) = \frac{8x}{11}$. Next highest $= \frac{3}{11}$ of $\frac{8x}{11} = \frac{24x}{121}$.

$\therefore \frac{3x}{11} - \frac{24x}{121} = 9 \quad \text{or} \quad 33x - 24x = 9 \times 121.$

or $9x = 9 \times 121$ or $x = 121$.

Hence, total score $= 121$.

EXERCISE 4

1. $5005 - 5000 \div 10.00 = ?$ **(Bank P.O. 1988)**
   (a) 0.5   (b) 50   (c) 5000   (d) 4505

2. On simplification, the expression $1 - [1 - \{1 - (1 - \overline{1 - 1})\}]$ yields
   (a) 0   (b) 1   (c) 2   (d) 3
                                                  (Teacher's Exam 1991)

3. How many pieces of 0.85 metres can be cut from a rod 42.5 metres long ?
   (a) 30   (b) 40   (c) 60   (d) None of these
                                                        (Bank P.O. 1994)

4. $b - [b - (a + b) - \{b - (b - a - b)\} + 2a] = ?$

(a) 2b   (b) b − a   (c) a + b   (d) None of these

5. $\frac{31}{10} \times \frac{3}{10} + \frac{7}{5} \div 20 = ?$

(Bank P.O. 1988)

(a) 0   (b) 1   (c) 100   (d) $\frac{107}{200}$

6. $\frac{16 - 6 \times 2 + 3}{23 - 3 \times 2} = ?$

(Bank P.O. 1988)

(a) $\frac{7}{17}$ (b) $\frac{23}{40}$ (c) $\frac{14}{23}$ (d) $\frac{2}{17}$

7. $\frac{(272 - 32)(124 + 176)}{17 \times 15 - 15} = ?$

(Bank P.O. 1991)

(a) 0   (b) 2.25   (c) 300   (d) None of these

8. $\left(\dfrac{1}{2\frac{1}{3}} + \dfrac{1}{1\frac{3}{4}} \right)$ is equal to

(I.Tax 1992)

(a) $4\frac{1}{12}$ (b) $\frac{7}{14}$ (c) $\frac{12}{49}$ (d) None of these

9. $\frac{46 + 18 \times 6 + 4}{12 \times 12 + 8 \times 12} = ?$

(Bank P.O. 1993)

(a) $\frac{20}{57}$ (b) $\frac{113}{912}$ (c) $\frac{113}{120}$ (d) $\frac{79}{120}$

10. $\frac{6}{119} \times \frac{63}{8} \times \frac{17}{9} = ?$

(Bank P.O. 1993)

(a) $\frac{2}{3}$ (b) $\frac{9}{14}$ (c) $\frac{3}{8}$ (d) $\frac{3}{4}$

11. $\frac{(11)^2 - (4)^2 \times 2}{4 \times 2} = ?$

(Bank P.O. 1993)

(a) 11   (b) $1\frac{1}{4}$ (c) $11\frac{1}{8}$ (d) 121

12. $12\frac{1}{2} \times 3\frac{3}{5} \div 1\frac{4}{5} = ?$

(S.B.I.P.O. 1991)

(a) 45   (b) 81   (c) 405   (d) None of these

13. How many $\frac{1}{8}$ s are there in $37\frac{1}{2}$?

(S.B.I.P.O. 1988)

(a) 300   (b) 400   (c) 500   (d) Can't be determined

14. $5.75 - \frac{3}{7} \times 15\frac{3}{4} + 2\frac{2}{35} \div 1.44 = ?$

(C.B.I., 1991)

(a) $\frac{2}{5}$ (b) $\frac{3}{7}$ (c) $\frac{4}{11}$ (d) $\frac{2}{9}$

15. $7\frac{1}{2} - \left[2\frac{1}{4} \div \left\{ 1\frac{1}{4} - \frac{1}{2}\left(1\frac{1}{2} - \frac{1}{3} - \frac{1}{6} \right) \right\} \right]$ is equal to

(U.D.C., 1993)

(a) $\dfrac{2}{9}$ (b) $4\dfrac{1}{2}$ (c) $9\dfrac{1}{2}$ (d) $1\dfrac{77}{228}$

16. $1 + 1 \div \left\{ 1 + 1 \div \left(1 + \dfrac{1}{3} \right) \right\}$ is equal to

     (a) $1\dfrac{1}{3}$ (b) $1\dfrac{4}{7}$ (c) $1\dfrac{1}{8}$ (d) $1\dfrac{2}{3}$

17. $.6 \times .6 + .6 \div 6 = ?$
     (a) .16   (b) .46   (c) .37   (d) .42

18. $4 - 3.6 \div 4 + 0.2 \times 0.5 = ?$
     (a) 3.2   (b) .2   (c) 1.65   (d) .15

19. $108 \div 48$ of $\dfrac{1}{4} + \dfrac{2}{5} \times 3\dfrac{3}{4} = ?$

     (a) $8\dfrac{3}{4}$ (b) $6\dfrac{1}{4}$ (c) $2\dfrac{1}{2}$ (d) $10\dfrac{1}{2}$

20. $\dfrac{\dfrac{1}{4} + \dfrac{1}{4} \div 1\dfrac{1}{4}}{\dfrac{1}{4} \times \dfrac{1}{4} + 2\dfrac{1}{4}} = ?$

     (a) $\dfrac{16}{25}$ (b) $\dfrac{32}{185}$ (c) $\dfrac{36}{185}$ (d) None of these

21. $\dfrac{\dfrac{1}{5} \div \dfrac{1}{5} \text{ of } \dfrac{1}{5}}{\dfrac{1}{5} \text{ of } \dfrac{1}{5} \div \dfrac{1}{5}} = ?$

     (Railway, 1991)

     (a) 1   (b) $\dfrac{1}{25}$ (c) 25   (d) 125

22. $5 - \left[\dfrac{3}{4} + \left\{ 2\dfrac{1}{2} - \left(0.5 + \overline{\dfrac{1}{6} - \dfrac{1}{7}} \right) \right\} \right]$ is equal to   **(Clerk's Grade, 1993)**

     (a) $1\dfrac{19}{84}$ (b) $2\dfrac{61}{84}$ (c) $2\dfrac{23}{84}$ (d) $2\dfrac{47}{84}$

23. $\dfrac{3\dfrac{1}{4} - \dfrac{4}{5} \text{ of } \dfrac{5}{6}}{4\dfrac{1}{3} \div \dfrac{1}{5} - \left(\dfrac{3}{10} + 21\dfrac{1}{5} \right)}$ is equal to

     (a) $\dfrac{1}{6}$ (b) $2\dfrac{7}{12}$ (c) $15\dfrac{1}{2}$ (d) $21\dfrac{1}{2}$

24. The value of $48 \div 12 \times \left(\dfrac{9}{8} \text{ of } \dfrac{4}{3} \div \dfrac{3}{4} \text{ of } \dfrac{2}{3} \right)$ is

     (C.B.I. 1991)

(a) $1\frac{1}{3}$ (b) 3   (c) $5\frac{1}{3}$ (d) 12

25. $\left\{7\frac{1}{2}+\frac{1}{2}\div\frac{1}{2}\text{ of }\frac{1}{4}-\frac{2}{5}\times2\frac{1}{3}\div1\frac{7}{8}\text{ of }\left(1\frac{2}{5}-1\frac{1}{3}\right)\right\}=?$

(a) $3\frac{1}{5}$ (b) $2\frac{1}{24}$ (c) $4\frac{1}{30}$ (d) None of these

26. $\left(4.59\times1.8\div3.6+5.4\text{ of }\frac{1}{9}-\frac{1}{5}\right)=?$

(a) 3.105   (b) 2.705   (c) 2.695   (d) None of these

27. $\frac{3}{4}\div2\frac{1}{4}\text{ of }\frac{2}{3}-\dfrac{\frac{1}{2}-\frac{1}{3}}{\frac{1}{2}+\frac{1}{3}}\times3\frac{1}{3}+\frac{5}{6}=?$

(a) $\frac{7}{18}$ (b) $\frac{49}{54}$ (c) $\frac{2}{3}$ (d) $\frac{1}{6}$

28. $\dfrac{\frac{1}{2}\div4+20}{\frac{1}{2}\times4+20}=?$

(Bank P.O. 1990)

(a) $\frac{81}{88}$ (b) $2\frac{3}{11}$ (c) $\frac{161}{176}$ (d) 1

29. $\dfrac{17.28\div?}{3.6\times0.2}=2$

(S.B.I.P.O Exam 1988)

(a) 120   (b) 1.20   (c) 12   (d) 0.12

30. The value of $\dfrac{9^2\times18^4}{3^{16}}$ is

(C.B.I. 1991)

(a) $\frac{2}{3}$ (b) $\frac{4}{9}$ (c) $\frac{16}{81}$ (d) $\frac{32}{243}$

31. $\frac{3}{8}$ is what part of $\frac{1}{12}$?

(Railways 1991)

(a) $\frac{3}{7}$ (b) $\frac{1}{12}$ (c) $\frac{4}{3}$ (d) None of these

32. $3\frac{1}{4}+4\frac{1}{6}+?+\frac{1}{4}=10$

(a) $2\frac{1}{6}$ (b) $4\frac{1}{3}$ (c) $1\frac{1}{3}$ (d) $2\frac{1}{3}$

33. $4\frac{1}{2}+3\frac{1}{6}+?+2\frac{1}{3}=13\frac{2}{5}$

(S.B.I.P.O, 1987)

(a) $3\frac{2}{5}$ (b) $1\frac{2}{5}$ (c) $4\frac{1}{5}$ (d) $4\frac{1}{6}$

34. $15\dfrac{2}{3}\times 3\dfrac{1}{6}+6\dfrac{1}{3}=11\dfrac{7}{18}+?$

   (a) $39\dfrac{5}{9}$ (b) $137\dfrac{4}{9}$ (c) $29\dfrac{7}{9}$ (d) None of these

35. $\dfrac{5}{6}\div\dfrac{6}{7}\times ?-\dfrac{8}{9}\div 1\dfrac{3}{5}+\dfrac{3}{4}\times 3\dfrac{1}{3}=2\dfrac{7}{9}$ **(G.I.C.A.A.O. 1988)**

   (a) $\dfrac{7}{6}$ (b) $\dfrac{6}{7}$ (c) 1   (d) None of these

36. By how much is two third of 57 more than one third of 90 ?

   (a) 8   (b) 38   (c) 30   (d) 28

      (Bank P.O. 1993)

37. If $45-[\,28-\{37-(15-*)\}\,]=58$, Then * is equal to **(C.B.I. 1993)**

   (a) -19 (b) 19   (c) 29   (d) -29

38. The missing figures at * and ** in $\left(9\dfrac{3}{*}\right)\times\left(**\dfrac{7}{9}\right)=16\dfrac{2}{3}$ will

respectively be   **(C.B.I. 1993)**

   (a) 1, 8   (b) 5, 1   (c) 8, 1   (d) 7, 2

39. $8\dfrac{1}{4}-4\dfrac{1}{5}+2.8+\dfrac{4}{?}-2.32=5.33$ **(Hotel Management 1993)**

   (a) 5   (b) .5   (c) .05   (d) None of these

40. $6\dfrac{2}{3}$ of $7.26\div .45$ of $?=8\dfrac{32}{117}$ **(Hotel Management 1993)**

   (a) $\dfrac{1}{13}$ (b) 13   (c) $13\dfrac{1}{9}$ (d) None of these

41. $5\dfrac{2}{5}$ of $140+?=800$ **(Bank P.O. 1994)**

   (a) 28   (b) 36   (c) 44   (d) 52

42. $1+\cfrac{1}{1+\cfrac{1}{1-\dfrac{1}{6}}}=?$

   (a) $\dfrac{6}{11}$ (b) $\dfrac{16}{11}$ (c) $\dfrac{7}{6}$ (d) $\dfrac{1}{6}$

43. The value of $1+\cfrac{1}{2+\cfrac{1}{1-\dfrac{1}{3}}}$ is :

    (I. Tax 1989)

   (a) $\dfrac{2}{7}$ (b) $\dfrac{7}{9}$ (c) $\dfrac{9}{7}$ (d) $\dfrac{13}{7}$

44. The simplification of $\dfrac{1}{2+\dfrac{1}{2+\dfrac{1}{2-\dfrac{1}{2}}}}$ yields :

(C.B.I. 1993)

   (*a*) $\dfrac{4}{9}$ (*b*) $\dfrac{8}{19}$ (*c*) $\dfrac{4}{18}$ (*d*) $\dfrac{8}{21}$

45. The value of $4-\dfrac{5}{1+\dfrac{1}{3+\dfrac{1}{2+\dfrac{1}{4}}}}$ is :

(U.D.C. 1993)

   (*a*) $\dfrac{40}{31}$ (*b*) $\dfrac{4}{9}$ (*c*) $\dfrac{1}{8}$ (*d*) $\dfrac{31}{40}$

46. The simplification of $\left(\dfrac{75983 \times 75983 - 45983 \times 45983}{30000}\right)$ yields :

   (*a*) 121796   (*b*) 121866   (*c*) 121956   (*d*) 121966

(Clerk's Grade 1993)

47. The value of $\left(\dfrac{343 \times 343 \times 343 + 257 \times 257 \times 257}{343 \times 343 - 343 \times 257 + 257 \times 257}\right)$ is :

   (*a*) 8600   (*b*) 800   (*c*) 600   (*d*) 2600

48. Four children A, B, C and D divide a bag of sweets. A takes $\frac{1}{3}$ of them, B $\frac{2}{5}$ th of the remainder and the rest is equally shared between C and D. What fraction of the sweets did C or D get ?

   (*a*) $\dfrac{1}{5}$ (*b*) $\dfrac{1}{17}$ (*c*) $\dfrac{1}{6}$ (*d*) $\dfrac{1}{4}$

49. The value of $1+\dfrac{1}{4\times 3}+\dfrac{1}{4\times 3^2}+\dfrac{1}{4\times 3^3}$ is :

   (*a*) $\dfrac{121}{108}$ (*b*) $\dfrac{3}{2}$ (*c*) $\dfrac{31}{2}$ (*d*) None of these

50. The value of $\dfrac{1}{4}+\dfrac{1}{4\times 5}+\dfrac{1}{4\times 5\times 6}$ correct to four decimal places is :

   (*a*) 0.3075   (*b*) 0.3082   (*c*) 0.3083   (*d*) 0.3085

(U.D.C. Exam 1993)

51. $\dfrac{1}{1.2.3}+\dfrac{1}{2.3.4}+\dfrac{1}{3.4.5}+\dfrac{1}{4.5.6}$ is equal to :

   (*a*) $\dfrac{7}{30}$ (*b*) $\dfrac{11}{30}$ (*c*) $\dfrac{13}{30}$ (*d*) $\dfrac{17}{30}$

52. The value of $\dfrac{1}{3+\dfrac{2}{2+\dfrac{1}{2}}}$ is

    (S.S.C. 1987)

    (a) $\dfrac{5}{19}$ (b) $\dfrac{19}{5}$ (c) $\dfrac{4}{5}$ (d) $\dfrac{5}{4}$

53. A boy was asked to mulitiply a certain number by 25. He multiplied it by 52 and got his answer more than the correct one by 324. The number to be multiplied was :   (C.B.I. 1990)

    (a) 12   (b) 15   (c) 25   (d) 32

54. A student was asked to multiply a given number by $\dfrac{8}{17}$. Instead, he divided the given number by $\dfrac{8}{17}$. His answer was 225 more than the correct answer. The given number was :   (Central Excise 1989)

    (a) 8   (b) 17   (c) 64   (d) 136

55. What fraction must be subtracted from the sum of $\dfrac{1}{4}$ and $\dfrac{1}{6}$ to have an average of $\dfrac{1}{12}$ of all the three fractions ?   (S.B.I.P.O. Exam 1988)

    (a) $\dfrac{1}{2}$ (b) $\dfrac{1}{3}$ (c) $\dfrac{1}{4}$ (d) $\dfrac{1}{6}$

56. The smallest fraction which should be subtracted from the sum of $1\dfrac{3}{4}$, $2\dfrac{1}{2}$, $5\dfrac{7}{12}$, $3\dfrac{1}{3}$ and $2\dfrac{1}{4}$ to make the result a whole number is

    (a) $\dfrac{5}{12}$ (b) $\dfrac{7}{12}$ (c) $\dfrac{1}{2}$ (d) 7   (C.B.I 1991)

57. On sports day, if 30 children were made to stand in a column, 16 columns could be formed. If 24 children were made to stand in a column, how many columns could be formed ?   (Bank P.O. 1993)

    (a) 45   (b) 20   (c) 22   (d) 29

58. A third of Vinod's marks in Mathematics exceeds a half of his marks in Social Studies by 30. If he got 240 marks in the two subjects together, how many marks did he get in Social Studies ?   (Bank P.O. 1989)

    (a) 40   (b) 60   (c) 80   (d) None of these

59. If $\dfrac{1}{8}$ of a pencil is black, $\dfrac{1}{2}$ of the remaining is white and the remaining $3\dfrac{1}{2}$ cm is blue, then the total length of pencil is

    (a) 6 cm   (b) 7 cm   (c) 8 cm   (d) 11 cm

60. The number of students in each section of a school is 24. After admitting new students, three new sections were started. Now, the total number of sections is 16 and there are 21 students in each section. The number of new students admitted is   (Bank P.O. 1991)

(a) 24   (b) 14   (c) 48   (d) 114

61. In a garden, there are 10 rows and 12 columns of mango trees. The distance between two trees is 2 metres and a distance of one metre is left from all sides of the boundary of the garden. The length of the garden is   **(Bank P.O. 1991)**

(a) 20 m   (b) 22 m   (c) 24 m   (d) 26 m

62. In a school, $\frac{1}{6}$ th of the girls and $\frac{1}{7}$ th of the boys took part in N.C.C. camp. What fraction of the total number of students in the college took part in the camp ?

(a) $\frac{13}{40}$ (b) $\frac{13}{80}$ (c) $\frac{2}{13}$ (d) Data inadequate

63. In an office, $\frac{3}{4}$ of the staff can neither type nor take shorthand. However, $\frac{1}{5}$ th can type and $\frac{1}{3}$ rd can take shorthand. What part of the whole staff can do both ?

(a) $\frac{1}{5}$ (b) $\frac{3}{40}$ (c) $\frac{13}{40}$ (d) $\frac{17}{60}$

64. One third of the boys and one half of the girls of a college participate in a social work project. If the number of participating students is 300 out of which 100 are boys, what is the total number of students in the college ?   **(Bank P.O., 1990)**

(a) 500   (b) 600   (c) 700   (d) 800

65. The expression $\left(1 - \frac{1}{3}\right)\left(1 - \frac{1}{4}\right)\left(1 - \frac{1}{5}\right) \dots \left(1 - \frac{1}{m}\right)$ when simplified yields   **(C.B.I., 1993)**

(a) $\frac{1-m}{m}$ (b) $\frac{2}{m}$ (c) $\frac{2}{m}(m-1)$ (d) $\frac{2}{m(m+1)}$

66. When simplied, the product $\left(2 - \frac{1}{3}\right)\left(2 - \frac{3}{5}\right)\left(2 - \frac{5}{7}\right) \dots \left(2 - \frac{999}{1001}\right)$ is equal to   **(C.B.I. 1990)**

(a) $\frac{991}{1001}$ (b) $\frac{1001}{13}$ (c) $\frac{1003}{13}$ (d) None of these

67. A class starts at 10 a.m. and lasts till 1.27 p.m. Four periods are held during this interval. After every period, 5 minutes are given free to the students. The exact duration of each period is

(a) 42 minutes   (b) 48 minutes   (c) 51 minutes   (d) 53 minutes

68. A light was seen at intervals of 13 seconds. It was seen for the first time at 1 hr 54 min 50 secs. a. m. and the last time at 3 hrs 17 min 49 secs. a.m. How many times was light seen ?

(a) 378   (b) 375   (c) 360   (d) 384

69. A person gave Rs 2500 to his eldest son, $\frac{5}{12}$ of the whole property to the second son and to the youngest as much as to the first and second son together. How much did the youngest son get ?

    (*a*) Rs 10000   (*b*) Rs 15000   (*c*) Rs 20000   (*d*) Rs 25000

                                              (Assistant Grade 1990)

70. $\frac{1}{4}$ of Nikhil's money is equal to $\frac{1}{6}$ of Yogesh's money. If both together have Rs. 600, the difference between their amounts is **(Bank P.O. 1989)**

    (*a*) Rs 50   (*b*) Rs 120   (*c*) Rs 240   (*d*) Rs 360

71. If $\frac{x}{y} = \frac{4}{5}$, the value of $\left(\frac{5}{8} + \frac{y-x}{y+x}\right)$ is   **(Assistant Grade 1993)**

    (*a*) $\frac{49}{72}$ (*b*) $\frac{53}{72}$ (*c*) $\frac{23}{72}$ (*d*) None of these

72. If $\frac{a}{2b} = \frac{3}{2}$, then the value of $\frac{2a+b}{a-2b}$ equals :

    (*a*) $\frac{1}{7}$ (*b*) 7   (*c*) 7.1   (*d*) None of these

73. If $\frac{a}{b} = \frac{1}{5}$, then $\frac{5a+2b}{5a-2b}$ is equal to :   **(C.B.I. 1990)**

    (*a*) 3   (*b*) – 3   (*c*) – 5   (*d*) – 1

74. If $\frac{a}{3} = \frac{b}{4} = \frac{c}{7}$, the value of $\frac{a+b+c}{c}$ is :

    (*a*) 7   (*b*) 2   (*c*) $\frac{1}{2}$ (*d*) $\frac{1}{7}$

75. If $(a-b)$ is 6 more than $(c+d)$ and $(a+b)$ is 3 less than $(c-d)$, then $(a-c)$ is :   **(Hotel Management 1993)**

    (*a*) .5   (*b*) 1   (*c*) 1.5   (*d*) None of these

76. A tin of oil was $\frac{4}{5}$ full. When 6 bottles of oil were taken out and four bottles of oil were poured into it, it was $\frac{3}{4}$ full. How many bottles of oil can the tin contain ?   **(Assistant Grade 1993)**

    (*a*) 10   (*b*) 20   (*c*) 30   (*d*) 40

77. If we multiply a fraction by itself and divide the product by its reciprocal, the fraction thus obtained is $18\frac{26}{27}$. The original fraction is :

    (*a*) $\frac{8}{27}$ (*b*) $2\frac{2}{3}$ (*c*) $1\frac{1}{3}$ (*d*) None of these

                                              (L.I.C.A.A.O. 1988)

78. A boy multiplied 423 by a number and obtained 65589 as his answer. If both the fives in the answer are wrong and all other figures are correct, the correct answer is :

(*a*) 62389   (*b*) 61189   (*c*) 62189   (*d*) 60489

79. In a family, the father took $\frac{1}{4}$ of the cake and he had 3 times as much
as others had. The total number of family members is :
(*a*) 3   (*b*) 7   (*c*) 10   (*d*) 12
                                                         (Railway Exam 1991)

80. The charges of hired car are Rs 4 per km for the first 60 km, Rs 5 per
km for the next 60 km and Rs 8 for every 5 km for further journey. If
the balance amount left over with Subhash is $\frac{1}{4}$ of what he paid towards
the charges of the hired car for travelling 320 km, how much money
did he have initially with him ?
(*a*) Rs 1075   (*b*) Rs 1255   (*c*) Rs 1540   (*d*) None of these

81. The rent of a guest house was Rs 50 per day for first three days, Rs 100
per day for next 5 days and Rs 300 per day for other days. The
registration fee in the beginning is Rs 50. If one has to pay Rs 1300,
for how many days he availed of this facility ?   **(Bank P.O. 1991)**
(*a*) 7   (*b*) 8   (*c*) 9   (*d*) 10

82. In a certain office, $\frac{1}{3}$ of the workers are women, $\frac{1}{2}$ of the women are
married and $\frac{1}{3}$ of the married women have children. If $\frac{3}{4}$ of the men are
married and $\frac{2}{3}$ of the married men have children, what part of workers
are without children ?   **(S.B.I.P.O., 1987)**
(*a*) $\frac{5}{18}$ (*b*) $\frac{4}{9}$ (*c*) $\frac{11}{18}$ (*d*) $\frac{17}{36}$

83. A train starts full of passengers. At the first station, it drops one third
of passengers and takes 280 more. At the second station, it drops one
half of the new total and takes 12 more . On arriving at the third station,
it is found to have 248 passengers. The number of passengers in the
beginning was :   **(Teacher's Exam, 1991)**
(*a*) 156   (*b*) 288   (*c*) 564   (*d*) 608

84. One test tube contains some acid and another test tube contains an equal
quantity of water. To prepare a solution, 20 grams of the acid is poured
into the second test tube. Then two thirds of the so formed solution is
poured from the second tube into the first. If the fluid in first test tube
is four times that in the second, what quantity of water was taken
initially?
(*a*) 40 grams   (*b*) 60 grams   (*c*) 80 grams   (*d*) 100 grams

85. From a group of boys and girls, 15 girls leave. There are then left 2
boys for each girl. After this, 45 boys leave. There are then 5 girls for
each boy. The number of girls in the beginning was :

(a) 40   (b) 43   (c) 29   (d) 50
(**Assistant Grade 1991**)

86.   A worker may claim 15 p for each km which he travels by taxi and 5 p for each km which he drives his own car. If in one week he claimed Rs 5 for travelling 80 km how many kms did he travel by taxi ?

(a) 10   (b) 20   (c) 30   (d) 40

87.   In an examination, a student scores 4 marks for every correct answer and loses 1 mark for every wrong answer. If he attempts all 75 questions and secures 125 marks, the number of questions he attempts correctly, is :

(a) 35   (b) 40   (c) 42   (d) 46

88.   Each boy contributed rupees equal to the number of girls and each girl contributed rupees equal to the number of boys in a class of 60 students. If the total contribution thus collected is Rs 1600, how many boys are there in the class ?   (**Bank P.O. 1992**)

(a) 30   (b) 25   (c) 50   (d) Data inadequate

89.   The value of 36 coins of 10 p and 20 p is Rs 6.60. The number of 20 p coins is

(a) 16   (b) 20   (c) 28   (d) 30

90.   Madhuri had 85 currency notes in all, some of which are of Rs 100 denomination and the remaining of Rs 50 denomination. The total amount of all these currency notes was Rs 5000. How much amount (in Rs) did she have in the denomination of Rs 50 ?   (**Bank P.O., 1993**)

(a) 3500   (b) 70   (c) 1500   (d) None of these

91.   The sum of three fractions is $2\frac{11}{24}$. When the largest fraction is divided by the smallest, the fraction thus obtained is $\frac{7}{6}$ which is $\frac{1}{3}$ more than the middle one. The fractions are   (**Hotel Management 1993**)

(a) $\frac{3}{5}, \frac{4}{7}, \frac{2}{3}$ (b) $\frac{7}{8}, \frac{5}{6}, \frac{3}{4}$ (c) $\frac{7}{9}, \frac{2}{3}, \frac{3}{5}$ (d) None of these

92.   A number of friends decided to go on a picnic and planned to spend Rs 96 on eatables. Four of them, however, did not turn up. As a consequence, the remaining ones had to contributed Rs 4 each extra. The number of those who attended the picnic was

(a) 24   (b) 16   (c) 12   (d) 8

93.   A man distributed Rs 100 equally among his friends. If there had been 5 more friends, each would have received one rupee less. How many friends had he ?   (**C.B.I. 1991**)

(a) 20   (b) 25   (c) 30   (d) 35

94.   In a group of cows and hens, the number of legs are 14 more than twice the number of heads. The number of cows is   (**Teacher's Exam 1991**)

(a) 5   (b) 7   (c) 10   (d) 12

95. An enterprising businessman earns an income of Re 1 on the first day of his business. On every subsequent day, he earns an income which is just double of that made on the previous day. On the 10th day of business, he earns an income of :

(a) Rs 2^9 (b) Rs 2^{10} (c) Rs 10^2 (d) Rs 10

ANSWERS

1. (d)	**2.** (a)	**3.** (d)	**4.** (d)	**5.** (b)	**6.** (a)	**7.** (c)	**8.** (d)	**9.** (d)
10. (d)	**11.** (c)	**12.** (d)	**13.** (a)	**14.** (b)	**15.** (b)	**16.** (b)	**17.** (b)	**18.** (a)
19. (d)	**20.** (c)	**21.** (c)	**22.** (c)	**23.** (c)	**24.** (d)	**25.** (c)	**26.** (d)	**27.** (c)
28. (c)	**29.** (c)	**30.** (c)	**31.** (d)	**32.** (d)	**33.** (a)	**34.** (d)	**35.** (b)	**36.** (a)
37. (b)	**38.** (c)	**39.** (d)	**40.** (b)	**41.** (c)	**42.** (b)	**43.** (c)	**44.** (b)	**45.** (c)
46. (d)	**47.** (c)	**48.** (a)	**49.** (a)	**50.** (c)	**51.** (a)	**52.** (a)	**53.** (a)	**54.** (d)
55. (d)	**56.** (a)	**57.** (b)	**58.** (d)	**59.** (c)	**60.** (a)	**61.** (b)	**62.** (c)	**63.** (d)
64. (c)	**65.** (b)	**66.** (d)	**67.** (b)	**68.** (d)	**69.** (b)	**70.** (b)	**71.** (b)	**72.** (b)
73. (b)	**74.** (b)	**75.** (c)	**76.** (d)	**77.** (b)	**78.** (d)	**79.** (c)	**80.** (a)	**81.** (d)
82. (c)	**83.** (b)	**84.** (a)	**85.** (a)	**86.** (a)	**87.** (b)	**88.** (d)	**89.** (d)	**90.** (b)
91. (b)	**92.** (d)	**93.** (a)	**94.** (b)	**95.** (a)				

SOLUTIONS

1. Given Expression $= 5005 - 5000 \div 10$
$$= 5005 - 500 = 4505.$$

2. Given Exp. $= 1 - [1 - \{1 - (1 - \overline{1 - 1})\}]$
$$= 1 - [1 - \{1 - (1 - 0)\}] = 1 - [1 - \{1 - 1\}]$$
$$= 1 - [1 - 0] = (1 - 1) = 0.$$

3. Number of pieces $= \dfrac{42.5}{0.85} = \dfrac{42.50}{0.85} = \dfrac{4250}{85} = 50.$

4. Given Exp. $= b - [b - (a + b) - \{b - (b - \overline{a - b})\} + 2a]$
$$= b - [b - a - b - \{b - (b - a + b)\} + 2a]$$
$$= b - [- a - \{b - 2b + a + 2a\}]$$
$$= b - [- a - \{- b + 3a\}] = b - [- a + b - 3a]$$
$$= b - [- 4a + b] = b + 4a - b = 4a.$$

5. Given Exp. $= \dfrac{31}{10} \times \dfrac{3}{10} + \dfrac{7}{5} \times \dfrac{1}{20} = \left(\dfrac{93}{100} + \dfrac{7}{100}\right) = \dfrac{100}{100} = 1.$

6. Given Exp. $= \dfrac{16 - 12 + 3}{23 - 6} = \dfrac{7}{17}.$

7. Given Exp. $= \left(\dfrac{240 \times 300}{255 - 15}\right) = \left(\dfrac{240 \times 300}{240}\right) = 300.$

8. Given Exp. $= \dfrac{1}{(7/3)} + \dfrac{1}{(7/4)} = \left(\dfrac{3}{7} + \dfrac{4}{7}\right) = \dfrac{7}{7} = 1.$

9. Given Exp. $= \left(\dfrac{46 + 108 + 4}{144 + 96}\right) = \dfrac{158}{240} = \dfrac{79}{120}.$

10. Given Exp. $= \dfrac{6}{119} \times \dfrac{63}{8} \times \dfrac{17}{9} = \dfrac{3}{4}.$

11. Given Exp. $= \left(\dfrac{121 - 32}{8}\right) = \dfrac{89}{8} = 11\dfrac{1}{8}.$

12. Given Exp. $= \dfrac{25}{2} \times \dfrac{18}{5} \div \dfrac{9}{5} = \dfrac{25}{2} \times \dfrac{18}{5} \times \dfrac{5}{9} = 25.$

13. Required number $= \dfrac{(75/2)}{(1/8)} = \left(\dfrac{75}{2} \times \dfrac{8}{1}\right) = 300.$

14. Given Exp. $= \dfrac{575}{100} - \dfrac{3}{7} \times \dfrac{63}{4} + \dfrac{72}{35} \div \dfrac{144}{100}$

$= \dfrac{575}{100} - \dfrac{27}{4} + \dfrac{72}{35} \times \dfrac{100}{144} = \dfrac{575}{100} - \dfrac{27}{4} + \dfrac{10}{7}$

$= \dfrac{575 - 675}{100} + \dfrac{10}{7} = \left(\dfrac{10}{7} - 1\right) = \dfrac{3}{7}.$

15. Given Exp. $= \dfrac{15}{2} - \left[\dfrac{9}{4} \div \left\{\dfrac{5}{4} - \dfrac{1}{2}\left(\dfrac{3}{2} - \dfrac{1}{3} - \dfrac{1}{6}\right)\right\}\right]$

$= \dfrac{15}{2} - \left[\dfrac{9}{4} \div \left\{\dfrac{5}{4} - \dfrac{1}{2}\left(\dfrac{18 - 4 - 2}{12}\right)\right\}\right]$

$= \dfrac{15}{2} - \left[\dfrac{9}{4} \div \left\{\dfrac{5}{4} - \dfrac{1}{2}\right\}\right] = \dfrac{15}{2} - \left[\dfrac{9}{4} \div \dfrac{3}{4}\right]$

$= \dfrac{15}{2} - \left[\dfrac{9}{4} \times \dfrac{4}{3}\right] = \left(\dfrac{15}{2} - 3\right) = \dfrac{9}{2} = 4\dfrac{1}{2}.$

16. Given Exp. $= 1 + 1 \div \left\{1 + 1 \div \dfrac{4}{3}\right\} = 1 + 1 \div \left\{1 + 1 \times \dfrac{3}{4}\right\}$

$= 1 + 1 \div \left\{1 + \dfrac{3}{4}\right\} = 1 + 1 \div \dfrac{7}{4} = 1 + 1 \times \dfrac{4}{7} = 1 + \dfrac{4}{7} = 1\dfrac{4}{7}.$

17. Given Exp. $= .6 \times .6 + .6 \div 6$

$= .36 + \dfrac{.6}{6} = .36 + .1 = .46.$

18. Given Exp. $= 4 - \dfrac{3.6}{4} + 0.2 \times 0.5$

$= 4 - 0.9 + 0.1 = 4.1 - 0.9 = 3.2$

19. Given Exp. $= 108 \div 48$ of $\dfrac{1}{4} + \dfrac{2}{5} \times \dfrac{15}{4}$

$= 108 \div 12 + \dfrac{3}{2} = \left(\dfrac{108}{12} + \dfrac{3}{2}\right) = \left(9 + \dfrac{3}{2}\right) = \dfrac{21}{2} = 10\dfrac{1}{2}.$

20. Given Exp. $= \dfrac{\dfrac{1}{4} + \dfrac{1}{4} \div \dfrac{5}{4}}{\dfrac{1}{4} \times \dfrac{1}{4} + \dfrac{9}{4}} = \dfrac{\dfrac{1}{4} + \dfrac{1}{4} \times \dfrac{4}{5}}{\dfrac{1}{16} + \dfrac{9}{4}} = \dfrac{\dfrac{1}{4} + \dfrac{1}{5}}{\dfrac{1}{16} + \dfrac{9}{4}} = \dfrac{\left(\dfrac{9}{20}\right)}{\left(\dfrac{37}{16}\right)}$

$= \left(\dfrac{9}{20} \times \dfrac{16}{37}\right) = \dfrac{36}{185}.$

21. Given Exp. $= \dfrac{\dfrac{1}{5} \div \dfrac{1}{25}}{\dfrac{1}{25} \div \dfrac{1}{5}} = \dfrac{\dfrac{1}{5} \times 25}{\dfrac{1}{25} \times 5} = \dfrac{5}{(1/5)} = \left(5 \times \dfrac{5}{1}\right) = 25.$

22. Given Exp. $= 5 - \left[\dfrac{3}{4} + \left\{\dfrac{5}{2} - \left(\dfrac{1}{2} + \dfrac{7-6}{42}\right)\right\}\right]$

$= 5 - \left[\dfrac{3}{4} + \left\{\dfrac{5}{2} - \left(\dfrac{1}{2} + \dfrac{1}{42}\right)\right\}\right]$

$= 5 - \left[\dfrac{3}{4} + \left\{\dfrac{5}{2} - \dfrac{22}{42}\right\}\right] = 5 - \left[\dfrac{3}{4} + \dfrac{83}{42}\right] = 5 - \left[\dfrac{229}{84}\right]$

$= \left(\dfrac{420 - 229}{84}\right) = \dfrac{191}{84} = 2\dfrac{23}{84}.$

23. Given Exp. $= \dfrac{\dfrac{13}{4} - \dfrac{4}{5} \text{ of } \dfrac{5}{6}}{\dfrac{13}{3} \div \dfrac{1}{5} - \left(\dfrac{3}{10} + \dfrac{106}{5}\right)} = \dfrac{\dfrac{13}{4} - \dfrac{2}{3}}{\dfrac{13}{3} \div \dfrac{1}{5} - \left(\dfrac{215}{10}\right)}$

$= \dfrac{\left(\dfrac{31}{12}\right)}{\left(\dfrac{13}{3} \times 5\right) - \dfrac{215}{10}} = \dfrac{(31/12)}{\dfrac{65}{2} - \dfrac{43}{2}} = \dfrac{(31/12)}{\left(\dfrac{130 - 129}{6}\right)} = \dfrac{(31/12)}{(1/6)}$

$= \left(\dfrac{31}{12} \times \dfrac{6}{1}\right) = \dfrac{31}{2} = 15\dfrac{1}{2}.$

24. Given Exp. $= 48 \div 12 \times \left(\dfrac{9}{8} \text{ of } \dfrac{4}{3} \div \dfrac{3}{4} \text{ of } \dfrac{2}{3}\right)$

$= 4 \times \left(\dfrac{3}{2} \div \dfrac{1}{2}\right) = 4 \times \left(\dfrac{3}{2} \times \dfrac{2}{1}\right) = 4 \times 3 = 12.$

25. Given Exp. $= \left\{\dfrac{15}{2} + \dfrac{1}{2} \div \dfrac{1}{2} \text{ of } \dfrac{1}{4} - \dfrac{2}{5} \times \dfrac{7}{3} \div \dfrac{15}{8} \text{ of } \left(\dfrac{7}{5} - \dfrac{4}{3}\right)\right\}$

$= \left\{\dfrac{15}{2} + \dfrac{1}{2} \div \dfrac{1}{8} - \dfrac{2}{5} \times \dfrac{7}{3} \div \dfrac{15}{8} \text{ of } \dfrac{1}{15}\right\}$

$= \left\{\dfrac{15}{2} + \dfrac{1}{2} \div \dfrac{1}{8} - \dfrac{2}{5} \times \dfrac{7}{3} \div \dfrac{1}{8}\right\} = \left\{\dfrac{15}{2} + \dfrac{1}{2} \times \dfrac{8}{1} - \dfrac{2}{5} \times \dfrac{7}{3} \times \dfrac{8}{1}\right\}$

$$= \left\{ \frac{15}{2} + 4 - \frac{112}{15} \right\} = \left(\frac{225 + 120 - 224}{30} \right) = \frac{121}{30} = 4\frac{1}{30}.$$

26. Given Exp. $= \frac{459}{100} \times \frac{18}{10} \div \frac{36}{10} + \frac{54}{10}$ of $\frac{1}{9} - \frac{1}{5}$

$$= \frac{459}{100} \times \frac{18}{10} \times \frac{10}{36} + \frac{3}{5} - \frac{1}{5} = \frac{459}{200} + \frac{3}{5} - \frac{1}{5}$$

$$= \left(\frac{459 + 120 - 40}{200} \right) = \left(\frac{539}{200} \right) = 2.695.$$

27. Given Exp. $= \frac{3}{4} \div \frac{9}{4}$ of $\frac{2}{3} - \dfrac{\left(\dfrac{3-2}{6}\right)}{\left(\dfrac{3+2}{6}\right)} \times \frac{10}{3} + \frac{5}{6}$

$$= \frac{3}{4} \div \frac{3}{2} - \frac{1}{6} \times \frac{6}{5} \times \frac{10}{3} + \frac{5}{6} = \frac{3}{4} \times \frac{2}{3} - \frac{2}{3} + \frac{5}{6}$$

$$= \left(\frac{1}{2} - \frac{2}{3} + \frac{5}{6} \right) = \left(\frac{3 - 4 + 5}{6} \right) = \frac{4}{6} = \frac{2}{3}.$$

28. Given Exp. $= \dfrac{\dfrac{1}{2} \div 4 + 20}{\dfrac{1}{2} \times 4 + 20} = \dfrac{\dfrac{1}{2} \times \dfrac{1}{4} + 20}{2 + 20} = \dfrac{\dfrac{1}{8} + 20}{22} = \left(\frac{161}{8} \times \frac{1}{22} \right) = \frac{161}{176}.$

29. Let $\dfrac{17.28 \div x}{3.6 \times 0.2} = 2.$ Then

$$\frac{17.28}{x} = 1.44\, x \text{ or } x = \frac{17.28}{1.44} = \frac{1728}{144} = 12$$

30. $\dfrac{9^2 \times 18^4}{3^{16}} = \dfrac{(3^2)^2 \times (3 \times 3 \times 2)^4}{3^{16}} = \dfrac{3^4 \times 3^4 \times 3^4 \times 2^4}{3^{16}} = \dfrac{3^{12} \times 2^4}{3^{16}} = \dfrac{2^4}{3^4} = \dfrac{16}{81}.$

31. Let x of $\dfrac{1}{12} = \dfrac{3}{8}.$ Then $\dfrac{x}{12} = \dfrac{3}{8} \Leftrightarrow x = \left(12 \times \dfrac{3}{8} \right) = \dfrac{9}{2}.$

32. Let $\dfrac{13}{4} + \dfrac{25}{6} + x + \dfrac{1}{4} = 10.$ Then, $x = 10 - \left(\dfrac{13}{4} + \dfrac{25}{6} + \dfrac{1}{4} \right)$

or $x = 10 - \left(\dfrac{39 + 50 + 3}{12} \right) = \left(10 - \dfrac{92}{12} \right) = \left(\dfrac{120 - 92}{12} \right) = \dfrac{28}{12} = \dfrac{7}{3} = 2\dfrac{1}{3}.$

33. Let $\dfrac{9}{2} + \dfrac{19}{6} + x + \dfrac{7}{3} = \dfrac{67}{5}.$ Then $x = \dfrac{67}{5} = \left(\dfrac{9}{2} + \dfrac{19}{6} + \dfrac{7}{3} \right)$

or $x = \dfrac{67}{5} - \left(\dfrac{27 + 19 + 14}{6} \right) = \left(\dfrac{67}{5} - \dfrac{60}{6} \right) = \left(\dfrac{67}{5} - 10 \right) = \dfrac{17}{5} = 3\dfrac{2}{5}.$

34. Let $\dfrac{47}{3} \times \dfrac{19}{6} + \dfrac{19}{3} = \dfrac{205}{18} + x.$

Then $\dfrac{893}{18} + \dfrac{19}{3} = \dfrac{205}{18} + x$ or $x = \left(\dfrac{893}{18} + \dfrac{19}{3} \right) - \dfrac{205}{18}$

or $x = \left(\dfrac{893 + 114}{18} \right) - \dfrac{205}{18} = \left(\dfrac{1007 - 205}{18} \right) = \left(\dfrac{802}{18} \right) = 44 \dfrac{5}{9}.$

35. Let $\dfrac{5}{6} \div \dfrac{6}{7} \times x - \dfrac{8}{9} \div \dfrac{8}{5} + \dfrac{3}{4} \times \dfrac{10}{3} = \dfrac{25}{9}.$

Then, $\dfrac{5}{6} \times \dfrac{7}{6} \times x - \dfrac{8}{9} \times \dfrac{5}{8} + \dfrac{5}{2} = \dfrac{25}{9}$

or $\dfrac{35}{36} x - \dfrac{5}{9} + \dfrac{5}{2} = \dfrac{25}{9}$ or $\dfrac{35}{36} x = \dfrac{25}{9} + \dfrac{5}{9} - \dfrac{5}{2}$

or $\dfrac{35}{36} x = \dfrac{10}{3} - \dfrac{5}{2} = \dfrac{5}{6}$ or $x = \dfrac{5}{6} \times \dfrac{36}{35} = \dfrac{6}{7}.$

36. Required excess $= \left(\dfrac{2}{3} \times 57 - \dfrac{1}{3} \times 90 \right) = (38 - 30) = 8.$

37. Let $45 - [28 - \{37 - (15 - x)\}] = 58.$
Then $45 - [28 - \{37 - 15 + x\}] = 58$
or $45 - [28 - \{22 + x\}] = 58$ or $45 - [28 - 22 - x] = 58$
or $45 - [6 - x] = 58$ or $45 - 6 + x = 58$ or $39 + x = 58$
or $x = (58 - 39) = 19.$

38. Substituting the given values, we have
$9 \dfrac{3}{8} \times 1 \dfrac{7}{9} = \dfrac{75}{8} \times \dfrac{16}{9} = \dfrac{150}{9} = \dfrac{50}{3} = 16 \dfrac{2}{3}.$

39. Let $\dfrac{33}{4} - \dfrac{21}{5} + \dfrac{28}{10} + \dfrac{4}{x} - \dfrac{232}{100} = \dfrac{533}{100}$

Then $\dfrac{4}{x} = \dfrac{533}{100} + \dfrac{232}{100} + \dfrac{21}{5} - \dfrac{33}{4} - \dfrac{28}{10}$ or $\dfrac{4}{x} = \dfrac{765}{100} + \dfrac{84 - 165 - 56}{20}$

or $\dfrac{4}{x} = \dfrac{765}{100} - \dfrac{137}{20}$ or $\dfrac{4}{x} = \dfrac{765 - 685}{20}$ or $\dfrac{4}{x} = \dfrac{80}{20} = \dfrac{4}{1}$

So, $x = 1.$

40. Let $\dfrac{20}{3}$ of $\dfrac{726}{100} \div \dfrac{45}{100}$ of $x = \dfrac{968}{117}$

or $\dfrac{242}{5} \div \dfrac{45x}{100} = \dfrac{968}{117}$ or $\dfrac{242}{5} \times \dfrac{100}{45x} = \dfrac{968}{117}$

or $x = \dfrac{242}{5} \times \dfrac{100}{45} \times \dfrac{117}{968}$ or $x = 13.$

41. Let $\dfrac{27}{5}$ of $140 + x = 800.$ Then $27 \times 28 + x = 800$
$\therefore \ 756 + x = 80$ or $x = (800 - 756) = 44.$

42. Given Exp. $= 1 + \dfrac{1}{1 + \dfrac{1}{1 - \dfrac{1}{6}}} = 1 + \dfrac{1}{1 + \dfrac{1}{(5/6)}} = 1 + \dfrac{1}{1 + \dfrac{6}{5}} = 1 + \dfrac{1}{(11/5)}$

$= \left(1 + \dfrac{5}{11}\right) = \dfrac{16}{11}.$

43. Given Exp. $= 1 + \dfrac{1}{2 + \dfrac{1}{1 - \dfrac{1}{3}}} = 1 + \dfrac{1}{2 + \dfrac{1}{(2/3)}} = 1 + \dfrac{1}{2 + \dfrac{3}{2}}$

$= 1 + \dfrac{1}{(7/2)} = \left(1 + \dfrac{2}{7}\right) = \dfrac{9}{7}.$

44. Given Exp. $= \dfrac{1}{2 + \dfrac{1}{2 + \dfrac{1}{2 - \dfrac{1}{2}}}} = \dfrac{1}{2 + \dfrac{1}{2 + \dfrac{1}{(3/2)}}} = \dfrac{1}{2 + \dfrac{1}{2 + \dfrac{2}{3}}}$

$= \dfrac{1}{2 + \dfrac{1}{(8/3)}} = \dfrac{1}{2 + \dfrac{3}{8}} = \dfrac{1}{(19/8)} = \dfrac{8}{19}.$

45. Given Exp. $= 4 - \dfrac{5}{1 + \dfrac{1}{3 + \dfrac{1}{2 + \dfrac{1}{4}}}} = 4 - \dfrac{5}{1 + \dfrac{1}{3 + \dfrac{1}{(9/4)}}}$

$= 4 - \dfrac{5}{1 + \dfrac{1}{3 + \dfrac{4}{9}}} = 4 - \dfrac{5}{1 + \dfrac{1}{(31/9)}} = 4 - \dfrac{5}{1 + \dfrac{9}{31}}$

$= 4 - \dfrac{5}{(40/31)} = \left(4 - \dfrac{5 \times 31}{40}\right) = \left(4 - \dfrac{31}{8}\right) = \dfrac{1}{8}.$

46. Given Exp. $= \dfrac{(75983)^2 - (45983)^2}{30000}$

$= \dfrac{(75983 + 45983)\,(75983 - 45983)}{30000} = \dfrac{121966 \times 30000}{30000} = 121966.$

47. Given Exp. $= \dfrac{(343)^3 + (257)^3}{(343)^2 - 343 \times 257 + (257)^2}$

$= \left(\dfrac{a^3 + b^3}{a^2 - ab + b^2}\right)$, where $a = 343$ and $b = 257$

$= (a + b) = (343 + 257) = 600.$

48. A's share $= \frac{1}{3}$. Remainder $= \left(1 - \frac{1}{3}\right) = \frac{2}{3}$.

B's share $= \frac{2}{5}$ of $\frac{2}{3} = \frac{4}{15}$. Rest $= \left(\frac{2}{3} - \frac{4}{15}\right) = \frac{6}{15} = \frac{2}{5}$.

C's share $= D$'s share $= \frac{1}{2}$ of $\frac{2}{5} = \frac{1}{5}$.

49. Given Exp. $= 1 + \dfrac{1}{4 \times 3} + \dfrac{1}{4 \times 3^2} + \dfrac{1}{4 \times 3^3}$

$$= \frac{4 \times 3^3 + 3^2 + 3 + 1}{4 \times 3^3} = \frac{108 + 9 + 3 + 1}{108} = \frac{121}{108}.$$

50. Given. Exp. $= \dfrac{5 \times 6 + 6 + 1}{4 \times 5 \times 6} = \dfrac{37}{120} = 0.3083.$

51. Given Exp. $= \dfrac{4.5.6 + 5.6 + 2.6 + 2.3}{1.2.3.4.5.6} = \dfrac{120 + 30 + 12 + 6}{720} = \dfrac{168}{720} = \dfrac{21}{90} = \dfrac{7}{30}.$

52. Given Exp. $= \dfrac{1}{3 + \dfrac{4}{5}} = \dfrac{5}{19}$.

53. Let the required number be x. Then,
$52x - 25x = 324$ or $27x = 324$ or $x = 12$.
$\therefore$ Required number $= 12$.

54. Let the given number be x.
$$\left(x \div \frac{8}{17}\right) - \left(x \times \frac{8}{17}\right) = 225.$$

or $\left(x \times \dfrac{17}{8}\right) - \left(x \times \dfrac{8}{17}\right) = 225$ or $\dfrac{17x}{8} - \dfrac{8x}{17} = 225$

or $289x - 64x = 225 \times 136$ or $x = \dfrac{225 \times 136}{225} = 136.$

55. $\dfrac{1}{4} + \dfrac{1}{6} - x = 3 \times \dfrac{1}{12}$ or $x = \dfrac{1}{6}.$

56. Sum of given numbers $= \dfrac{7}{4} + \dfrac{5}{2} + \dfrac{67}{12} + \dfrac{10}{3} + \dfrac{9}{4}$

$$= \left(\frac{21 + 30 + 67 + 40 + 27}{12}\right) = \frac{185}{12}.$$

The whole number just less than $\dfrac{185}{12}$ is 15.

Let $\dfrac{185}{12} - x = 15$. Then, $x = \left(\dfrac{185}{12} - 15\right) = \dfrac{5}{12}.$

57. Total number of children $= (30 \times 16) = 480$

Number of columns of 24 children each $= \left(\dfrac{480}{24}\right) = 20.$

58. $\frac{1}{3}M - \frac{1}{2}S = 30$, $S + M = 240$

$\therefore$ $3S - 2M = 180$, $S + M = 240$

On solving, we get : $S = 132$.

59. Let, total length $= x$ cm.

Black part $= \frac{x}{8}$. Remaining $\left(x - \frac{x}{8}\right) = \frac{7x}{8}$.

White part $= \frac{1}{2} \times \frac{7x}{8} = \frac{7x}{16}$.

Remaining part $= \left(\frac{7x}{8} - \frac{7x}{16}\right) = \frac{7x}{16}$.

$\therefore$ $\frac{7x}{16} = \frac{7}{2}$ or $x = \frac{16}{2} = 8$ cm.

60. Original number of sections $= (16 - 3) = 13$.

Original number of students $= (24 \times 13) = 312$.

Present number of students $= (21 \times 16) = 336$.

Number of new students admitted $= (336 - 312) = 24$.

61. Each row contains 12 plants.

Leaving 2 corner plants, 10 plants in between have (10×2) metres & 1 metre on each side is left.

$\therefore$ Length $= (20 + 2)$ m $= 22$ m.

62. Out of 6 girls, 1 took part in N.C.C.

Out of 7 boys, 1 took part in N.C.C.

$\therefore$ Out of 13 students, 2 took part in N.C.C.

$\therefore$ $\frac{2}{13}$ of the total number took part in N.C.C.

63. Let total number be x.

Then, the number who can type or take short hand $= \left(x - \frac{3x}{4}\right) = \frac{x}{4}$.

Let A = set of persons who can type & B = set of persons who can take short hand.

$\therefore$ $n(A \cup B) = \frac{x}{4}$, $n(A) = \frac{x}{5}$ & $n(B) = \frac{x}{3}$.

Now $n(A \cap B) = n(A) + n(B) - n(A \cup B) = \left(\frac{x}{5} + \frac{x}{3} - \frac{x}{4}\right)$

$= \left(\frac{12x + 20x - 15x}{60}\right)$

$= \frac{17x}{60} = \frac{17}{60}$ of the whole.

64. Number of boys who participate $= 100$.

$\therefore$ $\frac{1}{3}$ of boys $= 100$ or total number of boys $= 300$.

Number of girls who participate = 200.

$\frac{1}{2}$ of girls = 200 or total number of girls = 400.

∴ Total number of students = (300 + 400) = 700.

65. $\left(1-\frac{1}{3}\right)\left(1-\frac{1}{4}\right)\left(1-\frac{1}{5}\right)\cdots\left(1-\frac{1}{m}\right)=\frac{2}{3}\times\frac{3}{4}\times\frac{4}{5}\times\cdots\times\frac{m-1}{m}=\frac{2}{m}.$

66. $\left(2-\frac{1}{3}\right)\left(2-\frac{3}{5}\right)\left(2-\frac{5}{7}\right)\cdots\left(2-\frac{999}{1001}\right)$

$=\frac{5}{3}\times\frac{7}{5}\times\frac{9}{7}\times\cdots\times\frac{1003}{1001}=\frac{1003}{3}.$

67. Time between 10 a.m. and 13.27 hours = 3 hrs 27 min. = 207 min.
For three period in between free time = 15 min.
∴ Remaining time = (207 – 15) min = 192 min.

Duration of each of the 4 periods = $\left(\frac{192}{4}\right)$ min. = 48 min.

68.

	Hrs.		Min.		Sec.
	3	—	17	—	49
(–)	1	—	54	—	50
	1	—	22	—	59

∴ Total time = (1 × 60 + 22) min. + 59 sec.
= (82 × 60 + 59) sec. = 4979.

Number of times the light is seen = $\left(\frac{4979}{13}+1\right)$ = 384.

69. Let total property be worth of Rs. x. Then

$2500+\frac{5x}{12}+\left(2500+\frac{5x}{12}\right)=x.$

or $2\left(2500+\frac{5x}{12}\right)=x$ or $5000+\frac{5x}{6}=x$ or $x-\frac{5x}{6}=5000$

$\frac{x}{6}=5000$ or $x=30000.$

∴ Youngest son gets = Rs. $\left(2500+\frac{5\times30000}{12}\right)$ = Rs. 15000.

70. $\frac{1}{4}N=\frac{1}{6}Y$ & $N+Y=600$

or $N=\frac{2}{3}Y.$ So, $\frac{2}{3}Y+Y=600$ or $\frac{5}{3}Y=600$

∴ $Y=\left(600\times\frac{3}{5}\right)=360$ & $N=\left(\frac{2}{3}\times360\right)=240.$

∴ $Y-N=(360-240)=120.$

71. $\left(\dfrac{5}{8} + \dfrac{y-x}{y+x}\right) = \left(\dfrac{5}{8} + \dfrac{1-\dfrac{x}{y}}{1+\dfrac{x}{y}}\right) = \left(\dfrac{5}{8} + \dfrac{1-\dfrac{4}{5}}{1+\dfrac{4}{5}}\right)$

$= \dfrac{5}{8} + \dfrac{(1/5)}{(9/5)} = \left(\dfrac{5}{8} + \dfrac{1}{5} \times \dfrac{5}{9}\right) = \left(\dfrac{5}{8} + \dfrac{1}{9}\right) = \dfrac{53}{72}.$

72. $\dfrac{a}{2b} = \dfrac{3}{2} \Rightarrow \dfrac{a}{b} = \left(2 \times \dfrac{3}{2}\right) = 3.$

$\dfrac{2a+b}{a-2b} = \dfrac{2\left(\dfrac{a}{b}\right)+1}{\left(\dfrac{a}{b}\right)-2} = \dfrac{2 \times 3 + 1}{3 - 2} = 7.$

73. $\dfrac{5a+2b}{5a-2b} = \dfrac{5\left(\dfrac{a}{b}\right)+2}{5\left(\dfrac{a}{b}\right)-2} = \dfrac{5 \times \dfrac{1}{5} + 2}{5 \times \dfrac{1}{5} - 2} = \dfrac{3}{1-2} = -3.$

74. Let $\dfrac{a}{3} = \dfrac{b}{4} = \dfrac{c}{7} = k.$ Then, $a = 3k, b = 4k$ & $c = 7k.$

$\therefore \dfrac{a+b+c}{c} = \dfrac{3k+4k+7k}{7k} = \dfrac{14k}{7k} = 2.$

75. $(a-b) - (c+d) = 6$ & $(c-d) - (a+b) = 3.$
$\Rightarrow (a-c) - (b+d) = 6$ & $(c-a) - (b+d) = 3$
$\Rightarrow (b+d) = (a-c) - 6$ & $(b+d) = (c-a) - 3$
$\therefore (a-c) - 6 = (c-a) - 3$ or $2(a-c) = 3$ or $(a-c) = \dfrac{3}{2} = 1.5.$

76. $\dfrac{4}{5} - 2$ bottles $= \dfrac{3}{4}$ or 2 bottles $\equiv \left(\dfrac{4}{5} - \dfrac{3}{4}\right) = \dfrac{1}{20}$

$\therefore$ 40 bottles will fill the can.

77. Let the fraction be $\dfrac{a}{b}.$ Then,

$\left(\dfrac{a}{b} \times \dfrac{a}{b}\right) \div \dfrac{b}{a} = \dfrac{512}{27}$ or $\dfrac{a}{b} \times \dfrac{a}{b} \times \dfrac{a}{b} = \dfrac{512}{27}.$

$\therefore \left(\dfrac{a}{b}\right)^3 = \left(\dfrac{8}{3}\right)^3$ or $\dfrac{a}{b} = \dfrac{8}{3}$ or $\dfrac{a}{b} = 2\dfrac{2}{3}.$

78. Among the given choices only 60489 is a multiple of 423.

79. Let there be $(x+1)$ members.

Father's share $= \dfrac{1}{4}$, share of each other member $= \dfrac{3}{4x}.$

$\therefore 3\left(\dfrac{3}{4x}\right) = \dfrac{1}{4}$ or $4x = 36$ or $x = 9.$

$\therefore$ Total number of family members $= 10$.

80. Hire charges $=$ Rs. $\left(60 \times 4 + 60 \times 5 + \dfrac{8}{5} \times 200\right) =$ Rs. 860.

Now, suppose Subhash had Rs. x with him initially.

Then, $x - 860 = \dfrac{1}{4} \times 860$ or $x = 1075$.

81. $(50 + 50 \times 3 + 100 \times 5 + x \times 300) = 1300$
or $300x = 600$ or $x = 2$.
$\therefore$ Total number of days $= (3 + 5 + 2)$ days $= 10$ days.

82. Let the total number of workers be x. Then,

$W = \dfrac{x}{3}$ and $M = \dfrac{2x}{3}$

Women having children $= \dfrac{1}{3}$ of $\dfrac{1}{2}$ of $\dfrac{1}{3} x = \dfrac{x}{18}$.

Men having children $= \dfrac{2}{3}$ of $\dfrac{3}{4}$ of $\dfrac{2x}{3} = \dfrac{x}{3}$.

Workers having children $= \left(\dfrac{x}{18} + \dfrac{x}{3}\right) = \dfrac{7x}{18}$.

Workers having no children $= \left(x - \dfrac{7x}{18}\right) = \dfrac{11x}{18}$

$= \dfrac{11}{18}$ of all workers.

83. Let the number of passengers in the beginning be x.

After 1st station, passengers $= \left(x - \dfrac{x}{3}\right) + 280 = \left(\dfrac{2x}{3} + 280\right)$

After 2nd station, passengers $= \left(\dfrac{2x}{3} + 280\right) - \dfrac{1}{2}\left(\dfrac{2x}{3} + 280\right) + 12$

$\therefore \dfrac{1}{2}\left(\dfrac{2x}{3} + 280\right) + 12 = 248$

or $\dfrac{2x}{3} + 280 = 2 \times 236$ or $\dfrac{2x}{3} = 192$

$\therefore x = \left(192 \times \dfrac{3}{2}\right) = 288$.

84. Suppose each tube contains x gms initially.

$4\left[\dfrac{1}{3}(x + 20)\right] = x + \dfrac{2}{3}(x + 20)$ or $\dfrac{2}{3}(x + 20) = x$ or $\dfrac{x}{3} = \dfrac{40}{3}$.

$\therefore x = 40$.

85. Let at present there be x boys.
Then, the number of girls at present $= 5x$.

Before the boys have left :

Number of boys $= x + 45$ and number of girls $= 5x$

$\therefore\ x + 45 = 2\,(5x) \Rightarrow 9x = 45 \Rightarrow x = 5.$

Hence, the number of girls in the begining $= 5x + 15 = 25 + 15 = 40$.

86. Let the distance covered by taxi be x km.

Then, distance covered by car $= (80 - x)$ km.

$\dfrac{15}{100}\,x + \dfrac{5}{100}\,(80 - x) = 5$ or $\dfrac{3x}{20} + \dfrac{80 - x}{20} = 5$

or $3x + 80 - x = 100$ or $x = 10$ km.

87. Let the number of correct answers be x.

Number of incorrect answers $= (75 - x)$.

$4x - (75 - x) = 125$ or $5x = 200$ or $x = 40$.

88. Let the number of boys $= x$.

Then, number of girls $= (60 - x)$.

$\therefore\ x\,(60 - x) + (60 - x)\,x = 1600$

or $60x - x^2 + 60x - x^2 = 1600$ or $2x^2 - 120x + 1600 = 0$

or $x^2 - 60x + 800 = 0$ or $(x - 40)\,(x - 20) = 0$.

$\therefore\ x = 40$ or 20.

So, we are not definite. Hence, data is inadequate.

89. Let the number of 20 paise coins be x.

Then, number of 10 paise coins $= (36 - x)$.

$10\,(36 - x) + 20x = 660$ or $10x = 300$ or $x = 30$.

90. Let the number of 50-rupee notes $= x$

Then, the number of 100-rupee notes $= (85 - x)$.

$50x + 100\,(85 - x) = 5000$ or $x + 2\,(85 - x) = 100$ or $x = 70$.

91. Let largest fraction be x and smallest be y.

Then $\dfrac{x}{y} = \dfrac{7}{6}$ or $y = \dfrac{6}{7}\,x$

Let the middle one be z.

Then, $x + \dfrac{6}{7}\,x + z = \dfrac{59}{24}$

$\therefore\ z = \left(\dfrac{59}{24} - \dfrac{13x}{7}\right)$

$\therefore\ \dfrac{59}{24} - \dfrac{13x}{7} + \dfrac{1}{3} = \dfrac{7}{6}$ or $\dfrac{13x}{7} = \dfrac{59}{24} + \dfrac{1}{3} - \dfrac{7}{6} = \dfrac{59 + 8 - 28}{24}$

$\therefore\ \dfrac{13x}{7} = \dfrac{39}{24}$ or $x = \left(\dfrac{39}{24} \times \dfrac{7}{13}\right) = \dfrac{7}{8}$.

$\therefore\ x = \dfrac{7}{8},\ y = \dfrac{6}{7} \times \dfrac{7}{8} = \dfrac{3}{4}$ & $z = \dfrac{59}{24} - \dfrac{13}{7} \times \dfrac{7}{8} = \dfrac{20}{24} = \dfrac{5}{6}$.

$\therefore$ Fractions are $\dfrac{7}{8},\ \dfrac{5}{6},\ \dfrac{3}{4}$.

92. Suppose total number $= x$. Then,

$$\frac{96}{x-4} - \frac{96}{x} = 4 \text{ or } \frac{1}{x-4} - \frac{1}{x} = \frac{4}{96}$$

or $\dfrac{x-(x-4)}{x(x-4)} = \dfrac{1}{24}$ or $x^2 - 4x - 96 = 0$

or $(x-12)(x+8) = 0$ or $x = 12$.

∴ Number of students attending the picnic $= (12-4) = 8$.

93. Suppose he had x friends. Then,

$$\frac{100}{x} - \frac{100}{x+5} = 1 \text{ or } \frac{1}{x} - \frac{1}{x+5} = \frac{1}{100}$$

$$\frac{x+5-x}{x(x+5)} = \frac{1}{100} \text{ or } x^2 + 5x - 500 = 0 \text{ or } (x+25)(x-20) = 0$$

∴ $x = 20$.

94. Let the number of cows be x and the number of hens be y. Then,

$4x + 2y = 2(x+y) + 14$ or $2x + (2x + 2y) = (2x + 2y) + 14$

or $2x = 14$ or $x = 7$.

95. 2nd day he earns $= 2 = 2^{(2-1)}$

3rd day he earns $= 2^{(3-1)}$ and so on.

On 10th day he earns $2^{(10-1)} = 2^9$ rupees.

---

5. Square Roots & Cube Roots

Square Root : If $x^2 = y$, we say that square root of y is x and we write, $\sqrt{y} = x$.

Thus, $\sqrt{4} = 2$, $\sqrt{9} = 3$, $\sqrt{196} = 14$ etc.

Square Root By Factorization :

Rule : *Suppose we have to find the square root of a number which is a perfect square. Express this number as the product of prime factors. Now, take the product of these prime factors choosing one out of every pair of the same primes.*

Ex. 1. Evaluate : $\sqrt{6084}$.

Sol. Resolving 6084 into prime factors, we get :

$$6084 = 2^2 \times 3^2 \times 13^2$$

$$\therefore \sqrt{6084} = (2 \times 3 \times 13) = 78.$$

2	6084
2	3042
3	1521
3	507
13	169
	13

General Method :

Ex. 2. Find the square root of 1471369.

Sol.

```
   1  | 1̅ 47̅ 13̅ 69̅   (1213
      | 1
  22  | 47
      | 44
 241  |  313
      |  241
2423  |  7269
      |  7269
      |     ×
```

$$\therefore \sqrt{1471369} = 1213.$$

Explanation : In the given number mark off the digits in pairs. Each pair and the remaining one digit is called a period.

Now, $1^2 = 1$. On subtracting, we get 0 as remainder.

Now, bring down the next period, i.e. 47.

Now, trial divisor is $1 \times 2 = 2$ and trial dividend is 47.

So, we take 22 as divisor & put 2 as quotient. The remainder is 3.

We bring down the next period which is 13.

Now, trial divisor is $12 \times 2 = 24$ and trial dividend is 313. So, we take 241 as dividend & 1 as quotient.

The remainder is 72.

Bring down the next period, i.e. 69.

Now, the trial divisor is $121 \times 2 = 242$ and the trial dividend is 7269.

So, we take 3 as quotient and 2423 as divisor.

The remainder is then zero.

∴ $\sqrt{1471369} = 1213.$

Square Root of Decimal Fractions : We make even number of decimal places by affixing a zero, if necessary. Now, we mark off periods and extract the square root as shown below.

Ex. 3. *Evaluate* $\sqrt{175.2976}$.

Sol.

1	$\overline{1}\ \overline{75}\ .\ \overline{29}\ \overline{76}$	(13.24
	1	
23	75	
	69	
262	629	
	524	
2644	10576	
	10576	
	×	

∴ $\sqrt{175.2976} = 13.24.$

Ex. 4. *Evaluate* $\sqrt{0.9}$ *upto 3 places of decimal.*

Sol.

9	$0.\overline{90}\ \overline{00}\ \overline{00}$	(.948
	81	
184	900	
	736	
1888	16400	
	15104	

∴ $\sqrt{0.9} = 0.948.$

Remarks : (i) $\sqrt{ab} = \sqrt{a} \times \sqrt{b}$ (ii) $\sqrt{\dfrac{a}{b}} = \dfrac{\sqrt{a}}{\sqrt{b}}$.

Ex. 5. *Evaluate :*   (i) $\sqrt{48} \times \sqrt{12}$ (ii) $\dfrac{\sqrt{128}}{\sqrt{162}}$.

Sol.   (i) $\sqrt{48} \times \sqrt{12} = \sqrt{48 \times 12} = \sqrt{2 \times 2 \times 12 \times 12} = (2 \times 12) = 24.$

(ii) $\dfrac{\sqrt{128}}{\sqrt{162}} = \sqrt{\dfrac{128}{162}} = \sqrt{\dfrac{64}{81}} = \dfrac{\sqrt{64}}{\sqrt{81}} = \dfrac{8}{9}.$

Ex. 6. *If* $\sqrt{14} = 3.7416$, *find the value of* $\sqrt{\dfrac{2}{7}}$.

Sol. $\sqrt{\dfrac{2}{7}} = \sqrt{\dfrac{2 \times 7}{7 \times 7}} = \dfrac{\sqrt{14}}{\sqrt{7 \times 7}} = \dfrac{\sqrt{14}}{7} = \dfrac{3.7416}{7} = 0.5345.$

Ex. 7. *If* $\sqrt{15} = 3.8729$, *find the value of* $\left(\dfrac{\sqrt{5} + \sqrt{3}}{\sqrt{5} - \sqrt{3}}\right)$.

Sol. $\dfrac{\sqrt{5}+\sqrt{3}}{\sqrt{5}-\sqrt{3}} = \dfrac{(\sqrt{5}+\sqrt{3})}{(\sqrt{5}-\sqrt{3})} \times \dfrac{(\sqrt{5}+\sqrt{3})}{(\sqrt{5}+\sqrt{3})} = \dfrac{(\sqrt{5}+\sqrt{3})^2}{(5-3)}$

$$= \frac{5+3+2\sqrt{5}\times\sqrt{3}}{2} = \frac{8+2\sqrt{15}}{2} = (4+\sqrt{15})$$

$$= (4+3.8729) = 7.8729.$$

Ex. 8. *Evaluate :* $\sqrt{\dfrac{.036 \times .025 \times .49}{.81 \times .016 \times .064}}$.

Sol. The sum of decimal places in the numerator and the denominator of the radicand being the same, we may remove the decimal places.

$\therefore$ Given Expression $= \sqrt{\dfrac{36 \times 25 \times 49}{81 \times 16 \times 64}} = \left(\dfrac{6 \times 5 \times 7}{9 \times 4 \times 8}\right) = \dfrac{35}{48}$.

Cube Root : *The cube root of a given number x is the number whose cube is x. We denote the cube root of x by* $\sqrt[3]{x}$.

Thus, $\sqrt[3]{8} = (2 \times 2 \times 2)^{1/3} = 2,\ \sqrt[3]{343} = (7 \times 7 \times 7)^{1/3} = 7$ etc.

Rule For Finding The Cube Root : Resolve the given number as the product of prime factors and take the product of prime factors, choosing one out of three of the same prime factors.

Ex. 9. *Find the cube root of 2744.*

Sol. Resolving 2744 as the product of prime factors, we get :

$$2744 = 2^3 \times 7^3.$$

$\therefore \sqrt[3]{2744} = (2 \times 7) = 14.$

2	2744
2	1372
2	686
7	343
7	49
	7

EXERCISE 5

Mark ($\sqrt{}$) against the correct answer :

1. $\sqrt{64009}$ is equal to :

    (*a*) 803   (*b*) 363   (*c*) 347   (*d*) 253

2. $\sqrt{248 + \sqrt{51 + \sqrt{169}}}$ is equal to :

    (*a*) 14   (*b*) 16   (*c*) 16.6   (*d*) 18.8

3. $\sqrt{176 + \sqrt{2401}}$ is equal to :

    (*a*) 14   (*b*) 15   (*c*) 18   (*d*) 24

4. The value of $\sqrt{15612 + \sqrt{154 + \sqrt{225}}}$ is :

    (*a*) 13   (*b*) 15   (*c*) 25   (*d*) 125

                                                    (Central Excise & I. Tax 1990)

5. $\sqrt{0.01 + \sqrt{0.0064}}$ is equal to :

    (*a*) 0.3   (*b*) 0.03   (*c*) 0.42   (*d*) None

6. $\dfrac{1872}{\sqrt{?}} = 234$

    (*a*) 324   (*b*) 256   (*c*) 64   (*d*) 8

7. $\dfrac{2592}{\sqrt{?}} = 324$

    (*a*) 8   (*b*) 16   (*c*) 64   (*d*) 144

8. $140\sqrt{?} + 315 = 1015$

                                                                          (Bank P.O. 1994)

    (*a*) 5   (*b*) 16   (*c*) 25   (*d*) 36

9. $\dfrac{2707}{\sqrt{?}} = 27.07$

                                                                        (Bank P.O. 1993)

    (*a*) 10   (*b*) 100   (*c*) 1000   (*d*) 10000

10. $\sqrt{81} + \sqrt{0.81} = 10.09 - ?$

                                                                         (Bank P.O. 1992)

    (*a*) 1.19   (*b*) 1.1   (*c*) 1   (*d*) 0.19

11. $\sqrt{\dfrac{32.4}{?}} = 2$

                                                              (Hotel Management 1993)

    (*a*) 9   (*b*) .9   (*c*) .09   (*d*) None

12. $\sqrt{\dfrac{?}{169}} = \dfrac{54}{39}$

    (*a*) 108   (*b*) 324   (*c*) 2916   (*d*) 4800

13. $\dfrac{\sqrt{24} + \sqrt{216}}{\sqrt{96}} = ?$

                                                                (Railways 1991)

    (*a*) $2\sqrt{6}$ (*b*) 2   (*c*) $6\sqrt{2}$ (*d*) $\dfrac{2}{\sqrt{6}}$

14. $\dfrac{\sqrt{32} + \sqrt{48}}{\sqrt{8} + \sqrt{12}} = ?$

                                                                (Bank P.O. 1990)

    (*a*) $\sqrt{2}$ (*b*) 2   (*c*) 4   (*d*) 8

15. If $\sqrt{1 + \dfrac{x}{144}} = \dfrac{13}{12}$, then x is equal to :

                                                                         (U.D.C. 1993)

    (*a*) 1   (*b*) 12   (*c*) 13   (*d*) 25

16. If $\sqrt{1 + \dfrac{x}{169}} = \dfrac{14}{13}$, then x is equal to :

    (*a*) 1   (*b*) 13   (*c*) 27   (*d*) None

17. $\sqrt{\dfrac{.289}{.00121}}$ is equal to :

                                                              (Railways 1992)

    (*a*) $\dfrac{170}{11}$ (*b*) $\dfrac{17}{110}$ (*c*) $\dfrac{17}{11}$ (*d*) $\dfrac{0.17}{11}$

18. $\sqrt{\dfrac{36.1}{102.4}}$ is equal to :

    (a) $\dfrac{29}{32}$ (b) $\dfrac{19}{72}$ (c) $\dfrac{19}{32}$ (d) $\dfrac{29}{62}$

19. If $\dfrac{\sqrt{1296}}{x} = \dfrac{x}{2.25}$, then the value of x is :

    (a) 6   (b) 7   (c) 8   (d) 9

20. If $\sqrt{6084} = 78$, then the value of
$(\sqrt{60.84} + \sqrt{.6084} + \sqrt{.006084} + \sqrt{.00006084})$ is :

    (a) 86.658   (b) 8.6658   (c) .86658   (d) 866.58

21. If $\sqrt{841} = 29$, then the value of
$(\sqrt{841} + \sqrt{8.41} + \sqrt{0.0841} + \sqrt{0.000841})$ is :

    (a) 322.19   (b) 32.219   (c) 34.179   (d) 31.129

22. $\sqrt{110\dfrac{1}{4}} = ?$

    (a) 19.5   (b) 10.25   (c) 10.5   (d) 11.5

23. $\sqrt{\dfrac{.081 \times .484}{.0064 \times 6.25}}$ is equal to :

                                              (N.D.A. 1994)

    (a) 9   (b) 0.9   (c) 99   (d) 0.99

24. $\sqrt{\dfrac{0.204 \times 42}{0.07 \times 3.4}}$ is equal to :

    (a) 6   (b) 0.6   (c) 0.06   (d) $\dfrac{1}{6}$

25. $\sqrt{\dfrac{9.5 \times .0085 \times 18.9}{.0017 \times 1.9 \times 2.1}}$ is equal to :

    (a) 0.15   (b) 0.5   (c) 15   (d) 250

26. $\sqrt{\dfrac{0.081 \times 0.324 \times 4.624}{1.5625 \times 0.0289 \times 72.9 \times 64}}$ is equal to :   **(Assistant Grade 1990)**

    (a) 24   (b) 2.4   (c) 0.024   (d) None

27. $\sqrt{\dfrac{1.21 \times 0.9}{1.1 \times 0.11}}$ is equal to :

    (a) 2   (b) 3   (c) 9   (d) 11

28. $\sqrt{1\dfrac{9}{16}}$ is equal to :

    (a) $1\dfrac{3}{4}$ (b) $1\dfrac{1}{4}$ (c) 1.125   (d) None

29. If $\dfrac{x}{\sqrt{2.25}} = 550$, then the value of x is :   **(Bank P.O. 1988)**

    (a) 825   (b) 82.5   (c) 3666.66   (d) 2

30. $\sqrt{.00059049} = ?$

(a) .243   (b) .0243   (c) .00243   (d) .000243

31. The least perfect square number divisibly by 3, 4, 5, 6 and 8 is :

(a) 900   (b) 1200   (c) 2500   (d) 3600

32. If $\sqrt{5} = 2.236$, then the value of $\dfrac{1}{\sqrt{5}}$ is :

(a) .367   (b) .745   (c) .447   (d) None

33. If $\sqrt{3} = 1.732$, then value of $\sqrt{\dfrac{3}{4}}$ is :

(a) 0.577   (b) 0.866   (c) 0.433   (d) None

34. If $\sqrt{5} = 2.236$ and $\sqrt{3} = 1.732$, the value of $\dfrac{1}{\sqrt{5} + \sqrt{3}}$ is :

(a) 0.504   (b) 0.252   (c) 0.362   (d) None

35. If $\sqrt{2} = 1.4142$, the value of $\dfrac{7}{(3 + \sqrt{2})}$ is :

(a) 1.5858   (b) 4.4142   (c) 3.4852   (d) 3.5858

36. If $a = \dfrac{\sqrt{5} + 1}{\sqrt{5} - 1}$ and $b = \dfrac{\sqrt{5} - 1}{\sqrt{5} + 1}$, the value of $\left(\dfrac{a^2 + ab + b^2}{a^2 - ab + b^2}\right)$ is :

(a) $\dfrac{3}{4}$ (b) $\dfrac{4}{3}$ (c) $\dfrac{3}{5}$ (d) $\dfrac{5}{3}$

(C.B.I. 1990)

37. The expression $(2 + \sqrt{2}) + \dfrac{1}{(2 + \sqrt{2})} + \dfrac{1}{\sqrt{2} - 2}$ equals :

(a) 2   (b) $2\sqrt{2}$ (c) $2 - \sqrt{2}$ (d) $2 + \sqrt{2}$

(Hotel Management 1993)

38. If $\sqrt{24} = 4.899$, the value of $\sqrt{\dfrac{8}{3}}$ is :

(a) 1.333   (b) 1.633   (c) 2.666   (d) 0.544

39. If $\sqrt{75.24 + x} = 8.71$, the value of x is :

(a) 6.241   (b) 62.41   (c) .6241   (d) None

40. $\left(\dfrac{\sqrt{7} + \sqrt{5}}{\sqrt{7} - \sqrt{5}} + \dfrac{\sqrt{7} - \sqrt{5}}{\sqrt{7} + \sqrt{5}}\right)$ is equal to :

(a) $2(\sqrt{7} + \sqrt{5})$ (b) $2(\sqrt{7} - \sqrt{5})$ (c) 2   (d) 12

41. $\dfrac{1}{(\sqrt{9} - \sqrt{8})}$ is equal to :

(a) $(3 - 2\sqrt{2})$ (b) $(3 + 2\sqrt{2})$

(c) $\dfrac{1}{2}(3 - 2\sqrt{2})$ (d) $\dfrac{1}{2}(3 + 2\sqrt{2})$

42. $(2\sqrt{27} - \sqrt{75} + \sqrt{12})$ is equal to :

(a) $\sqrt{3}$ (b) $2\sqrt{3}$ (c) $3\sqrt{3}$ (d) $4\sqrt{3}$

43. $\dfrac{1}{(\sqrt{9} - \sqrt{8})} - \dfrac{1}{(\sqrt{8} - \sqrt{7})} + \dfrac{1}{(\sqrt{7} - \sqrt{6})} - \dfrac{1}{(\sqrt{6} - \sqrt{5})} + \dfrac{1}{(\sqrt{5} - \sqrt{4})}$
- is equal to :

    (*a*) 0   (*b*) 1   (*c*) 5   (*d*) $\dfrac{1}{3}$

44. $\dfrac{\sqrt{8750}}{\sqrt{14}}$ is equal to :

    (*a*) 24.75   (*b*) 27.25   (*c*) 25   (*d*) 35

45. $\sqrt{50} \times \sqrt{98}$ is equal to :

    (*a*) 65.95   (*b*) 63.75   (*c*) 70.25   (*d*) 70

46. If $\sqrt{6} = 2.449$, then the value of $\dfrac{3\sqrt{2}}{2\sqrt{3}}$ is :   **(N.D.A. 1994)**

    (*a*) 0.6122   (*b*) 1.223   (*c*) 1.2245   (*d*) 0.8163

47. The square root of $(7 + 2\sqrt{10})$ is :

    (*a*) $(\sqrt{5} + \sqrt{2})$ (*b*) $(\sqrt{3} + \sqrt{4})$ (*c*) $(\sqrt{6} + 1)$ (*d*) $(2 + \sqrt{5})$

48. The square root of $(8 + 2\sqrt{15})$ is :   **(C.D.S. 1992)**

    (*a*) $(\sqrt{2} + \sqrt{6})$ (*b*) $(\sqrt{5} + \sqrt{3})$ (*c*) $(2\sqrt{3} + 5\sqrt{5})$ (*d*) $2 + \sqrt{6}$

49. The square root of $(3 + \sqrt{5})$ is :

    (*a*) $\left(\dfrac{\sqrt{3}}{2} + \dfrac{1}{\sqrt{2}} \right)$ (*b*) $\left(\dfrac{\sqrt{3}}{2} - \dfrac{1}{\sqrt{2}} \right)$

    (*c*) $\left(\dfrac{\sqrt{5}}{2} - \dfrac{1}{\sqrt{2}} \right)$ (*d*) $\left(\sqrt{\dfrac{5}{2}} + \sqrt{\dfrac{1}{2}} \right)$

50. If $\sqrt{2} = 1.4142$, then $\dfrac{\sqrt{2}}{(2 + \sqrt{2})}$ is equal to :

    (*a*) 0.4713   (*b*) 0.2071   (*c*) 0.4142   (*d*) 0.828

51. If $\sqrt{2} = 1.4142$, the square root of $\left(\dfrac{\sqrt{2} - 1}{\sqrt{2} + 1} \right)$ is equal to :   **(I. Tax 1990)**

    (*a*) 0.732   (*b*) 0.3652   (*c*) 1.3142   (*d*) 0.4142

52. If $\sqrt{2} = 1.4142$, then $\left(\dfrac{4 + \sqrt{2}}{\sqrt{2} + 1} \right)$ is equal to :

    (*a*) 2.1236   (*b*) 2.2426   (*c*) 2.4136   (*d*) 2.3216

53. The greatest number of four digits which is a perfect square, is :

    (*a*) 9996   (*b*) 9801   (*c*) 9900   (*d*) 9604

54. The largest number of five digits which is a perfect square, is :

    (*a*) 99999   (*b*) 99764   (*c*) 99976   (*d*) 99856

55. The least number of 4 digits which is a perfect square, is :

    (*a*) 1000   (*b*) 1016   (*c*) 1036   (*d*) 1024

56. What is the smallest number to be subtracted from 549162 in order to make it a perfect square ?   **(C.D.S. 1993)**

    (*a*) 28   (*b*) 36   (*c*) 62   (*d*) 81

57. The least number to be added to 269 to make it a perfect square, is :

(a) 31   (b) 16   (c) 7   (d) 20

58. The least square number which is exactly divisible by 10, 12, 15 and 18, is :   **(C.B.I. 1993)**

    (a) 360   (b) 400   (c) 900   (d) 1600

59. The least number by which 294 must be multiplied to make it a perfect square, is :

    (a) 2   (b) 3   (c) 6   (d) 24

60. The least number by which 1470 must be divided to get a number which is a perfect square, is :

    (a) 6   (b) 5   (c) 15   (d) 30

61. $\dfrac{\dfrac{1}{\sqrt{9}} - \dfrac{1}{\sqrt{11}}}{\dfrac{1}{\sqrt{9}} + \dfrac{1}{\sqrt{11}}} \times \dfrac{10 + \sqrt{99}}{?} = \dfrac{1}{2}$

                                           (Hotel Management 1993)

    (a) 2   (b) 3   (c) 4   (d) None

62. $\left(\dfrac{\sqrt{7} + \sqrt{5}}{\sqrt{7} - \sqrt{5}}\right)$ is equal to :   **(Assistant Grade 1993)**

    (a) $6 + \sqrt{35}$ (b) $6 - \sqrt{35}$ (c) 2   (d) 1

63. Which one of the following numbers has rational square root ?

    (a) 0.4   (b) 0.09   (c) 0.9   (d) 0.025

                                           (Assistant Grade 1993)

64. The value of $\sqrt{2}$ upto three places of decimal is :

    (a) 1.410   (b) 1.412   (c) 1.413   (d) 1.414

                                           (Assistant Grade 1994)

65. If $a = 5 + 2\sqrt{6}$, then the value of $\left(\sqrt{a} - \dfrac{1}{\sqrt{a}}\right)$ is :

    (a) $2\sqrt{2}$ (b) $3\sqrt{2}$ (c) $2\sqrt{3}$ (d) $3\sqrt{3}$

66. $\sqrt{12 + \sqrt{12 + \sqrt{12 + \dots}}} = ?$ **(C.B.I. 1990)**

    (a) 3   (b) 4   (c) 6   (d) greater than 6

67. If $a = \sqrt{3 + \sqrt{3 + \sqrt{3 + \dots}}}$, then which of the following is true ?

    (a) $2 < a < 3$ (b) $a > 3$ (c) $3 < a < 4$ (d) $a = 3$

68. The value of $\sqrt{0.4}$ is :

    (a) 0.2   (b) 0.02   (c) 0.63   (d) 0.51

69. The value of $\sqrt{0.121}$ is :

    (a) 0.11   (b) 1.1   (c) 0.347   (d) 0.011

70. The value of $\sqrt{0.064}$ is :

    (a) 0.8   (b) 0.08   (c) 0.008   (d) 0.252

71. The value of $\sqrt{\dfrac{0.16}{0.4}}$ is :

    (a) 0.2　　　　(b) 0.02　　　　(c) 0.63　　　　(d) None

72. If $2 * 3 = \sqrt{13}$ and $3 * 4 = 5$, then the value of $5 * 12$ is :

    (a) $\sqrt{17}$　　(b) $\sqrt{29}$　　(c) 12　　　　(d) 13

    (Central Excise & I. Tax 1990)

73. If $x * y * z = \sqrt{\dfrac{(x+2)(y+3)}{(z+1)}}$, the value of $(6 * 15 * 3)$ is :

    (a) 2　　　　(b) 3　　　　(c) 4　　　　(d) None

    (Hotel Management 1993)

74. If $\sqrt{.04 \times .4 \times a} = .004 \times .4 \times \sqrt{b}$, then $\dfrac{a}{b}$ is :

    (a) 16×10^{-4}　(b) 16×10^{-3}　(c) 16×10^{-5}　(d) None

75. A man plants 15376 apple trees in his garden and arranges them so that there are as many rows as there are apple trees in the row, then the number of rows is :

    (a) 126　　　　(b) 124　　　　(c) 134　　　　(d) 144

76. A General wishes to draw up his 36581 soldiers in the form of a solid square. After arranging them, he found that some of them are left over. How many are left ?

    (a) 81　　　　(b) 65　　　　(c) 100　　　　(d) None

77. A group of students decided to collect as many paise from each member of the group as is the number of members. If the total collection amounts to Rs. 59.29, the number of members in the group is :

    (a) 67　　　　(b) 77　　　　(c) 87　　　　(d) 57

78. $\sqrt[3]{\sqrt{.000064}}$ = ?　　　　**(Hotel Management 1993)**

    (a) .02　　　　(b) .2　　　　(c) 2　　　　(d) None

79. The largest four-digit number which is a perfect cube, is :

    (a) 9999　　　　(b) 9261　　　　(c) 8000　　　　(d) None

    (Hotel Management 1993)

80. By what least number 675 be multiplied to obtain a number which is a perfect cube ?　　　　**(C.B.I. 1993)**

    (a) 5　　　　(b) 6　　　　(c) 7　　　　(d) 8

81. By what least number 4320 be multiplied to obtain a number which is a perfect cube ?

    (a) 10　　　　(b) 30　　　　(c) 20　　　　(d) 50

82. What is the smallest number by which 3600 be divided to make it a perfect cube ?

    (a) 9　　　　(b) 50　　　　(c) 300　　　　(d) 450

83. The cube root of .000216 is :

    (a) .6　　　　(b) .06　　　　(c) .006　　　　(d) None

84. $\sqrt[3]{4\dfrac{12}{125}} = ?$

    (a) $1\dfrac{3}{5}$ (b) $1\dfrac{2}{5}$ (c) $1\dfrac{4}{5}$ (d) $2\dfrac{2}{5}$

ANSWERS

1. (d)	**2.** (b)	**3.** (b)	**4.** (d)	**5.** (a)	**6.** (c)	**7.** (c)	**8.** (c)	**9.** (d)
10. (d)	**11.** (d)	**12.** (b)	**13.** (b)	**14.** (b)	**15.** (d)	**16.** (c)	**17.** (a)	**18.** (a)
19. (d)	**20.** (b)	**21.** (b)	**22.** (c)	**23.** (d)	**24.** (a)	**25.** (c)	**26.** (c)	**27.** (b)
28. (b)	**29.** (a)	**30.** (b)	**31.** (d)	**32.** (c)	**33.** (b)	**34.** (b)	**35.** (a)	**36.** (b)
37. (a)	**38.** (b)	**39.** (c)	**40.** (d)	**41.** (b)	**42.** (c)	**43.** (c)	**44.** (c)	**45.** (d)
46. (c)	**47.** (a)	**48.** (b)	**49.** (d)	**50.** (c)	**51.** (d)	**52.** (b)	**53.** (b)	**54.** (d)
55. (d)	**56.** (d)	**57.** (d)	**58.** (c)	**59.** (c)	**60.** (d)	**61.** (a)	**62.** (a)	**63.** (b)
64. (d)	**65.** (a)	**66.** (b)	**67.** (a)	**68.** (c)	**69.** (c)	**70.** (d)	**71.** (c) ·	**72.** (d)
73. (d)	**74.** (c)	**75.** (b)	**76.** (c)	**77.** (b)	**78.** (b)	**79.** (b)	**80.** (a)	**81.** (d)
82. (d)	**83.** (b)	**84.** (a)						

SOLUTIONS

1.

```
 2  | 6̄ 4̄0̄ 0̄9̄   (253
    |  4
45  | 240
    | 225
503 | 1509
    | 1509
    |    ×
```

$\therefore \ \sqrt{64009} = 253.$

2. Given Exp. $= \sqrt{248 + \sqrt{51 + 13}} = \sqrt{248 + \sqrt{64}}$

$$= \sqrt{248 + 8} = \sqrt{256} = 16.$$

3.

```
 4  | 2̄4̄ 0̄1̄   (49
    | 16
89  | 801
    | 801
    |   ×
```

$\therefore \ \sqrt{2401} = 49.$

$\therefore \ \sqrt{176 + \sqrt{2401}} = \sqrt{176 + 49} = \sqrt{225} = 15.$

4. Given Exp. $= \sqrt{15612 + \sqrt{154 + 15}} = \sqrt{15612 + \sqrt{169}}$

$= \sqrt{15612 + 13} = \sqrt{15625} = 125.$

5. $\sqrt{0.0064} = \sqrt{\dfrac{64}{10000}} = \dfrac{\sqrt{64}}{\sqrt{10000}} = \dfrac{8}{100} = .08.$

$\therefore \ \sqrt{0.01 + \sqrt{0.0064}} = \sqrt{0.01 + 0.08} = \sqrt{0.09} = 0.3.$

6. Let $\dfrac{1872}{\sqrt{x}} = 234.$ Then, $\sqrt{x} = \dfrac{1872}{234} = 8.$

$\therefore \ x = (8 \times 8) = 64.$

7. Let $\dfrac{2592}{\sqrt{x}} = 324.$ Then, $\sqrt{x} = \dfrac{2592}{324} = 8.$

$\therefore \ x = (8 \times 8) = 64.$

8. Let $140\sqrt{x} + 315 = 1015.$ Then, $140\sqrt{x} = (1015 - 315)$

$\therefore \ 140\sqrt{x} = 700 \ $ or $ \ \sqrt{x} = 5.$ So, $x = (5 \times 5) = 25.$

9. Let $\dfrac{2707}{\sqrt{x}} = 27.07.$ Then, $\sqrt{x} = \dfrac{2707}{27.07} = \dfrac{2707}{2707} \times 100 = 100.$

$\therefore \ x = 100 \times 100 = 10000.$

10. Let $\sqrt{81} + \sqrt{0.81} = 10.09 - x.$

Then, $\sqrt{81} + \sqrt{\dfrac{81}{100}} = 10.09 - x$

or $9 + \dfrac{9}{10} = 10.09 - x \ $ or $ \ 9.9 = 10.09 - x$

$\therefore \ x = 10.09 - 9.9 = 0.19.$

11. Let $\sqrt{\dfrac{32.4}{x}} = 2.$ Then $\dfrac{32.4}{x} = 4$

or $4x = 32.4 \ $ or $ \ x = 8.1.$

12. Let $\sqrt{\dfrac{x}{169}} = \dfrac{54}{39}.$ Then, $\dfrac{x}{169} = \dfrac{54}{39} \times \dfrac{54}{39}.$

$\therefore \ x = \left(\dfrac{54}{39} \times \dfrac{54}{39} \times 169 \right) = 324.$

13. $\dfrac{\sqrt{24} + \sqrt{216}}{\sqrt{96}} = \dfrac{\sqrt{4 \times 6} + \sqrt{6 \times 36}}{\sqrt{16 \times 6}} = \dfrac{2\sqrt{6} + 6\sqrt{6}}{4\sqrt{6}} = \dfrac{8\sqrt{6}}{4\sqrt{6}} = 2.$

14. $\dfrac{\sqrt{32} + \sqrt{48}}{\sqrt{8} + \sqrt{12}} = \dfrac{\sqrt{16 \times 2} + \sqrt{16 \times 3}}{\sqrt{4 \times 2} + \sqrt{4 \times 3}} = \dfrac{4\,(\sqrt{2} + \sqrt{3})}{2\,(\sqrt{2} + \sqrt{3})} = 2.$

15. $\sqrt{1 + \dfrac{x}{144}} = \dfrac{13}{12} \Rightarrow 1 + \dfrac{x}{144} = \dfrac{169}{144}$

$\therefore \ \dfrac{x}{144} = \left(\dfrac{169}{144} - 1 \right) \ $ or $ \ \dfrac{x}{144} = \dfrac{25}{144} \ $ or $ \ x = 25.$

16. $\sqrt{1 + \dfrac{x}{169}} = \dfrac{14}{13}$ or $\left(1 + \dfrac{x}{169}\right) = \dfrac{196}{169}$.

$\therefore \dfrac{x}{169} = \left(\dfrac{196}{169} - 1\right) = \dfrac{27}{169}$ or $x = 27$.

17. $\sqrt{\dfrac{.289}{.00121}} = \sqrt{\dfrac{.28900}{.00121}} = \sqrt{\dfrac{28900}{121}} = \dfrac{170}{11}$.

18. $\sqrt{\dfrac{36.1}{102.4}} = \sqrt{\dfrac{361}{1024}} = \dfrac{\sqrt{361}}{\sqrt{1024}} = \dfrac{29}{32}$.

19.

	3	12 96	(36
		9	
	66	396	
		396	
		$\times$	

$\therefore \dfrac{\sqrt{1296}}{x} = \dfrac{x}{2.25} \Rightarrow \dfrac{36}{x} = \dfrac{x}{2.25}$.

$\therefore x^2 = (36 \times 2.25)$ or $x = \sqrt{36 \times 2.25} = 6 \times 1.5 = 9$.

20. Given Exp. $= \sqrt{\dfrac{6084}{10^2}} + \sqrt{\dfrac{6084}{10^4}} + \sqrt{\dfrac{6084}{10^6}} + \sqrt{\dfrac{6084}{10^8}}$

$= \dfrac{\sqrt{6084}}{10} + \dfrac{\sqrt{6084}}{100} + \dfrac{\sqrt{6084}}{1000} + \dfrac{\sqrt{6084}}{10000}$

$= \left(\dfrac{78}{10} + \dfrac{78}{100} + \dfrac{78}{1000} + \dfrac{78}{10000}\right)$

$= (7.8 + .78 + .078 + .0078) = 8.6658$.

21. Given Exp. $= \sqrt{841} + \sqrt{\dfrac{841}{100}} + \sqrt{\dfrac{841}{10000}} + \sqrt{\dfrac{841}{1000000}}$

$= \left(29 + \dfrac{29}{10} + \dfrac{29}{100} + \dfrac{29}{1000}\right)$

$= (29 + 2.9 + 0.29 + .029) = 32.219$.

22. $\sqrt{110\dfrac{1}{4}} = \sqrt{\dfrac{441}{4}} = \dfrac{\sqrt{441}}{\sqrt{4}} = \dfrac{21}{2} = 10.5$.

23. Sum of decimal places in the numerator and denominator under the radical sign being the same, we remove the decimal places.

$\therefore$ Given Exp. $= \sqrt{\dfrac{81 \times 484}{64 \times 625}} = \dfrac{9 \times 22}{8 \times 25} = 0.99$.

24. Given Exp. $= \sqrt{\dfrac{204 \times 42}{7 \times 34}} = \sqrt{36} = 6$.

25. Given Exp. $= \sqrt{\dfrac{95 \times 85 \times 189}{17 \times 19 \times 21}} = \sqrt{5 \times 5 \times 9} = 15.$

26. Given Exp. $= \sqrt{\dfrac{81 \times 324 \times 4624}{15625 \times 289 \times 729 \times 64}} = \left(\dfrac{9 \times 18 \times 68}{125 \times 17 \times 27 \times 8}\right)$

$$= \dfrac{3}{125} = 0.024.$$

27. Given Exp. $= \sqrt{\dfrac{121 \times 9}{11 \times 11}} = \sqrt{9} = 3.$

28. $\sqrt{1\dfrac{9}{16}} = \sqrt{\dfrac{25}{16}} = \dfrac{5}{4} = 1\dfrac{1}{4}.$

29. $\dfrac{x}{\sqrt{2.25}} = 550 \Rightarrow \dfrac{x}{1.5} = 550$ or $x = (550 \times 1.5)$

$$\therefore \ x = \left(\dfrac{550 \times 15}{10}\right) = 825.$$

30. $\sqrt{59049} = 243.$

$$\therefore \ \sqrt{.00059049} = \sqrt{\dfrac{59049}{10^8}} = \dfrac{\sqrt{59049}}{10000} = \dfrac{243}{10000} = .0243.$$

31. l.c.m. of 3, 4, 5, 6, 8 is 120.

Now, $120 = 2 \times 2 \times 2 \times 3 \times 5.$

To make it a perfect square it must be multiplied by $2 \times 3 \times 5.$

So, required number $= 2^2 \times 2^2 \times 3^2 \times 5^2 = 3600.$

32. $\dfrac{1}{\sqrt{5}} = \dfrac{1}{\sqrt{5}} \times \dfrac{\sqrt{5}}{\sqrt{5}} = \dfrac{\sqrt{5}}{5} = \dfrac{2.236}{5} = 0.447.$

33. $\sqrt{\dfrac{3}{4}} = \dfrac{\sqrt{3}}{\sqrt{4}} = \dfrac{\sqrt{3}}{2} = \dfrac{1.732}{2} = 0.866.$

34. $\dfrac{1}{(\sqrt{5}+\sqrt{3})} = \dfrac{1}{(\sqrt{5}+\sqrt{3})} \times \dfrac{(\sqrt{5}-\sqrt{3})}{(\sqrt{5}-\sqrt{3})} = \dfrac{(\sqrt{5}-\sqrt{3})}{(5-3)}$

$$= \left(\dfrac{2.236 - 1.732}{2}\right) = \dfrac{0.504}{2} = 0.252.$$

35. $\dfrac{7}{(3+\sqrt{2})} = \dfrac{7}{(3+\sqrt{2})} \times \dfrac{(3-\sqrt{2})}{(3-\sqrt{2})} = \dfrac{7(3-\sqrt{2})}{(9-2)}$

$$= (3 - \sqrt{2}) = (3 - 1.4142) = 1.5858.$$

36. $a = \dfrac{\sqrt{5}+1}{\sqrt{5}-1} \times \dfrac{\sqrt{5}+1}{\sqrt{5}+1} = \dfrac{(\sqrt{5}+1)^2}{(5-1)} = \dfrac{5+1+2\sqrt{5}}{4} = \left(\dfrac{3+\sqrt{5}}{2}\right)$

$b = \dfrac{\sqrt{5}-1}{\sqrt{5}+1} \times \dfrac{\sqrt{5}-1}{\sqrt{5}-1} = \dfrac{(\sqrt{5}-1)^2}{(5-1)} = \dfrac{5+1-2\sqrt{5}}{4} = \left(\dfrac{3-\sqrt{5}}{2}\right)$

$\therefore \ a^2 + b^2 = \dfrac{(3+\sqrt{5})^2}{4} + \dfrac{(3-\sqrt{5})^2}{4} = \dfrac{(3+\sqrt{5})^2 + (3-\sqrt{5})^2}{4}$

$$= \frac{2(9+5)}{4} = 7.$$

Also, $ab = \frac{(3+\sqrt{5})}{2} \cdot \frac{(3-\sqrt{5})}{2} = \frac{(9-5)}{4} = 1.$

$$\therefore \frac{a^2+ab+b^2}{a^2-ab+b^2} = \frac{(a^2+b^2)+ab}{(a^2+b^2)-ab} = \frac{7+1}{7-1} = \frac{8}{6} = \frac{4}{3}.$$

37. Given Exp. $= (2+\sqrt{2}) + \frac{1}{(2+\sqrt{2})} \times \frac{(2-\sqrt{2})}{(2-\sqrt{2})} - \frac{1}{(2-\sqrt{2})} \times \frac{(2+\sqrt{2})}{(2+\sqrt{2})}$

$$= (2+\sqrt{2}) + \frac{(2-\sqrt{2})}{(4-2)} - \frac{(2+\sqrt{2})}{(4-2)}$$

$$= (2+\sqrt{2}) + \frac{1}{2}(2-\sqrt{2}) - \frac{1}{2}(2+\sqrt{2}) = 2.$$

38. $\sqrt{\dfrac{8}{3}} = \sqrt{\dfrac{8\times3}{3\times3}} = \dfrac{\sqrt{24}}{3} = \dfrac{4.899}{3} = 1.633.$

39. On squaring both sides we get :

$75.24 + x = (8.71)^2$ or $x = (8.71)^2 - 75.24 = 75.8641 - 75.24$
$\therefore x = 0.6241.$

40. Given Exp. $= \dfrac{(\sqrt{7}+\sqrt{5})}{(\sqrt{7}-\sqrt{5})} \times \dfrac{(\sqrt{7}+\sqrt{5})}{(\sqrt{7}+\sqrt{5})} + \dfrac{(\sqrt{7}-\sqrt{5})}{\sqrt{7}+\sqrt{5}} \times \dfrac{(\sqrt{7}-\sqrt{5})}{(\sqrt{7}-\sqrt{5})}$

$$= \frac{(\sqrt{7}+\sqrt{5})^2}{(7-5)} + \frac{(\sqrt{7}-\sqrt{5})^2}{(7-5)} = \frac{(\sqrt{7}+\sqrt{5})^2 + (\sqrt{7}-\sqrt{5})^2}{2}$$

$$= \frac{2(7+5)}{2} = 12.$$

41. $\dfrac{1}{(\sqrt{9}-\sqrt{8})} = \dfrac{1}{(\sqrt{9}-\sqrt{8})} \times \dfrac{(\sqrt{9}+\sqrt{8})}{(\sqrt{9}+\sqrt{8})} = \dfrac{\sqrt{9}+\sqrt{8}}{(9-8)} = (3+2\sqrt{2}).$

42. $2\sqrt{27} - \sqrt{75} + \sqrt{12} = 2\sqrt{9\times3} - \sqrt{25\times3} + \sqrt{4\times3}$
$$= 6\sqrt{3} - 5\sqrt{3} + 2\sqrt{3} = 3\sqrt{3}.$$

43. $\dfrac{1}{\sqrt{9}-\sqrt{8}} = \dfrac{1}{\sqrt{9}-\sqrt{8}} \times \dfrac{\sqrt{9}+\sqrt{8}}{\sqrt{9}+\sqrt{8}} = \dfrac{(\sqrt{9}+\sqrt{8})}{(9-8)} = (\sqrt{9}+\sqrt{8}).$

Similarly, $\dfrac{1}{(\sqrt{8}-\sqrt{7})} = (\sqrt{8}+\sqrt{7}), \dfrac{1}{(\sqrt{7}-\sqrt{6})} = (\sqrt{7}+\sqrt{6})$

and $\dfrac{1}{(\sqrt{5}-\sqrt{4})} = (\sqrt{5}+\sqrt{4}).$

$\therefore$ Given Exp.
$= (\sqrt{9}+\sqrt{8}) - (\sqrt{8}+\sqrt{7}) + (\sqrt{7}+\sqrt{6}) - (\sqrt{6}+\sqrt{5}) + (\sqrt{5}+\sqrt{4})$
$= (\sqrt{9}+\sqrt{4}) = (3+2) = 5.$

44. $\dfrac{\sqrt{8750}}{\sqrt{14}} = \sqrt{\dfrac{8750}{14}} = \sqrt{625} = 25.$

45. $\sqrt{50} \times \sqrt{98} = \sqrt{50\times98} = \sqrt{4900} = 70.$

46. $\dfrac{3\sqrt{2}}{2\sqrt{3}} = \dfrac{3\sqrt{2}}{2\sqrt{3}} \times \dfrac{\sqrt{3}}{\sqrt{3}} = \dfrac{\sqrt{6}}{2} = \dfrac{2.449}{2} = 1.2245.$

47. Choose two numbers a & b s.t. $a^2 + b^2 = 7$ & $ab = \sqrt{10}$.

∴ Clearly, such numbers are $\sqrt{5}$ and $\sqrt{2}$.

∴ $(7 + 2\sqrt{10}) = [(\sqrt{5})^2 + (\sqrt{2})^2 + 2\sqrt{5} \times \sqrt{2}] = (\sqrt{5} + \sqrt{2})^2.$

∴ $\sqrt{7 + 2\sqrt{10}} = (\sqrt{5} + \sqrt{2}).$

48. $(8 + 2\sqrt{15}) = [(\sqrt{5})^2 + (\sqrt{3})^2 + 2 \times \sqrt{5} \times \sqrt{3}] = (\sqrt{5} + \sqrt{3})^2.$

∴ $\sqrt{8 + 2\sqrt{15}} = (\sqrt{5} + \sqrt{3}).$

49. $\sqrt{3 + \sqrt{5}} = \sqrt{a} + \sqrt{b}$. Then, $3 + \sqrt{5} = a + b + 2\sqrt{ab}$

∴ $a + b = 3$ and $2\sqrt{ab} = \sqrt{5}$ or $ab = \dfrac{5}{4}$.

$a - b = \sqrt{(a+b)^2 - 4ab} = \sqrt{9 - 5} = 2.$

Solving $a + b = 3$ & $a - b = 2$, we get $a = \dfrac{5}{2}$ & $b = \dfrac{1}{2}$.

∴ $\sqrt{3 + \sqrt{5}} = \left(\sqrt{\dfrac{5}{2}} + \sqrt{\dfrac{1}{2}} \right)$

50. $\dfrac{\sqrt{2}}{(2 + \sqrt{2})} = \dfrac{\sqrt{2}}{(2 + \sqrt{2})} \times \dfrac{(2 - \sqrt{2})}{(2 - \sqrt{2})} = \dfrac{2\sqrt{2} - 2}{(4 - 2)} = \dfrac{2(\sqrt{2} - 1)}{2}$

$= (\sqrt{2} - 1) = (1.4142 - 1) = 0.4142.$

51. $\dfrac{\sqrt{2} - 1}{\sqrt{2} + 1} = \dfrac{(\sqrt{2} - 1)}{(\sqrt{2} + 1)} \times \dfrac{(\sqrt{2} - 1)}{(\sqrt{2} - 1)} = (\sqrt{2} - 1)^2$

∴ $\sqrt{\left(\dfrac{\sqrt{2} - 1}{\sqrt{2} + 1} \right)} = (\sqrt{2} - 1) = (1.4142 - 1) = 0.4142.$

52. $\dfrac{4 + \sqrt{2}}{\sqrt{2} + 1} = \dfrac{(4 + \sqrt{2})}{(\sqrt{2} + 1)} \times \dfrac{(\sqrt{2} - 1)}{(\sqrt{2} - 1)} = (3\sqrt{2} - 2)$

$= (3 \times 1.4142 - 2) = 2.2426.$

53. Greatest number of four digits = 9999.

Now $9999 = (99)^2 + 198$. So, $(99)^2 = (9999 - 198) = 9801$.

∴ Required number = 9801.

54. Largest number of 5 digits is 99999.

```
   3  | 9 99 99   (316
      | 9
   ───┼────────
   61 | 99
      | 61
   ───┼────────
  626 | 3899
      | 3756
   ───┼────────
      | 143
```

∴ Required number = $(99999 - 143) = 99856$.

55. Least number of 4 digits is 1000.

$$\begin{array}{r|ll} 3 & \overline{10}\ \overline{00} & (31 \\ & 9 & \\ \hline 61 & 100 & \\ & 61 & \\ \hline & 39 & \end{array}$$

$\therefore (31)^2 < 1000 < (32)^2$.

$\therefore$ Least number to be added to 1000 to make it a perfect square

$$= [(32)^2 - 1000] = (1024 - 1000) = 24.$$

$\therefore$ Required number $= (1000 + 24) = 1024$.

56.

$$\begin{array}{r|ll} 7 & \overline{54}\ \overline{91}\ \overline{62} & (741 \\ & 49 & \\ \hline 144 & 591 & \\ & 576 & \\ \hline 1481 & 1562 & \\ & 1481 & \\ \hline & 81 & \end{array}$$

$\therefore$ Required number to be subtracted $= 81$.

57.

$$\begin{array}{r|ll} 1 & \overline{2}\ \overline{69} & (16 \\ & 1 & \\ \hline 26 & 169 & \\ & 156 & \\ \hline & 13 & \end{array}$$

$\therefore$ Required number to be added $= (17)^2 - 269 = (289 - 269) = 20$.

58. L.C.M. of 10, 12, 15, 18 $= 180 = 2 \times 2 \times 3 \times 3 \times 5 = 2^2 \times 3^2 \times 5$.

To make it a perfect square it must be multiplied by 5.

$\therefore$ Required number $= (2^2 \times 3^2 \times 5^2) = 900$.

59. $294 = 7 \times 7 \times 2 \times 3$.

To make it a perfect square it must be multiplied by 2×3 i.e. 6.

$\therefore$ Required number $= 6$.

60. $1470 = 7 \times 7 \times 5 \times 6$.

To make it a perfect square it must be divided by 5×6, i.e. 30.

$\therefore$ Required number $= 30$.

61. Let $\dfrac{\left(\dfrac{1}{\sqrt{9}} - \dfrac{1}{\sqrt{11}}\right)}{\left(\dfrac{1}{\sqrt{9}} + \dfrac{1}{\sqrt{11}}\right)} \times \dfrac{10 + \sqrt{99}}{x} = \dfrac{1}{2}$. Then,

$$x = \frac{\sqrt{11} - \sqrt{9}}{\sqrt{11} + \sqrt{9}} \times \frac{\sqrt{11} - \sqrt{9}}{\sqrt{11} - \sqrt{9}} \times (10 + \sqrt{99}) \times 2$$

$$= \frac{(\sqrt{11} - \sqrt{9})^2}{(11 - 9)} \times (10 + \sqrt{99}) \times 2 = (11 + 9 - 2\sqrt{99})(10 + \sqrt{99})$$
$$= 2(10 - \sqrt{99})(10 + \sqrt{99}) = 2(100 - 99) = 2.$$

62. $\dfrac{\sqrt{7} + \sqrt{5}}{\sqrt{7} - \sqrt{5}} = \dfrac{(\sqrt{7} + \sqrt{5})}{(\sqrt{7} - \sqrt{5})} \times \dfrac{(\sqrt{7} + \sqrt{5})}{(\sqrt{7} + \sqrt{5})} = \dfrac{(\sqrt{7} + \sqrt{5})^2}{(7 - 5)}$

$$= \frac{7 + 5 + 2\sqrt{7} \times \sqrt{5}}{2} = \frac{12 + 2\sqrt{35}}{2} = (6 + \sqrt{35}).$$

63. $\sqrt{0.09} = \sqrt{\dfrac{9}{100}} = \dfrac{3}{10} = 0.3$; which is rational.

∴ 0.09 has rational square root.

64.

```
    1  | 2.00 00 00   (1.414
       | 1
   24  | 100
       |  96
  281  |  400
       |  281
 2824  | 11900
       | 11296
```

∴ $\sqrt{2} = 1.414.$

65. $a = (5 + 2\sqrt{6}) = [(\sqrt{3})^2 + (\sqrt{2})^2 + 2 \times \sqrt{3} \times \sqrt{2}] = (\sqrt{3} + \sqrt{2})^2.$

∴ $\sqrt{a} = (\sqrt{3} + \sqrt{2})$ & $\dfrac{1}{\sqrt{a}} = \dfrac{1}{(\sqrt{3} + \sqrt{2})} \times \dfrac{(\sqrt{3} - \sqrt{2})}{(\sqrt{3} - \sqrt{2})} = (\sqrt{3} - \sqrt{2}).$

∴ $\sqrt{a} - \dfrac{1}{\sqrt{a}} = (\sqrt{3} + \sqrt{2}) - (\sqrt{3} - \sqrt{2}) = 2\sqrt{2}.$

66. Let the given expression give the value x.

Then, $x = \sqrt{12 + x} \Leftrightarrow x^2 = 12 + x$

∴ $x^2 - x - 12 = 0$ or $(x - 4)(x + 3) = 0$ or $x = 4.$

67. $a = \sqrt{3 + a} \Rightarrow a^2 = 3 + a$

$$\Rightarrow a^2 - a - 3 = 0 \text{ or } a = \frac{1 + \sqrt{1 + 12}}{2} = \frac{1 + \sqrt{13}}{2}$$

∴ $a = \dfrac{1 + 3.60}{2} = \dfrac{4.6}{2} = 2.3.$

∴ $2 < a < 3.$

68.

```
    6  | .40 00   (.63
       |  36
  123  |  400
       |  369
```

$\therefore \ \sqrt{.4} = .63.$

69. $\sqrt{0.121} = \sqrt{0.1210} = \sqrt{\dfrac{1210}{10000}} = \dfrac{\sqrt{1210}}{100} = \dfrac{34.7}{100} = 0.347.$

70. $\sqrt{0.064} = \sqrt{0.0640} = \sqrt{\dfrac{640}{10000}} = \dfrac{\sqrt{640}}{100} = \dfrac{25.2}{100} = 0.252.$

71. $\sqrt{\dfrac{0.16}{0.4}} = \sqrt{\dfrac{0.16}{0.40}} = \sqrt{\dfrac{16}{40}} = \sqrt{\dfrac{4}{10}} = \sqrt{0.4} = \sqrt{0.40} = 0.63.$

Now, See. Ex. 67

72. $a * b = \sqrt{a^2 + b^2}.$ So, $5 * 12 = \sqrt{5^2 + (12)^2} = \sqrt{25 + 144} = \sqrt{169} = 13.$

73. $(6 * 15 * 3) = \sqrt{\dfrac{(6+2)\,(15+3)}{(3+1)}} = \sqrt{\dfrac{8 \times 18}{4}} = \sqrt{36} = 6.$

74. $\dfrac{\sqrt{a}}{\sqrt{b}} = \dfrac{.004 \times .4}{\sqrt{.04 \times .4}} \Rightarrow \dfrac{a}{b} = \dfrac{.004 \times .4 \times .004 \times .4}{.04 \times .4} = \dfrac{.0000064}{.04}$

$\therefore \ \dfrac{a}{b} = \dfrac{.00064}{4} = .00016 = \dfrac{16}{10^5} = 16 \times 10^{-5}.$

75.

```
      1  | 1 53 76   (126
         | 1
     22  |   53
         |   44
    244  |  976
         |  976
         |    ×
```

$\therefore$ Number of rows = 126.

76.

```
      1  | 3 65 81   (191
         | 1
     29  |  265
         |  261
    381  |   481
         |   381
         |   100
```

$\therefore$ Number of men left over = 100.

77. Money collected = (59.29×100) paise = 5929 paise.

$\therefore$ Number of members = $\sqrt{5929} = 77.$

78. $\sqrt{.000064} = \sqrt{\dfrac{64}{10^6}} = \dfrac{8}{10^3} = \dfrac{8}{1000} = .008.$

$$\therefore \sqrt[3]{\sqrt{.000064}} = \sqrt[3]{.008} = \sqrt[3]{\frac{8}{1000}} = \frac{2}{10} = 0.2.$$

79. Clearly, 9261 is a perfect cube satisfying the given property.

80. $675 = 5 \times 5 \times 3 \times 3 \times 3.$

To make it a perfect cube it must be multiplied by 5.

81. $4320 = 2^3 \times 3^3 \times 2^2 \times 5.$

To make it a perfect cube, it must be multiplied by 2×5^2 i.e. 50.

82. $3600 = 2^3 \times 5^2 \times 3^2 \times 2.$

To make it a perfect cube, it must be divided by $5^2 \times 3^2 \times 2$ i.e. 450.

83. $(.000216)^{1/3} = \left(\frac{216}{10^6}\right)^{1/3} = \left(\frac{6 \times 6 \times 6}{10^2 \times 10^2 \times 10^2}\right)^{1/3} = \frac{6}{10^2} = \frac{6}{100} = .06.$

84. $\sqrt[3]{4\frac{12}{125}} = \sqrt[3]{\frac{512}{125}} = \left(\frac{8 \times 8 \times 8}{5 \times 5 \times 5}\right)^{1/3} = \frac{8}{5} = 1\frac{3}{5}.$

6. AVERAGE

Formula : Average $= \left(\dfrac{Sum\,of\,observations}{Number\,of\,observations} \right)$.

Solved Problems

Ex.1. *Find the average of all prime numbers between 30 and 50.*

Sol. There are five prime numbers between 30 and 50.

They are 31, 37, 41, 43 and 47.

$\therefore$ Required average $= \dfrac{(31+37+41+43+47)}{5} = \dfrac{199}{5} = 39.8$.

Ex. 2. *Find the average of first 30 natural numbers.*

Sol. Sum of first 30 natural numbers $= \dfrac{30 \times 31}{2} = 465$.

$\therefore$ Required average $= \dfrac{465}{30} = 15.5$.

Ex. 3. *Find the average of first 25 multiples of 3.*

Sol. Required average $= \dfrac{3\,(1+2+3+\ldots+25)}{25} = \left(\dfrac{3 \times 25 \times 26}{2 \times 25} \right) = 39$.

Ex. 4. *The average age of a class of 39 students is 15 years. If the age of the teacher be included, then the average increases by 3 months. Find the age of the teacher.*

Sol. Total age of 39 persons $= (39 \times 15)$ years $= 585$ years.

Average age of 40 persons $= 15$ years 3 months $= \dfrac{61}{4}$ years.

Total age of 40 persons $= \left(\dfrac{61}{4} \times 40 \right)$ years $= 610$ years.

$\therefore$ Age of the teacher $= (610 - 585)$ years $= 25$ years.

Ex. 5. *The average weight of 10 oarsmen in a boat is increased by 1.8 kg when one of the crew, who weighs 53 kg is replaced by a new man. Find the weight of the new man.*

Sol. Total weight increased $= (1.8 \times 10)$ kg $= 18$ kg.

$\therefore$ Weight of the new man $= (53 + 18)$ kg $= 71$ kg.

Ex. 6. *The average of 11 results is 60. If the average of first six results is 58 and that of the last six is 63, find the sixth result.*

Sol. Sixth result $= (6 \times 58 + 6 \times 63 - 11 \times 60) = 66$.

Ex. 7. *Distance between two stations A and B is 778 km. Hari Mohan covers the journey from A to B at 84 km per hour and returns back to A with a uniform speed of 56 km per hour. Find his average speed during the whole journey.*

Sol. Required average speed $= \dfrac{2xy}{x+y}$ km/hr.

$$= \frac{2 \times 84 \times 56}{(84+56)} \text{ km/hr} = \left(\frac{2 \times 84 \times 56}{140}\right) \text{ km/hr} = 67.2 \text{ km/hr}.$$

Ex. 8. *The average weight of A, B, C is 45 kg. If the average weight of A and B be 40 kg and that of B and C be 43 kg, find the weight of B.*

Sol. $A + B + C = (45 \times 3)$ kg $= 135$ kg .

$\quad A + B = (40 \times 2) = 80$ kg $\&$ $B + C = (43 \times 2) = 86$ kg .

$\therefore$ $B = (A+B) + (B+C) - (A+B+C) = (80+86-135)$ kg $= 31$ kg .

Ex. 9. *There are two sections A and B of a class, consisting of 36 and 44 students respectively. If the average weight of section A is 40 kg and that of section B is 35 kg, find the average weight of the whole class.*

Sol. Total weight of $(36 + 44)$ students

$$= (36 \times 40 + 44 \times 35) \text{ kg} = 2980 \text{ kg}.$$

$\therefore$ Average weight of the whole class $= \left(\dfrac{2980}{80}\right)$ kg

$$= 37.25 \text{ kg}.$$

Ex. 10. *A batsman makes a score of 87 runs in the 17th inning and thus increases his average by 3. Find his average after 17th inning.*

Sol. Let the average after 17th inning $= x$.

Then, average after 16th inning $= (x - 3)$.

$\therefore$ $16(x-3) + 87 = 17x$ or $x = (87 - 48) = 39$.

Ex. 11. *Nine persons went to a hotel for taking their meals. Eight of them spent Rs. 12. each on their meals and the ninth spent Rs 8 more than the average expenditure of all the nine. What was the total money spent by them ?*

Sol. Let the total expenditure be x . Then, average $= \dfrac{x}{9}$.

$\therefore$ $8 \times 12 + \left(\dfrac{x}{9} + 8\right) = x$ or $\left(x - \dfrac{x}{9}\right) = 104$.

or $\dfrac{8x}{9} = 104$ or $x = \left(\dfrac{104 \times 9}{8}\right) = 117$.

$\therefore$ Total money spent by them $=$ Rs 117.

Ex. 12. *There were 35 students in a hostel. Due to the admission of 7 new students, the expenses of the mess were increased by Rs 42 per day while the average expenditure per head diminished by Re 1. What was the original expenditure of the mess ?*

Sol. Let the original average expenditure be Rs x. Then,

$42(x-1) - 35x = 42$.

$\Rightarrow 7x = 84 \Rightarrow x = 12$.

$\therefore$ Original expenditure = Rs (35×12) = Rs 420 .

EXERCISE 6

Mark a tick ($\sqrt{}$)against the correct answer :

1. The average of first five prime numbers is :   **(Assistant Grade 1994)**
    (a) 4.5   (b) 5   (c) 5.6   (d) 7.5

2. The average of first five multiples of 3 is :
    (a) 3   (b) 9   (c) 12   (d) 15
    (I.Tax & Central Excise 1988)

3. The average of first 50 natural numbers is :
    (a) 12.25   (b) 21.25   (c) 25   (d) 25.5

4. The mean of $1^2, 2^2, 3^2, 4^2, 5^2, 6^2, 7^2$ is :   **(U.D.C. Exam 1993)**
    (a) 40   (b) 20   (c) 30   (d) 10

5. The average of all odd numbers upto 100 is :
    (a) 51   (b) 50   (c) 49.5   (d) 49

6. If a, b, c, d, e are five consecutive odd numbers, their average is :
    (Bank P.O. 1989)

    (a) $5(a+4)$ (b) $\dfrac{abcde}{5}$

    (c) $5(a+b+c+d+e)$ (d) None of these

7. The average of 7 consecutive numbers is 33. The largest of these numbers is :
    (a) 36   (b) 33   (c) 30   (d) 28

8. The average of four consecutive even numbers is 27. The largest of these numbers is :   **(Assistant Grade 1994)**
    (a) 36   (b) 32   (c) 30   (d) 28

9. On a certain day, temperatures recorded in a city are as follows :

Time :	6 A.M.	12 A.M.	6 P.M.	12 P.M.
Temp :	12.4°C	18.8°C	16.6°C	10°C

    The average temperature for the day is :
    (a) 12°C   (b) 14.45°C   (c) 15.2°C   (d) 15.8°C

10. The average height of 30 boys out of a class of 50, is 160 cm. If the average height of the remaining boys is 165 cm, the average height of the whole class (in cm) is :
    (a) 161   (b) 162   (c) 163   (d) 164

11. There are three sections of a class in a school. The number of students in the three sections is 38, 32 and 40 and the average age of the students in these sections separately is 15.3 years, 16.5 years and 15.9 years respectively. What is the average age of the class ?
   (*a*) 15.9 yrs   (*b*) 15.92 yrs   (*c*) 15.96 yrs   (*d*) None
   (Hotel Management 1993)

12. The average of three numbers is 20. If two numbers are 16 and 22, the third is :
   (*a*) 22   (*b*) 20   (*c*) 19   (*d*) 18

13. The average of two numbers is M. If one number is N, then the other number is :   **(Assistant Grade 1994)**
   (*a*) $2N$ (*b*) $2M$ (*c*) $M - N$ (*d*) $2M - N$

14. The average of five results is 46 and that of the first four is 45. The fifth result is :
   (*a*) 1   (*b*) 10   (*c*) 12.5   (*d*) 50

15. The average of Kanchan's marks in 7 subjects is 75. His average in six subjects excluding Science is 72. How many marks did he get in Science ?   **(Bank P.O., 1993)**
   (*a*) 72   (*b*) 90   (*c*) 93   (*d*) None of these

16. The average of eight numbers is 14. The average of six of these numbers is 16. The average of the remaining two numbers is : **(Bank P.O. 1994)**
   (*a*) 4   (*b*) 8   (*c*) 16   (*d*) Data inadequate

17. The average price of three items of furniture is Rs 15000. If their prices are in the ratio 3 : 5 : 7, the price of the cheapest item is :
   (*a*) Rs 9000   (*b*) Rs 15000   (*c*) Rs 18000   (*d*) Rs 21000

18. Of the three numbers, second is twice the first and is also thrice the third. If the average of the three numbers is 44, the largest number is :
   (*a*) 24   (*b*) 36   (*c*) 72   (*d*) 108
   (I. Tax & Central Excise 1989)

19. The average of ten numbers is 7. If each number is multiplied by 12, then the average of new set of numbers is :   **(Assistant Grade 1994)**
   (*a*) 7   (*b*) 19   (*c*) 82   (*d*) 84

20. A man spends Rs 1800 monthly on an average for the first four months and Rs 2000 monthly for the next eight months and saves Rs 5600 a year. His average monthly income is :
   (*a*) Rs 2000   (*b*) Rs 2200   (*c*) Rs 2400   (*d*) Rs 2600

21. The average age of 30 students of a class is 12 years. The average age of a group of 5 of the students is 10 years and that of another group of 5 of them is 14 years. What is the average age of the remaining students?   **(Bank P.O. 1990)**
   (*a*) 8 years   (*b*) 10 years   (*c*) 12 years   (*d*) 14 years

22. A class has two sections, in one of which there are 40 students with an average of 14.5 years. The average of the class is 14.2 years. If there be 32 students in the other section, its average age is :
    (*a*) 13.5 years   (*b*) 13.6 years   (*c*) 13.7 years   (*d*) None

23. The average of 50 numbers is 38. If two numbers, namely 45 and 55 are discarded, the average of the remaining numbers is : **(C.B.I. 1990)**
    (*a*) 36.5   (*b*) 37   (*c*) 37.5   (*d*) 37.52

24. The mean of 100 observations was calculated as 40. It was found later on that one of the observations was misread as 83 instead of 53. The correct mean is : **(C.B.I. 1993)**
    (*a*) 39   (*b*) 39.7   (*c*) 40.3   (*d*) 42.7

25. The average of six numbers is 30. If the average of first four is 25 and that of last three is 35, the fourth number is :
    (*a*) 25   (*b*) 30   (*c*) 35   (*d*) 40

26. The average of 11 observations is 60. If the average of first five observations is 58 and that of the last five is 56, then the sixth observation is : **(Assistant Grade 1993)**
    (*a*) 90   (*b*) 110   (*c*) 85   (*d*) 100

27. In seven given numbers, the average of first four numbers is 4 and that of the last four numbers is also 4. If the average of these seven numbers is 3, the fourth number is : **(I.Tax & Central Excise 1992)**
    (*a*) 3   (*b*) 4   (*c*) 7   (*d*) 11

28. The average of 25 results is 18. The average of first twelve of them is 14 and that of last twelve is 17. The thirteenth result is :
    (*a*) 28   (*b*) 78   (*c*) 72   (*d*) 85

29. Out of four numbers, the average of first three is 16 and that of the last three is 15. If the last number is 18, the first number is :
    (*a*) 20   (*b*) 21   (*c*) 23   (*d*) 25

30. Mukesh has twice as much money as Sohan and Sohan has 50% more money than what Pankaj has. If the average money with them is Rs 110, then Mukesh has : **(Assistant Grade 1994)**
    (*a*) Rs 55   (*b*) Rs 60   (*c*) Rs 90   (*d*) Rs 180

31. A motorist travels to a place 150 km away at an average speed of 50 km per hour and returns at 30 km per hour. His average speed for the whole journey in km per hour is : **(Bank P.O. 1991)**
    (*a*) 35   (*b*) 37   (*c*) 37.5   (*d*) 40

32. The total of the present ages of *P*, *Q*, *R* and *S* is 96 years. To find out *Q*'s present age, which of the following informations given in statements *A* and *B* is/are sufficient ? **(Bank P.O. 1994)**
    A. The average age of *P*, *Q* and *S* is 20 years.
    B. The average age of *R* and *S* is 25 years.
    (*a*) Both A and B are needed   (*b*) Both A and B are not sufficient

(c) Only B is sufficient   (d) Only A is sufficient

33. The average of 5 numbers is 7. When 3 new numbers are added, the average of the eight numbers is 8.5. The average of the three new numbers is :

    (a) 11   (b) 7.75   (c) 8.5   (d) 7

34. The average age of 30 students is 9 years. If the age of their teacher is included, it becomes 10 years. The age of the teacher (in years) is : **(Assistant Grade 1994)**

    (a) 27   (b) 31   (c) 35   (d) 40

35. The average age of 24 boys and the teacher is 15 years. When the teacher's age is excluded, the average decreases by 1. What is the age of the teacher ? **(Bank P.O. 1994)**

    (a) 38 years   (b) 39 years   (c) 40 years   (d) Data inadequate

36. The average weight of 50 balls is 2 lbs. If the weight of the container be included, the average weight will increase by 0.05 lbs. The weight of the container is :

    (a) 4.55 lbs   (b) 2.2 lbs   (c) 2.3 lbs   (d) 2.5 lbs

37. The average weight of 29 students is 28 kg. By the admission of a new student, the average weight is reduced to 27.8 kg. The weight of the new student is :

    (a) 22 kg   (b) 21.6 kg   (c) 22.4 kg   (d) 21 kg

38. The average salary per month of 30 employees in a compnay is Rs 4000. If the manager's salary is added, the average salary increases to Rs 4300, what is the salary of the manager ? **(Bank P.O. 1993)**

    (a) Rs 10000   (b) Rs 13000   (c) Rs 12000   (d) Rs 13300

39. The average age of 40 students of a class is 15 years. When 10 new students are admitted, the average is increased by 0.2 years. The average age of new students is : **(Assistant Grade 1993)**

    (a) 15.2 yrs   (b) 16 yrs   (c) 16.2 yrs   (d) 16.4 yrs

40. The average weight of 8 men is increased by 1.5 kg when one of the men who weighs 65 kg is replaced by a new man. The weight of the new man is :

    (a) 76 kg   (b) 76.5 kg   (c) 76.7 kg   (d) 77 kg

41. The average weight of 9 mangoes increases by 20 g if one of them weighing 120 g is replaced by another. The weight of the new mango is : **(Assistant Grade 1994)**

    (a) 180 g   (b) 200 g   (c) 260 g   (d) 300 g

42. The average weight of 6 men decreases by 3 kg when one of them weighing 80 kg is replaced by a new man. The weight of the new man is : **(U.D.C. Exam 1993)**

    (a) 56 kg   (b) 58 kg   (c) 62 kg   (d) 76 kg

43. The average of 5 consecutive numbers is n. If the next two numbers are also included, the average will

    (*a*) increase by 1   (*b*) remain the same

    (*c*) increase by 1.4   (*d*) increase by 2

44. The average age of a committee of eight members is 40 years. A member aged 55 years retired and his place was taken by another member aged 39 years. The average age of the present committee is :

    (*a*) 39 years   (*b*) 38 years   (*c*) 36 years   (*d*) 35 years

                                              (Teacher's Exam 1991)

45. A cricketer has a certain average for 9 innings. In the tenth inning, he scores 100 runs, thereby increasing his average by 8 runs. His new average is :   **(Bank P.O. 1991)**

    (*a*) 20 runs   (*b*) 24 runs   (*c*) 28 runs   (*d*) 32 runs

46. A man whose bowling average is 12.4, takes 5 wickets for 26 runs and thereby decreases his average by 0.4. The number of wickets, taken by him before his last match is :   **(C.B.I. 1991)**

    (*a*) 85   (*b*) 78   (*c*) 72   (*d*) 64

47. The mean temperature of Monday to Wednesday was 37°C and of Tuesday to Thursday was 34°C. If the temperature on Thursday was $\frac{4}{5}$ th that of Monday, the temperature on Thursday was :

    (*a*) 36.5°C   (*b*) 36°C   (*c*) 35.5°C   (*d*) 34°C

48. A team of 8 persons joins in a shooting competition. The best marksman scored 85 points. If he had scored 92 points, the average score for the team would have been 84. The number of points, the team scored, was :   **(C.B.I. 1993)**

    (*a*) 672   (*b*) 665   (*c*) 645   (*d*) 588

49. The average weight of 3 men A, B and C is 84 kg. Another man D joins the group and the average now becomes 80 kg. If another man E, whose weight is 3 kg more than that of D, replaces A then the average weight of B, C, D and E becomes 79 kg. The weight of A is :   **(Bank P.O. 1989)**

    (*a*) 70 kg   (*b*) 72 kg   (*c*) 75 kg   (*d*) 80 kg

50. Three years ago, the average age of A, B and C was 27 years and that of B and C, 5 years ago was 20 years. A's present age is :

    (*a*) 30 yrs   (*b*) 35 yrs   (*c*) 40 yrs   (*d*) 48 yrs

51. Three years ago, the average age of a family of 5 members was 17 years. A baby having been born, the average age of the family is the same today . The present age of the baby is :   **(Assistant Grade 1992)**

    (*a*) 2 yrs   (*b*) 2.4 yrs   (*c*) 3 yrs   (*d*) 1.5 yrs

52. Five years ago, the average age of A, B, C and D was 45 years. With E joining them now, the average of all the five is 49 years. How old is E ?   **(Bank P.O. 1988)**

(a) 25 yrs   (b) 40 yrs   (c) 45 yrs   (d) 64 yrs

53. Five years ago, the average age of *P* and *Q* was 15 years. Average age of *P*, *Q* and *R* today is 20 years. How old will *R* be after 10 years ?

(a) 35 yrs   (b) 40 yrs   (c) 30 yrs   (d) 50 yrs

(Bank P.O. 1989)

54. The average age of boys in the class is twice the number of girls in the class. If the ratio of boys and girls in the class of 36 be 5 : 1, what is the total of the ages (in years) of the boys in the class ?

(a) 490   (b) 196   (c) 420   (d) 360

(Bank P.O. 1989)

55. In a cricket eleven, the average of eleven players is 28 years. Out of these, the average ages of three groups of three players each are 25 years, 28 years and 30 years respectively. If in these groups, the captain and the youngest player are not included, and the captain is eleven years older than the youngest player, what is the age of the captain ?

(a) 33 years   (b) 34 years   (c) 35 years   (d) 36 years

(Hotel Management 1992)

56. After replacing an old member by a new member, it was found that the average age of five members of a club is the same as it was 3 years ago. What is the difference between the ages of the replaced and the new member ?

(a) 15 yrs   (b) 8 yrs   (c) 4 yrs   (d) 2 yrs

57. The average age of a class is 15.8 years. The average age of the boys in the class is 16.4 yrs while that of the girls is 15.4 years. What is the ratio of boys to girls in the class ?   **(Hotel Management 1993)**

(a) 1 : 2   (b) 3 : 4   (c) 3 : 5   (d) None of these

58. The average age of 3 children in a family is 20% of the average age of the father and the eldest child. The total age of the mother and the youngest child is 39 years. If the father's age is 26 years, what is the age of second child ?

(a) 15 yrs   (b) 18 yrs   (c) 20 yrs   (d) Can not be determined

ANSWERS

1. (c)	**2.** (b)	**3.** (d)	**4.** (b)	**5.** (b)	**6.** (d)	**7.** (a)	**8.** (c)	**9.** (b)
10. (b)	**11.** (d)	**12.** (a)	**13.** (d)	**14.** (d)	**15.** (c)	**16.** (b)	**17.** (a)	**18.** (c)
19. (d)	**20.** (c)	**21.** (c)	**22.** (d)	**23.** (c)	**24.** (b)	**25.** (a)	**26.** (a)	**27.** (d)
28. (b)	**29.** (b)	**30.** (d)	**31.** (c)	**32.** (b)	**33.** (a)	**34.** (d)	**35.** (b)	**36.** (a)
37. (a)	**38.** (d)	**39.** (b)	**40.** (d)	**41.** (d)	**42.** (c)	**43.** (a)	**44.** (b)	**45.** (c)
46. (a)	**47.** (b)	**48.** (b)	**49.** (c)	**50.** (c)	**51.** (a)	**52.** (c)	**53.** (c)	**54.** (d)
55. (c)	**56.** (a)	**57.** (d)	**58.** (d)					

1. Average $= \left(\dfrac{2+3+5+7+11}{5} \right) = \dfrac{28}{5} = 5.6$.

2. Average $= \dfrac{3\,(1+2+3+4+5)}{5} = \dfrac{45}{5} = 9$.

3. Sum of first n natural numbers $= \dfrac{n\,(n+1)}{2}$

So, average of first n natural numbers $= \dfrac{n\,(n+1)}{2n} = \dfrac{n+1}{2}$.

$\therefore$ Average $= \left(\dfrac{50+1}{2} \right) = \dfrac{51}{2} = 25.5$.

4. $1^2 + 2^2 + 3^2 + \ldots + n^2 = \dfrac{n\,(n+1)\,(2n+1)}{6}$

$\therefore 1^2 + 2^2 + 3^2 + \ldots + 7^2 = \left(\dfrac{7 \times 8 \times 15}{6} \right) = 140$.

$\therefore$ Required average $= \left(\dfrac{140}{7} \right) = 20$.

5. Sum of odd numbers upto 100

$= 1 + 3 + 5 + 7 + \ldots + 95 + 97 + 99$

$= (1+99) + (3+97) + (5+95) + \ldots$ upto 25 pairs.

$= 100 + 100 + 100 + \ldots (25 \text{ times}) = 2500$.

$\therefore$ Average $= \left(\dfrac{2500}{50} \right) = 50$.

6. Clearly, $b = a + 2$, $c = a + 4$, $d = a + 6$ and $e = a + 8$.

$\therefore$ Average

$= \dfrac{a + (a+2) + (a+4) + (a+6) + (a+8)}{5} = \left(\dfrac{5a+20}{5} \right) = (a+4)$.

7. Let the numbers be $x, x+1, x+2, x+3, x+4, x+5$ and $x+6$.

Then , $\dfrac{x+x+1+x+2+x+3+x+4+x+5+x+6}{7} = 33$

or $\dfrac{7x+21}{7} = 33$ or $\dfrac{7\,(x+3)}{7} = 33$ or $x+3 = 33$ or $x = 30$.

$\therefore$ Largest number $= x + 6 = (30 + 6) = 36$.

8. Let the numbers be $x, x+2, x+4$ and $x+6$. Then,

$\dfrac{x+x+2+x+4+x+6}{4} = 27 \Rightarrow \dfrac{4x+12}{4} = 27 \Rightarrow x+3 = 27 \Rightarrow x = 24$.

$\therefore$ Largest number $= (24 + 6) = 30$.

9. Average $= \dfrac{12.4 \times 6 + 18.8 \times 6 + 16.6 \times 6 + 10 \times 6}{24}$

$$= \left(\frac{74.4 + 112.8 + 99.6 + 60}{24}\right) = \frac{346.8}{24} = 14.45 \,.$$

10. Required average $= \left(\dfrac{30 \times 160 + 20 \times 165}{50}\right) = 162 \text{ cm}\,.$

11. Required average $= \left(\dfrac{38 \times 15.3 + 32 \times 16.5 + 40 \times 15.9}{38 + 32 + 40}\right)$

$$= \left(\frac{581.4 + 528 + 636}{110}\right) = \frac{1745.4}{110} = 15.867 \,.$$

12. Total sum of three numbers $= (20 \times 3) = 60$.
    Third number $= 60 - (16 + 22) = 22$.

13. Total sum of two numbers $= 2\,M$.
    $\therefore$ Other number $= (2\,M - N)$.

14. Fifth result $= (5 \times 46 - 4 \times 45) = 50$.

15. Marks in Science $= (7 \times 75 - 6 \times 72) = 93$.

16. Total sum of remaining two $= (8 \times 14 - 6 \times 16) = 16$.

    $\therefore$ Average of these two numbers $= \dfrac{16}{2} = 8$.

17. Let their prices be $3x, 5x$ and $7x$.
    Then, $3x + 5x + 7x = (15000 \times 3)$ or $x = 3000$.
    Cost of cheapest item $= 3x = $ Rs 9000 .

18. Let 3rd number be x. Then, second number $= 3x$.

    $\therefore$ First number $= \dfrac{3x}{2}$.

    $\therefore x + 3x + \dfrac{3x}{2} = (44 \times 3)$ or $\dfrac{11x}{2} = 44 \times 3$ or $x = 24$.

    Largest number $=$ 2nd number $= 3x = 72$.

19. Average of new set $= (12 \times 7) = 84$.

20. Total annual income $= $ Rs $(1800 \times 4 + 2000 \times 8 + 5600) = $ Rs 28800 .

    $\therefore$ Average monthly income $= $ Rs $\left(\dfrac{28800}{12}\right) = $ Rs 2400 .

21. Total age of 20 students $= (30 \times 12) - (5 \times 10 + 5 \times 14) = 240$ years .

    $\therefore$ Required average $= \left(\dfrac{240}{20}\right) = 12$ years .

22. Total age of 32 students $= (72 \times 14.2 - 40 \times 14.5)$ years
    $\qquad\qquad\qquad\qquad\quad = (1022.4 - 580)$ years $= 442.4$ years .

    $\therefore$ Required average $= \dfrac{442.4}{32} = 13.825$ years .

23. Total sum of 48 numbers $= [\,50 \times 38 - (45 + 55)\,] = 1800$.

    $\therefore$ Required average $= \dfrac{1800}{48} = 37.5$.

24. Correct sum $= (40 \times 100 + 53 - 83) = 3970$.

∴ Correct mean $= \dfrac{3970}{100} = 39.7$.

25. Fourth number $= (4 \times 25 + 3 \times 35 - 6 \times 30) = 25$.

26. Sixth observation $= [\, 60 \times 11 - (58 \times 5 + 56 \times 5)\,] = 90$.

27. Fourth number $= (4 \times 4 + 4 \times 4 - 7 \times 3) = 11$.

28. Thirteenth result $= [\, 25 \times 18 - (12 \times 14 + 12 \times 17)\,] = 78$.

29. Sum of 2nd & 3rd number $= (3 \times 15 - 18) = 27$.

∴ First number $= (3 \times 16 - 27) = 21$.

30. Suppose Pankaj has Rs x.

Then, Sohan has 150% of Rs $x = $ Rs $\left(\dfrac{150\,x}{100}\right) = $ Rs $\left(\dfrac{3x}{2}\right)$.

Mukesh has Rs $3x$.

∴ $x + \dfrac{3x}{2} + 3x = (110 \times 3)$ or $\dfrac{11x}{2} = 110 \times 3$ or $x = 60$.

∴ Mukesh has Rs 180.

31. Average speed $= \dfrac{2xy}{x+y}$ km/hr $= \left(\dfrac{2 \times 50 \times 30}{50 + 30}\right)$ km/hr $= 37.5$ km/hr .

32. Clearly, both A and B are not sufficient.

33. Sum of three new numbers $= (8 \times 8.5 - 5 \times 7) = 33$.

∴ Their average $= \dfrac{33}{3} = 11$.

34. Age of the teacher $= (31 \times 10 + 30 \times 9) = 40$ years.

35. Age of the teacher $= (25 \times 15 - 24 \times 14) = 39$ years.

36. Weight of the container $= (51 \times 2.05 - 50 \times 2)$ lbs.
$= (104.55 - 100)$ lbs $-= 4.55$ lbs.

37. Weight of the new student $= (30 \times 27.8 - 29 \times 28)$ kg $= 22$ kg .

38. Salary of the manager $= $ Rs $(31 \times 4300 - 30 \times 4000) = $ Rs 13300 .

39. Sum of ages of 10 new students $= (50 \times 15.2 - 40 \times 15) = 160$ years.

∴ Average age of new students $= \dfrac{160}{10}$ years $= 16$ years.

40. Total weight increased $= (8 \times 1.5)$ kg $= 12$ kg .
Weight of new man $= (65 + 12)$ kg $= 77$ kg .

41. Total weight increased $= (9 \times 20)$ gm $= 180$ gm .
Weight of new mango $= (120 + 180)$ gm $= 300$ gm .

42. Total weight decreased $= (6 \times 3)$ kg $= 18$ kg .
Weight of new man $= (80 - 18)$ kg $= 62$ kg .

43. Let five consecutive numbers be $x, x+1, x+2, x+3, \& x+4$.

Their average $= \dfrac{5x + 10}{5} = (x + 2)$.

Average of 7 numbers $= \dfrac{(5x+10) + (x+5) + (x+6)}{7} = \dfrac{7x + 21}{7} = (x + 3)$.

So, the average increased by 1.

44. Required average $= \left(\dfrac{8 \times 40 - 55 + 39}{8}\right) = \dfrac{304}{8} = 38$ years.

45. Let average for 9 innings be x. Then,

$\dfrac{9x + 100}{10} = x + 8 \implies 10x + 80 = 9x + 100 \implies x = 20$.

$\therefore$ New average $= (x + 8) = 28$ runs.

46. Let the number of wickets taken before the last match be x.

Then, $\dfrac{12.4x + 26}{x + 5} = 12 \implies 12.4x + 26 = 12x + 60$

$\implies 0.4x = 34 \implies x = \dfrac{34}{0.4} = \dfrac{340}{4} = 85$.

47. $M + T + W = (3 \times 37) = 111,\ T + W + Th = (3 \times 34) = 102$.

Now, $Th = \dfrac{4}{5} M \implies M = \dfrac{5}{4} Th$.

$(M + T + W) - (T + W + Th) = 9 \implies M - Th = 9$

$\implies \left(\dfrac{5}{4} Th - Th = 9\right)$ or $Th = 36$.

48. Let the total score be x.

$\therefore \dfrac{x + 92 - 85}{8} = 84 \implies x + 7 = 672 \implies x = 665$.

49. $A + B + C = (84 \times 3) = 252$ kg, $A + B + C + D = (80 \times 4) = 320$ kg.

$\therefore D = (320 - 252)$ kg $= 68$ kg, $E = (68 + 3)$ kg $= 71$ kg.

$B + C + D + E = (79 \times 4) = 316$ kg.

Now $(A + B + C + D) - (B + C + D + E) = (320 - 316)$ kg $= 4$ kg.

$\therefore A - E = 4 \implies A = (4 + E) = 75$ kg.

50. Present age of $(A + B + C) = (27 \times 3 + 3 \times 3) = 90$ years.

Present age of $(B + C) = (20 \times 2 + 2 \times 5) = 50$ years.

$\therefore$ A's present age $= (90 - 50)$ years $= 40$ years.

51. Total age of 5 members, 3 years ago $= (17 \times 5) = 85$ years.

Total age of 5 members now $= (85 + 3 \times 5) = 100$ years.

Total age of 6 members now $= (17 \times 6) = 102$ years.

Age of the baby $= 2$ years.

52. $(A + B + C + D)$, five years ago $= (45 \times 4) = 180$ years.

$(A + B + C + D)$, now $= (180 + 5 \times 4)$ years $= 200$ years.

$A + B + C + D + E$, now $= (49 \times 5)$ years $= 245$ years.

$\therefore E$, now $= (245 - 200) = 45$ years.

53. $(P + Q)$, five years ago $= (15 \times 2) = 30$ years.

$(P + Q)$, now $= (30 + 5 \times 2)$ years $= 40$ years.

$(P + Q + R)$, now $= (20 \times 3)$ years $= 60$ years.

$\therefore R$, now $= (60 - 40)$ years $= 20$ years.

R, after 10 years $= (20 + 10)$ years $= 30$ years.

54. Number of boys $= \left(36 \times \dfrac{5}{6}\right) = 30$, Number of girls $= 6$.

Average age of boys $= (2 \times 6) = 12$ years .

$\therefore$ Total age of boys $= (30 \times 12)$ years $= 360$ years .

55. Let the age of youngest player be x .

Then, age of the captain $= (x + 11)$.

$\therefore\ 3 \times 25 + 3 \times 28 + 3 \times 30 + x + x + 11 = 11 \times 28$.

$\Rightarrow\ 75 + 84 + 90 + 2x + 11 = 308 \Rightarrow 2x = 48 \Rightarrow x = 24$.

$\therefore$ Age of the captain $= (x + 11) = 35$ years .

56. Age decreased $= (5 \times 3)$ years $= 15$ years .

So, the required difference $= 15$ years .

57. Let the ratio be $k : 1$. Then,

$k \times 16.4 + 1 \times 15.4 = (k + 1) \times 15.8$

or $(16.4 - 15.8)\, k = (15.8 - 15.4)$ or $k = \dfrac{0.4}{0.6} = \dfrac{2}{3}$.

$\therefore$ Required ratio $= \dfrac{2}{3} : 1 = 2 : 3$.

58. Since the total or average age of all the family members is not given, the given data is inadequate. So, the age of second child cannot be determined.

---

7. Problems On Numbers

Ex. 1. *If 30% of a certain number is 12.6, then find the number.*

(Assistant Grade 1994)

Sol. Let the required number be x.

Then $\dfrac{30}{100} x = 12.6$ or $x = \left(\dfrac{12.6 \times 100}{30}\right) = 42$.

∴ Required number = 42 .

Ex. 2. *The average of four consecutive even numbers is 27. Find the largest of these numbers.* (Assistant Grade 1994)

Sol. Let the four consecutive even numbers be $x, x+2, x+4$ & $x+6$.

Their total sum = $(27 \times 4) = 108$.

∴ $x + x + 2 + x + 4 + x + 6 = 108$ or $4x = 96$ or $x = 24$.

∴ Largest number = $(x + 6) = 30$.

Ex. 3. **A number consists of two digits. The sum of the digit is 9. If 63 is subtracted from the number, its digits are interchanged. Find the number.**

Sol. Let ten's digit = x . Then, unit's digit = $(9 - x)$.

$10x + (9 - x) - 63 = 10 (9 - x) + x$

or $9x - 54 = 90 - 9x$ or $18x = 144$ or $x = 8$.

∴ Ten's digit = 8 and unit's digit = 1.

Hence, the required number is 81.

Ex. 4. *A fraction becomes $\dfrac{2}{3}$ when 1 is added to both, its numerator and denominator. And, it becomes $\dfrac{1}{2}$ when 1 is subtracted from both the numerator and denominator.*

Find the fraction.

Sol. Let the required fraction be $\dfrac{x}{y}$. Then,

$\dfrac{x+1}{y+1} = \dfrac{2}{3} \Rightarrow 3x - 2y = -1$ ...(i)

And, $\dfrac{x-1}{y-1} = \dfrac{1}{2} \Rightarrow 2x - y = 1$ ...(ii)

Solving (i) & (ii), we get $x = 3$, $y = 5$.

∴ Required fraction = $\dfrac{3}{5}$.

EXERCISE 7

Mark ($\sqrt{}$) against the correct answer :

1. One–fourth of one-third of two-fifth of a number is 15. What will be 40% of that number ?   **(Bank P.O. 1994)**
   (a) 120   (b) 180   (c) 270   (d) 350

2. Three–fourth of a number exceeds its one–third by 60. The number is :   **(Hotel Management 1993)**
   (a) 108   (b) 144   (c) 184   (d) None of these

3. The number which when added to 10 times itself gives 264, is :
   (a) 20   (b) 22   (c) 24   (d) 26
                                                                 (U.D.C. 1993)

4. A number when divided by 4 is reduced by 21. The number is :
   (a) 18   (b) 20   (c) 28   (d) 38
                                                                 (U.D.C. 1993)

5. Four–fifth of a certain number is 64. Half of that number is :
   (a) 16   (b) 32   (c) 40   (d) 80
                                                                 (Railways 1991)

6. A number exceeds 20% of itself by 40. The number is :
   (a) 50   (b) 60   (c) 80   (d) 320
                                                                 (Assistant Grade 1990)

7. If 16% of 40% of a number is 8, the number is :
   (a) 320   (b) 225   (c) 200   (d) 125
                                                                 (Assistant Grade 1990)

8. A number exceeds its four–seventh by 18. What is the number ?
   (a) 36   (b) 49   (c) 63   (d) None of these
                                                                 (Bank P.O. 1991)

9. A positive number when decreased by 4 is equal to 21 times the reciprocal of the number. The number is :
   (a) 3   (b) 5   (c) 7   (d) 9

10. The sum of a positive number and its reciprocal is thrice the difference of the number and its reciprocal. The number is :
    (a) $\sqrt{2}$ (b) $\frac{1}{\sqrt{2}}$ (c) $\sqrt{3}$ (d) $\frac{1}{\sqrt{3}}$

11. A number whose fifth part increased by 4 is equal to its fourth part diminished by 10, is :
    (a) 240   (b) 260   (c) 280   (d) 270

12. A number is as much greater than 36 as is less than 86. The number is :
    (a) 63   (b) 72   (c) 61   (d) 57

13. If 10 be added to four times a certain number, the result is 5 less than five times the number. The number is :
    (a) 15 (b) 20 (c) 25 (d) 35

14. If a number is subtracted from the square of its one-half, the result is 48. The square root of the number is :
    (a) 8 (b) 6 (c) 5 (d) 4

15. The sum of the squares of two numbers is 3341 and the difference of their squares is 891. The numbers are : **(Hotel Management 1993)**
    (a) 25, 46 (b) 35, 46 (c) 25, 36 (d) None of these

16. The sum of two numbers is 15 and the sum of their squares is 113. The numbers are :
    (a) 4, 11 (b) 5, 10 (c) 6, 9 (d) 7, 8

17. The product of two numbers is 120 and the sum of their squares is 289. The sum of the numbers is :
    (a) 20 (b) 23 (c) 169 (d) None of these

18. The difference of two numbers is 11 and $\frac{1}{5}$th of their sum is 9. The numbers are : **(Railways 1991)**
    (a) 31, 20 (b) 30, 19 (c) 29, 18 (d) 28, 17

19. Two different natural numbers are such that their product is less than their sum. One of the numbers must be : **(C.B.I. 1990)**
    (a) 1 (b) 2 (c) 3 (d) None of these

20. The difference between the squares of two numbers is 256000 and the sum of the numbers is 1000. The numbers are :
    (a) 600, 400 (b) 640, 360 (c) 628, 372 (d) None of these

21. The difference between the squares of two consecutive numbers is 35. The smaller number is :
    (a) 14 (b) 15 (c) 17 (d) 18

22. The sum of the squares of three consecutive odd numbers is 251. The numbers are :
    (a) 1, 3, 5 (b) 3, 5, 7 (c) 5, 7, 9 (d) 7, 9, 11

23. Two numbers are such that the square of one is 224 less than 8 times the square of the other. If the numbers be in the ratio of 3 : 4, the numbers are : **(Hotel Management 1993)**
    (a) 12, 16 (b) 6, 8 (c) 9, 12 (d) None of these

24. The difference of two numbers is 20% of the larger number. If the smaller number is 12, the larger one is : **(Assistant Grade 1994)**
    (a) 16 (b) 15 (c) 18 (d) 20

25. Three numbers are in the ratio of 3 : 4 : 6 and their product is 1944. The largest of these numbers is. : **(Hotal Management 1993)**
    (a) 6 (b) 12 (c) 18 (d) None of these

26. Three numbers are in the ratio 4 : 5 : 6 and their average is 25. The largest number is :
    (a) 30   (b) 32   (c) 36   (d) 42

27. There are two numbers such that the sum of twice the first and thrice the second is 39, while the sum of thrice the first and twice the second is 36. The larger of the two is :
    (a) 9   (b) 6   (c) 8   (d) 12

28. The sum of three numbers is 136. If the ratio between first and second be 2 : 3 and that between second and third is 5 : 3, then the second number is :
    (a) 40   (b) 48   (c) 72   (d) 60

29. The sum of three numbers is 264. If the first number be twice the second and third number be one– third of the first, then the second number is :
    (a) 48   (b) 54   (c) 72   (d) 84

30. The sum of two consecutive odd numbers in a set of three consecutive odd numbers is 5 more than the third number. What is the second of these numbers ?   **(Bank P.O. 1994)**
    (a) 5   (b) 7   (c) 9   (d) 11

31. The ratio between a two– digit number and the sum of the digits of that number is 4 : 1 . If the digit in the unit place is 3 more than the digit in the ten's place, what is that number ?   **(Bank P.O. 1993)**
    (a) 24   (b) 63   (c) 36   (d) None of these

32. The difference between a two–digit number and the number obtained by interchanging the digits is 27. What is the difference between the digits of the number ?   **(Bank P.O.1993)**
    (a) 3   (b) 6   (c) 9   (d) 5

33. In a two–digit number, the sum of the digits is 15. If 9 is added to the number, the digits are reversed. The number is :
    (a) 96   (b) 87   (c) 78   (d) 69

34. A certain number of two digits is three times the sum of its digits and if 45 be added to it, the digits are reversed, The number is :
    (a) 23   (b) 27   (c) 32   (d) 72

35. Two numbers are such that the ratio between them is 4 : 7.If each is increased by 4, the ratio becomes 3 : 5 . The larger number is :
    (a) 36   (b) 48   (c) 56   (d) 64

36. The difference between the digits of a two– digit number is 4. What is the digit in unit's place ? To find out the answer, which of the informations given in the statements P and Q is / are sufficient.
    P : The difference between the number and the number obtained by interchanging the positions of the digits is 36.

Q : The sum of the digits of that number is 12.
(a) Only P is sufficient   (b) Only Q is sufficient
(c) Both P and Q are needed   (d) Either P or Q is sufficient

(Bank P.O. 1993)

37. The denominator of a fraction is 3 more than the numerator. If 4 is added

to both the numerator and the denominator, the fraction becomes $\frac{4}{5}$. The

fraction is :

(a) $\frac{5}{8}$ (b) $\frac{7}{10}$ (c) $\frac{8}{11}$ (d) $\frac{10}{13}$

38. A fraction becomes $\frac{5}{2}$ when 3 is added to both the numerator and the

denominator and it becomes 4 when 1 is subtracted from both the
numerator and denominator. The numerator of the given fraction is :
(a) 13   (b) 15   (c) 17   (d) 14

39. The sum of the numerator and denominator of a fraction is 11. If 1 is
added to the numerator and 2 is subtracted from the denominator, it
becomes $\frac{2}{3}$. The fraction is :

(a) $\frac{5}{6}$ (b) $\frac{6}{5}$ (c) $\frac{3}{8}$ (d) $\frac{8}{3}$

40. The sum of the digits of a two-digit number is 9 less than the number.
Which of the following digits is at unit place of the number ?
(a) 1   (b) 2   (c) 4   (d) Data inadequate

(Bank P.O. 1992)

41. On dividing 50 into two parts such that the sum of their reciprocals is
$\frac{1}{12}$, we get the parts as :

(a) 20, 30   (b) 24, 26   (c) 28, 22   (d) 36, 14

42. Of the three numbers, the sum of the first two is 45; the sum of the
second and the third is 55 and the sum of the third and thrice the first
is 90. The third number is :
(a) 20   (b) 25   (c) 30   (d) 35

43. The difference between two numbers is 1365. When larger number is
divided by the smaller one, the quotient is 6 and the remainder is 15.
The smaller number is :
(a) 240   (b) 360   (c) 270   (d) 295

44. The sum of two numbers is 184. If one third of the one exceeds one
seventh of another by 8, the smaller number is :
(a) 64   (b) 72   (c) 84   (d) 76

45. 243 has been divided into three parts such that half of the first part,
one-third of the second part and one-fourth of the third part are equal.
The largest part is :

(a) 74   (b) 86   (c) 92   (d) 108

46. A number consists of two digits whose sum is 8. If 18 is added to the number, its digits are interchanged. The number is :
    (a) 26   (b) 62   (c) 53   (d) 35

47. The sum of the squares of two numbers is 68 and the square of their difference is 36. The product of the two numbers is :
    (a) 16   (b) 32   (c) 58   (d) 104

48. The sum of seven numbers is 235. The average of the first three is 23 and that of the last three is 42. The fourth number is :
    (a) 40   (b) 69   (c) 126   (d) 195

49. The sum of three consecutive odd numbers is 57. The middle one is :
    (a) 17   (b) 19   (c) 21   (d) 23

50. The sum of two numbers is twice their difference. If one of the numbers is 10, the other one is :   **(Railways 1991)**

    (a) $3\frac{1}{3}$ (b) $-3\frac{1}{3}$ (c) $4\frac{1}{4}$ (d) 30

51. If one-seventh of a number exceeds its eleventh part by 100, then the number is :   **(C.D.S. 1994)**
    (a) 770   (b) 1100   (c) 1825   (d) 1925

ANSWERS

1. (b)   2. (b)   3. (c)   4. (c)   5. (c)   6. (a)   7. (d)   8. (d)   9. (c)
10. (a)   11. (c)   12. (c)   13. (a)   14. (d)   15. (b)   16. (d)   17. (b)   18. (d)
19. (a)   20. (c)   21. (c)   22. (d)   23. (b)   24. (b)   25. (c)   26. (a)   27. (a)
28. (d)   29. (c)   30. (c)   31. (c)   32. (a)   33. (c)   34. (b)   35. (c)   36. (b)
37. (c)   38. (c)   39. (c)   40. (d)   41. (a)   42. (c)   43. (c)   44. (b)   45. (d)
46. (d)   47. (a)   48. (a)   49. (b)   50. (d)   51. (d)

SOLUTIONS

1. $\frac{1}{4}$ of $\frac{1}{3}$ of $\frac{2}{5}$ of $x = 15 \Leftrightarrow \frac{x}{30} = 15 \Leftrightarrow x = 450$.

   40% of $450 = \left(\frac{40}{100} \times 450\right) = 180$.

2. $\frac{3}{4}x - \frac{1}{3}x = 60 \Leftrightarrow 9x - 4x = 720 \Leftrightarrow x = 144$.

3. $x + 10x = 264 \Leftrightarrow 11x = 264 \Leftrightarrow x = 24$.

4. $\frac{x}{4} = (x - 21) \Leftrightarrow x = 4(x - 21) \Leftrightarrow 3x = 84 \Leftrightarrow x = 28$.

5. $\dfrac{4x}{5} = 64 \Leftrightarrow x = \left(64 \times \dfrac{5}{4}\right) = 80.$

Half of the number $= \left(\dfrac{1}{2} \times 80\right) = 40.$

6. $x - \dfrac{20}{100}x = 40 \Leftrightarrow x - \dfrac{x}{5} = 40 \Leftrightarrow \dfrac{4x}{5} = 40 \Leftrightarrow x = 50.$

7. $\dfrac{16}{100}$ of $\dfrac{40}{100}$ of $x = 8 \Leftrightarrow \dfrac{4}{25} \times \dfrac{2}{5} \times x = 8 \Leftrightarrow x = \left(\dfrac{8 \times 125}{8}\right) = 125.$

8. $x - \dfrac{4x}{7} = 18 \Leftrightarrow \dfrac{3x}{7} = 18 \Leftrightarrow x = \left(\dfrac{18 \times 7}{3}\right) = 42.$

9. $x - 4 = \dfrac{21}{x} \Leftrightarrow x^2 - 4x - 21 = 0 \Leftrightarrow (x-7)(x+3) = 0 \Leftrightarrow x = 7.$

10. $x + \dfrac{1}{x} = 3\left(x - \dfrac{1}{x}\right) \Leftrightarrow 2x = \dfrac{4}{x} \Leftrightarrow x^2 = 2 \Leftrightarrow x = \sqrt{2}.$

11. $\dfrac{x}{5} + 4 = \dfrac{x}{4} - 10 \Leftrightarrow \dfrac{x}{4} - \dfrac{x}{5} = 14 \Leftrightarrow x = (14 \times 20) = 280.$

12. $x - 36 = 86 - x \Leftrightarrow 2x = (86 + 36) \Leftrightarrow 2x = 122 \Leftrightarrow x = 61.$

13. $4x + 10 = 5x - 5 \Leftrightarrow x = 15.$

14. $\left(\dfrac{x}{2}\right)^2 - x = 48 \Leftrightarrow \dfrac{x^2}{4} - x = 48 \Leftrightarrow x^2 - 4x - 192 = 0$

$\Leftrightarrow (x - 16)(x + 12) = 0 \Leftrightarrow x = 16.$

$\therefore \sqrt{x} = 4.$

15. Let the numbers be a and b. Then,

$a^2 + b^2 = 3341...(i),\ a^2 - b^2 = 891...(ii)$

Adding, we get $2a^2 = 4232$ or $a^2 = 2116$ or $a = \sqrt{2116} = 46.$

Subtracting, we get $2b^2 = 2450$ or $b^2 = 1225$ or $b = \sqrt{1225} = 35.$

So, the numbers are 35 and 46.

16. Let the numbers be x and y. Then,

$x + y = 15$ and $x^2 + y^2 = 113.$

$\therefore 2xy = (x+y)^2 - (x^2 + y^2) = (225 - 113) = 112.$

$\therefore x - y = \sqrt{x^2 + y^2 - 2xy} = \sqrt{113 - 112} = 1.$

Solving $x + y = 15,\ x - y = 1$ we get $x = 8,\ y = 7.$

17. Let the numbers be x and y. Then,

$xy = 120$ and $x^2 + y^2 = 289.$

$(x+y)^2 = (x^2 + y^2) + 2xy = (289 + 240) = 529.$

$\therefore x + y = \sqrt{529} = 23.$

18. Let the numbers be x and y. Then,

$x - y = 11$ and $\dfrac{1}{5}(x + y) = 9$ or $x + y = 45.$

                                                  Quantitative Aptitude

Solving $x - y = 11$ & $x + y = 45$ we get $x = 28$, $y = 17$.

19. Since $1.x < 1 + x$, so one of the numbers is 1.

20. Let the numbers be x and y. Then,

$x^2 - y^2 = 256000$ and $x + y = 1000$.

On dividing, we get $x - y = 256$.

Solving $x + y = 1000$ & $x - y = 256$ we get $x = 628$ & $y = 372$.

21. Let the numbers be x and $(x + 1)$. Then,

$(x+1)^2 - x^2 = 35 \Leftrightarrow 2x + 1 = 35 \Leftrightarrow x = 17$.

∴ Smaller number = 17.

22. Let the numbers be x, $(x + 2)$ and $(x + 4)$.

Then, $x^2 + (x+2)^2 + (x+4)^2 = 251 \Rightarrow x^2 + 4x - 77 = 0$

∴ $(x + 11)(x - 7) = 0$ or $x = 7$.

So, the numbers are 7, 9 and 11.

23. Let the numbers be $3x$ and $4x$.

$16x^2 = 8 \times 9x^2 - 224$ or $56x^2 = 224$ or $x^2 = 4$ or $x = 2$.

∴ The numbers are 6 and 8.

24. Let the larger number be x. Then,

$x - 12 = \dfrac{20}{100} x \Leftrightarrow x - \dfrac{x}{5} = 12 \Leftrightarrow \dfrac{4x}{5} = 12 \Leftrightarrow x = 15$.

∴ Larger number = 15.

25. Let the numbers be $3x$, $4x$ and $6x$. Then,

$3x \times 4x \times 6x = 1944 \Leftrightarrow x^3 = 27 \Leftrightarrow x = 3$.

Largest number = $6x = 18$.

26. Let the numbers be $4x$, $5x$ and $6x$.

Total of these numbers = $(25 \times 3) = 75$.

∴ $4x + 5x + 6x = 75 \Leftrightarrow x = 5$.

∴ Largest number = $6x = 30$.

27. Let the numbers be x and y. Then,

$2x + 3y = 39$ and $3x + 2y = 36$

On solving we get $x = 6$ and $y = 9$.

∴ Larger number = 9.

28. $A : B = 2 : 3$ and $B : C = 5 : 3 = \dfrac{3}{5} \times 5 : \dfrac{3}{5} \times 3 = 3 : \dfrac{9}{5}$.

∴ $A : B : C = 2 : 3 : \dfrac{9}{5} = 10 : 15 : 9$.

∴ Second number = $\left(136 \times \dfrac{15}{34}\right) = 60$.

29. Let the numbers be $2x$, x and $\dfrac{2x}{3}$.

Then $2x + x + \dfrac{2x}{3} = 264$ or $11x = 792$ or $x = 72$.

∴ Second number = 72.

30. Let the numbers be $x, x + 2$ and $x + 4$.

$(x + x + 2) - (x + 4) = 5 \Leftrightarrow x = 7$.

∴ Second number = 9.

31. Let ten's digit be x. Then, unit's digit = $(x + 3)$

Sun of the digits = $x + (x + 3) = 2x + 3$.

Number = $10x + (x + 3) = 11x + 3$

∴ $\dfrac{11x + 3}{2x + 3} = \dfrac{4}{1} \Leftrightarrow 11x + 3 = 4(2x + 3) \Leftrightarrow x = 3$.

∴ Number = $(11x + 3) = 36$.

32. Let ten's digit be x and unit's digit be y.

Then, $(10x + y) - (10y + x) = 27 \Leftrightarrow 9(x - y) = 27 \Leftrightarrow x - y = 3$.

33. Let the ten's digit be x. Then, unit's digit = $(15 - x)$.

$10x + (15 - x) + 9 = 10(15 - x) + x$

∴ $18x = 126$ or $x = 7$.

∴ Number = 78.

34. Let the ten's digit be x and unit digit be y. Then,

$10x + y = 3(x + y) \Rightarrow 7x - 2y = 0$ ...(i)

$10x + y + 45 = 10y + x \Rightarrow y - x = 5$ ...(ii)

Solving (i) and (ii) we get : $x = 2$ and $y = 7$.

∴ Required number = 27.

35. Let the numbers be $4x$ and $7x$. Then,

$\dfrac{4x + 4}{7x + 4} = \dfrac{3}{5} \Leftrightarrow 5(4x + 4) = 3(7x + 4) \Leftrightarrow x = 8$.

∴ Larger number = $7x = 56$.

36. Let the ten's digit be x and unit's digit be $(x - 4)$.

P gives : $[10x + (x - 4)] - [10(x - 4) + x] = 36$

This does not give the value of x.

∴ Unit's place can not be found out.

Q gives : $x + x - 4 = 12$ or $x = 8$.

This gives unit's digit = 4.

Thus only Q is sufficient.

37. Let the fraction be $\dfrac{x}{x + 3}$.

Now, $\dfrac{x + 4}{x + 3 + 4} = \dfrac{4}{5} \Leftrightarrow 5(x + 4) = 4(x + 7) \Leftrightarrow x = 8$.

∴ The fraction is $\dfrac{8}{11}$.

38. Let the fraction be $\dfrac{x}{y}$.

Then, $\dfrac{x+3}{y+3}=\dfrac{5}{2} \Rightarrow 2x - 5y = 9$ ...(i)

And, $\dfrac{x-1}{y-1}=4 \Rightarrow x - 4y = -3$ ...(ii)

Solving (i) and (ii), we get : $x = 17$ and $y = 5$.

∴ Numerator of the given fraction is 17.

39. Let the fraction be $\dfrac{x}{y}$.

Then, $x + y = 11$ ...(i)

$\dfrac{x+1}{y-2}=\dfrac{2}{3} \Rightarrow 3(x+1) = 2(y-2)$ or $3x - 2y = -7$ ...(ii)

Solving (i) and (ii) we get : $x = 3$ and $y = 8$.

∴ The fraction is $\dfrac{3}{8}$.

40. Let the ten's digit be x and unit's digit be y.

$(10x + y) - (x + y) = 9$ or $x = 1$.

From this data, we can not find y, the unit's digit.

∴ Data is inadequate.

41. Let these parts be x and $(50 - x)$. Then,

$\dfrac{1}{x}+\dfrac{1}{50-x}=\dfrac{1}{12} \Rightarrow \dfrac{50-x+x}{x(50-x)}=\dfrac{1}{12}$

$\Rightarrow x^2 - 50x + 600 = 0$

$\Rightarrow (x - 30)(x - 20) = 0$

$\Rightarrow x = 30$ or $x = 20$.

∴ These parts are 30 and 20.

42. Let the numbers be x, y and z. Then,

$x + y = 45$, $y + z = 55$ and $3x + z = 90$.

$y = 45 - x$ & $z = 55 - y = 55 - (45 - x) = 10 + x$.

∴ $3x + 10 + x = 90$ or $x = 20$.

$y = (45 - 20) = 25$ and $z = (10 + 20) = 30$.

∴ Third number = 30.

43. Let the numbers be x and $1365 + x$.

Then, $1365 + x = 6x + 15$ or $x = 270$.

44. Let the numbers be x and $(184 - x)$.

∴ $\dfrac{x}{3}-\dfrac{(184-x)}{7}=8$ or $7x - 3(184 - x) = 168$ or $x = 72$.

∴ Smaller number is 72.

45. $\dfrac{A}{2}=\dfrac{B}{3}=\dfrac{C}{4}=x \Rightarrow A = 2x$, $B = 3x$ and $C = 4x$.

$\Rightarrow A : B : C = 2 : 3 : 4$.

∴ Largest part $=\left(243 \times \dfrac{4}{9}\right)= 108$.

46. Let ten's digit be x and unit's digit be y.

Then, $x + y = 8$ ...(i)

$(10x + y) + 18 = 10y + x$ or $y - x = 2$ ...(ii)

Solving (i) and (ii) we get $x = 3$ and $y = 5$.

∴ The number is 35.

47. $a^2 + b^2 = 68$ and $(a - b)^2 = 36$.

$(a - b)^2 = a^2 + b^2 - 2ab \Leftrightarrow 36 = 68 - 2ab \Leftrightarrow ab = 16.$

48. $23 \times 3 + x + 42 \times 3 = 235 \Leftrightarrow x = 40.$

49. Let the required numbers be x, $x + 2$ and $x + 4$.

$x + x + 2 + x + 4 = 57 \Leftrightarrow x = 17.$

∴ Middle number $= x + 2 = 19.$

50. Let the other number be x. Then,

$10 + x = 2(x - 10) \Rightarrow x = 30.$

51. Let the number be x. Then,

$\dfrac{x}{7} - \dfrac{x}{11} = 100 \Leftrightarrow 11x - 7x = 7700 \Leftrightarrow x = 1925.$

---

8. Problems On Ages

Ex. 1. *The ratio of the ages of Mona and Sona is 4 : 5. Twelve years hence, their ages will be in the ratio of 5 : 6. What will be Sona's age after 6 years ?*

Sol. Let their present ages be $4x$ & $6x$.

Then, $\dfrac{4x+12}{5x+12} = \dfrac{5}{6}$ or $x = 12$.

∴ Sona's age after 6 years $= (5x+6) = 66$ years.

Ex. 2. *Ramu was 4 times as old as his son 8 years ago. After 8 years, Ramu will be twice as old as his son. What are their present ages ?*

Sol. Let son's age 8 years ago be x years.

Then, Ramu's age at that time $= 4x$ years.

Son's age after 8 years $= (x+8) + 8 = (x+16)$ years.

Ramu's age after 8 years $= (4x+8) + 8 = (4x+16)$ years.

∴ $2(x+16) = 4x+16$ or $x = 8$.

∴ Son's present age $= (x+8) = 16$ years.

Ramu's present age $= (4x+8) = 40$ years.

Ex. 3. *A man is four times as old as his son. Five years ago, the man was nine times as old as his son was at that time. What is the present age of the man ?*

Sol. Let son's age $= x$. Then, man's age $= 4x$.

$9(x-5) = (4x-5)$ or $x = 8$.

∴ Man's present age $= 4x = 32$ years.

Ex. 4. *The sum of the ages of Aruna and her mother is 49 years. Also, 7 years ago, the mother's age was 4 times Aruna's age. Find the present age of Aruna's mother.*

Sol. Let Aruna's age 7 years ago be x.

Mother's age 7 years ago $= 4x$.

∴ $(x+7) + (4x+7) = 49$ or $x = 7$.

∴ Mother's present age $= (4x+7) = 35$ years.

Ex. 5. *The ages of A and B differ by 16 years. If 6 years ago, the elder one be 3 times as old as the younger one, find their present ages.*

Sol. Let A's age $= x$ & B's age $= (x+16)$.

$3(x-6) = (x+16-6)$ or $x = 14$.

∴ A's age $= 14$ years & B's age $= 30$ years.

EXERCISE 8

1. The ratio of the ages of Meena and Meera is 4 : 3. The sum of their ages is 28 years. The ratio of their ages after 8 years will be :
   (a) 4 : 3   (b) 12 : 11   (c) 7 : 4   (d) 6 : 5
   (Central Excise & I. Tax 1991)

2. The ages of Ram and Mukta are in the ratio of 3 : 5. After 9 years, the ratio of their ages will becomes 3 :4. The present age of Mukta (in years) is :   **(Assistant Grade 1994)**
   (a) 9   (b) 15   (c) 18   (d) 24

3. The ratio of the ages of Swati and Varun is 2 : 5. After 8 years, their ages will be in the ratio of 1 : 2. The difference in their present ages (in years) is :   **(C.B.I. 1993)**
   (a) 24   (b) 26   (c) 29   (d) 32

4. A father is twice as old as his son. 20 years ago, the age of the father was 12 times the age of the son. The present age of the father (in years) is :   **(Hotel Management 1992)**
   (a) 44   (b) 32   (c) 22   (d) 45

5. Five years ago, the total of the ages of a father and his son was 40 years. The ratio of their present ages is 4 : 1. What is the present age of the father ?   **(Bank P.O. 1994)**
   (a) 30 years   (b) 20 years   (c) 25 years   (d) None of these

6. One year ago, Mrs Promila was four times as old as her daughter Swati. Six years hence, Mrs Promila's age will exceed her daugther's age by 9 years. The ratio of the present ages of Promila and her daughter is :   **(C.B.I. 1993)**
   (a) 9 : 2   (b) 11 : 3   (c) 12 : 5   (d) 13 : 4

7. Sachin was twice as old as Ajay 10 years back. How old is Ajay today if Sachin will be 40 years old 10 years hence ?   **(Bank P.O. 1991)**
   (a) 20 years   (b) 10 years   (c) 30 years   (d) None of these

8. Ten years ago *A* was half of *B* in age. If the ratio of their present ages is 3 : 4, what will be the total of their present ages ? **(Bank P.O. 1991)**
   (a) 8 years   (b) 20 years   (c) 30 years   (d) 35 years

9. Sushil was thrice as old as Snehal 6 years back. Sushil will be $\frac{5}{3}$ times as old as Snehal 6 years hence. How old is Snehal today ?
   (a) 18 years   (b) 24 years   (c) 12 years   (d) 15 years
   (Bank P.O. 1992)

10. If 6 years are subtracted from the present age of Gulzar and the remainder is divided by 18, then the present age of his grandson Anup is obtained. If Anup is 2 years younger to Mahesh whose age is 5 years, then what is the present age of Gulzar ?   **(Bank P.O. 1993)**

(a) 96 years   (b) 84 years   (c) 48 years   (d) 60 years

11. The total of the ages of A, B and C at present is 90 years. Ten years ago, the ratio of their ages was 1 : 2 : 3. What is the age of B at present ?

    (a) 40 years   (b) 30 years   (c) 20 years   (d) 18 years
                                                                (Bank P.O. 1993)

12. The sum of the ages of A, B and C is 96 years. To find out B's age, which of the following information given in the statements P and Q is/are sufficient ?

    P : A is 6 years older than C

    Q : The total of B and C's ages is 56 years.   **(Bank P.O. 1994)**

    (a) P   (b) Q   (c) both P and Q   (d) None of these

13. Sneh's age is $\frac{1}{6}$ th of her father's age. Sneh's father's age will be twice of Vimal's age after 10 years. If Vimal's eighth birthday was celebrated two years before, then what is Sneh's present age ?   **(Bank P.O. 1992)**

    (a) 24 years   (b) 30 years   (c) $6\frac{2}{3}$ years   (d) None of these

14. Jayesh is as much younger to Anil as he is older to Prashant. If the sum of the ages of Anil and Prashant is 48 years, what is the age of Jayesh ?   **(Bank P.O. 1991)**

    (a) 20 years   (b) 30 years
    (c) 24 years   (d) Can not be determined

15. The sum of the ages of a father and son is 45 years. Five years ago, the product of their ages was four times the father's age at that time. The present age of father and son, respectively are :

    (a) 25 years, 10 years   (b) 36 years, 9 years
    (c) 39 years, 6 years   (d) None of these
                                                        (Hotel Management 1991)

16. Kamla got married 6 years ago. Today her age is $1\frac{1}{4}$ times her age at the time of marriage. Her son's age is $\frac{1}{10}$ times her age. Her son's age is :
                                                                (Bank P.O. 1988)

    (a) 2 years   (b) 3 years   (c) 4 years   (d) 5 years

17. Ten years ago, Chandrawati's mother was four times older than her daughter. After ten years, the mother will be twice older than daughter. The present age of Chandrawati is :   **(Bank P.O. 1990)**

    (a) 5 years   (b) 10 years   (c) 20 years   (d) 30 years

18. In 10 years, A will be twice as old as B was 10 years ago. If A is now 9 years older than B, the present age of B is :   **(L.I.C. 1989)**

    (a) 19 years   (b) 29 years   (c) 39 years   (d) 49 years

19. The age of father 10 years ago was thrice the age of his son. Ten years hence, the father's age will be twice that of his son. The ratio of their present ages is :

(a) 5 : 2   (b) 9 : 2   (c) 7 : 3   (d) 13 : 4

20. Two years ago a man was 6 times as old as his son. After 18 years, he will be twice as old as his son. Their present ages (in years) are :

(a) 32, 7   (b) 34, 9   (c) 36, 11   (d) None of these

(N.D.A. 1992)

21. The ages of two persons differ by 20 years. If 5 years ago, the elder one be 5 times as old as the younger one, their present ages (in years) are respectively : **(N.D.A. 1994)**

(a) 30, 10   (b) 25, 5   (c) 29, 9   (d) 50, 30

22. The difference between the ages of two persons is 10 years. 15 years ago, the elder one was twice as old as the younger one. The present age of the elder person is :

(a) 35 years   (b) 45 years   (c) 55 years   (d) 25 years

23. Three years ago the average age of A and B was 18 years. With C joining them now, the average becomes 22 years. How old is C now ?

(a) 24 years   (b) 27 years   (c) 28 years   (d) 30 years

24. Pushpa is twice as old as Rita was 2 years ago. If the difference of their ages be 2 years, how old is Pushpa today ?   **(Railways 1991)**

(a) 6 years   (b) 8 years   (c) 10 years   (d) 12 years

25. The ratio of the father's age of his son's age is 7 : 3. The product of their ages is 756. The ratio of their ages after 6 years will be :

(a) 5 : 2   (b) 2 : 1   (c) 11 : 7   (d) 13 : 9

26. Average age of A and B is 24 years and average age of B, C and D is 22 years. The sum of the ages of A, B, C and D is :   **(Bank P.O. 1992)**

(a) 90 years   (b) 96 years

(c) 114 years   (d) Data inadequate

27. The ratio of Meena's age to the age of her mother is 3 : 8. The difference of their ages is 35 years. The ratio of their ages after 4 years will be :

(a) 7 : 12   (b) 5 : 12   (c) 38 : 43   (d) 42 : 47

28. One year ago, a father was four times as old as his son. In 6 years time his age exceeds twice his son's age by 9 years. The ratio of their present ages is :

(a) 9 : 2   (b) 11 : 3   (c) 12 : 5   (d) 13 : 4

29. The age of Anu's father is four times his age. If 5 years ago, the father's age was seven times the age of his son at that time, what is Anu's father's present age ?

(a) 35 years   (b) 40 years   (c) 70 years   (d) 84 years

30. Ramlal is four times as old as his son. Four years hence, the sum of their ages will be 43 years. The present age of the son is :

(a) 5 years   (b) 7 years   (c) 8 years   (d) 10 years

31. Ratio of Ashok's age to Sandeep's age is 4 : 3. Ashok will be 26 years old after 6 years. How old is Sandeep now ?   **(Railways 1989)**

    (a) 12 years   (b) 15 years   (c) $19\frac{1}{2}$ years (d) 21 years

32. The ratio of Vimal's age and Aruna's age is 3 : 5 and the sum of their ages is 80 years. The ratio of their ages after 10 years will be :

    (a) 2 : 3   (b) 1 : 2   (c) 3 : 2   (d) 3 : 5

                                                     (Bank P.O. 1990)

33. The average age of five members of a family is 21 years. If the age of the grandfather be included, the average is increased by 9 years. The age of the grandfather is :

    (a) 66 years   (b) 72 years   (c) 75 years   (d) 84 years

34. The average age of 12 students is 20 years. If the age of one more student is included, the average decreases by 1. What is the age of the new student ?   **(Bank P.O. 1991)**

    (a) 5 years   (b) 7 years   (c) 9 years   (d) 11 years

35. The average age of an adult class is 40 years. Twelve new students with an average age of 32 years join the class, thereby decreasing the average of the class by 4 years. The original strength of the class was :

    (a) 10   (b) 11   (c) 12   (d) 15

                                             (Assistant Grade 1994)

ANSWERS

1. (d)   **2.** (b)   **3.** (a)   **4.** (a)   **5.** (d)   **6.** (d)   **7.** (a)   **8.** (d)   **9.** (c)

10. (d)   **11.** (b)   **12.** (c)   **13.** (d)   **14.** (c)   **15.** (b)   **16.** (b)   **17.** (c)   **18.** (c)

19. (c)   **20.** (a)   **21.** (a)   **22.** (a)   **23.** (a)   **24.** (b)   **25.** (b)   **26.** (d)   **27.** (b)

28. (b)   **29.** (b)   **30.** (b)   **31.** (b)   **32.** (a)   **33.** (b)   **34.** (b)   **35.** (c)

SOLUTIONS

1. Let Meena's age $= 4x$ & Meera's age $= 3x$.

    Then, $4x + 3x = 28 \Leftrightarrow x = 4$.

    $\therefore$ Meena's age $= 16$ years & Meera's age $= 12$ years.

    Ratio of their ages after 8 years $= (16 + 8) : (12 + 8) = 24 : 20 = 6 : 5.$.

2. Let Ram's age $= 3x$ & Mukta's age $= 5x$.

    $\therefore \dfrac{3x+9}{5x+9} = \dfrac{3}{4} \Leftrightarrow 4(3x+9) = 3(5x+9) \Leftrightarrow x = 3.$

    $\therefore$ Mukta's age $= 15$ years.

3. Let Swati's age $= 2x$ & Varun's age $= 5x$.

    $\therefore \dfrac{2x+8}{5x+8} = \dfrac{1}{2} \Leftrightarrow 2(2x+8) = (5x+8) \Leftrightarrow x = 8.$

    $\therefore$ Swati's age $= 16$ years & Varun's age $= 40$ years.

    Difference of their ages $= 24$ years.

4. Let son's age = x. Then, father's age = $2x$.
    $12 (x - 20) = (2x - 20) \Leftrightarrow x = 22$.
    $\therefore$ Father's present age = 44 years.

5. Let son's age = x. Then, father's age = $4x$.
    $(x - 5) + (4x - 5) = 40 \Leftrightarrow x = 10$.
    Present age of father = 40 years.

6. Let Swati's age 1 year ago = x.
    Then, Promila's age 1 year ago = $4x$.
    $(4x + 6) - (x + 6) = 9$ or $x = 3$.
    Present age of Promila = $(12 + 1)$ years = 13 years.
    Present age of Swati = $(3 + 1)$ years = 4 years.
    $\therefore$ Ratio of their ages = 13 : 4.

7. Sachin's age today = 30 years.
    Sachin's age 10 years back = 20 years.
    Ajay's age 10 years back = 10 years.
    Ajay's age today = 20 years.

8. Let A's age 10 years ago = x. Then, B's age 10 years ago = $2x$.
    $\dfrac{x + 10}{2x + 10} = \dfrac{3}{4} \Leftrightarrow 4(x + 10) = 3(2x + 10) \Leftrightarrow x = 5$.
    Total of their present ages = $(x + 10 + 2x + 10)$
    $\qquad\qquad\qquad\qquad = (3x + 20) = 35$ years.

9. Let Snehal's age 6 years back = x.
    Then, Sushil's age 6 years back = $3x$.
    $\dfrac{5}{3}(x + 6 + 6) = (3x + 6 + 6) \Leftrightarrow 5(x + 12) = 3(3x + 12) \Leftrightarrow x = 6$.
    Snehal today = $(x + 6)$ years = 12 years.

10. Anup's age = $(5 - 2)$ years = 3 years.
    Let Gulzar's age x years.
    Then, $\dfrac{x - 6}{18} = 3 \Leftrightarrow x - 6 = 54 \Leftrightarrow x = 60$.

11. Let their ages 10 years ago be x, $2x$ and $3x$ years.
    $\therefore$ $x + 10 + 2x + 10 + 3x + 10 = 90 \Leftrightarrow x = 10$.
    B's present age = $(2x + 10)$ = 30 years.

12. $A + B + C = 96$. Let $C = x$. Then, $A = x + 6$.
    $x + 6 + B + x = 96 \Rightarrow B + 2x = 90$.
    Now $B + C = 56 \Rightarrow B + x = 56$
    $\therefore$ $x = (90 - 56) = 34$.
    $\therefore$ $B + 2x = 90 \Rightarrow B = (90 - 68) = 22$.
    Thus both P and Q are needed.

13. Vimal's age after 10 years = $(8 + 2 + 10)$ years = 20 years.
    Sneh's father's age after 10 years = 40 years.
    Sneh's father's present age = 30 years.

Sneh's age $= \left(\frac{1}{6} \times 30\right)$ years $= 5$ years.

14. $A - J = J - P$ or $A + P = 2J$. So, $2J = 48$ or $J = 24$.

15. Let son's age $= x$ years. Then father's age $= (45 - x)$ years.
$(x - 5)(45 - x - 5) = 4(45 - x - 5) \Leftrightarrow (x - 5) = 4 \Leftrightarrow x = 9$.
$\therefore$ Their ages are 36 years and 9 years.

16. Let Kamla's age 6 years ago $= x$ years.
Kamla's present age $= (x + 6)$ years.
$\therefore$ $x + 6 = \frac{5}{4}x$ or $\frac{x}{4} = 6$ or $x = 24$.
$\therefore$ Kamla's present age $= 30$ years.
$\therefore$ Son's present age $= \left(\frac{1}{10} \times 30\right)$ years $= 3$ years.

17. Let Chandrawati's age 10 years ago be x years.
Her mother's age 10 years ago $= 4x$.
$(4x + 10) + 10 = 2(x + 10 + 10)$ or $2x = 20$ or $x = 10$.
$\therefore$ Present age of Chandrawati $= (x + 10) = 20$ years.

18. Let B's age $= x$ years. Then, A's age $= (x + 9)$ years.
$(x + 9 + 10) = 2(x - 10) \Leftrightarrow x = 39$.
$\therefore$ Present age of $B = 39$ years.

19. Let son's age 10 years ago $= x$.
Then, father's age 10 years ago $= 3x$.
$2(x + 10 + 10) = (3x + 10 + 10) \Leftrightarrow x = 20$.
Ratio of their present ages $= (3x + 10):(x + 10) = 70:30 = 7:3$.

20. Let son's age 2 years ago be x.
Man's age 2 years ago $= 6x$.
$2(x + 2 + 18) = (6x + 2 + 18) \Leftrightarrow 4x = 20 \Leftrightarrow x = 5$.
Their present ages are $(6x + 2)$ & $(x + 2)$ i.e. 32 years & 7 years.

21. Let their ages be x and $(x + 20)$ years.
$5(x - 5) = (x + 20 - 5)$ or $4x = 40$ or $x = 10$.
$\therefore$ Their present ages are 30 years & 10 years.

22. Let their ages be x and $(x + 10)$ years.
$(x + 10 - 15) = 2(x - 15) \Leftrightarrow x = 25$.
$\therefore$ Present age of the elder person $= 35$ years.

23. $(A + B)$'s age 3 years ago $= (18 \times 2)$ years $= 36$ years.
$\therefore$ $(A + B)$ now $= (36 + 3 + 3)$ years $= 42$ years.
$(A + B + C)$ now $= (22 \times 3)$ years $= 66$ years.
$\therefore$ C now $= (66 - 42)$ years $= 24$ years.

24. Let Rita's age 2 years ago $= x$ years.
Pushpa's age now $= 2x$ years.
$2x - (x + 2) = 2 \Rightarrow x = 4$.
$\therefore$ Pushpa's age now $= 8$ years.

25. Let their ages be $7x$ and $3x$ years. Then,

$7x \times 3x = 756 \Leftrightarrow x^2 = 36 \Leftrightarrow x = 6$.

$\therefore$ Their present ages are 42 years & 18 years.

Ratio of their ages after 6 years $= 48 : 24 = 2 : 1$.

26. $A + B = (24 \times 2) = 48$ & $B + C + D = (22 \times 3) = 66$.

With this data, we can not find $A + B + C + D$.

So, the data is inadequate.

27. Let their ages be $3x$ and $8x$.

Then, $8x - 3x = 35$ or $x = 7$.

So, their present ages are 21 years and 56 years.

Ratio of their ages after 4 years $= 25 : 60 = 5 : 12$.

28. Let son's age 1 year ago $= x$.

Father's age 1 year ago $= 4x$.

$(4x + 1 + 6) - 2(x + 1 + 6) = 9 \Leftrightarrow x = 8$.

$\therefore$ Ratio of present ages $= (4x + 1) : (x + 1) = 33 : 9 = 11 : 3$.

29. Let Anu's age $= x$. Then, father's age $= 4x$.

$7(x - 5) = (4x - 5) \Leftrightarrow 3x = 30 \Leftrightarrow x = 10$.

$\therefore$ Father's age $= 40$ years.

30. Let son's age $= x$. Then, Ramlal's age $= 4x$.

$(x + 4) + (4x + 4) = 43 \Leftrightarrow x = 7$.

$\therefore$ Present age of the son is 7 years.

31. Let their ages be $4x$ and $3x$ years.

Now $4x + 6 = 26 \Rightarrow x = 5$.

$\therefore$ Age of Sandeep $= 3x = 15$ years.

32. Let their ages be $3x$ and $5x$ years.

Then, $3x + 5x = 80 \Leftrightarrow x = 10$.

Ratio of their ages after 10 years $= (3x + 10) : (5x + 10)$
$$= 40 : 60 = 2 : 3.$$

33. Grand father's age $= (6 \times 30 - 5 \times 21)$ years $= 75$ years.

34. New average $= (20 - 1) = 19$.

$\therefore$ Age of new student $= (13 \times 19 - 12 \times 20)$ years $= 7$ years.

35. Let, original strength $= x$.

$\therefore \dfrac{40x + 12 \times 32}{x + 12} = 36$ or $x = 12$.

9. Surds & Indices

Laws of Indices :

$$\text{(i) } a^m \times a^n = a^{m+n} \qquad \text{(ii) } \frac{a^m}{a^n} = a^{m-n} \qquad \text{(iii) } (a^m)^n = a^{mn}$$

$$\text{(iv) } (ab)^n = a^n b^n \qquad \text{(v) } \left(\frac{a}{b}\right)^n = \frac{a^n}{b^n} \qquad \text{(vi) } a^0 = 1$$

Laws of Surds :

We write $\sqrt[n]{a} = a^{1/n}$ and it is called a surd of order n.

$$\text{(i) } (\sqrt[n]{a})^n = (a^{1/n})^n = a \qquad \text{(ii) } \sqrt[n]{ab} = \sqrt[n]{a} \cdot \sqrt[n]{b} \qquad \text{(iii) } \sqrt[n]{\frac{a}{b}} = \frac{\sqrt[n]{a}}{\sqrt[n]{b}}$$

$$\text{(iv) } (\sqrt[n]{a})^m = \sqrt[n]{a^m} \qquad \text{(v) } \sqrt[m]{\sqrt[n]{a}} = \sqrt[mn]{a}.$$

Solved Problems

Ex. 1. *Simplify :* $(i) \ (81)^{3/4}$ $(ii) \ \left(\dfrac{1}{64}\right)^{-5/6}$ $(iii) \ (256)^{-1/4}$

Sol. $(i) \ (81)^{3/4} = (3^4)^{3/4} = 3^{\left(4 \times \frac{3}{4}\right)} = 3^3 = 27.$

$(ii) \ \left(\dfrac{1}{64}\right)^{-5/6} = (64)^{5/6} = (2^6)^{5/6} = 2^{\left(6 \times \frac{5}{6}\right)} = 2^5 = 32.$

$(iii) \ (256)^{-1/4} = \left(\dfrac{1}{256}\right)^{1/4} = \left[\left(\dfrac{1}{4}\right)^4\right]^{1/4} = \left(\dfrac{1}{4}\right)^{\left(4 \times \frac{1}{4}\right)} = \dfrac{1}{4}.$

Ex. 2. *Simplify :* $\left(\dfrac{x^b}{x^c}\right)^{(b^2 + c^2 + bc)} \times \left(\dfrac{x^c}{x^a}\right)^{(c^2 + a^2 + ca)} \times \left(\dfrac{x^a}{x^b}\right)^{(a^2 + b^2 + ab)}$

Sol. Given Exp.

$= (x^{b-c})^{(b^2 + c^2 + bc)} \times (x^{c-a})^{(c^2 + a^2 + ca)} \times (x^{a-b})^{(a^2 + b^2 + ab)}$

$= x^{(b-c)(b^2 + c^2 + bc)} \times x^{(c-a)(c^2 + a^2 + ca)} \times x^{(a-b)(a^2 + b^2 + ab)}$

$= x^{(b^3 - c^3)} \times x^{(c^3 - a^3)} \times x^{(a^3 - b^3)}$

$= x^{(b^3 - c^3) + (c^3 - a^3) + (a^3 - b^3)} = x^0 = 1.$

Ex. 3. *Simplify* : $\left(\dfrac{2^{1/2}\times 3^{1/3}\times 4^{1/4}}{10^{-1/5}\times 5^{3/5}}\div\dfrac{3^{4/3}\times 5^{-7/5}}{4^{-3/5}\times 6}\right).$

Sol. Given Exp. $=\dfrac{2^{1/2}\times 3^{1/3}\times (2^2)^{1/4}}{(2\times 5)^{-1/5}\times 5^{3/5}}\times\dfrac{4^{-3/5}\times 6}{3^{4/3}\times 5^{-7/5}}$

$=\dfrac{2^{1/2}\times 3^{1/3}\times 2^{1/2}}{2^{-1/5}\times 5^{-1/5}\times 5^{3/5}}\times\dfrac{(2^2)^{-3/5}\times (2\times 3)}{3^{4/3}\times 5^{-7/5}}$

$=\dfrac{2^{1/2}\times 3^{1/3}\times 2^{1/2}}{2^{-1/5}\times 5^{-1/5}\times 5^{3/5}}\times\dfrac{2^{-6/5}\times 2\times 3}{3^{4/3}\times 5^{-7/5}}$

$=\dfrac{2^{\left(\frac{1}{2}+\frac{1}{2}+\frac{1}{5}-\frac{6}{5}+1\right)}\,3^{\left(\frac{1}{3}+1-\frac{4}{3}\right)}}{5^{\left(-\frac{1}{5}+\frac{3}{5}-\frac{7}{5}\right)}}$

$=(2^1\times 3^0\times 5^1)=(2\times 1\times 5)=10.$

Ex. 4. *Which is larger :* $\sqrt[3]{4}$ *or* $\sqrt[4]{5}$?

Sol. Given surds are of order 3 and 4, whose l.c.m. is 12.
We change each one of the given surds into a surd of order 12.

$\therefore\ \sqrt[3]{4}=4^{1/3}=4^{\left(\frac{1}{3}\times\frac{4}{4}\right)}=(4^{4/12})=(4^4)^{1/12}=(256)^{1/12}$

$\sqrt[4]{5}=5^{1/4}=5^{\left(\frac{1}{4}\times\frac{3}{3}\right)}=(5^{3/12})=(5^3)^{1/12}=(125)^{1/12},$

Clearly, $(256)^{1/12}>(125)^{1/12}$ or $\sqrt[3]{4}>\sqrt[4]{5}.$

EXERCISE 9

Mark ($\sqrt{}$) against the correct answer :

1. The value of $(\sqrt{8})^{1/3}$ is : **(C.D.S. 1991)**
   (a) 2   (b) 4   (c) $\sqrt{2}$ (d) 8

2. The value of $5^{1/4}\times(125)^{0.25}$ is : **(I. Tax 1992)**
   (a) $\sqrt{5}$ (b) $5\sqrt{5}$ (c) 5   (d) 25

3. The value of $\left(\dfrac{32}{243}\right)^{-4/5}$ is :
   (a) $\dfrac{4}{9}$ (b) $\dfrac{9}{4}$ (c) $\dfrac{16}{81}$ (d) $\dfrac{81}{16}$

4. $\left(\dfrac{1}{216}\right)^{-2/3}\div\left(\dfrac{1}{27}\right)^{-4/3}=?$ **(Hotel Management 1992)**

(a) $\frac{3}{4}$ (b) $\frac{2}{3}$ (c) $\frac{4}{9}$ (d) $\frac{1}{8}$

5. $\dfrac{2^{n+4} - 2.2^n}{2.2^{n+3}} + 2^{-3}$ is equal to :

         (Assistant Grade 1994)

    (a) 2^{n+1} (b) $-2^{n+1} + \frac{1}{8}$ (c) $\frac{9}{8} - 2^n$ (d) 1

6.   If $5\sqrt{5} \times 5^3 \div 5^{-3/2} = 5^{a+2}$, the value of a is :   **(Assistant Grade 1994)**

    (a) 4   (b) 5   (c) 6   (d) 8

7.   If $\sqrt{2^n} = 64$, then the value of n is :   **(Assistant Grade 1990)**

    (a) 2   (b) 4   (c) 6   (d) 12

8. $\dfrac{(0.6)^0 - (0.1)^{-1}}{\left(\frac{3}{2^3}\right)^{-1} \cdot \left(\frac{3}{2}\right)^3 + \left(-\frac{1}{3}\right)^{-1}}$ is equal to :

         (C.D.S. 1993)

    (a) $-\frac{3}{2}$ (b) $-\frac{1}{2}$ (c) $\frac{2}{3}$ (d) $\frac{3}{2}$

9.   If $\dfrac{9^n \times 3^5 \times (27)^3}{3 \times (81)^4} = 27$, then n equals :

    (a) 0   (b) 2   (c) 3   (d) 4

10.   If $\dfrac{9^n (3^2)(3^{-n/2})^{-2} - 27^n}{3^{3m}(2^3)} = \dfrac{1}{27}$, then

         (C.D.S. 1992)

    (a) $m - n = 2$ (b) $m - n = 1$ (c) $m - n = -2$ (d) $m - n = -1$

11.   If $(\sqrt{3})^5 \times 9^2 = 3^\alpha \times 3\sqrt{3}$, then α equals :

    (a) 2   (b) 3   (c) 4   (d) 5

12.   The simplified form of $\dfrac{x^{7/2} \cdot \sqrt{y^3}}{x^{5/2} \cdot \sqrt{y}}$ is :

    (a) $\frac{x^2}{y}$ (b) $\frac{x^3}{y^2}$ (c) $\frac{x^6}{y^3}$ (d) xy

13. $\left(\dfrac{1}{1 + x^{n-m}} + \dfrac{1}{1 + x^{m-n}}\right)$ is equal to :

    (a) 0   (b) 1   (c) $\frac{1}{2}$ (d) x^{m+n}

14.   If x, y, z are real numbers, then the value of :

    $\sqrt{x^{-1}y} \cdot \sqrt{y^{-1}z} \cdot \sqrt{z^{-1}x}$ is :

    (a) xyz (b) $\sqrt{xyz}$ (c) $\frac{1}{xyz}$ (d) 1

15. $\dfrac{1}{1 + x^{(b-a)} + x^{(c-a)}} + \dfrac{1}{1 + x^{(a-b)} + x^{(c-b)}} + \dfrac{1}{1 + x^{(b-c)} + x^{(a-c)}} = ?$

    (a) x^{a-b-c} (b) 1   (c) 0   (d) 3

16. $\left(\dfrac{x^b}{x^c}\right)^{(b+c-a)} \cdot \left(\dfrac{x^c}{x^a}\right)^{(c+a-b)} \cdot \left(\dfrac{x^a}{x^b}\right)^{(a+b-c)} = ?$

    (a) x^{abc} (b) x^{a+b+c} (c) $x^{ab+bc+ca}$ (d) 1

17. If $pqr = 1$, then $\left(\dfrac{1}{1+p+q^{-1}} + \dfrac{1}{1+q+r^{-1}} + \dfrac{1}{1+r+p^{-1}}\right) = ?$

    (a) 0   (b) $\dfrac{1}{pq}$ (c) pq (d) 1

18. $\left(\dfrac{x^a}{x^b}\right)^{(a+b)} \times \left(\dfrac{x^b}{x^c}\right)^{(b+c)} \times \left(\dfrac{x^c}{x^a}\right)^{(c+a)} = ?$

    (a) 0   (b) x^{abc} (c) x^{a+b+c} (d) 1

19. $\left(\dfrac{x^a}{x^b}\right)^{1/ab} \times \left(\dfrac{x^b}{x^c}\right)^{1/bc} \times \left(\dfrac{x^c}{x^a}\right)^{1/ca} = ?$

    (a) 1   (b) $x^{1/abc}$ (c) $x^{1/(ab+bc+ca)}$ (d) None

20. If $2^{x+4} - 2^{x+2} = 3$, then x is equal to :
    (a) 0   (b) 2   (c) -1 (d) -2

21. If $2^{x-1} + 2^{x+1} = 320$, then x is equal to :   **(C.D.S. 1991)**
    (a) 6   (b) 8   (c) 5   (d) 7

22. If $2^{2x-1} = \dfrac{1}{8^{x-3}}$, then the value of x is :

    (a) 3   (b) 2   (c) 0   (d) -2

23. If $\left(\dfrac{a}{b}\right)^{x-1} = \left(\dfrac{b}{a}\right)^{x-3}$, then x is equal to :

    (a) 1   (b) $\dfrac{1}{2}$ (c) 2   (d) $\dfrac{7}{2}$

24. If $2^x \times 8^{1/5} = 2^{1/5}$, then x is equal to :   **(C.D.S. 1993)**
    (a) $\dfrac{1}{5}$ (b) $-\dfrac{1}{5}$ (c) $\dfrac{2}{5}$ (d) $-\dfrac{2}{5}$

25. If $\sqrt{5 + \sqrt[3]{x}} = 3$, then x is equal to :
    (a) 125   (b) 64   (c) 27   (d) 9

26. If $5^{x+3} = (25)^{3x-4}$, then the value of x is :

(a) $\dfrac{5}{11}$ (b) $\dfrac{11}{5}$ (c) $\dfrac{11}{3}$ (d) $\dfrac{13}{5}$

27. If $\sqrt[3]{32} = 2^x$, then x is equal to :

(a) 5   (b) 3   (c) $\dfrac{3}{5}$ (d) $\dfrac{5}{3}$

28. If $a^x = b^y = c^z$ and $b^2 = ac$, then y equals :

(a) $\dfrac{xz}{x+z}$ (b) $\dfrac{xz}{2\,(x-z)}$ (c) $\dfrac{xz}{2\,(z-x)}$ (d) $\dfrac{2xz}{(x+z)}$

29. If $2^x = 3^y = 6^{-z}$, then $\left(\dfrac{1}{x} + \dfrac{1}{y} + \dfrac{1}{z}\right)$ is equal to :

(a) 0   (b) 1   (c) $\dfrac{3}{2}$ (d) $-\dfrac{1}{2}$

30. If $x = y^a$, $y = z^b$ and $z = x^c$, then the value of abc is :

(a) 4   (b) 3   (c) 2   (d) 1

31. $\sqrt{2}, \sqrt[3]{4}$ and $\sqrt[4]{6}$ in ascending order are :

(a) $\sqrt{2}, \sqrt[3]{4}, \sqrt[4]{6}$ (b) $\sqrt[4]{6}, \sqrt{2}, \sqrt[3]{4}$
(c) $\sqrt[4]{6}, \sqrt[3]{4}, \sqrt{2}$ (d) $\sqrt{2}, \sqrt[4]{6}, \sqrt[3]{4}$

32. If m and n are whole numbers such that $m^n = 121$, then the value of $(m-1)^{n+1}$ is :   **(Assistant Grade 1993)**

(a) 1   (b) 10   (c) 121   (d) 1000

33. If $1 - x^8 = 65$ and $1 - x^4 = 64$, the value of x is :

(a) $\pm\dfrac{1}{\sqrt{2}}$ (b) $\pm\sqrt{2}$ (c) $\pm\dfrac{1}{2\sqrt{2}}$ (d) $\pm 2\sqrt{2}$

34. If $[3^m \div (3^m)^2]^{1/m} = 81$, the value of m is :

(a) 3   (b) 6   (c) -3 (d) -6

35. If $2^a + 3^b = 17$ and $2^{a+2} - 3^{b+1} = 5$, the values of a and b respectively are :

(a) 2, 3   (b) $-2, 3$ (c) $2, -3$ (d) 3, 2

ANSWERS

1. (c)   **2.** (c)   **3.** (d)   **4.** (c)   **5.** (d)   **6.** (a)   **7.** (d)   **8.** (a)   **9.** (c)
10. (b)   **11.** (d)   **12.** (d)   **13.** (b)   **14.** (d)   **15.** (b)   **16.** (d)   **17.** (d)   **18.** (d)
19. (a)   **20.** (d)   **21.** (d)   **22.** (b)   **23.** (c)   **24.** (d)   **25.** (b)   **26.** (b)   **27.** (d)
28. (d)   **29.** (b)   **30.** (d)   **31.** (d)   **32.** (d)   **33.** (c)   **34.** (b)   **35.** (d)

$$\boxed{\textbf{SOLUTIONS}}$$

1. $(\sqrt{8})^{1/3} = (8^{1/2})^{1/3} = 8^{\left(\frac{1}{2} \times \frac{1}{3}\right)} = 8^{1/6} = (2^3)^{1/6} = 2^{\left(3 \times \frac{1}{6}\right)} = 2^{1/2} = \sqrt{2}.$

2. $5^{1/4} \times (125)^{0.25} = 5^{0.25} \times (5^3)^{0.25} = 5^{0.25} \times 5^{(3 \times 0.25)}$
$$= 5^{0.25} \times 5^{0.75} = 5^{(0.25 + 0.75)} = 5^1 = 5.$$

3. $\left(\dfrac{32}{243}\right)^{-4/5} = \left(\dfrac{243}{32}\right)^{4/5} = \left(\dfrac{3^5}{2^5}\right)^{4/5} = \left[\left(\dfrac{3}{2}\right)^5\right]^{4/5} = \left(\dfrac{3}{2}\right)^{\left(5 \times \frac{4}{5}\right)}$

$$= \left(\dfrac{3}{2}\right)^4 = \dfrac{3^4}{2^4} = \dfrac{81}{16}.$$

4. $\left(\dfrac{1}{216}\right)^{-2/3} \div \left(\dfrac{1}{27}\right)^{-4/3} = (216)^{2/3} \div (27)^{4/3} = (6^3)^{2/3} \div (3^3)^{4/3}$

$$= 6^{\left(3 \times \frac{2}{3}\right)} \div 3^{\left(3 \times \frac{4}{3}\right)} = 6^2 \div 3^4 = \dfrac{36}{81} = \dfrac{4}{9}.$$

5. Given Exp. $= \dfrac{2^n \cdot 2^4 - 2 \cdot 2^n}{2 \cdot 2^n \cdot 2^3} + \dfrac{1}{2^3} = \dfrac{2^n(2^4 - 2)}{2^n(2 \cdot 2^3)} + \dfrac{1}{2^3}$

$$= \left(\dfrac{16 - 2}{16} + \dfrac{1}{8}\right) = \left(\dfrac{7}{8} + \dfrac{1}{8}\right) = 1.$$

6. $\dfrac{5\sqrt{5} \times 5^3}{5^{-3/2}} = 5^{a+2} \Leftrightarrow \dfrac{5^{3/2} \times 5^3}{5^{-3/2}} = 5^{a+2}$

$$\therefore \; 5^{\left(\frac{3}{2} + 3 + \frac{3}{2}\right)} = 5^{a+2} \text{ or } 5^6 = 5^{a+2}.$$
$$\therefore \; a + 2 = 6 \text{ or } a = 4.$$

7. $\sqrt{2^n} = 64 \Leftrightarrow 2^{n/2} = 64 = 2^6.$

$$\therefore \; \dfrac{n}{2} = 6 \text{ or } n = 12.$$

8. Given Exp. $= \dfrac{1 - \left(\dfrac{1}{10}\right)^{-1}}{\left(\dfrac{2^3}{3}\right) \cdot \left(\dfrac{3}{2}\right)^3 + (-3)^1} = \dfrac{1 - 10}{\dfrac{2^3}{3} \cdot \dfrac{3^3}{2^3} - 3} = \dfrac{-9}{9 - 3} = \dfrac{-9}{6} = \dfrac{-3}{2}.$

9. $\dfrac{9^n \times 3^5 \times (27)^3}{3 \times (81)^4} = 27 \Rightarrow \dfrac{3^{2n} \times 3^5 \times (3^3)^3}{3 \times (3^4)^4} = 3^3.$

or $\dfrac{3^{2n} \times 3^5 \times 3^9}{3^1 \times 3^{16}} = 3^3$ or $3^{2n+5+9} = 3^3 \times 3^1 \times 3^{16}$ or $3^{2n+14} = 3^{20}$

$\therefore \ 2n + 14 = 20$ or $2n = 6$ or $n = 3$.

10. $\dfrac{9^n \,(3^2)\,(3^{-n/2})^{-2} - 27^n}{3^{3m}\,(2^3)} = \dfrac{1}{27} \Rightarrow \dfrac{3^{2n} \cdot 3^2 \cdot 3^{\left(-\frac{n}{2}\right) \times (-2)} - (3^3)^n}{3^{3m} \cdot 2^3} = \dfrac{1}{3^3}$

or $\dfrac{3^{2n} \cdot 3^2 \cdot 3^n - 3^{3n}}{3^{3m} \cdot 2^3} = \dfrac{1}{3^3}$ or $\dfrac{3^{3n}\,(9-1)}{3^{3m} \cdot 8} = \dfrac{1}{3^3}$

or $3^{3n-3m} = 3^{-3}$. So, $3n - 3m = -3$ or $m - n = 1$.

11. $(\sqrt{3})^5 \times 9^2 = 3^\alpha \times 3\sqrt{3} \Rightarrow (3^{1/2})^5 \times (3^2)^2 = 3^\alpha \times 3^1 \times 3^{1/2}$

$\therefore \ 3^{5/2} \times 3^4 = 3^\alpha \times 3^1 \times 3^{1/2}$ or $3^{\left(\frac{5}{2}+4\right)} = 3^{\left(\alpha+1+\frac{1}{2}\right)}$

or $3^{13/2} = 3^{\alpha+\frac{3}{2}}$. So, $\alpha + \dfrac{3}{2} = \dfrac{13}{2}$ or $\alpha = \left(\dfrac{13}{2} - \dfrac{3}{2}\right) = 5$.

12. Given Exp. $= \dfrac{x^{7/2} \cdot y^{3/2}}{x^{5/2} \cdot y^{1/2}} = x^{\left(\frac{7}{2}-\frac{5}{2}\right)} \cdot y^{\left(\frac{3}{2}-\frac{1}{2}\right)} = xy$.

13. Given Exp. $= \left(\dfrac{1}{1 + \dfrac{x^n}{x^m}} + \dfrac{1}{1 + \dfrac{x^m}{x^n}}\right) = \dfrac{x^m}{(x^m + x^n)} + \dfrac{x^n}{(x^m + x^n)}$

$= \dfrac{(x^m + x^n)}{(x^m + x^n)} = 1.$

14. $\sqrt{x^{-1}y} \cdot \sqrt{y^{-1}z} \cdot \sqrt{z^{-1}x} = \sqrt{\dfrac{y}{x}} \cdot \sqrt{\dfrac{z}{y}} \cdot \sqrt{\dfrac{x}{z}} = \dfrac{\sqrt{y}}{\sqrt{x}} \times \dfrac{\sqrt{z}}{\sqrt{y}} \times \dfrac{\sqrt{x}}{\sqrt{z}} = 1.$

15. Given Exp. $= \dfrac{1}{1 + \dfrac{x^b}{x^a} + \dfrac{x^c}{x^a}} + \dfrac{1}{1 + \dfrac{x^a}{x^b} + \dfrac{x^c}{x^b}} + \dfrac{1}{1 + \dfrac{x^b}{x^c} + \dfrac{x^a}{x^c}}$

$= \left(\dfrac{x^a}{x^a + x^b + x^c} + \dfrac{x^b}{x^b + x^a + x^c} + \dfrac{x^c}{x^c + x^b + x^a}\right) = \left(\dfrac{x^a + x^b + x^c}{x^a + x^b + x^c}\right) = 1.$

16. Given Exp. $= x^{(b-c)\,(b+c-a)} \cdot x^{(c-a)\,(c+a-b)} \cdot x^{(a-b)\,(a+b-c)}$

$= x^{(b^2-c^2)+(c^2-a^2)+(a^2-b^2)} \cdot x^{-a\,(b-c)-b\,(c-a)-c\,(a-b)} = x^0 \cdot x^0 = 1.$

17. Given Exp. $= \dfrac{q}{q + pq + 1} + \dfrac{r}{r + qr + 1} + \dfrac{p}{p + pr + 1}$

$= \dfrac{q}{q + pq + 1} + \dfrac{1}{1 + q + pq} + \dfrac{pq}{pq + 1 + q} \qquad \left[\because \ r = \dfrac{1}{pq}\right]$

$$= \left(\frac{q+1+pq}{q+1+pq}\right) = 1.$$

18. Given Exp. $= x^{(a-b)(a+b)} \times x^{(b-c)(b+c)} \times x^{(c-a)(c+a)}$

$$= x^{(a^2-b^2)+(b^2-c^2)+(c^2-a^2)} = x^0 = 1.$$

19. Given Exp. $= x^{(a-b)/ab} \cdot x^{(b-c)/bc} \cdot x^{(c-a)/ca}$

$$= x^{\left(\frac{1}{b}-\frac{1}{a}\right)+\left(\frac{1}{c}-\frac{1}{b}\right)+\left(\frac{1}{a}-\frac{1}{c}\right)} = x^0 = 1.$$

20. $2^{x+4} - 2^{x+2} = 3 \Leftrightarrow 2^{x+2}(2^2-1) = 3 \Leftrightarrow 2^{x+2} = 1 = 2^0.$

$\therefore x+2 = 0$ or $x = -2.$

21. $2^{x-1} + 2^{x+1} = 320 \Leftrightarrow 2^{x-1}(1+2^2) = 320 \Leftrightarrow 2^{x-1} = 64 = 2^6.$

$\therefore x-1 = 6$ or $x = 7.$

22. $2^{2x-1} = \dfrac{1}{8^{x-3}} \Leftrightarrow 2^{2x-1} = \dfrac{1}{(2^3)^{(x-3)}}$

$$\Leftrightarrow 2^{2x-1} = \frac{1}{2^{3x-9}} \Leftrightarrow 2^{2x-1} = 2^{9-3x}$$

$\therefore 2x-1 = 9-3x$ or $5x = 10$ or $x = 2.$

23. $\left(\dfrac{a}{b}\right)^{x-1} = \left(\dfrac{b}{a}\right)^{x-3} \Leftrightarrow \left(\dfrac{a}{b}\right)^{x-1} = \left(\dfrac{a}{b}\right)^{3-x}$

$\therefore x-1 = 3-x$ or $2x = 4$ or $x = 2.$

24. $2^x \times 8^{1/5} = 2^{1/5} \Leftrightarrow \dfrac{2^x \times 2^{3/5}}{2^{1/5}} = 1 \Leftrightarrow 2^x \times 2^{\left(\frac{3}{5}-\frac{1}{5}\right)} = 1$

or $2^{\left(x+\frac{2}{5}\right)} = 2^0.$ So, $x + \dfrac{2}{5} = 0$ or $x = -\dfrac{2}{5}.$

25. On squaring both sides, we get :
$5 + \sqrt[3]{x} = 9$ or $\sqrt[3]{x} = 4.$
Cubing both sides, we get $x = (4 \times 4 \times 4) = 64.$

26. $5^{x+3} = (25)^{3x-4} = (5^2)^{3x-4}$

or $5^{x+3} = 5^{2(3x-4)}$ or $5^{x+3} = 5^{6x-8}$

$\therefore x+3 = 6x-8$ or $5x = 11$ or $x = \dfrac{11}{5}.$

27. $\sqrt[3]{32} = 2^x \Rightarrow (2^5)^{1/3} = 2^x \Rightarrow 2^x = 2^{5/3}. \quad \therefore x = \dfrac{5}{3}.$

28. Let $a^x = b^y = c^z = k.$
Then $a = k^{1/x}, b = k^{1/y}$ and $c = k^{1/z}.$

$b^2 = ac \Rightarrow k^{2/y} = k^{1/x} \cdot k^{1/z} \Rightarrow k^{2/y} = k^{\left(\frac{1}{x}+\frac{1}{z}\right)}$

$\therefore \dfrac{2}{y} = \dfrac{1}{x} + \dfrac{1}{z}$ or $\dfrac{2}{y} = \dfrac{x+z}{xz}$ or $y = \dfrac{2xz}{(x+z)}$

29. $2^x = 3^y = 6^{-z} = k \Rightarrow 2 = k^{1/x}, 3 = k^{1/y}$ & $6 = k^{-1/z}$

Now $2 \times 3 = 6 \Rightarrow k^{1/x} \times k^{1/y} = k^{-1/z} \Rightarrow k^{\left(\frac{1}{x} + \frac{1}{y}\right)} = k^{-1/z}$.

$\therefore \dfrac{1}{x} + \dfrac{1}{y} = -\dfrac{1}{z}$ or $\dfrac{1}{x} + \dfrac{1}{y} + \dfrac{1}{z} = 1$.

30. $x = y^a = (z^b)^a = z^{ab} = (x^c)^{ab} = x^{abc}$. $\qquad \therefore abc = 1$.

31. Given surds are of order 2, 3, 4 whose l.c.m. is 12.

Changing each one of given surds to that of order 12, we get :

$\sqrt{2} = 2^{1/2} = 2^{\left(\frac{1}{2} \times \frac{6}{6}\right)} = (2^6)^{1/12} = (64)^{1/12}$

$\sqrt[3]{4} = 4^{1/3} = 4^{\left(\frac{1}{3} \times \frac{4}{4}\right)} = 4^{4/12} = (4^4)^{1/12} = (256)^{1/12}$

$\sqrt[4]{6} = 6^{1/4} = 6^{\left(\frac{1}{4} \times \frac{3}{3}\right)} = 6^{3/12} = (6^3)^{1/12} = (216)^{1/12}$

Now, $(64)^{1/12} < (216)^{1/12} < (256)^{1/12}$

$\therefore \sqrt{2} < \sqrt[4]{6} < \sqrt[3]{4}$.

32. Clearly, $m = 11$ and $n = 2$.

$\therefore (m-1)^{n+1} = (11-1)^3 = 10^3 = 1000$.

33. On dividing, we get $\dfrac{1-x^8}{1-x^4} = \dfrac{65}{64}$

or $\dfrac{(1-x^4)(1+x^4)}{(1-x^4)} = \dfrac{65}{64}$ or $1 + x^4 = \dfrac{65}{64}$

$\therefore x^4 = \left(\dfrac{65}{64} - 1\right) = \dfrac{1}{64}$ or $x = \left(\dfrac{1}{2^6}\right)^{1/4} = \pm\dfrac{1}{2^{3/2}} = \pm\dfrac{1}{2\sqrt{2}}$

34. $\left[\dfrac{3^{m^2}}{(3^m)^2}\right]^{1/m} = 81 \Rightarrow \left(\dfrac{3^{m^2}}{3^{2m}}\right)^{1/m} = 3^4$

or $(3^{m^2 - 2m})^{1/m} = 3^4$ or $3^{m(m-2) \cdot \frac{1}{m}} = 3^4$

or $3^{m-2} = 3^4$ or $m - 2 = 4$ or $m = 6$.

35. Given equations are :

$2^a + 3^b = 17, 2^2 \cdot 2^a - 3 \cdot 3^b = 5$

or $x + y = 17$ & $4x - 3y = 5$, where $x = 2^a$ & $y = 3^b$.

On solving, we get : $x = 8$ and $y = 9$.

$\therefore 2^a = 8 = 2^3$ and $3^b = 9 = 3^2$ $\qquad \therefore a = 3$ and $b = 2$.

10. Percentage

Percent : *By a certain percent we mean that many hundredths.* Thus, x percent means x hundredths, written as $x\%$.

To express $x\%$ as a fraction : We have, $x\% = \dfrac{x}{100}$.

Thus, $15\% = \dfrac{15}{100} = \dfrac{3}{20}$; $24\% = \dfrac{24}{100} = \dfrac{6}{25}$ etc.

To express $\dfrac{a}{b}$ as a percent : We have $\dfrac{a}{b} = \left(\dfrac{a}{b} \times 100\right)\%$.

Thus, $\dfrac{3}{4} = \left(\dfrac{3}{4} \times 100\right)\% = 75\%$, $\dfrac{6}{5} = \left(\dfrac{6}{5} \times 100\right)\% = 120\%$ etc.

$0.6 = \dfrac{6}{10} = \dfrac{3}{5} = \left(\dfrac{3}{5} \times 100\right)\% = 60\%$.

Solved Problems

Ex. 1. *Express each of the following as a fraction :*
(i) 56%   (ii) 4%   (iii) 0.6%   (iv) 0.08%

Sol. (i) $56\% = \dfrac{56}{100} = \dfrac{14}{25}$.

(ii) $4\% = \dfrac{4}{100} = \dfrac{1}{25}$.

(iii) $0.6\% = \dfrac{0.6}{100} = \dfrac{6}{1000} = \dfrac{3}{500}$.

(iv) $0.08\% = \dfrac{0.08}{100} = \dfrac{8}{10000} = \dfrac{1}{1250}$.

Ex. 2. *Express each of the following as a decimal :*
(i) 28%   (ii) 6%   (iii) 0.2%   (iv) 0.04%

Sol. (i) $28\% = \dfrac{28}{100} = .28$.

(ii) $6\% = \dfrac{6}{100} = .06$.

(iii) $0.2\% = \dfrac{0.2}{100} = .002$.

(iv) $0.04\% = \dfrac{0.04}{100} = .0004$.

Ex. 3. *Express each of the following as rate per cent :*

(i) $\dfrac{23}{36}$ (ii) .004   (iii) $6\dfrac{3}{4}$

Sol. (i) $\dfrac{23}{36} = \left(\dfrac{23}{36} \times 100\right)\% = \left(\dfrac{575}{9}\right)\% = 63\dfrac{8}{9}\%.$

(ii) $.004 = \dfrac{4}{1000} = \left(\dfrac{4}{1000} \times 100\right)\% = .4\%.$

(iii) $6\dfrac{3}{4} = \dfrac{27}{4} = \left(\dfrac{27}{4} \times 100\right)\% = 675\%.$

Ex. 4. (i) *What percent of 72 is 6 ?*

(ii) *What per cent of 7 is 84 ?*

(iii) *What per cent of 2.4 kg is 8 gms ?*

(iv) *What per cent of 6.5 litres is 130 ml ?*

Sol. (i) Required percentage $= \left(\dfrac{6}{72} \times 100\right)\% = 8\dfrac{1}{3}\%.$

(ii) Required percentage $= \left(\dfrac{84}{7} \times 100\right)\% = 1200\%.$

(iii) Required percentage $= \left(\dfrac{8}{2.4 \times 1000} \times 100\right)\% = \dfrac{1}{3}\%.$

(iv) Required percentage $= \left(\dfrac{130}{6.5 \times 1000} \times 100\right)\% = 2\%.$

TWO IMPORTANT RULES (Short Cut Methods) :

(i) If A is $R\%$ more than B, then :

B is less than A by $\left\{\dfrac{R}{(100 + R)} \times 100\right\}\%.$

(ii) If A is $R\%$ less than B, then

B is more than A by $\left\{\dfrac{R}{(100 - R)} \times 100\right\}\%.$

Ex. 5. *If A's income is 33% more than that of B, then how much percent is B's income less than that of A ?*

Sol. Required percentage $= \left\{\dfrac{33}{(100 + 33)} \times 100\right\}\% = 24.8\%.$

Ex. 6. *If A's height is 24% less than that of B, then how much per cent is B's height more than that of A ?*

Sol. Required percentage

$= \left\{\dfrac{24}{(100 - 24)} \times 100\right\}\% = \left(\dfrac{24}{76} \times 100\right)\% = 31.57\%.$

TWO IMPORTANT RULES (Short Cut Method) :

(*i*)   If the price of a commodity increases by $R\%$, then reduction in consumption, not to increase the expenditure is :

$$\left\{\frac{R}{(100+R)}\times100\right\}\%.$$

(*ii*) If the price of a commodity decreases by $R\%$, then the increase in consumption, not to decrease the expenditure is :

$$\left\{\frac{R}{(100-R)}\times100\right\}\%.$$

Ex. 7. *If the price of tea is increased by 20%, find by how much percent must a householder reduce her consumption of tea so as not to increase the expenditure ?*

Sol. Reduction in Consumption $=\left\{\dfrac{R}{(100+R)}\times100\right\}\%$

$$=\left(\frac{20}{120}\times100\right)\%=16\frac{2}{3}\%.$$

Ex. 8. *If the price of sugar decreases by 20%, find by how much percent must a house holder increase her consumption of sugar so as not to decrease the expenditure ?*

Sol. Increase in consumption

$$=\left\{\frac{R}{(100-R)}\times100\right\}\%=\left(\frac{20}{80}\times100\right)\%=25\%.$$

RESULTS ON POPULATION (Formulae) :

Let the population of a town be P now and suppose it increases at the rate of $R\%$ per annum, then :

(*i*) Population after n years $=P\left(1+\dfrac{R}{100}\right)^{n}.$

(*ii*) Population n years ago $=\dfrac{P}{\left(1+\dfrac{R}{100}\right)^{n}}.$

Ex. 9. *The population of a town is 176400. If it increases at the rate of 5% per annum, what will be its population 2 years hence ?*
What was it 2 years ago ?

Sol. Population after 2 years $=176400\times\left(1+\dfrac{5}{100}\right)^{2}$

$$=\left(176400\times\frac{21}{20}\times\frac{21}{20}\right)=194481.$$

Population 2 years ago $= \dfrac{176400}{\left(1 + \dfrac{5}{100}\right)^2} = \left(176400 \times \dfrac{20}{21} \times \dfrac{20}{21}\right) = 160000.$

RESULTS ON DEPRECIATION (Formulae) :

Let the present value of a machine be *P*. Suppose it depreciates at the rate of *R%* per annum. Then :

(*i*) Value of the machine after *n* years $= P\left(1 - \dfrac{R}{100}\right)^n.$

(*ii*) Value of the machine *n* years ago $= \dfrac{P}{\left(1 - \dfrac{R}{100}\right)^n}.$

Ex. 10. *The value of a machine depreciates at the rate of 10% per annum. If its present value is Rs. 162000, what will be its worth after 2 years? What was the value of the machine 2 years ago ?*

Sol. Value of the machine after 2 years

$= \text{Rs.} \left[162000 \times \left(1 - \dfrac{10}{100}\right)^2\right] = \text{Rs.} \left(162000 \times \dfrac{9}{10} \times \dfrac{9}{10}\right) = \text{Rs. } 131220.$

Value of the machine 2 years ago

$= \text{Rs.} \left\{ \dfrac{162000}{\left(1 - \dfrac{10}{100}\right)^2} \right\} = \text{Rs.} \left(162000 \times \dfrac{10}{9} \times \dfrac{10}{9}\right) = \text{Rs. } 200000.$

Ex. 11. *Two numbers are less than a third number by 30% and 37% respectively. How much percent is the second number less than the first ?*

Sol. Let the third number be 100.

Then, first number = 70 and second number = 63.

∴ Second number is less than the first by

$= \left(\dfrac{70 - 63}{70} \times 100\right)\% = 10\%.$

Ex. 12. *1 litre of water is added to 5 litres of a 20% solution of alcohol in water. Find the strength of alcohol in the new solution.*

Sol. Alcohol in 5 litres = (20% of 5 litres) $= \left(\dfrac{20}{100} \times 5\right) = 1$ litre.

Alcohol in 6 litres of new mix. = 1 litre.

∴ Percentage of alcohol $= \left(\dfrac{1}{6} \times 100\right)\% = 16\dfrac{2}{3}\%.$

Ex. 13. *From the salary of an officer, 10% is deducted as house rent, 15% of the rest he spends on children's education and 10% of the balance, he spends on clothes. Then, he is left with Rs. 4131. Find his total salary.*

Sol. Let his total salary be Rs. x. Then,

90% of 85% of 90% of $x = 4131$

or $\dfrac{90}{100} \times \dfrac{85}{100} \times \dfrac{90}{100} x = 4131$

$\therefore x = \dfrac{4131 \times 100 \times 100 \times 100}{90 \times 85 \times 90} = 6000.$

Hence, the salary of the officer is Rs. 6000.

Ex. 14. *Due to a reduction of $6\frac{1}{4}$ % in the prices of sugar, a man is able to buy 1 kg more for Rs. 120. Find the original and reduced rate of sugar.*

Sol. Let original rate be Rs. x per kg.

Reduced Rate $= $ Rs. $\left(100 - \dfrac{25}{4}\right) \cdot \dfrac{1}{100} x = \dfrac{15x}{16}$ per kg.

$\therefore \dfrac{120}{\dfrac{15x}{16}} - \dfrac{120}{x} = 1$ or $\dfrac{128}{x} - \dfrac{120}{x} = 1$ or $x = 8.$

$\therefore$ Original rate $=$ Rs. 8 per kg.

Reduced rate $=$ Rs. $\left(\dfrac{15}{16} \times 8\right)$ per kg $=$ Rs. 7.50 per kg.

Ex. 15. *If A earns $33\frac{1}{3}$% more than B, then B earns less than A by :*

(a) $16\frac{2}{3}$ %   (b) 20%   (c) 25%   (d) $33\frac{1}{3}$ %

(C.D.S. 1994)

Sol. Required percentage $= \left[\dfrac{\left(\dfrac{100}{3}\right)}{\left(100 + \dfrac{100}{3}\right)} \times 100\right]$ %

$= \left(\dfrac{100}{400} \times 100\right)$ % $= 25$ %.

$\therefore$ The correct answer is (c).

Ex. 16. *If A's salary is 20% less than B's salary, by how much percent is B's salary more than A's ?*   (Central Excise & I. Tax. 1993)

(a) $16\frac{2}{3}$%   (b) 20%   (c) 25%   (d) $33\frac{1}{3}$%

Sol. Required percentage $= \left[\dfrac{20}{(100 - 20)} \times 100\right]$ % $= 25\%$

$\therefore$ The correct answer is (c).

Ex. 17. *Find the missing figures :*

(*i*) ($\cdots$? $\cdots$) % of 25 = **2.125**

(*ii*) **9% of** ($\cdots$? $\cdots$) = **6.3**

(*iii*) **0.25 % of** ($\cdots$? $\cdots$) = **.04**

Sol. (*i*) Let *x*% of 25 = 2.125.

Then, $\dfrac{x}{100} \times 25 = 2.125$ or $x = (2.125 \times 4) = 8.5$.

(*ii*) Let 9% of *x* = 6.3.

Then, $\dfrac{9}{100} x = 6.3$ or $x = \left(\dfrac{6.3 \times 100}{9} \right) = 70$.

(*iii*) Let 0.25% of *x* = .04.

Then, $\dfrac{0.25}{100} x = .04$ or $x = \left(\dfrac{.04 \times 100}{0.25} \right) = 16$.

Ex. 18. *Which is greatest in* $16\frac{2}{3}\%$, $\frac{2}{15}$ *and 0.17 ?*

Sol. $16\frac{2}{3}\% = \left(\dfrac{50}{3} \times \dfrac{1}{100} \right) = \dfrac{1}{6} = 0.166$,

$\dfrac{2}{15} = 0.133$ & the third number is 0.17.

Clearly, 0.17 is the greatest.

EXERCISE 10

Mark a tick (√) against the correct answer :

1. .02 = ? %   **(Bank P.O. 1986)**

    (*a*) 20   (*b*) 2   (*c*) .02   (*d*) .2

2. $12\frac{1}{2}$ % is equivalent to :

    (*a*) 0.8   (*b*) 1.25   (*c*) 0.125   (*d*) 12.5

3. 5 out of 2250 parts of earth is sulphur. What is the percentage of sulphur in earth ?   **(Assistant Grade, 1990)**

    (*a*) $\dfrac{11}{50}$ (*b*) $\dfrac{2}{9}$ (*c*) $\dfrac{1}{45}$ (*d*) $\dfrac{2}{45}$

4. 45 × ? = 25% of 900   **(Bank P.O. 1991)**

    (*a*) 16.20   (*b*) 500   (*c*) 4   (*d*) 5

5. 218% of 1674 = ? × 1800   **(S.B.I.P.O. 1991)**

    (*a*) 4   (*b*) 0.5   (*c*) 6   (*d*) None of these

6. 13937.869 ÷ 199.54 + 15% of 201 = ?   **(Bank P.O. 1994)**

    (*a*) 150   (*b*) 90   (*c*) 80   (*d*) 100

7. 63% of $3\frac{4}{7}$ is :

    (*Assistant Grade 1994*)

    (*a*) 2.25   (*b*) 2.40   (*c*) 2.50   (*d*) 2.75

8. If 30% of a number is 12.6, then the number is

(a) 41   (b) 51   (c) 52   (d) 42

(Assistant Grade 1994)

9. 5% of (25% of Rs. 1600) is :
   (a) Rs. 5   (b) Rs. 17.50   (c) Rs. 20   (d) Rs. 25

10. $8\frac{1}{3}$ % of ? = 150

    (Bank P.O. 1993)

    (a) 1250   (b) 1800   (c) 1700   (d) 1400

11. 35% of 30 = 25% of ? + 1   **(Bank P.O. 1993)**
    (a) 28   (b) 38   (c) 42   (d) 32

12. What percent is 3% of 5% ?
    (a) 60%   (b) 50%   (c) 15%   (d) 30%

13. ?% of $6144 = 2\frac{1}{2} \times 245.76$

    (S.B.I.P.O. 1991)

    (a) 16   (b) 20   (c) 5   (d) 10

14. 12.5% of 192 = 50% of ?   **(Bank P.O. 1991)**
    (a) 48   (b) 96   (c) 24   (d) None

15. $\dfrac{30 \% \text{ of } 80}{?} = 24$

    (C.B.I. 1989)

    (a) $\dfrac{3}{10}$ (b) $\dfrac{3}{17}$ (c) 1   (d) 2

16. What is 25% of 25% equal to ?
    (a) 6.25   (b) .625   (c) .0625   (d) .00625

17. 45% of ? + 30% of 90 = 30% of 210.   **(Bank P.O. 1994)**
    (a) 120   (b) 80   (c) 60   (d) 90

18. One fourth of one third of two fifth of a number is 15. What will be 40% of that number ?   **(Bank P.O. 1994)**
    (a) 120   (b) 350   (c) 270   (d) 180

19. If 37% of a number is 990.86, what will be approximately 19% of that number ?   **(Bank P.O. 1994)**
    (a) 600   (b) 400   (c) 500   (d) 700

20. If 15% of 40 is greater than 25% of a number by 2, the number is :
    (a) 16   (b) 20   (c) 24   (d) 32

    (Assistant Grade 1992)

21. What percent of 7.2 kg is 18 gms ?
    (a) 25%   (b) 2.5%   (c) .25%   (d) .025%

22. If 40% of 40% of x = 40, then x is :
    (a) 100   (b) 400   (c) 250   (d) 1000

23. $\sqrt{3.6\% \text{ of } 40}$ = ?
    (a) 2.8   (b) 1.8   (c) 1.2   (d) None

24. By how much percent is four-fifth of 70 lesser than five-seventh of 112?
    (a) 42%   (b) 30%   (c) 24%   (d) 36%

25. What will be 160% of a number whose 200% is 140 ?

(a) 200   (b) 160   (c) 140   (d) 112
(Clerk's Grade 1993)

26. If 75% of a number is added to 75, the result is the number itself. Then, the number is : **(Assistant Grade 1993)**

(a) 400   (b) 300   (c) 60   (d) 50

27. Subtracting 40% of a number from the number, we get the result as 30. The number is : **(U.D.C. Exam 1993)**

(a) 28   (b) 50   (c) 52   (d) 70

28. If three fifth of a number is 40 more than 40% of the same number. What is the number ? **(Bank P.O. 1994)**

(a) 100   (b) 150   (c) 200   (d) 400

29. A number, on subtracting 15 from it, reduces to its 80%. What is 40% of that number ? **(Bank P.O. 1994)**

(a) 60   (b) 45   (c) 30   (d) 90

30. Calculation shows that an angle is $37\frac{1}{2}°$. The size obtained by drawing and measurement is 36°. The error percent is :

(a) $1\frac{1}{2}$ (b) 3   (c) 4   (d) $4\frac{1}{6}$

31. The population of a town has increased from 133575 to 138918. The percent increase in population is **(Clerk's Grade 1993)**

(a) 2.5   (b) 3   (c) 3.5   (d) 4

32. If X is 90% of Y, what percent of X is Y ?

(a) 101.1   (b) 190   (c) 90   (d) 111.1

33. If x% of y is the same as $\frac{4}{5}$ of 80, then the value of xy is :

(a) 320   (b) 400   (c) 640   (d) None
(Hotel Management 1993)

34. Subtracting 6% of x from x is equivalent to multiplying x by how much?

(a) .94   (b) 9.4   (c) .094   (d) 94

35. If 8% of x = 4% of y, then 20% of x is : **(L.I.C. 1991)**

(a) 10% of y (b) 16% of y (c) 80% of y (d) None of these

36. (x% of y + y% of x) = ? **(C.B.I. 1991)**

(a) x% of y (b) y% of x (c) 2% of xy (d) xy% of 3

37. If 90% of A = 30% of B and $B = x$% of A, then x is equal to :

(a) 900   (b) 300   (c) 800   (d) 600

38. x% of y is y% of ?

(a) x (b) $\dfrac{x}{100}$ (c) $100x$ (d) $\dfrac{y}{100}$

39. A number increased by $37\frac{1}{2}$ % gives 33. The number is :

(a) 27   (b) 25   (c) 24   (d) 22

40. The number which when decreased by $27\frac{1}{2}$ % gives 87, is :

    (*a*) 120   (*b*) 110   (*c*) 135   (*d*) 58

41. 40 quintals is what percent of 2 metric tonnes ?

    (*a*) 20%   (*b*) 2%   (*c*) 200%   (*d*) 150%

42. It is known that 20% of the mangoes are rotten. If the number of rotten mangoes is 35, then the total number of mangoes is :

    (*a*) 150   (*b*) 175   (*c*) 180   (*d*) 185

                                                 (I. Tax & Central Excise 1992)

43. If 70% of students in a school are boys and the number of girls is 504, the number of boys is :

    (*a*) 1680   (*b*) 1176   (*c*) 1276   (*d*) None of these

44. A student has to secure 40% marks to pass. He gets 178 marks and fails by 22 marks. The maximum marks are :   **(Assistant Grade 1994)**

    (*a*) 200   (*b*) 500   (*c*) 800   (*d*) 1000

45. A house-owner was having his house painted. He was advised that he would require 25 kg of paint. Allowing for 15% wastage and assuming that the paint is available in 2kg cans, what would be the cost of paint purchased, if one can cost Rs. 16 ?   **(Hotel Management 1992)**

    (*a*) Rs. 240   (*b*) Rs. 180   (*c*) Rs. 160   (*d*) Rs. 360

46. A reduction of 12.5% in the price of a dining table brought down its price to Rs. 4375. The original price (in Rs.) of the table was :

    (*a*) 6000   (*b*) 5400   (*c*) 5200   (*d*) 5000

                                                     (Assistant Grade 1994)

47. Of the total amount received by Kiran, 20% was spent on purchases and 5% of the remaining on transportation. If he is left with Rs. 1520, the initial amount was :

    (*a*) Rs. 2800   (*b*) Rs. 2000   (*c*) Rs. 2400   (*d*) Rs. 1600

48. In a library, 20% books are in Hindi, 50% of the remaining are in English and the remaining 9000 are in various other languages. What is the total number of books in English ?   **(Bank P.O. 1993)**

    (*a*) 4000   (*b*) 3000   (*c*) 2250   (*d*) None of these

49. Avinash spends 30% of his income on scooter petrol, $\frac{1}{4}$ of the remaining on house rent and the balance on food. If he spends Rs. 300 on petrol, then what is the expenditure on house rent ?   **(Bank P.O., 1990)**

    (*a*) Rs. 525   (*b*) Rs. 1000   (*c*) Rs. 675   (*d*) Rs. 175

50. A man spends 35% of his income on house rent, 75% of the remaining on other items. What percentage of income does he save ?

    (*a*) 16.25   (*b*) 34.50   (*c*) 48.75   (*d*) None

51. The price of jute has been reduced by 20%. If the reduced price is Rs. 800 per quintal, the original price per quintal was

(a) Rs. 900   (b) Rs. 640   (c) Rs. 960   (d) Rs. 1000
(I. Tax & Central Excise 1992)

52. Swati spends 40% of her salary on food, 25% on house rent, 15% on entertainment and 5% on conveyance. If her saving at the end of a month is Rs. 1200, then her salary per month (in Rs.) is :
(a) 4000   (b) 6000   (c) 8000   (d) 10000

53. Samir spends 40% of his salary on food articles and one third of the remaining on transport. If he saves Rs. 450 per month which is half of the balance after spending on food items and transport, what is his monthly salary ?   **(S.B.I.P.O. 1991)**
(a) Rs. 4500   (b) Rs. 2250   (c) Rs. 1125   (d) Rs. 2500

54. Kamal has some apples. He sold 40% more than he ate. If he sold 70 apples, how many did he eat ?
(a) 50   (b) 90   (c) 18   (d) 42

55. $\frac{5}{9}$ part of the population in a village are males. If 30% of the males are married, the percentage of unmarried females in the total population is :
(a) 70%   (b) 40%   (c) $27\frac{7}{9}\%$ (d) 20%

56. In an examination, 1100 boys and 900 girls appeared. 50% of the boys and 40% of the girls passed the examination. The percentage of candidates failed is :   **(Assistant Grade 1993)**
(a) 45   (b) 45.5   (c) 54.5   (d) 59.2

57. A school has only three classes which contain 40, 50 and 60 students respectively. The pass percentages of these classes are 10, 20 and 10 respectively. The pass percentage of the school is :
(a) $13\frac{1}{3}$ (b) 15   (c) 20   (d) $16\frac{2}{3}$

58. 30% of A's salary is equal to 20% of $\frac{3}{5}$ th of B's salary. If B's salary is Rs. 2400, what is A's salary ?
(a) Rs. 1880   (b) Rs. 1000   (c) Rs. 960   (d) Rs. 2160

59. Alekh secured 50% marks in Hindi, 60% in English and 70% in Maths as well as in Science. What were his total marks if the maximum marks obtainable in each of these 4 subjects was 50 ?   **(Bank P.O. 1989)**
(a) 125   (b) 120   (c) 250   (d) 150

60. If $x\%$ of a is the same as $y\%$ of b, then $z\%$ of b is
(a) $\frac{yz}{x}\%$ of a (b) $\frac{xy}{z}\%$ of a (c) $\frac{xz}{y}\%$ of a (d) None of these

61. In a city, 35% of the population is composed of migrants, 20% of whom are from rural areas. Of the local population, 48% is female while this figure for rural and urban migrants is 30% and 40% respectively. If the total population of the city is 728400, what is its female population ?

    (*a*) 324138   (*b*) 349680   (*c*) 509940   (*d*) None

                                                         (Hotel Management 1993)

62. *A's* marks in Biology are 20 less than 25% of the total marks obtained by him in Biology, Maths and Drawing. If his marks in Drawing be 50, what are his marks in Maths ?   **(Bank P.O. 1993)**

    (*a*) 40   (*b*) 45   (*c*) 50   (*d*) Can't be determined

63. An increase of Rs. 60 in the monthly salary of Madan made it 50% of the monthly salary of Kamal. What is Madan's present monthly salary ?   **(Bank P.O. 1990)**

    (*a*) Rs. 180   (*b*) Rs. 240   (*c*) Rs. 300   (*d*) Data inadequate

64. From a container having pure milk, 20% is replaced by water and the process is repeated thrice. At the end of the third operation, the milk is :

    (*a*) 40% pure   (*b*) 50% pure   (*c*) 51.2% pure (*d*) 58.8% pure

65. A man bought a house for Rs. 5 lakhs and rents it. He puts $12\frac{1}{2}$% of each month's rent aside for repairs, pays Rs. 1660 as annual taxes and realises 10% on his investment thereafter. The monthly rent of the house is :

    (*a*) Rs. 5000   (*b*) Rs. 4920   (*c*) Rs. 2500   (*d*) Rs. 2460

                                                         (Teacher's Exam 1991)

66. In a public school, $\frac{1}{5}$ th of girls and $\frac{1}{4}$th of boys are under 12 years of age. If the total strength of the school is 1000 and number of girls is $\frac{2}{5}$th of the total, what part of the total strength of the school is accounted for by those which are 12 years or more of age ?   **(C.B.I. 1993)**

    (*a*) 23%   (*b*) 45%   (*c*) 55%   (*d*) 77%

67. The salaries of *A* and *B* together amount to Rs. 2000. A spends 95% of his salary and *B*, 85% of his. If now, their savings are the same, what is *A*'s salary ?

    (*a*) Rs. 1500   (*b*) Rs. 1250   (*c*) Rs. 750   (*d*) Rs. 1600

68. A debtor can pay 87 paise in the rupee, but if his creditors would take 20% of his debts, he could pay them and have Rs. 42 left. His debts and assets respectively are   **(Hotel Management 1992)**

    (*a*) Rs. 600, Rs. 522   (*b*) Rs. 500, Rs. 521

    (*c*) Rs. 400, Rs. 520   (*d*) Rs. 1000, Rs. 525

69. 300 grams of sugar solution has 40% sugar in it. How much sugar should be added to make it 50% in the solution ?   **(Assistant Grade 1993)**

(a) 10 gms   (b) 40 gms   (c) 60 gms   (d) 80 gms

70. The quantity of water (in ml) needed to reduce 9 ml shaving lotion containing 50% alcohol to a lotion containing 30% alcohol, is :
    (a) 4   (b) 5   (c) 6   (d) 7

71. To a sugar solution of 3 litres containing 40% sugar, one litre of water is added. The percentage of sugar in the new solution is :
    (a) $13\frac{1}{3}\%$ (b) 15%   (c) 30%   (d) 33%

72. The price of an article is cut by 20%. To restore it to the former value, the new price must be increased by :   **(Assistant Grade 1994)**

    (a) 20%   (b) 25%   (c) $16\frac{2}{3}\%$ (d) 24%

73. The income of a broker remains unchanged though the rate of commission is increased from 4% to 5%. The percentage of slump in business is :
    (a) 1%   (b) 8%   (c) 20%   (d) 80%

74. In an examination, there are 3 papers of Mathematics of 100 marks each. A boy secures 60% in the first paper and 70% in the second paper. In order to secure 70% in the aggregate the percentage of marks he should secure in third paper will be :   **(C.B.I. 1993)**
    (a) 90%   (b) 80%   (c) 75%   (d) 70%

75. A candidate scoring 25% marks in an examination fails by 30 marks while another candidate who scores 50% marks gets 20 marks more than those required to pass. The pass percentage is :
    (a) 25%   (b) 35%   (c) 40%   (d) 50%

76. Two numbers are less than a third number by 30% and 37% respectively. How much percent is the second number less than the first ?
    (a) 10%   (b) 7%   (c) 4%   (d) 3%

77. A bag contains 600 coins of 25p denomination and 1200 coins of 50p denomination. If 12% of 25p coins and 24% of 50p coins are removed, the percentage of money removed from the bag is nearly :
    (a) 30%   (b) 21.6%   (c) 17.8%   (d) 15.6%

78. 5% of income of A is equal to 15% of income of B and 10% of income of B is equal to 20% of income of C. If income of C is Rs. 2000, then total income of A, B & C is :   **(Bank P.O. 1990)**
    (a) Rs. 6000   (b) Rs. 18000   (c) Rs. 20000   (d) Rs. 14000

79. In an examination, A got 10% marks less than B, B got 25% marks more than C and C got 20% less than D. If A got 360 marks out of 500, the percentage of marks obtained by D was :   **(Teacher's Exam 1991)**
    (a) 70   (b) 75   (c) 80   (d) 85

80. If the numerator of a fraction be increased by 15% and its denominator be diminished by 8%, the value of the fraction is $\frac{15}{16}$. The original fraction is

(a) $\frac{3}{5}$ (b) $\frac{3}{4}$ (c) $\frac{3}{7}$ (d) $\frac{2}{3}$

81. In an examination, 35% of total students failed in Hindi, 45% failed in English and 20% in both. The percentage of those who passed in both the subjects is :
    (a) 10   (b) 20   (c) 30   (d) 40

82. Raman's salary was decreased by 50% and subsequently increased by 50%. He has a loss of :
    (a) 0%   (b) 25%   (c) 0.25%   (d) 2.5%

83. Arvind spends 75% of his income. His income is increased by 20% and he increased his expenditure by 10%. His savings are increased by :
    (a) 10%   (b) 25%   (c) $37\frac{1}{2}$%   (d) 50%

84. There are 600 boys in a hostel. Each plays either hockey or football or both. If 75% play hockey and 45% play football, how many play both?
    (a) 48   (b) 60   (c) 80   (d) 120

85. In a certain office, 72% of the workers prefer tea and 44% prefer coffee. If each of them prefers tea or coffee and 40 like both, the total number of workers in the office is :
    (a) 200   (b) 240   (c) 250   (d) 320

86. In an examination, 80% of the students passed in English, 85% in Mathematics and 75% in both English and Mathematics. If 40 students failed in both the subjects, the total number of students is :
    (a) 200   (b) 400   (c) 600   (d) 800

                                     (Assistant Grade 1994)

87. In an examination, 35% candidates failed in one subject and 42% failed in another subject while 15% failed in both the subjects. If 2500 candidates appeared at the examination, how many passed in either subject but not in both ?   **(Hotel Management 1993)**
    (a) 325   (b) 1175   (c) 2125   (d) None of these

88. p is six times as large as q. The percent that q is less than p, is :
    (a) $83\frac{1}{3}$ (b) $16\frac{2}{3}$ (c) 90   (d) 60

                                       (C.B.I. 1990)

89. The boys and girls in a college are in the ratio 3 : 2. If 20% of the boys and 25% of the girls are adults, the percentage of students who are not adults is :
    (a) 58%   (b) 67.5%   (c) 78%   (d) 82.5%

90. In an election between two candidates, a candidate who gets 40% of total votes is defeated by 15000 votes. The number of votes polled by the winning candidate is :
    (a) 6000   (b) 10000   (c) 22500   (d) 45000

91. In an election between two candidates, one got 55% of total valid votes. 20% of the votes were invalid. If the total number of votes was 7500, the number of valid votes that the other candidate got was :
(a) 2700   (b) 2900   (c) 3000   (d) 3100
                                                (Central Excise 1989)

92. At an election involving two candidates, 68 votes were declared invalid. The winning candidate scores 52% and wins by 98 votes. The total number of votes polled is :   **(Bank P.O. 1990)**
(a) 2518   (b) 2450   (c) 2382   (d) None

93. *A*'s income is 25% more than *B*'s income. *B*'s income in terms of *A*'s income is :   **(Assistant Grade 1994)**
(a) 75%   (b) 80%   (c) 90%   (d) 96%

94. Anil's height is 20% less than Deepak's. How much is Deepak's height more than Anil's ?
(a) $16\frac{2}{3}$%   (b) 18%   (c) 20%   (d) 25%

95. Water tax is increased by 20% but its consumption is decreased by 20%. Then, the increase or decrease in the expenditure of the money is :
(a) No change   (b) 5% decrease
(c) 4% increase   (d) 4% decrease
                                                        (C.B.I. 1991)

96. On increasing the price of T.V. sets by 30%, their sale decreases by 20%. What is the effect on the revenue receipts of the shop ?
(a) 4% increase   (b) 4% decrease
(c) 8% increase   (d) 8% decrease **(Bank P.O. 1990)**

97. A man spends 75% of his income. His income increases by 20% and he increased his expenditure by 15%. His savings are then increased by
(a) 33%   (b) $33\frac{1}{3}$%   (c) 35%   (d) 40%

98. The price of sugar increases by 20%. By what percent must a house wife reduce the consumption of sugar, so that the expenditure on sugar is the same as before ?   **(Hotel Management 1992)**
(a) $16\frac{2}{3}$ (b) 20   (c) 80   (d) $83\frac{1}{3}$

99. The price of oil is increased by 25%. If the expenditure is not allowed to increase, the ratio between the reduction in consumption and the original consumption is :
(a) 1 : 3   (b) 1 : 4   (c) 1 : 5   (d) 1 : 6

100. The price of sugar is increased by 20%. As a result, a family decreases its consumption by 25%. The expenditure of the family on sugar will be decreased by :   **(Assistant Grade 1994)**
(a) 10%   (b) 5%   (c) 14%   (d) 15%

101. If the price of sugar rises from Rs 6 per kg to Rs 7.50 per kg, a person, to have no increase in his expenditure on sugar, will have to reduce his consumption of sugar by :

(*a*) 15%   (*b*) 20%   (*c*) 25%   (*d*) 30%

102. The price of sugar increases by 32%. A family reduces its consumption so that the expenditure of the sugar is up by 10% only. If the total consumption of sugar before the price rise was 10 kg per month, then the consumption of sugar per month at present (in kg) is :

(*a*) $8\dfrac{1}{3}$ (*b*) $8\dfrac{1}{2}$ (*c*) $8\dfrac{3}{4}$ (*d*) 9

(C.B.I. 1993)

103. Prices register an increase of 10% on food grains and 15% on other items of expenditure. If the ratio of an employee's expenditure on food grains and other items be 2 : 5, by how much should his salary be increased in order that he may maintain the same level of consumption as before, his present salary being Rs. 2590 ?

(*a*) Rs. 323.75   (*b*) Rs. 350   (*c*) Rs. 360.50   (*d*) None

104. The population of a town increases by 15% annually. If its population was 8000 in 1995, what will it be in 1997 ?

(*a*) 9200   (*b*) 10400   (*c*) 9600   (*d*) 10580

105. The population of a town is 18000. It increases by 10% during first year and by 20% during the second year. The population after 2 years will be :

(*a*) 19800   (*b*) 21600   (*c*) 23760   (*d*) None

106. The value of a **sewing** machine depreciates every year by 4%. Its value at present is Rs. 200. What will be its value after 2 years ?

(*a*) Rs. $\left(200 \times \dfrac{23}{5}\right)$ (*b*) Rs. $\left[200 \times \left(\dfrac{24}{25}\right)^2\right]$

(*c*) Rs. $\left[200 \times \left(\dfrac{25}{26}\right)^2\right]$ (*d*) Rs. $\left[200 \times \left(\dfrac{26}{25}\right)^2\right]$

(Assistant Grade 1994)

107. The population of a city increases at the rate of 5% annually. Its present population is 1,85,220. Its population 3 years ago was :

(*a*) 181500   (*b*) 183433   (*c*) 160000   (*d*) 127783

108. The value of a machine depreciates at the rate of 10% every year. It was purchased 3 years ago. If its present value is Rs. 8748, its purchase price was :

(*a*) Rs. 10000   (*b*) Rs. 11372.40   (*c*) Rs. 12000   (*d*) None

109. A ball pen factory decided to reduce its production by 10% over that of previous month for next 3 months starting from February 1994. In January 1994, it produced 3000 ball pens. How many ball pens were produced in March 1994 ? **(Bank P.O. 1993)**

    (*a*) 2700   (*b*) 2430   (*c*) 2187   (*d*) 2400

110. The present population of a country estimated to be 10 crores is expected to increase to 13.31 crores during the next three years. The uniform rate of growth is :

    (*a*) 8%   (*b*) 12.7%   (*c*) 10%   (*d*) 15%

111. A building worth Rs 133,100 is constructed on land worth Rs. 72,900. After how many years will the value of both be the same if land appreciates at 10% p.a. and building depreciates at 10% p.a. ?

    (*a*) $2\frac{1}{2}$ (*b*) 2   (*c*) $1\frac{1}{2}$ (*d*) 3

                                     (Hotel Management 1992)

112. The population of a town increases 4% annually but is decreased by emigration annually to the extent of (1/2) %. What will be the increase percent in 3 years ? **(C.B.I. 1991)**

    (*a*) 9.8   (*b*) 10   (*c*) 10.5   (*d*) 10.8

113. The current birth rate per thousand is 32, whereas corresponding death rate is 11 per thousand. The net growth rate in terms of population increase in percent is given by

    (*a*) 0.021%   (*b*) 0.0021%   (*c*) 21%   (*d*) 2.1%

114. A reduction of 21% in the price of wheat enables a person to buy 10.5 kg more for Rs. 100. What is the reduced price per kg ?

    (*a*) Rs. 2   (*b*) Rs. 2.25   (*c*) Rs. 2.30   (*d*) Rs. 2.50

115. A man's basic pay for a 40 hour week is Rs. 20. Overtime is paid for at 25% above the basic rate. In a certain week, he worked overtime and his total wage was Rs. 25. He, therefore, worked for a total of :

    (*a*) 45 hours   (*b*) 47 hours   (*c*) 48 hours   (*d*) 50 hours

                                            (C.B.I. 1991)

116. Salaries of *A*, *B* and *C* are in the ratio 1 : 2 : 3. Salary of *B* and *C* together is Rs. 6000. By what percent is salary of *C* more than that of *A* ?

    (*a*) 300   (*b*) 600   (*c*) 100   (*d*) 200

                                            (Bank P.O. 1992)

117. The price of a table is Rs. 400 more than that of a chair. If 6 tables and 6 chairs together cost Rs. 4800, by what percent is the price of the chair less than that of the table ? **(Bank P.O. 1992)**

    (*a*) 200   (*b*) 400   (*c*) 100   (*d*) None of these

118. If the side of a square is increased by 25%, then its area is increased by :

    (*a*) 25%   (*b*) 55%   (*c*) 40.5%   (*d*) 56.25%

119. The length and breadth of a square are increased by 40% and 30% respectively. The area of the resulting rectangle exceeds the area of the square by : **(I. Tax & Central Excise 1988)**
    (a) 42%   (b) 62%   (c) 82%   (d) None
120. The length of a rectangle is increased by 20% and the width is decreased by 20%. The area decreases by : **(U.D.C. 1993)**
    (a) 0.8%   (b) 1.2%   (c) 4%   (d) 8%
121. The length of a rectangle is increased by 60%. By what percent would the width have to be decreased to maintain the same area ?
    (a) $37\frac{1}{2}$%   (b) 60%   (c) 75%   (d) None
    (S.B.I.P.O. 1988)
122. If the radius of a circle is decreased by 50%, its area is reduced by :
    (a) 25%   (b) 50%   (c) 75%   (d) None
123. For a sphere of radius 10 cm, the numerical value of surface area is what percent of the numerical value of its volume ?
    (a) 24%   (b) 26.5%   (c) 30%   (d) 45%
124. The radius of a sphere is increased by 50%. The increase in surface area of the sphere is :
    (a) 100%   (b) 125%   (c) 150%   (d) 200%
125. A cricket team won 40% of the total number of matches it played during a year. If it lost 50% of the matches played and 20 matches were drawn, the total number of matches played by the team during the year was :
    (a) 200   (b) 100   (c) 50   (d) 40
126. In a market survey, 20% opted for product A whereas 60% opted for product B. The remaining individuals were not certain. If the difference between those who opted for product B and those who were uncertain was 720, how many individuals were covered in the survey ?
    (a) 3600   (b) 1440   (c) 1800   (d) Data inadequate
    (Bank P.O. 1993)
127. Arun gave a portion of the money he had to Gopal. Gopal in turn gave 40% of what he got from Arun to Dinesh. How much money did Dinesh get ? To find out the answer, which of the following informations given in statements (P) and (Q) is/are sufficient ? **(Bank P.O. 1993)**
    P : Arun had Rs. 4,000 with him.
    Q : The difference between the amounts of Gopal and Dinesh was Rs. 500.
    (a) Only Q is sufficient.   (b) Only P is sufficient.
    (c) Either P or Q is sufficient.
    (d) Both P and Q together are needed.
128. The price of an article was increased by p%. Later the new price was decreased by p%. If the latest price was Re 1, the original price was

(a) Re 1

(b) Rs. $\left(\dfrac{1-p^2}{100}\right)$

(c) Rs. $\left(\dfrac{10000}{10000-p^2}\right)$

(d) Rs. $\left(\dfrac{\sqrt{1-p^2}}{100}\right)$

(C.B.I. 1990)

ANSWERS

1. (b)	**2.** (c)	**3.** (b)	**4.** (d)	**5.** (d)	**6.** (d)	**7.** (a)	**8.** (d)	**9.** (c)
10. (b)	**11.** (b)	**12.** (a)	**13.** (d)	**14.** (a)	**15.** (c)	**16.** (c)	**17.** (b)	**18.** (d)
19. (c)	**20.** (a)	**21.** (c)	**22.** (c)	**23.** (c)	**24.** (b)	**25.** (d)	**26.** (b)	**27.** (b)
28. (c)	**29.** (c)	**30.** (c)	**31.** (d)	**32.** (d)	**33.** (d)	**34.** (a)	**35.** (d)	**36.** (c)
37. (b)	**38.** (a)	**39.** (c)	**40.** (a)	**41.** (c)	**42.** (b)	**43.** (b)	**44.** (b)	**45.** (a)
46. (d)	**47.** (b)	**48.** (d)	**49.** (d)	**50.** (a)	**51.** (d)	**52.** (c)	**53.** (b)	**54.** (a)
55. (c)	**56.** (c)	**57.** (a)	**58.** (c)	**59.** (a)	**60.** (c)	**61.** (d)	**62.** (d)	**63.** (d)
64. (c)	**65.** (b)	**66.** (d)	**67.** (a)	**68.** (a)	**69.** (c)	**70.** (c)	**71.** (c)	**72.** (b)
73. (c)	**74.** (b)	**75.** (c)	**76.** (a)	**77.** (b)	**78.** (b)	**79.** (c)	**80.** (b)	**81.** (d)
82. (b)	**83.** (d)	**84.** (d)	**85.** (c)	**86.** (b)	**87.** (b)	**88.** (a)	**89.** (c)	**90.** (d)
91. (a)	**92.** (a)	**93.** (b)	**94.** (d)	**95.** (d)	**96.** (a)	**97.** (c)	**98.** (a)	**99.** (c)
100. (a)	**101.** (b)	**102.** (a)	**103.** (d)	**104.** (d)	**105.** (c)	**106.** (b)	**107.** (c)	**108.** (c)
109. (c)	**110.** (c)	**111.** (d)	**112.** (d)	**113.** (d)	**114.** (a)	**115.** (c)	**116.** (d)	**117.** (d)
118. (d)	**119.** (c)	**120.** (c)	**121.** (a)	**122.** (c)	**123.** (c)	**124.** (b)	**125.** (a)	**126.** (c)
127. (a)	**128.** (c)							

SOLUTIONS

1. $.02 = \dfrac{2}{100} = \left(\dfrac{2}{100} \times 100\right)\% = 2\%.$

2. $12\dfrac{1}{2}\% = \dfrac{25}{2 \times 100} = \dfrac{1}{8} = 0.125.$

3. Percentage of Sulphur $= \left(\dfrac{5}{2250} \times 100\right)\% = \dfrac{2}{9}\%.$

4. Let $45 \times x = 25\%$ of 900. Then, $x = \left(\dfrac{25}{100} \times 900 \times \dfrac{1}{45}\right) = 5.$

5. Let 218% of $1674 = x \times 1800.$

Then, $x = \left(\dfrac{218}{100} \times 1674 \times \dfrac{1}{1800}\right) = 2.0274.$

6. Given Exp. $= \dfrac{13937.869}{199.54} + \dfrac{15}{100} \times 201 = 69.85 + 30.15 = 100.$

7. 63% of $3\frac{4}{7} = \frac{63}{100} \times \frac{25}{7} = \frac{9}{4} = 2.25.$

8. Let 30% of $x = 12.6$. Then, $x = \left(12.6 \times \frac{100}{30}\right) = 42.$

9. 5% of $(25\%$ of $1600) = \frac{5}{100} \times \left(\frac{25}{100} \times 1600\right) = 20.$

10. Let $8\frac{1}{3}\%$ of $x = 150$. Then, $\frac{25}{3 \times 100} \times x = 150.$

    $\therefore \; x = \left(150 \times \frac{300}{25}\right) = 1800.$

11. Let 35% of $30 = 25\%$ of $x + 1$.

    Then, $\frac{35}{100} \times 30 = \frac{25}{100} \times x + 1$ or $\frac{x}{4} = \left(\frac{21}{2} - 1\right) = \frac{19}{2}$

    $\therefore \; x = \left(\frac{19}{2} \times 4\right) = 38.$

12. Required percentage $= \left(\frac{3\%}{5\%} \times 100\right)\% = \left[\frac{(3/100)}{(5/100)} \times 100\right]\% = 60\%.$

13. Let $x\%$ of $6144 = \frac{5}{2} \times 245.76$

    Then, $x = \left(\frac{5}{2} \times 245.76 \times \frac{100}{6144}\right) = 10.$

14. Let $\frac{12.5}{100} \times 192 = \frac{50}{100} \times x$. Then, $x = \frac{12.5 \times 192}{100} \times 2 = 48.$

15. Let $\frac{30\% \text{ of } 80}{x} = 24$. Then,

    $x = \frac{30\% \text{ of } 80}{24} = \left(\frac{30}{100} \times \frac{80}{24}\right) = 1.$

16. 25% of $25\% = \frac{25}{100} \times \frac{25}{100} = \frac{1}{16} = .0625.$

17. Let $\frac{45}{10} \times x + \frac{30}{100} \times 90 = \frac{30}{100} \times 210$

    Then, $\frac{9x}{20} = (63 - 27) = 36$ or $x = \frac{36 \times 20}{9} = 80.$

18. Let $\frac{1}{4} \times \frac{1}{3} \times \frac{2}{5} \times x = 15$. Then, $x = 15 \times 30 = 450.$

    Now, 40% of $450 = \frac{40}{100} \times 450 = 180.$

19. Let 37% of $x = 990.86$. Then, $\frac{37}{100} \times x = 990.86$

or $x = \dfrac{990.86 \times 100}{37} = \dfrac{99086}{37} = 2678.$

Now, 19% of $2678 = \dfrac{19}{100} \times 2678 = 508.82$ or 500 approx.

20. $\dfrac{15}{100} \times 40 - \dfrac{25}{100} \times x = 2$ or $\dfrac{x}{4} = (6 - 2) = 4$ or $x = 16.$

21. Required percentage $= \left(\dfrac{18}{7200} \times 100 \right) = 0.25\%.$

22. $\dfrac{40}{100} \times \dfrac{40}{100} \times x = 40 \Rightarrow x = \dfrac{40 \times 100 \times 100}{40 \times 40} = 250.$

23. $\sqrt{3.6\% \text{ of } 40} = \sqrt{\dfrac{3.6}{100} \times 40} = \sqrt{\dfrac{144}{100}} = \dfrac{12}{10} = 1.2.$

24. $\dfrac{4}{5} \times 70 = 56$ & $\dfrac{5}{7} \times 112 = 80$

Decrease over $80 = (80 - 56) = 24$

Decrease over $100 = \left(\dfrac{24}{80} \times 100 \right)\% = 30\%.$

25. Let 200% of $x = 140$. Then, $\dfrac{200}{100} \times x = 140$ or $x = 70.$

Now, 160% of $70 = \dfrac{160}{100} \times 70 = 112.$

26. 75% of $x + 75 = x \Rightarrow x - \dfrac{75}{100} x = 75$

$\therefore x - \dfrac{3}{4} x = 75$ or $\dfrac{x}{4} = 75$ or $x = 75 \times 4 = 300.$

27. $x - 40\%$ of $x = 30 \Rightarrow x - \dfrac{40}{100} x = 30 \Rightarrow x - \dfrac{2}{5} x = 30$

$\therefore \dfrac{3x}{5} = 30$ or $x = \left(30 \times \dfrac{5}{3} \right) = 50.$

28. $\dfrac{3}{5} x - 40\%$ of $x = 40 \Rightarrow \dfrac{3}{5} x - \dfrac{40}{100} x = 40.$

or $\dfrac{3}{5} x - \dfrac{2}{5} x = 40$ or $\dfrac{x}{5} = 40$ or $x = (40 \times 5) = 200.$

29. $x - 15 = \dfrac{80}{100} x \Rightarrow x - 15 = \dfrac{4}{5} x \Rightarrow x - \dfrac{4}{5} x = 15.$

$\therefore \dfrac{x}{5} = 15$ or $x = (15 \times 5) = 75.$

Now, 40% of $75 = \left(\dfrac{40}{100} \times 75 \right) = 30.$

30. Error on $37\frac{1}{2} = \left(37\frac{1}{2} - 36\right) = 1\frac{1}{2}$.

$\therefore$ Error on $\dfrac{75}{2} = \dfrac{3}{2}$.

Error on $100 = \left(\dfrac{3}{2} \times \dfrac{2}{75} \times 100\right) = 4\%$.

31. Increase on $133575 = (138918 - 133575) = 5343$

$\therefore$ Increase on $100 = \left(\dfrac{5343}{133575} \times 100\right)\% = 4\%$.

32. $X = \dfrac{90}{100}Y \Rightarrow X = \dfrac{9}{10}Y \Rightarrow Y = \dfrac{10}{9}X \Rightarrow \dfrac{Y}{X} = \dfrac{10}{9}$.

$\therefore$ Required percentage $= \left(\dfrac{Y}{X} \times 100\right) = \left(\dfrac{10}{9} \times 100\right)\% = 111.1$.

33. $\dfrac{x}{100} \times y = \dfrac{4}{5} \times 80 \Rightarrow xy = 64 \times 100 = 6400$.

34. Let $x - 6\%$ of $x = xz$. Then, 94% of $x = xz$

or $\dfrac{94 \cdot}{100} x \times \dfrac{1}{x} = z$ or $z = .94$.

35. $\dfrac{8}{100}x = \dfrac{4}{100}y \Rightarrow x = \left(\dfrac{4}{100}y \times \dfrac{100}{8}\right) = \dfrac{1}{2}y$.

$\therefore 20\%$ of $x = 20\%$ of $\dfrac{1}{2}y = 10\%$ of y.

36. $\dfrac{x}{100}y + \dfrac{y}{100}x = \dfrac{2xy}{100} = 2\%$ of xy.

37. $\dfrac{90}{100}A = \dfrac{30}{100}B \Rightarrow B = \dfrac{90}{100} \times \dfrac{100}{30}A = \dfrac{300}{100}A = 300\%$ of A.

$\therefore x = 300$.

38. $x\%$ of $y = \dfrac{x}{100} \times y = \dfrac{y}{100}$ of $x = y\%$ of x.

39. $137\frac{1}{2}\%$ of $x = 33 \Rightarrow \dfrac{275}{2 \times 100}x = 33$.

$\therefore x = \left(\dfrac{33 \times 200}{275}\right) = 24$.

40. $\left(100 - 27\frac{1}{2}\right)\%$ of $x = 87 \Rightarrow 72\frac{1}{2}\%$ of $x = 87$.

$\therefore \dfrac{145}{2 \times 100} \times x = 87$ or $x = \dfrac{87 \times 200}{145} = 120$.

41. Note that 1 metric tonne = 10 quintals.

$\therefore$ Required percentage $= \left(\dfrac{40}{2 \times 10} \times 100\right)\% = 200\%$.

42. 20% of $x = 35 \Rightarrow \dfrac{20}{100} x = 35$ or $x = (35 \times 5) = 175$.

43. 30% of $x = 504 \Rightarrow \dfrac{30}{100} x = 504 \Rightarrow x = \left(504 \times \dfrac{100}{30} \right) = 1680$.

$\therefore$ Number of boys $= 70\%$ of $1680 = \left(\dfrac{70}{100} \times 1680 \right) = 1176$.

44. 40% of $x = 178 + 22$ or $\dfrac{40}{100} x = 200$ or $x = \left(200 \times \dfrac{100}{40} \right) = 500$.

45. 15% of $x + 25 = x \Rightarrow x - \dfrac{15}{100} x = 25$ or $\dfrac{17x}{20} = 25$

or $x = \dfrac{25 \times 20}{17} = 29.41$ or 30 kg.

So, he must purchase 15 cans.

Total cost $=$ Rs. $(16 \times 15) =$ Rs. 240.

46. 87.5% of $x = 4375 \Rightarrow \dfrac{87.5}{100} x = 4375$.

$\therefore$ $x = \left(\dfrac{4375 \times 100}{87.5} \right) = 5000$.

47. Purchases $= 20\%$ of $x = \dfrac{x}{5}$. Balance $= x - \dfrac{x}{5} = \dfrac{4x}{5}$.

Transportation $= 5\%$ of $\dfrac{4x}{5} = \dfrac{5}{100} \times \dfrac{4x}{5} = \dfrac{x}{25}$.

Balance $= \dfrac{4x}{5} - \dfrac{x}{25} = \dfrac{19x}{25}$.

$\therefore$ $\dfrac{19x}{25} = 1520 \Rightarrow x = \dfrac{1520 \times 25}{19} = 2000$.

48. Hindi Books $= 20\%$ of $x = \dfrac{20}{100} x = \dfrac{x}{5}$.

Remaining $= \left(x - \dfrac{x}{5} \right) = \dfrac{4x}{5}$.

English Books $= 50\%$ of $\dfrac{4x}{5} = \dfrac{50}{100} \times \dfrac{4x}{5} = \dfrac{2x}{5}$.

Remaining $= \left(\dfrac{4x}{5} - \dfrac{2x}{5} \right) = \dfrac{2x}{5}$.

$\therefore$ $\dfrac{2x}{5} = 9000$ or $x = \dfrac{9000 \times 5}{2} = 22500$.

49. Spent on scooter petrol $= \dfrac{30}{100} x = \dfrac{3x}{10}$.

Remaining $= \left(x - \dfrac{3x}{10} \right) = \dfrac{7x}{10}$.

House Rent $= \frac{1}{4} \times \frac{7x}{10} = \frac{7x}{40}$.

Now, $\frac{3x}{10} = 300 \Rightarrow x = \frac{300 \times 10}{3} = 1000$.

$\therefore$ House Rent $= \frac{7 \times 1000}{40} = 175$.

50. House rent $= \frac{35}{100} x = \frac{7x}{20}$. Remaining $= \left(x - \frac{7x}{20}\right) = \frac{13x}{20}$.

Other expenditures $= \left(\frac{75}{100} \times \frac{13x}{20}\right) = \frac{39x}{80}$

Saving $= \left(\frac{13x}{20} - \frac{39x}{80}\right) = \frac{13x}{80}$.

$\therefore$ Saving percent $= \left(\frac{13x}{80} \times \frac{1}{x} \times 100\right) = \frac{65}{4}\% = 16.25\%$.

51. 80% of $x = 800 \Rightarrow \frac{80}{100} x = 800 \Rightarrow x = 800 \times \frac{100}{80} = 1000$.

52. Saving $= [100 - (40 + 25 + 15 + 5)]\% = 15\%$.

$\therefore$ 15% of $x = 1200 \Rightarrow \frac{15}{100} x = 1200 \Rightarrow x = \left(1200 \times \frac{100}{15}\right) = 8000$.

53. Money spent on food articles $= 40\%$ of $x = \frac{40}{100} x = \frac{2x}{5}$.

Balance $= \left(x - \frac{2x}{5}\right) = \frac{3x}{5}$.

Money spent on transport $= \frac{1}{3} \times \frac{3x}{5} = \frac{x}{5}$.

Balance now $= \left(\frac{3x}{5} - \frac{x}{5}\right) = \frac{2x}{5}$.

$\therefore \frac{1}{2} \times \frac{2x}{5} = 450 \Rightarrow x = (450 \times 5) = 2250$.

54. Suppose he ate x apples.

Then, apples sold $= 140\%$ of $x = \left(\frac{140}{100} \times x\right) = \frac{7x}{5}$.

$\frac{7x}{5} = 70 \Rightarrow x = 70 \times \frac{5}{7} = 50$.

55. Let, total population $= x$. Males $= \frac{5}{9} x$.

Married males $= 30\%$ of $\frac{5}{9} x = \frac{30}{100} \times \frac{5}{9} x = \frac{x}{6}$.

Married females $= \frac{x}{6}$.

Total females $= \left(x - \dfrac{5}{9} x \right) = \dfrac{4x}{9}$.

Unmarried females $= \left(\dfrac{4x}{9} - \dfrac{x}{6} \right) = \dfrac{5x}{18}$.

$\therefore$ Required percentage $= \left(\dfrac{5x}{18} \times \dfrac{1}{x} \times 100 \right) \% = 27 \dfrac{7}{9} \%$.

56. Number of failures $= (50\%$ of $1100 + 60\%$ of $900)$

$$= \left(\dfrac{50}{100} \times 1100 + \dfrac{60}{100} \times 900 \right) = 1090.$$

Required percentage $= \left(\dfrac{1090}{2000} \times 100 \right) \% = 54.5\%$.

57. Number of passed candidates $= \left(\dfrac{10}{100} \times 40 + \dfrac{20}{100} \times 50 + \dfrac{10}{100} \times 60 \right)$

$$= (4 + 10 + 6) = 20.$$

Pass percentage $= \dfrac{20}{(40 + 50 + 60)} \times 100 = \left(\dfrac{20}{150} \times 100 \right) \% = 13 \dfrac{1}{3} \%$.

58. $30\% A = 20\%$ of $\dfrac{3}{5} B \Rightarrow \dfrac{30A}{100} = \dfrac{20}{100} \times \dfrac{3}{5} B$

$\therefore A = \dfrac{20}{100} \times \dfrac{3}{5} \times \dfrac{100}{30} B = \dfrac{2}{5} B = \left(\dfrac{2}{5} \times 2400 \right) = 960.$

59. Total marks $= 50\%$ of $50 + 60\%$ of $50 + 70\%$ of $50 + 70\%$ of 50

$$= \left(\dfrac{50}{100} \times 50 + \dfrac{60}{100} \times 50 + \dfrac{70}{100} \times 50 + \dfrac{70}{100} \times 50 \right)$$

$$= (25 + 30 + 35 + 35) = 125.$$

60. $x\%$ of $a = y\%$ of $b \Rightarrow \dfrac{x}{100} a = \dfrac{y}{100} b \Rightarrow b = \left(\dfrac{x}{100} \times \dfrac{100}{y} \right) a = \left(\dfrac{x}{y} \right) a$

$\therefore z\%$ of $b = \left(z\% \text{ of } \dfrac{x}{y} \right) a = \left(\dfrac{xz}{y \times 100} \right) a = \left(\dfrac{xz}{y} \right) \%$ of a.

61. Migrants $= 35\%$ of $728400 = \dfrac{35}{100} \times 728400 = 254940$.

Local population $= (728400 - 254940) = 473460$.
Rural population $= 20\%$ of $473460 = 94692$.
Urban population $= (254940 - 94692) = 160248$.
$\therefore$ Female population
$= 48\%$ of $473460 + 30\%$ of $94692 + 40\%$ of 160248

$= \left(\dfrac{48}{100} \times 473460 + \dfrac{30}{100} \times 94692 + \dfrac{40}{100} \times 160248 \right)$

$= 227260.8 + 28407.6 + 64099.2 = 896660.$

62. Let $B + M + D = x$.

Then, $B = (25\%$ of $x - 20) = \left(\dfrac{25}{100}x - 20\right) = \left(\dfrac{x}{4} - 20\right)$ & $D = 50$

$\therefore \dfrac{x}{4} - 20 + M + 50 = x$ or $M = \left(\dfrac{3x}{4} - 30\right)$.

So, marks in Maths cannot be determined.

63. $M + 60 = 50\%$ of K. Clearly, M cannot be determined.

64. Let total quantity of original milk = 1000 gm.

Milk after first operation = 80% of 1000 = 800 gm.

Milk after second operation = 80% of 800 = 640 gm.

Milk after third operation = 80% of 640 = 512 gm.

$\therefore$ Strength of final mixture = 51.2%.

65. Suppose monthly rent = Rs. x. Then,

$12x - \dfrac{25}{2}\%$ of $12x - 1660 = 10\%$ of 500000

$\Rightarrow 12x - \dfrac{25}{200} \times 12x - 1660 = 50000$

$\Rightarrow \dfrac{21x}{2} = 51660$ or $x = \left(51660 \times \dfrac{2}{21}\right) = 4920.$

66. Girls $= \left(\dfrac{2}{5} \times 1000\right) = 400$, Boys = 600.

Under 12 years $= \left(\dfrac{1}{5} \times 400 + \dfrac{1}{4} \times 600\right) = 230.$

Above 12 years = (1000 − 230) = 770.

Required percentage $= \left(\dfrac{770}{1000} \times 100\right)\% = 77\%.$

67. Let A's salary $= x$. Then, B's $= (2000 - x)$

5% of A = 15% of B, i.e. $\dfrac{5}{100}x = \dfrac{15}{100}(2000 - x)$ or $x = 1500.$

68. Let total debt $= x$. Asset with him $= \dfrac{87}{100}x$.

After paying 20% of the debt, he is left with 80% of the debt plus Rs. 42.

$\therefore$ 80% of $x + 42 = \dfrac{87}{100}x$ or $\dfrac{87}{100}x - \dfrac{80}{100}x = 42$ or $x = 600$.

$\therefore$ Debt = Rs. 600 & Assets $= \dfrac{87}{100} \times 600 = $ Rs. 522.

69. Sugar $= \left(\dfrac{40}{100} \times 300\right)$ gms = 120 gms, water = 180 gms.

Let x gm sugar may be added.

Then, $\dfrac{120+x}{300+x} \times 100 = 50 \Rightarrow 240 + 2x = 300 + x \Rightarrow x = 60.$

70. Alcohol in 9 ml $= \left(\dfrac{50}{100} \times 9\right)$ ml $= 4.5$ ml, water $= 4.5$ ml.

Let the water to be added be x ml.

Then, $\dfrac{4.5}{9+x} \times 100 = 30 \Rightarrow 450 = 270 + 30x \Rightarrow x = 6$ ml.

71. Sugar $= \left(\dfrac{40}{100} \times 3\right)$ litres $= 1.2$ litres, water $= 1.8$ litres.

New percentage $= \left(\dfrac{1.2}{4} \times 100\right)\% = 30\%.$

72. Let original price $= 100.$ New price $= 80.$
Increase on $80 = 20$

Increase on $100 = \left(\dfrac{20}{80} \times 100\right)\% = 25\%.$

73. Let the business value changes from x to y.

4% of $x = 5\%$ of $y \Rightarrow \dfrac{4}{100} x = \dfrac{5}{100} y \Rightarrow y = \dfrac{4}{5} x.$

Change in business $= \left(x - \dfrac{4}{5} x\right) = \dfrac{x}{5}.$

Percentage slump $= \left(\dfrac{x}{5} \times \dfrac{1}{x} \times 100\right)\% = 20\%.$

74. $60 + 70 + x = \dfrac{70}{100} \times 300$ or $x = 80\%.$

75. Let total marks $= x$.
25% of $x + 30 = (50\%$ of $x) - 20$

$\Rightarrow \dfrac{25}{100} x + 30 = \dfrac{50}{100} x - 20 \Rightarrow \left(\dfrac{x}{2} - \dfrac{x}{4}\right) = 50$

$\Rightarrow \dfrac{x}{4} = 50 \Rightarrow x = 200.$

$\therefore$ Pass marks $= (25\%$ of $200) + 30 = \left(\dfrac{25}{100} \times 200 + 30\right) = 80.$

$\therefore$ Pass percentage $= \left(\dfrac{80}{200} \times 100\right)\% = 40\%.$

76. Let, third number be x. Then,

First number $= 70\%$ of $x = \dfrac{7x}{10},$

Second number $= 63\%$ of $x = \dfrac{63x}{100}.$

Required Percentage $= \left(\dfrac{7x}{100} \times \dfrac{10}{7x} \times 100 \right)\% = 10\%.$

77. Total money $= \left(600 \times \dfrac{25}{100} + 1200 \times \dfrac{50}{100} \right) = $ Rs. 750.

25 paise coins removed $= \left(\dfrac{12}{100} \times 600 \right) = 72.$

50 paise coins removed $= \left(\dfrac{24}{100} \times 1200 \right) = 288.$

Money removed $= \left(72 \times \dfrac{25}{100} + 288 \times \dfrac{50}{100} \right) = $ Rs. 162.

Required percentage $= \left(\dfrac{162}{750} \times 100 \right)\% = 21.6\%.$

78. $\dfrac{5}{100} A = \dfrac{15}{100} B \ \& \ \dfrac{10}{100} B = \dfrac{20}{100} C$

$\therefore \ A = 3B$ and $B = 2C = 2 \times 2000 = 4000$

$\therefore \ A = 3 \times 4000 = 12000.$

$\therefore \ A + B + C = (12000 + 4000 + 2000) = 18000.$

79. $A = \dfrac{90}{100} B, B = \dfrac{125}{100} C$ and $C = \dfrac{80}{100} D.$

$\therefore \ B = \dfrac{10}{9} A, C = \dfrac{4}{5} B$ and $D = \dfrac{5}{4} C.$

$B = \dfrac{10}{9} \times 360 = 400, C = \dfrac{4}{5} \times 400 = 320 \ \& \ D = \dfrac{5}{4} \times 320 = 400.$

Percentage of $D = \left(\dfrac{400}{500} \times 100 \right)\% = 80\%.$

80. Let the given fraction be $\dfrac{x}{y}$.

Then, $\dfrac{115\% \text{ of } x}{92\% \text{ of } y} = \dfrac{15}{16} \Rightarrow \dfrac{115x}{92y} = \dfrac{15}{16} \Rightarrow \dfrac{x}{y} = \left(\dfrac{15}{16} \times \dfrac{92}{115} \right) = \dfrac{3}{4}.$

81. $n(A) = 35, n(B) = 45, n(A \cap B) = 20.$

$n(A \cup B) = n(A) + n(B) - n(A \cap B) = (35 + 45 - 20) = 60.$

$\therefore$ Number failed in one or the other or both $= 60.$

$\therefore$ Number passed $= 40\%.$

82. Let original salary $=$ Rs. 100.

New final salary $= 150\%$ of $(50\%$ of $100)$

$= \left(\dfrac{150}{100} \times \dfrac{50}{100} \times 100 \right) = $ Rs. 75.

$\therefore$ Decrease $= 25\%.$

83. Let income $= 100.$ Expenditure $= 75 \ \&$ Savings $= 25.$

New income = 120, New expenditure = $\left(\dfrac{110}{100} \times 75\right) = \dfrac{165}{2}$.

New savings = $\left(120 - \dfrac{165}{2}\right) = \dfrac{75}{2}$.

Increase in savings = $\left(\dfrac{75}{2} - 25\right) = \dfrac{25}{2}$.

Increase percent = $\left(\dfrac{25}{2} \times \dfrac{1}{25} \times 100\right)\% = 50\%$.

84. $n(A) = \left(\dfrac{75}{100} \times 600\right) = 450$, $n(B) = \left(\dfrac{45}{100} \times 600\right) = 270$ and

$n(A \cup B) = 600$.

$\therefore\ n(A \cap B) = n(A) + n(B) - n(A \cup B) = (450 + 270 - 600) = 120$.

85. Let total number be x. Then,

$n(A) = \dfrac{72}{100}\, x = \dfrac{18x}{25}$, $n(B) = \dfrac{44}{100}\, x = \dfrac{11x}{25}$ & $n(A \cap B) = 40$.

$n(A \cup B) = n(A) + n(B) - n(A \cap B)$

$\Rightarrow x = \dfrac{18x}{25} + \dfrac{11x}{25} - 40 \Rightarrow \dfrac{29x}{25} - x = 40$ or $\dfrac{4x}{25} = 40$

$\therefore\ x = \left(\dfrac{25 \times 40}{4}\right) = 250$.

86. Let the total number of students be x.

Number passed in one or both is given by :

$n(A \cup B) = n(A) + n(B) - n(A \cap B)$

$\qquad = 80\%$ of $x + 85\%$ of $x - 75\%$ of x

$\qquad = \left(\dfrac{80}{100}\, x + \dfrac{85}{100}\, x - \dfrac{75}{100}\, x\right) = \dfrac{90}{100}\, x = \dfrac{9x}{10}$.

Failed in both = $\left(x - \dfrac{9x}{100}\right) = \dfrac{x}{10}$.

$\therefore\ \dfrac{x}{10} = 40$ or $x = 400$.

87. Failed in 1st subject = $\left(\dfrac{35}{100} \times 2500\right) = 875$.

Failed in 2nd subject = $\left(\dfrac{42}{100} \times 2500\right) = 1050$.

Failed in both = $\left(\dfrac{15}{100} \times 2500\right) = 375$.

Failed in 1st subject only = $(875 - 375) = 500$

Failed in 2nd subject only = $(1050 - 375) = 675$.

Passed in 2nd only + Passed in 1st only = $(675 + 500) = 1175$.

88. $p = 6q$, so q is less than p by $5q$.

Note that q has been compared with p.

∴ Required percentage $= \left(\dfrac{5q}{p} \times 100\right)\% = \left(\dfrac{5q}{6q} \times 100\right)\% = 83\dfrac{1}{3}\%$.

89. Suppose boys $= 3x$ and girls $= 2x$.

Not adults $= \left(\dfrac{80}{100} \times 3x\right) + \left(\dfrac{75}{100} \times 2x\right) = \left(\dfrac{12x}{5} + \dfrac{3x}{2}\right) = \dfrac{39x}{10}$.

Required percentage $= \left(\dfrac{39x}{10} \times \dfrac{1}{5x} \times 100\right)\% = 78\%$.

90. Let the votes polled by the winning candidate be x.

Defeated candidate gets $(x - 15000)$ votes.

40% of $[x + (x - 15000)] = (x - 15000)$

$\dfrac{2}{5}(2x - 15000) = x - 15000$ or $4x - 30000 = 5x - 75000$

or $x = 45000$.

91. Valid votes in all $= 80\%$ of $7500 = 6000$.

Valid votes polled by another candidate $= 45\%$ of 6000

$= \left(\dfrac{45}{100} \times 6000\right) = 2700$.

92. Let the valid votes be x.

Then, 52% of $x - 48\%$ of $x = 98 \Rightarrow 4\%$ of $x = 98$.

∴ $\dfrac{4}{100}x = 98$ or $x = 98 \times 25 = 2450$.

∴ Total votes polled $= (2450 + 68) = 2518$.

93. $A = (125\%)$ of $B \Rightarrow A = \dfrac{125}{100}B$.

∴ $B = \dfrac{100}{125}A = \dfrac{4}{5}A = \left(\dfrac{4}{5} \times 100\right)\%$ of $A = 80\%$ of A.

94. Excess of Deepak's height over Anil $= \left[\dfrac{20}{(100 - 20)} \times 100\right]\% = 25\%$.

95. Let original consumption $= 100$ units & Tax $=$ Rs. 100 per unit.

Then original expenditure $=$ Rs. 100×100

New expenditure $= 80 \times 120 =$ Rs. 9600.

Decrease in expenditure $= \left(\dfrac{400}{100 \times 100} \times 100\right)\% = 4\%$.

96. Let cost per T.V. $=$ Rs. 100 & original sale $= 100$ T.V.

Revenue Receipt $=$ Rs. (100×100).

New Receipt $=$ Rs. $(130 \times 80) =$ Rs. 10400.

Increase in receipt $= \left(\dfrac{400}{100 \times 100} \times 100\right)\% = 4\%$.

97. Let income be Rs 100.

Then, expenditure = Rs 75, saving = Rs 25
New income = Rs 120

New expenditure = Rs = $\left(\dfrac{115}{100} \times 75\right)$ = Rs $\dfrac{345}{4}$

Now, saving = Rs = $\left(120 - \dfrac{345}{4}\right)$ = Rs $\dfrac{135}{4}$

Increase% in saving = $\left(\dfrac{35}{4 \times 25} \times 100\right)$ = 35 %.

98. Reduction in Consumption = $\left[\dfrac{r}{(100+r)} \times 100\right]\%$ = $\left(\dfrac{20}{120} \times 100\right)\%$

$= 16\dfrac{2}{3}\%.$

99. Let original comsumption be 1 unit costing Rs 100.
New cost = Rs. 125.

New consumption = $\left(\dfrac{1}{125} \times 100\right) = \dfrac{4}{5}$ unit .

$\dfrac{\text{Reduction in consumption}}{\text{original consumption}} = \dfrac{\left(1 - \dfrac{4}{5}\right)}{1} = \dfrac{1}{5}$ i.e., 1 : 5.

100. Let original consumption = 100 units & original price = Rs. 100/unit.
Original expenditure = Rs. (100 × 100) = Rs. 10000.
New expenditure = Rs. (120 × 75) = Rs. 9000.

∴ Decrease in expenditue = $\left(\dfrac{1000}{10000} \times 100\right)\%$ = 10%.

101. Let original consumption = 100 kg & new consumption = x kg
∴ 100 × 6 = x × 7.50 ⟹ x = 80 kg.
∴ Reduction in consumption = 20%.

102. Let original rate = Rs. x/kg. Consumption = 10 kg.
Expenditure = Rs. 10x.
New expenditure = 110% of *Rs*. 10x = 11x.

New rate = 132% of $x = \dfrac{33x}{25}$.

New consumption = $\dfrac{\text{Expenditure}}{\text{Rate}} = \left(11x \times \dfrac{25}{33x}\right) = \dfrac{25}{3}$ kg. = $8\dfrac{1}{3}$ kg.

103. Let expenditures on food grains and other items be Rs. 2x and
Rs. 5x.
2x + 5x = 2590   or x = 370.
∴ F = 2 × 370 = 740, O = 5 × 370 = 1850.
New expenditures = 110% of 740 + 115% of 1850

$$= \left(\frac{110}{100} \times 740 + \frac{115}{100} \times 1850 \right)$$

$$= \text{Rs. } (814 + 2127.50) = \text{Rs. } 2941.50$$

$$\therefore \text{ Desired increase} = \text{Rs. } (2941.50 - 2590) = \text{Rs. } 351.50.$$

104. Population in 1997 $= 8000 \times \left(1 + \frac{15}{100} \right)^2 = \left(8000 \times \frac{23}{20} \times \frac{23}{20} \right) = 10580.$

105. Required population $= 18000 \times \left(1 + \frac{10}{100} \right) \times \left(1 + \frac{20}{100} \right)$

$$= \left(18000 \times \frac{11}{10} \times \frac{6}{5} \right) = 23760.$$

106. Value after 2 years $= \text{Rs. } \left[200 \times \left(1 - \frac{4}{100} \right)^2 \right] = \text{Rs. } \left[200 \times \left(\frac{24}{25} \right)^2 \right]$

107. Population 3 years ago $= \dfrac{185220}{\left(1 + \dfrac{5}{100} \right)^3} = \left(185220 \times \frac{20}{21} \times \frac{20}{21} \times \frac{20}{21} \right)$

$$= 160000.$$

108. $P \times \left(1 - \frac{10}{100} \right)^3 = 8748 \Rightarrow P = \left(8748 \times \frac{10}{9} \times \frac{10}{9} \times \frac{10}{9} \right) = \text{Rs. } 12000.$

109. Required number $= 3000 \times \left(1 - \frac{10}{100} \right)^2 = 3000 \times \frac{9}{10} \times \frac{9}{10} = 2430.$

110. 10 crores $\times \left(1 + \frac{R}{100} \right)^3 = 13.31$ crores.

$$\therefore \left(1 + \frac{R}{100} \right)^3 = \frac{13.31 \text{ crores}}{10 \text{ crores}} = \frac{13.31}{10} = \frac{1331}{1000} = \left(\frac{11}{10} \right)^3.$$

So, $\left(1 + \frac{R}{100} \right) = \frac{11}{10}$ or $\frac{R}{100} = \left(\frac{11}{10} - 1 \right) = \frac{1}{10}$ or $R = 10.$

111. $72900 \left(1 + \frac{10}{100} \right)^n = 133100 \times \left(1 - \frac{10}{100} \right)^n$

$$\therefore \left(\frac{11}{10} \right)^n \times \left(\frac{10}{9} \right)^n = \frac{133100}{72900} = \frac{1331}{729}$$

$$\therefore \left(\frac{11}{9} \right)^n = \left(\frac{11}{9} \right)^3 \Rightarrow n = 3.$$

112. Let original population = 100.

Population after 3 years $= 100 \times \left(1 + \dfrac{3\frac{1}{2}}{100}\right)^3$

$$= 100 \times \frac{207}{200} \times \frac{207}{200} \times \frac{207}{200} = 110.87.$$

$\therefore$ Increase % = 10.8%.

113. Net growth on $1000 = (32 - 11) = 21$

Net growth on $100 = \left(\dfrac{21}{1000} \times 100\right) = 2.1\%.$

114. Let original price = Rs. x/kg. Reduced price $= \left(\dfrac{79}{100}x\right)$/kg.

$$\frac{100}{\dfrac{79x}{100}} - \frac{100}{x} = 10.5 \Rightarrow \frac{10000}{79x} - \frac{100}{x} = 10.5$$

$10000 - 7900 = 10.5 \times 79x \quad \text{or} \quad x = \dfrac{2100}{10.5 \times 79}$

$\therefore$ Reduced price = Rs. $\left(\dfrac{79}{100} \times \dfrac{2100}{10.5 \times 79}\right)$/kg = Rs. 2 per kg.

115. Basic rate = Rs. $\dfrac{20}{40}$ per hour.

Overtime rate = Rs. $\left(\dfrac{125}{100} \times \dfrac{20}{40}\right)$ per hour = Rs. $\dfrac{5}{8}$ per hr.

Let overtime hours $= x$.

Then, $\dfrac{5}{8}x = 5 \Rightarrow x = \dfrac{5 \times 8}{5} = 8$ hours.

So, he worked for $(40 + 8)$ hours = 48 hours.

116. Let $A = x$, $B = 2x$ and $C = 3x$.

Then, $2x + 3x = 6000 \Rightarrow x = 1200$.

$\therefore$ $A = 1200$ and $C = 3600$.

Required excess $= \left(\dfrac{2400}{1200} \times 100\right)\% = 200\%.$

117. $T = C + 400$. Now $6T + 6C = 4800$.

$\therefore$ $6(C + 400) + 6C = 4800$ or $C = 200$.

Thus, $C = 200$ & $T = (200 + 400) = 600$.

Required percentage $= \left(\dfrac{400}{600} \times 100\right)\% = 66\dfrac{2}{3}\%.$

118. Let side = 10 cm. Then, area = 100 cm^2.

New side = 125% of 10 = 12.5 cm. Area $= (12.5)^2 = 156.25$

$\therefore$ Increase percent = 56.25%.

119. Let $l = 10$m & $b = 10$m. Then, area = 100 m^2.

New length = 140% of 10 = 14 m.
New breadth = 130% of 10 = 13 m.

New area = (14×13) m^2 = 182 m^2.
Increase in area = 82%.

120. Let l = 10 m & b = 10 m. Then, area = 100 m^2.
New length = 120% of 10 = 12 m.
New breadth = 80% of 10 = 8 m.

New area = (12×8) m^2 = 96 m^2.
Decrease = 4%.

121. Let length = l and breadth = b.
Let the required decrease in breadth be x%.

Then, $\dfrac{160}{100} l \times \dfrac{(100-x)}{100} \times b = lb \Rightarrow 160(100-x) = 100 \times 100$

or $100 - x = \dfrac{10000}{160} = \dfrac{125}{2} \Rightarrow x = \left(100 - \dfrac{125}{2}\right) = 37\dfrac{1}{2}$.

122. Let, original radius be R. Then, area = πR^2.

New radius = 50% of $R = \dfrac{50}{100} R = \dfrac{R}{2}$.

New area = $\pi \times \left(\dfrac{R}{2}\right)^2 = \dfrac{\pi R^2}{4}$

Decrease = $\left(\pi R^2 - \dfrac{\pi R^2}{4}\right) = \dfrac{3\pi R^2}{4}$.

$\therefore$ Decrease % = $\left(\dfrac{3\pi R^2}{4} \times \dfrac{1}{\pi R^2} \times 100\right)$% = 75%.

123. Surface area = $4\pi R^2 = \dfrac{3}{R}\left(\dfrac{4}{3}\pi R^3\right) = \dfrac{3}{R} \times$ Volume

When $R = 10$, we have

$S = \dfrac{3}{10} V = \left(\dfrac{3}{10} \times 100\right)$% of V = 30% of V.

124. Let original radius = R, New radius = $\dfrac{150}{100} R = \dfrac{3}{2} R$.

Original Surface area = $4\pi R^2$

New surface area = $4\pi \left(\dfrac{3}{2} R\right)^2 = 9\pi R^2$.

$\therefore$ Increase = $\left(\dfrac{5\pi R^2}{4\pi R^2} \times 100\right)$% = 125%.

125. 40% of x + 50% of x + 20 = x

$$\Rightarrow \frac{40}{100}x + \frac{50}{100}x + 20 = x \quad \text{or} \quad x = 200.$$

126. Clearly, 20% were uncertain.

60% of $x - 20\%$ of $x = 720$

or 40% of $x = 720$ or $\frac{40}{100}x = 720$ or $x = \frac{720 \times 100}{40} = 1800.$

127. $P : A = 4000 \ \& \ Q : G - D = 500.$

Clearly, $D = 40\%$ of G or $G = \frac{100}{40}D = \frac{5}{2}D.$

$\therefore \ G - D = 500 \Rightarrow \frac{5}{2}D - D = 500$ or $D = \frac{1000}{3}.$

Thus, only Q is sufficient.

128. Let the original price be Rs. x.

$\therefore \ (100 - p)\%$ of $(100 + p)\%$ of $x = 1$

$\Rightarrow \dfrac{(100 - p)}{100} \times \dfrac{(100 + p)}{100} \times x = 1$

$\Rightarrow x = \dfrac{100 \times 100}{(100 - p)(100 + p)} = \dfrac{10000}{(10000 - p^2)}.$

---

11. Profit & Loss

Cost Price : *The price at which an article is purchased, is called its cost price, abbreviated as C.P.*

Selling Price : *The price at which an article is sold, is called its selling price, abbreviated as S.P.*

Profit or Gain =(S.P.) − (C.P.)

Loss = (C.P.) − (S.P.).

An Important Result : *Loss or gain is reckoned on C.P.*

FORMULAE :

(*i*) $Gain = (S.P.) - (C.P.)$

(*ii*) $Gain \% = \left(\dfrac{Gain \times 100}{C.P.} \right)$

(*iii*) $Loss = (C.P.) - (S.P.)$

(*iv*) $Loss \% = \left(\dfrac{Loss \times 100}{C.P.} \right)$

(*v*) $S.P. = \dfrac{(100 + Gain \%)}{100} \times C.P.$

(*vi*) $S.P. = \dfrac{(100 - Loss \%)}{100} \times C.P.$

(*vii*) $C.P. = \dfrac{100}{(100 + Gain \%)} \times S.P.$

(*viii*) $C.P. = \dfrac{100}{(100 - Loss \%)} \times S.P.$

(*ix*) If an article is sold at a gain of 35%, then S.P. = 135% of C.P.

(*x*) If an article is sold at a loss of 35%, then S.P. = 65% of C.P.

Solved Problems

Ex. 1. *A man buys an article for Rs. 27.50 and sells it for Rs. 28.60. Find his gain percent.*

Sol. C.P. = Rs. 27.50, S.P. = Rs. 28.60.

∴ Gain = Rs. (28.60 − 27.50) = Rs. 1.10.

∴ Gain % = $\left(\dfrac{1.10}{27.50} \times 100 \right) \% = 4\%.$

Ex. 2. *If a radio is purchased for Rs. 490 and sold for Rs. 465.50, find the loss per cent.*

Sol. C.P. = Rs. 490, S.P. = Rs. 465.50.

Loss = Rs. (490 − 465.50) = Rs. 24.50

∴ Loss % = $\left(\dfrac{24.50}{490} \times 100 \right) \% = 5\%.$

Ex. 3. *Find S.P., when :*
(i) C.P. = Rs. 56.25, gain = 20%
(ii) C.P. = Rs. 80.40, loss = 15%.

Sol. (i) S.P. = 120% of Rs. 56.25 = Rs. $\left(\dfrac{120}{100} \times 56.25 \right)$ = Rs. 67.50.

(ii) S.P. = 85% of Rs. 80.40 = Rs. $\left(\dfrac{85}{100} \times 80.40 \right)$ = Rs. 68.34.

Ex. 4. *Find C.P., when*
(i) S.P. = Rs. 40.60, gain = 16%
(ii) S.P. = Rs. 51.70, loss = 12%
Sol. (i) Let C.P. be x.

Then, 116% of $x = 40.60 \Leftrightarrow \dfrac{116}{100} x = 40.60$.

$\therefore\ x = \left(\dfrac{40.60 \times 100}{116} \right) = 35$.

$\therefore$ C.P. = Rs. 35.

(ii) Let C.P. be x.

Then, 88% of $x = 51.70 \Leftrightarrow \dfrac{88}{100} x = 51.70$.

$\therefore\ x = \left(\dfrac{51.70 \times 100}{88} \right) = 58.75$.

$\therefore$ C.P. = Rs. 58.75.

Ex. 5. *By selling a book for Rs. 115.20, a man loses 10%. At what price should he sell it to gain 5%?*

Sol. (**Short Cut Method**) : Let the new S.P. be Rs. x.

(100 – loss%) : (1st S.P.) = (100 + gain %) : (2nd S.P.)

or $\dfrac{(100 - 10)}{115.20} = \dfrac{100 + 5}{x}$ or $x = \left(\dfrac{105 \times 115.20}{90} \right) = 134.40$.

$\therefore$ New S.P. = Rs. 134.40.

Ex. 6. *A trader lost 20% by selling a watch for Rs. 1024. What percent shall he gain or lose by selling it for Rs. 1472?*

Sol. (**Short Cut Method**) : Let the gain be x%. Then,

80 : 1024 = (100 + x) : 1472   or $\dfrac{80}{1024} = \dfrac{100 + x}{1472}$

$\therefore\ 100 + x = \dfrac{80 \times 1472}{1024} = 115$. So, $x = 15\%$.

Ex. 7. *Ashok purchased a radio set and sold it to Shyam at a profit of 25% and Shyam sold it to Mohan at a loss of 10% and Mohan paid Rs. 675 for it. For how much did Ashok purchase it?*

Sol. (**Short Cut Method**) : Suppose Ashok purchased it for Rs. x.
Then, 90% of 125% of $x = 675$

$$\therefore \frac{90}{100} \times \frac{125}{100} \times x = 675 \Leftrightarrow x = \left(675 \times \frac{100}{125} \times \frac{100}{90}\right) = 600.$$

Ex. 8. *A man sold two houses for Rs. 675958 each. On one he gains 16% while on the other he loses 16%. How much does he gain or lose in the whole transaction ?*

Sol. (Short Cut Method) : In such a question, there is always a loss. The selling price is immaterial.

Formula : $\text{Loss}\% = \left(\dfrac{\text{Common loss \& gain }\%}{10}\right)^2.$

$$\therefore \text{ Loss }\% = \left(\frac{16}{10}\right)^2 \% = \left(\frac{64}{25}\right)\% = 2.56\%.$$

Ex. 9. *The original price of a T.V. set is Rs. 9000. The price is discounted by 20% and then raised by 10%. What is its new price ?*

Sol. New price = (110% of 80% of 9000)

$$= \text{Rs.} \left(\frac{110}{100} \times \frac{80}{100} \times 9000\right) = \text{Rs. } 7920.$$

Ex. 10. *The C.P. of 12 articles is equal to S.P. of 9 articles. Find the gain per cent.*

Sol. Let C.P. of each article be Re 1.

Then, C.P. of 9 articles = Rs. 9, S.P. of 9 articles = Rs. 12.

$$\therefore \text{ Gain }\% = \left(\frac{3}{9} \times 100\right)\% = 33\frac{1}{3}\%.$$

Ex. 11. *By selling 33 metres of cloth, one gains the selling price of 11 metres. Find the gain percent.*

Sol. (S.P. of 33 *m*) – (C.P. of 33*m*) = Gain = S.P. of 11 *m*.

$\therefore$ S.P. of 22 *m* = C.P. of 33 *m*.

Let C.P. of each metre be Re 1.

C.P. of 22*m* = Rs. 22, S.P. of 22 *m* = Rs. 33.

$$\therefore \text{ Gain }\% = \left(\frac{11}{22} \times 100\right)\% = 50\%.$$

Ex. 12. *Hari purchased 25 kg of wheat at Rs. 4 per kg and 35 kg of wheat at Rs. 4.50 per kg. He sold the mixture at Rs. 4.25 per kg. Find his gain or loss.*

Sol. Total C.P. = Rs. $(25 \times 4 + 35 \times 4.50)$ = Rs. 257.50.

Total S.P. = Rs. (60×4.25) = Rs. 255.

$\therefore$ Loss = Rs. $(257.50 - 255)$ = Rs. 2.50.

Ex. 13. *A man sells an article at a profit of 25%. If he had bought it at 20% less and sold it for Rs. 10.50 less, he would have gained 30%. Find the cost price of the article.*

Sol. (Short Cut Method) : Let the C.P. be Rs. *x*.

1st S.P. $= 125\%$ of Rs. $x = \dfrac{125}{100}x = \dfrac{5x}{4}$.

2nd C.P. $= 80\%$ of $x = \left(\dfrac{80}{100}x\right) = \dfrac{4x}{5}$.

2nd S.P. $= 130\%$ of $\dfrac{4x}{5} = \dfrac{130}{100} \times \dfrac{4x}{5} = \dfrac{26x}{25}$.

$\therefore \dfrac{5x}{4} - \dfrac{26x}{25} = 10.50$ or $\dfrac{21x}{100} = 10.50$

or $x = \dfrac{10.50 \times 100}{21} = 50$.

Hence, C.P. = Rs. 50.

Ex. 14. *A reduction of 20% in the price of sugar enables a purchaser to obtain 2.5 kg more for Rs. 160. Find the original rate and the reduced price per kg.*

Sol. Let original rate = Rs. x per kg.

New rate $= 80\%$ of $x =$ Rs. $\left(\dfrac{80}{100}x\right) =$ Rs. $\dfrac{4x}{5}$.

Original quantity for Rs. $160 = \dfrac{160}{x}$.

New quantity $= \left(160 \times \dfrac{5}{4x}\right) = \dfrac{200}{x}$.

$\therefore \dfrac{200}{x} - \dfrac{160}{x} = 2.5$ or $\dfrac{40}{x} = 2.5$ or $x = \dfrac{40}{2.5} = 16$.

$\therefore$ Original rate = Rs.16 per kg.

Reduced rate $= 80\%$ of Rs 16 = Rs. 12.80 per kg.

Ex. 15. *A grocer purchased 80 kg of rice at Rs. 13.50 per kg and mixed it with 120 kg rice at Rs. 16 per kg. At what rate per kg should he sell the mixture to gain 16% ?*

Sol. C.P. of 200 kg of mix. = Rs. $(80 \times 13.50 + 120 \times 16)$ = Rs. 3000.

S.P. $= 116\%$ of Rs. 3000 = Rs. $\left(\dfrac{116}{100} \times 3000\right) =$ Rs. 3480.

Rate of S.P. of the mixture = Rs. $\left(\dfrac{3480}{200}\right)$ per kg = Rs. 17.40 per kg.

Ex. 16. *A vendor sells 10 toffees for a rupee, gaining thereby 20%. How many did he buy for a rupee ?*

Sol. S.P. of 10 toffees = Re 1, Gain = 20%.

$\therefore$ C.P. of 10 toffees = Rs. $\left(\dfrac{100}{120} \times 1\right) =$ Re. $\dfrac{5}{6}$.

Re $\dfrac{5}{6}$ is the C.P. of 10

Re 1 is the C.P. of $\left(10 \times \dfrac{6}{5}\right) = 12$.

Thus, he bought 12 toffees for a rupee.

Ex. 17. *A vendor bought lemons at 6 for a rupee. How many for a rupee must he sell to gain 20% ?*

Sol. C.P. of 6 lemons = Re 1, Gain = 20%.

S.P. of 6 lemons = Rs. $\left(\dfrac{120}{100} \times 1\right) = $ Rs. $\dfrac{6}{5}$.

Rs. $\dfrac{6}{5}$ is the S.P. of 6.

Re 1 is the S.P. of $\left(6 \times \dfrac{5}{6}\right) = 5$.

So, he must sell 5 for a rupee.

Ex. 18. *A vendor bought a number of bananas at 6 for 5 rupees and sold at 4 for 3 rupees. Find his gain percent.*

Sol. Suppose, number bought = l.c.m. of 6, 5, 4, 3 = 60.

$\therefore$ C.P. = Rs. $\left(\dfrac{5}{6} \times 60\right) = $ Rs. 50.

S.P. = Rs. $\left(\dfrac{3}{4} \times 60\right) = $ Rs. 45.

$\therefore$ Loss % = $\left(\dfrac{5}{50} \times 100\right)$ % = 10%.

Ex. 19. *A dishonest dealer professes to sell his goods at cost price but uses a weight of 960 gms. for a kg weight. Find his gain per cent.*

Sol. (Short Cut Method) :

Formula : Gain % = $\left[\dfrac{\text{Error}}{(\text{True Value}) - (\text{Error})} \times 100\right]$ %.

$\therefore$ Gain % = $\left(\dfrac{40}{960} \times 100\right)$ % = $4\dfrac{1}{6}$ %.

Ex. 20. *Find the single discount equivalent to a series discount of 20%, 10% and 5%.*

Sol. (Short cut Method) : Let marked price be Rs. 100.

Then, Net S.P. = 95% of 90% of 80% of 100

$$= \left(\dfrac{95}{100} \times \dfrac{90}{100} \times \dfrac{80}{100} \times 100\right) = 68.40.$$

$\therefore$ Required discount = (100 − 68.40)% = 31.6%.

Ex. 21. *If a commission of 10% is given on the marked price of an article, the gain is 25%. Find the gain percent, if the commission is increased to 20%.*

Sol. Let marked price = Rs. 100. Then, commission = Rs. 10.

$\therefore$ S.P. = Rs. (100 − 10) = Rs. 90.

But, gain = 25%.

∴ C.P. = Rs. $\left(\dfrac{100}{125} \times 90\right)$ = Rs. 72.

New commission = Rs. 20.

New S.P. = Rs. (100 – 20) = Rs. 80.

∴ Gain% = $\left(\dfrac{8}{72} \times 100\right)\% = 11\dfrac{1}{9}\%$.

Ex. 22. *A trader marks his goods 20% above the cost price and allows a discount of 15% on it. Find his gain per cent.*

Sol. Let C.P. = Rs. 100. Then, marked price = Rs. 120.

∴ S.P. = 85% of Rs. 120 = Rs. 102.

∴ Gain % = 2%.

Ex. 23. *A shopkeeper allows a discount of 10% on the marked price. How much above cost price must he mark his goods to gain 8% ?*

Sol. Let C.P. = Rs. 100. Then, S.P. = Rs. 108.

Let, marked price be Rs. x.

90% of $x = 108 \Rightarrow x = \left(108 \times \dfrac{100}{90}\right) = 120$.

∴ Marked price = Rs. 120.

Ex. 24. *After getting two successive discounts, a shirt with a list price of Rs. 150 is available at Rs. 105. If the second discount is 12.5%, find the first discount.*

Sol. Let the first discount be $x\%$.

Then, 87.5% of $(100 - x)$ % of 150 = 105

or $\dfrac{87.5}{100} \times \dfrac{100-x}{100} \times 150 = 105$ or $100 - x = \left(\dfrac{105 \times 100 \times 100}{150 \times 87.5}\right) = 80$

∴ $x = (100 - 80) = 20\%$.

EXERCISE 11

1. Cost of 3 cricket balls = cost of 2 pairs of leg pads.
    Cost of 3 pairs of leg pads = cost of 2 pairs of gloves.
    Cost of 3 pairs of gloves = cost of 2 cricket bats.
    If a cricket bat costs Rs 54, what is the cost of a cricket ball ?
    (*a*) Rs 12   (*b*) Rs 14   (*c*) Rs 16   (*d*) Rs 18

    (Hotel Management, 1992)

2. If, by selling an article for Rs 100, a man gains Rs 15, then his gain percent is :

    (*a*) 15 %   (*b*) $12\dfrac{2}{3}$ %   (*c*) $17\dfrac{11}{17}$ %   (*d*) $17\dfrac{1}{4}$ %

3. What is the loss percent if a man loses Rs 10 on selling an article for Rs 100 ?

(a) $9\frac{1}{11}\%$ (b) 10 %   (c) $11\frac{1}{9}\%$ (d) None

4. A shopkeeper sold an article for Rs 2564.36. Approximately what was his profit percent if the cost price of the article was Rs 2400 ?
   (a) 7   (b) 8   (c) 12   (d) 60
   (Bank P.O., 1993)

5. When a commodity is sold for Rs 34.80, there is a loss of 25%. What is the cost price of the commodity ?   **(Bank P.O., 1989)**
   (a) Rs 46.40   (b) Rs 26.10   (c) Rs 43   (d) Rs 43.20

6. A man sold an article for Rs 247.50, thereby gaining $12\frac{1}{2}\%$. The cost of the article was :
   (a) Rs 225   (b) Rs 224   (c) Rs 220   (d) Rs 210

7. A retailer buys a radio for Rs 225. His overhead expenses are Rs 15. He sellls the radio for Rs 300. The profit percent of the retailer is :
   (a) 10   (b) 25   (c) 50   (d) 52
   (N.D.A.1987)

8. A shopkeeper bought an article for Rs 319.60. Approximately, at what price should he sell the article to make 25% profit ?   **(Bank P.O., 1994)**
   (a) Rs 400   (b) Rs 450   (c) Rs 500   (d) Rs 600

9. If the selling price of an article is $\frac{4}{3}$ times its cost price, the profit percent is :   **(Assistant Grade 1992)**
   (a) $33\frac{1}{3}$ (b) $25\frac{1}{4}$ (c) $20\frac{1}{2}$ (d) $20\frac{1}{3}$

10. There would be 10% loss if a toy is sold at Rs 10.80 per piece. At what price should it be sold to earn a profit of 20% ?   **(Bank P.O., 1991)**
    (a) Rs 12   (b) Rs 12.96   (c) Rs 14.40   (d) None

11. By selling an article for Rs 19.50, a dealer makes a profit of 30%. By how much should he increase his selling price so as to make a profit of 40% ?
    (a) Rs 1.50   (b) Rs 1.75   (c) Rs 2   (d) Rs 3

12. Rahim buys mangoes at the rate of 3 kg for Rs 21 and sells them at 5 kg for Rs 50. To earn Rs 102 as profit, he must sell :
    (a) 26 kg   (b) 32 kg   (c) 34 kg   (d) 56 kg
    (Assistant Grade, 1993)

13. If books bought at prices ranging from Rs 200 to Rs 350 are sold at prices ranging from Rs 300 to Rs 425, what is the greatest possible profit that might be made in selling eight books ?   **(S.B.I.P.O., 1988)**
    (a) Rs 400   (b) Rs 600
    (c) Cannot be determined   (d) None of these

14. The cost price of 20 articles is the same as selling price of 15 articles. The profit percent in the transaction is :   **(C.B.I., 1993)**

(a) 25   (b) 30   (c) 33 $\frac{1}{3}$ (d) 50

15. A man sells 320 mangoes at the cost price of 400 mangoes. His gain percent is
    (a) 10 %   (b) 15 %   (c) 20 %   (d) 25 %

16. If the cost price of 12 tables is equal to the selling price of 16 tables, the loss percent is :   **(Bank P.O., 1992)**
    (a) 15 %   (b) 20 %   (c) 25 %   (d) 30 %

17. If the selling price of 18 articles is equal to the C.P. of 21 articles, the loss or gain percent is :

    (a) $16\frac{2}{3}$ % gain (b) $14\frac{2}{7}$ % gain (c) $16\frac{2}{3}$ % loss (d) $14\frac{2}{7}$ % loss

18. A man sold 250 chairs and had a gain equal to selling price of 50 chairs. His profit percent is :   **(Teacher's Exam, 1991)**
    (a) 5 %   (b) 10 %   (c) 25 %   (d) 50 %

19. If by selling 110 mangoes, the C.P. of 120 mangoes is realised, the gain percent is :   **(Income Tax 1992)**

    (a) $11\frac{1}{9}$ %   (b) $9\frac{1}{9}$ %   (c) $10\frac{10}{11}$ %   (d) $9\frac{1}{11}$ %

20. A vendor loses the S.P. of 4 oranges on selling 36 oranges. His loss percent is :

    (a) $12\frac{1}{2}$ %   (b) $11\frac{1}{9}$ %   (c) 10 %   (d) None of these

21. By selling a pen for Rs 15, a man loses one-sixteenth of what it costs him. The cost price of the pen is :
    (a) Rs 18   (b) Rs 20   (c) Rs 21   (d) Rs 16

22. By selling an article, Sheetal earned a profit equal to $\frac{1}{4}$ th of the price he bought it. If he sold it for Rs 375, what was the cost price ?
    (a) Rs 281.75   (b) Rs 300   (c) Rs 312.50   (d) Rs 350

23. A shopkeeper, on selling a pen for Rs 10, loses $\frac{1}{11}$ of what it costs him. His cost price is :
    (a) Rs 9   (b) Rs 10   (c) Rs 11   (d) Rs 12

24. A fruit seller purchases oranges at the rate of 3 for Rs 5 and sells them at 2 for Rs 4. His profit in the transaction is :   **(Asstt. Grade, 1994)**
    (a) 10 %   (b) 15 %   (c) 20 %   (d) 25 %

25. If I purchased 11 books for Rs 10 and sold all the books at the rate of 10 books for Rs 11, the profit percent is :
    (a) 10 %   (b) 11 %   (c) 21 %   (d) 100 %

26. A man bought a number of oranges at 3 for a rupee and an equal number at 2 for a rupee. At what price per dozen should he sell them to make a profit of 20 % ?   **(U.D.C., 1993)**

(a) Rs 4   (b) Rs 5   (c) Rs 6   (d) Rs 7

27. A man buys eggs at 2 for Re 1 and an equal number at 3 for Rs 2 and sells the whole at 5 for Rs 3. His gain or loss percent is :

(a) $2\frac{2}{7}$ % loss   (b) $3\frac{6}{7}$ % gain   (c) $3\frac{2}{7}$ % loss   (d) $2\frac{6}{7}$ % gain

28. A man buys oranges at Rs 5 a dozen and an equal number at Rs 4 a dozen. He sells them at Rs 5.50 a dozen and makes a profit of Rs 50. How many oranges does he buy ?   **(RRB Exam, 1990)**

(a) 30 dozens   (b) 40 dozens   (c) 50 dozens   (d) 60 dozens

29. Ajay bought 15 kg of dal at the rate of Rs 14.50 per kg and 10 kg at the rate of Rs 13 per kg. He mixed the two and sold the mixture at the rate of Rs 15 per kg. What was his total gain in this transaction ?

(a) Rs 1.10   (b) Rs 16.50   (c) Rs 11   (d) Rs 27.50

(Bank P.O., 1993)

30. A producer of tea blends two varieties of tea from two tea gardens one costing Rs 18 per kg and another Rs 20 per kg in the ratio 5 : 3. If he sells the blended variety at Rs 21 per kg, then his gain percent is :

(a) 10   .   (b) 12   (c) 19   (d) 22

(C.B.I., 1993)

31. Gopal purchased 35 kg of rice at the rate of Rs 9.50 per kg and 30 kg at the rate of Rs 10.50 per kg. He mixed the two. Approximately, at what price per kg should he sell the mixture to make 35 % profit in the transaction ?   **(Bank P.O., 1994)**

(a) Rs 12   (b) Rs 12.50   (c) Rs 13   (d) Rs 13.50

32. Pure ghee costs Rs 100 per kg. After adulterating it with vegetable oil costing Rs 50 per kg, a shopkeeper sells the mixture at the rate of Rs 96 per kg, thereby making a profit of 20 %. In what ratio does he mix the two ?

(a) 1 : 2   (b) 3 : 2   (c) 3 : 1   (d) None of these

33. By mixing two qualities of pulses in the ratio 2 : 3 and selling the mixture at the rate of Rs 22 per kilogram, a shopkeeper makes a profit of 10 %. If the cost of the smaller quantity be Rs 14 per kg, the cost per kg of the larger quantity is :   **(Hotel Management, 1993)**

(a) Rs 23   (b) Rs 24   (c) Rs 25   (d) None of these

34. A dealer professing to sell his goods at cost price, uses a 900 gm weight for a kilogram. His gain percent is :

(a) 9   (b) 10   (c) 11   (d) $11\frac{1}{9}$

35. A dishonest dealer professes to sell his goods at cost price. But he uses a false weight and thus gains $6\frac{18}{47}$ %. For a kg, he uses a weight of :

(a) 953 gms   (b) 940 gms   (c) 960 gms   (d) 947 gms

36. A grain dealer cheats to the extent of 10 % while buying as well as selling, by using false weights. His total gain is :

    (a) 10 %   (b) 20 %   (c) $22\frac{2}{9}$ %   (d) 21 %

37. Toffees are bought at the rate of 3 for a rupee. To gain 50 %, they must be sold at :

    (a) 2 for a rupee   (b) 1 for a rupee
    (c) 4 for a rupee   (d) 5 for a rupee

38. By selling toffees at 20 for a rupee, a man loses 4 %. To gain 20 %, for one rupee, he must sell

    (a) 16 toffees   (b) 20 toffees
    (c) 24 toffees   (d) 25 toffees

39. By selling 45 lemons for Rs 40, a man loses 20 %. How many should he sell for Rs 24 to gain 20 % in the transaction ?

    (a) 16   (b) 18   (c) 20   (d) 22

    (Asstt. Grade, 1992)

40. Vikas bought paper sheets for Rs 7200 and spent Rs 200 on transport. Paying Rs 600, he had 330 boxes made, which he sold at Rs 28 each. His profit percentage is :   **(Bank P.O., 1991)**

    (a) 15.5   (b) 40   (c) 60   (d) None of these

41. Bhajan Singh purchased 120 reams of paper at Rs 80 per ream. He spent Rs 280 on transportation, paid octroi at the rate of 40 paise per ream and paid Rs 72 to the coolie. If he wants to have a gain of 8 %, what must be the selling price per ream ?   **(Bank P.O., 1988)**

    (a) Rs 90   (b) Rs 87.48   (c) Rs. 89   (d) Rs 86

42. A man gains 10 % by selling a certain article for a certain price. If he sells it at double the price, the profit made is :

    (a) 20 %   (b) 120 %   (c) 100 %   (d) 140 %

43. A person bought 20 litres of milk at the rate of Rs 8 per litre. He got it churned after spending Rs 10 and got 5 kg of cream and 20 litres of toned milk. If he sold the cream at Rs. 30 per kg and toned milk at Rs 4 per litre, his profit in the transaction is :   **(Teacher's Exam, 1991)**

    (a) 25 %   (b) 35.3 %   (c) 37.5 %   (d) 42.5 %

44. A sells a bicycle to B at a profit of 20 % and B sells it to C at a profit of 25 %. If C pays Rs 1500, what did A pay for it ?

    (a) Rs 825   (b) Rs 1000   (c) Rs 1100   (d) Rs 1125

    (Assistant Grade, 1994)

45. A bought a ratio set and spent Rs 110 on its repairs. He then sold it to B at 20 % profit, B sold it to C at a loss of 10 % and C sold it for Rs 1188 at a profit of 10 %. What is the amount for which A bought the radio set ?   **(Hotel Management, 1992)**

    (a) Rs 850   (b) Rs 890   (c) Rs 930   (d) Rs 950

46. If the manufacturer gains 10 %, the wholesale dealer 15 % and the retailer 25 %, then the cost of production of a table, the retail price of which is Rs 1265 was : **(C.B.I., 1992)**

(*a*) Rs 632.50　　(*b*) Rs 800　　(*c*) Rs 814　　(*d*) Rs 834.34

47. Kanak owns a plot worth Rs. 10000. He sells it to Raman at 10% profit Raman sells the plot back to Kanak at a loss of 10%. In the whole transaction, Kanak gets

(*a*) no profit no loss　　　　　　(*b*) profit of Rs. 2000
(*c*) profit of Rs. 1100　　　　　(*d*) profit of Rs. 1000

48. Two mixers and one T.V. cost Rs. 7000, while two T.V.s and a mixer cost Rs. 9800. The value of one T.V. is : **(S.B.I.P.O., 1987)**

(*a*) Rs. 2800　　(*b*) Rs. 2100　　(*c*) Rs.4200　　(*d*) Rs. 8400

49. A dealer sold two of his cattle for Rs. 500 each. On one of them he lost 10% and on the other, he gained 10%. His gain or loss percent in the entire transaction was : **(U.D.C., 1993)**

(*a*) 10% loss　　　　　　　　(*b*) 1% gain
(*c*) 1% loss　　　　　　　　(*d*) Neither loss nor gain

50. A man sells two houses at the rate of Rs. 1.995 lakhs each. On one he gains 5% and on the other, he loses 5%. His gain or loss percent in the whole transaction is : **(Income Tax, 1988)**

(*a*) 0.25% loss　　(*b*) 0.25% gain　(*c*) 2.5% loss　(*d*) 25% loss

51. A man sells two commodities for Rs. 4000 each, neither losing nor gaining in the deal. If he sold one commodity at a gain of 25%, the other commodity is sold at a loss of :

(*a*) $16\frac{2}{3}$%　　(*b*) $18\frac{2}{9}$%　　(*c*) 25%　　(*d*) None

52. A horse and a cow were sold for Rs. 12000 each. The horse was sold at a loss of 20% and the cow at a gain of 20%. The entire transaction resulted in : **(C.B.I., 1991)**

(*a*) no loss or gain　　　　　　(*b*) loss of Rs. 1000
(*c*) gain of Rs. 1000　　　　　(*d*) gain of Rs. 2000

53. A person earns 15% on an investment but loses 10% on another investment. If the ratio of the two investments be 3 : 5, what is the gain or loss on the two investments taken together ?

(*a*) $6\frac{1}{4}$ % loss　(*b*) $13\frac{1}{8}$ % gain (*c*) $13\frac{1}{8}$ % loss (*d*) None of these

54. The manufacturer of a certain item can sell all he can produce at the selling price of Rs. 60 each. If costs him Rs. 40 in materials and labour to produce each item and he has overhead expenses of Rs. 3000 per week in order to operate the plant. The number of units he should produce and sell in order to make a profit of at least Rs. 1000 per week, is :

    (*a*) 200   (*b*) 250   (*c*) 300   (*d*) 400

55. Monika purchased a pressure cooker at $\frac{9}{10}$th of its selling price and sold it at 8% more than its S.P. Her gain is
    (*a*) 20%   (*b*) 18%   (*c*) 10%   (*d*) 8%

56. An article is sold at a certain price. By selling it at $\frac{2}{3}$ of that price one loses 10%. The gain percent at original price is :
    (*a*) 20%   (*b*) $33\frac{1}{3}$%   (*c*) 35%   (*d*) 40%

57. The selling price of an article is Rs. 39. If its cost price is numerically equal to its profit percent, then its cost price (in Rs.) is :
    (*a*) 25   (*b*) 30   (*c*) 35   (*d*) 37

58. A grocer sells rice at a profit of 10% and uses weights which are 20% less than the market weight. The total gain earned by him will be :
    (*a*) 30%   (*b*) 35%   (*c*) 37.5%   (*d*) None of these

59. A dealer sold three-fourth of his articles at a gain of 20% and the remaining at C.P. The gain earned by him in the whole transaction is :
    (*a*) 25%   (*b*) 20%   (*c*) 15%   (*d*) 10%

60. A man purchased sugar worth Rs. 400. He sold (3/4) th at a loss of 10% and the remainder at a gain of 10%. On the whole, he gets
    (*a*) a loss of 5%   (*b*) a gain of $5\frac{1}{2}$%
    (*c*) a loss of $5\frac{1}{19}$%   (*d*) a loss of $5\frac{5}{19}$%

61. Two-third of a consignment was sold at a profit of 5% and the remainder at a loss of 2%. If the total profit was Rs. 400, the value of the consignment (in rupees) was :
    (*a*) 20000   (*b*) 15000   (*c*) 12000   (*d*) 10000

62. Vivek purchased 120 tables at a price of Rs. 110 per table. He sold 30 tables at a profit of Rs. 12 per table and 75 tables at a profit of Rs. 14 per table. The remaining tables were sold at a loss of Rs. 7 per table. What is the average profit per table ?
    (*a*) Rs. 12.875   (*b*) Rs. 10.04   (*c*) Rs. 10.875   (*d*) Rs. 12.80

63. Hemant sold 10 sarees for a total profit of Rs. 460 and 12 sarees for a total profit of Rs. 144. At what profit per saree should he sell the remaining 20 sarees so that he gets an average profit of Rs. 18 per saree ?
    (*a*) Rs. 7.40   (*b*) Rs. 7.60   (*c*) Rs. 7.80   (*d*) Rs. 8.00

64. A fruitseller has 24 kg of apples. He sells a part of these at 20% gain and the balance at a loss of 5%. If on the whole he earns a profit of 10%, the amount of apples sold at a loss is :
    (*a*) 6 kg   (*b*) 4.6 kg   (*c*) 9.6 kg   (*d*) 11.4 kg

65. The C.P. of two watches taken together is Rs. 840. If by selling one at a profit of 16% and the other at a loss of 12%, there is no loss or gain in the whole transaction, then the C.P. of the two watches are respectively
    (*a*) Rs. 360, Rs. 480   (*b*) Rs. 480, Rs. 360
    (*c*) Rs. 380, Rs. 460   (*d*) Rs. 400, Rs. 440

66. The C.P. of an article is 40% of the S.P. The percent that the S.P. is of C.P. is :   **(C.B.I., 1990)**
    (*a*) 250   (*b*) 240   (*c*) 60   (*d*) 40

67. A machine is sold at a profit of 10%. Had it been sold for Rs. 80 less, there would have been a loss of 10%. The C.P. of the machine is :
    (*a*) Rs. 350   (*b*) Rs. 400   (*c*) Rs. 450   (*d*) Rs. 520

68. If an article is sold at 5% gain instead of 5% loss, the seller gets Rs. 6.72 more. The C.P. of the article is :   **(C.B.I., 1992)**
    (*a*) Rs. 67.20   (*b*) Rs. 120   (*c*) Rs. 134.40 (*d*) Rs. 240

69. If by selling an article there would have been a loss of $2\frac{1}{2}$% and by selling it at Rs 6 more than the earlier S.P., there would have been a profit of 5 %. Then the C.P. of the article is :
    (*a*) Rs 78   (*b*) Rs 80   (*c*) Rs 82   (*d*) Rs 84

70. A person bought an article and sold it at a loss of 10 %. If he had bought it for 20% less and sold it for Rs 55 more, he would have had a profit of 40%. The C.P. of the article is :
    (*a*) Rs 200   (*b*) Rs 225   (*c*) Rs 250   (*d*) None of these

71. A man bought an article and sold it at a gain of 5 %. If he had bought it at 5% less and sold it for Re 1 less, he would have made a profit of 10%. The C.P. of the article was :   **(Income Tax, 1989)**
    (*a*) Rs 100   (*b*) Rs 150   (*c*) Rs 200   (*d*) Rs 500

72. Kishan bought a certain quantity of rice at the rate of Rs 150 per quintal and 10% of the rice was spoiled. At what price should he sell the remainder to gain 20% of his outlay ?
    (*a*) Rs 190 per quintal   (*b*) Rs 200 per quintal
    (*c*) Rs 210 per quintal   (*d*) Rs 215 per quintal

73. A reduction of 25% in the price of eggs will enable one to buy 4 dozen more eggs for Rs 96. What is the price per dozen ?   **(C.B.I., 1992)**
    (*a*) Rs 6   (*b*) Rs 8   (*c*) Rs 8.50   (*d*) Rs 9

74. An article when sold at a gain of 5% yields Rs 15 more than when sold at a loss of 5%. What is the C.P. ?   **(Assistant Grade, 1992)**
    (*a*) Rs 64   (*b*) Rs 80   (*c*) Rs 150   (*d*) Rs 200

75. Raghu bought 4 dozen oranges at Rs 12 per dozen and 2 dozen oranges at Rs 16 per dozen. He sold them all to earn 20% profit. At what price per dozen did he sell the oranges ?   **(Bank P.O. 1991)**

    (a) Rs 14.40   (b) Rs 16   (c) Rs 16.80   (d) Rs 19.20

76. Nandlal purchased 20 dozen notebooks at Rs 48 per dozen. He sold 8 dozen at 10% profit and the remaining 12 dozen with 20% profit. What is his profit percentage in this transaction ?   **(Bank P.O., 1993)**

    (a) 15   (b) 16   (c) 7.68   (d) 19.2

77. Profit after selling a commodity for Rs 425 is the same as the loss after selling it for Rs 355. What is the cost of the commodity ?

    (a) Rs 385   (b) Rs 390   (c) Rs 395   (d) Rs 400

78. An article when sold for Rs 840 earns a profit which is double the amount of loss when the same article is sold for Rs 600. What is the C.P. of the article ?   **(Bank P.O., 1993)**

    (a) Rs 500   (b) Rs 680   (c) Rs 720   (d) Data inadequate

79. The profit earned by selling an article for Rs 900 is double the loss incurred when the same article is sold for Rs 450. At what price should the article be sold to make 25% profit ?   **(Bank P.O., 1994)**

    (a) Rs 600   (b) Rs 750   (c) Rs 800   (d) Data inadequate

80. The percent profit made when a article is sold for Rs 78 is twice as much as when it is sold for Rs 69. What is the cost price of the article ?

    (a) Rs 51   (b) Rs 55.50   (c) Rs 60   (d) None

81. Profit earned by selling an article for Rs 1060 is 20% more than the loss incurred by selling the article for Rs 950. At what price should the article be sold to earn 20% profit ?   **(Bank P.O. 1992)**

    (a) Rs 980   (b) Rs 1080   (c) Rs 1800   (d) None

82. A man sold an article for Rs 75 and lost something. Had he sold it for Rs 96, his gain would have been double the former loss. The C.P. of the article is :

    (a) Rs 81   (b) Rs 82   (c) Rs 83   (d) Rs 85.50

83. A dealer sold an article at a loss of $2\frac{1}{2}$ %. Had he sold it for Rs 100 more, he would have gained $7\frac{1}{2}$ %. To gain $12\frac{1}{2}$ %, he should sell it for :

    (a) Rs 850   (b) Rs 925   (c) Rs 1080   (d) Rs 1125

84. A single discount equivalent to a discount series of 40% and 20% is :

    (a) 50 %   (b) 52 %   (c) 55 %   (d) 60 %

                                    (Income Tax, 1988)

85. A single discount equivalent to a discount series of 30%, 20% and 10% is :   **(Assistant Grade, 1994)**

    (a) 50 %   (b) 49.6 %   (c) 49.4 %   (d) 51 %

86. Successive discounts of x % and y % are equivalent to a single discount of

    (a) $(x+y)$ %   (b) $\left(x-y-\dfrac{xy}{100}\right)$ %

(c) $\left(x + y - \dfrac{xy}{100}\right)\%$ (d) $\left(x + y + \dfrac{xy}{100}\right)\%$

87. A table is offered for Rs 300 with 20% and 10% off. If in addition, a discount of 5% is offered on cash payment, then the cash price of the table is :   **(C.B.I., 1993)**

(a) Rs 240   (b) Rs 216   (c) Rs 210   (d) Rs 205.20

88. On a Rs 10000 payment order, a person has a choice between 3 successive discounts of 10%, 10% and 30% and 3 successive discounts of 40%, 5% and 5%. By choosing the better offer, he can save :

(a) Rs 200   (b) Rs 255   (c) Rs 400   (d) Rs 433

89. The marked price of a fan is Rs 620. Due to off season, a 15% discount is allowed. The S.P. of the fan is :   **(Clerk's Grade, 1993)**

(a) Rs 427   (b) Rs 527   (c) Rs 537   (d) Rs 547

90. A bag marked at Rs 80 is sold for Rs 68. The rate of discount is :

(a) 20 %   (b) $17\dfrac{11}{17}\%$ (c) 15 %   (d) 12 %

91. A tradesman marks his goods 30% above the C.P. If he allows a discount of $6\dfrac{1}{4}\%$, then his gain percent is :

(a) $23\dfrac{3}{4}\%$ (b) 22 %   (c) $21\dfrac{7}{8}\%$ (d) None

92. The difference between a discount of 40% on Rs 500 and two successive discounts of 36% and 4% on the same amount is :   **(C.B.I., 1990)**

(a) Nil   (b) Rs 2   (c) Rs 7.20   (d) Rs 1.93

93. At what percentage above the C.P. must an article be marked so as to gain 33% after allowing a customer a discount of 5% ?

(a) 38 %   (b) 40 %   (c) 43 %   (d) 48 %

94. A dealer marks his goods 20% above C.P. He then allows some discount on it & makes a profit of 8%. The rate of discount is :

(a) 4 %   (b) 6 %   (c) 10 %   (d) 12 %

                                               (Assistant Grade, 1992)

95. Rajesh buys an article with 25% discount on its marked price. He makes a profit of 10% by selling it at Rs 660. The marked price is :

(a) Rs 600   (b) Rs 685   (c) Rs 700   (d) Rs 800

                                               (Bank P.O., 1991)

96. What price should a shopkeeper mark on an article, costing him Rs 153, to gain 20% after allowing a discount of 15% ?

(a) Rs 224   (b) Rs 216   (c) Rs 184   (d) Rs 162

                              (I. Tax & Central Excise, 1992)

97. A video cassette is listed at Rs 150, with a discount of 20%. What additional discount must be offered to bring the net price to Rs 108 ?

(a) 15%   (b) $12\dfrac{1}{2}\%$ (c) 10%   (d) 8%

98. If the S.P. of Rs 24 results in a 20% discount on list price, what S.P. would result in a 30% discount on list price ?

   (*a*) Rs 27   (*b*) Rs 21   (*c*) Rs 20   (*d*) Rs 9

                                                        (Assistant Grade, 1994)

99. A house was sold for Rs y by giving a discount of x %. Then, its list price is :

   (*a*) $\dfrac{100y}{1-(x/100)}$ (*b*) $\dfrac{100y}{100-x}$ (*c*) $\dfrac{100y}{1-x}$ (*d*) None of these

100. A trader allows two successive discounts of 20% and 10%. If he sells an article for Rs 108, then the marked price of the article is :

   (*a*) Rs 150   (*b*) Rs 148   (*c*) Rs 142   (*d*) Rs 140

101. A customer purchased an office bag with a price tag of Rs 600 in a sale where 25% discount was being offered on the tag price. The customer was given a further discount of 10%. The final amount paid by the customer was :   **(Bank P.O., 1993)**

   (*a*) Rs 565   (*b*) Rs 540   (*c*) Rs 405   (*d*) Rs 390

102. A shopkeeper earns a profit of 12% on selling a book at 10% discount on the printed price. The ratio of the cost price to the printed price of the book is :   **(G.I.C.A.A.O, 1988)**

   (*a*) 50 : 61   (*b*) 45 : 56   (*c*) 99 : 125   (*d*) 55 : 69

103. A retailer buys 30 articles from a wholesaler at the price of 27. If he sells this at their marked price, the gain percent in the transaction is :

   (*a*) $9\dfrac{1}{11}$ %   (*b*) 10 %   (*c*) $11\dfrac{1}{9}$ %   (*d*) $16\dfrac{2}{3}$ %

                                                        (Teacher's Exam, 1991)

104. Pankaj bought a bag with 20% discount on the original price. He got a profit of Rs 50,by selling it at a price 150% of the price at which he bought. What was the original price of the bag ?   **(Bank P.O., 1993)**

   (*a*) Rs 125   (*b*) Rs 150   (*c*) Rs 175   (*d*) Rs 200

105. Anil bought a T.V. with 20% discount on the labelled price. Had he bought it with 25% discount, he would have saved Rs 500. At what price did he buy the T.V. ?   **(Bank P.O., 1990)**

   (*a*) Rs 16000   (*b*) Rs 12000   (*c*) Rs 10000   (*d*) Rs 5000

106. A retailer buys a sewing machine at a discount of 15% and sells it for Rs 1955. Thus, he makes a profit of 15%. The discount is :

   (*a*) Rs 300   (*b*) Rs 290   (*c*) Rs 275   (*d*) Rs 270

                                                        (L.I.C.A.A.O., 1988)

107. A discount of 30% on the marked price of a toy reduces its S.P. by Rs 30. What is the new S.P. ?   **(C.B.I., 1992)**

   (*a*) Rs 130   (*b*) Rs 100   (*c*) Rs 70   (*d*) Rs 21

108. A cloth merchant announces 25% rebate in prices. If one needs to have a rebate of Rs 40, then how many shirts each costing Rs 32, he should purchase ?

    (*a*) 5   (*b*) 6   (*c*) 7   (*d*) 10

109. If a commission of 10% is given on the written price of an article, the gain is 20%. If the commission is increased to 20%, the gain is :

    (*a*) $6\frac{2}{3}\%$ (*b*) $7\frac{1}{4}\%$ (*c*) $12\frac{1}{2}\%$ (*d*) $13\frac{1}{3}\%$

110. A shopkeeper professes to sell all things at a discount of 10%, but increases the S.P. of each article by 20%. His gain on each article is :   **(Assistant Grade, 1994)**

    (*a*) 6 %   (*b*) 8 %   (*c*) 10 %   (*d*) 12 %

111. Even after reducing the marked price of a transistor by Rs 32, a shopkeeper makes a profit of 15%. If the cost price be Rs 320, what percentage of profit would he have made if he had sold the transistor at the marked price ?   **(Hotel Management, 1993)**

    (*a*) 10%   (*b*) 20%   (*c*) 25%   (*d*) None of these

112. After allowing a discount of 10% on M.P., a shopkeeper charges Rs 540 for a watch. Had he not allowed any discount, he would have made a profit of 20%. What was the C.P. of the watch ?

    (*a*) Rs 648   (*b*) Rs 600   (*c*) Rs 500   (*d*) None of these

ANSWERS

1. (*c*)	**2.** (*c*)	**3.** (*d*)	**4.** (*a*)	**5.** (*a*)	**6.** (*c*)	**7.** (*b*)	**8.** (*a*)	**9.** (*a*)
10. (*c*)	**11.** (*a*)	**12.** (*c*)	**13.** (*d*)	**14.** (*c*)	**15.** (*d*)	**16.** (*b*)	**17.** (*c*)	**18.** (*c*)
19. (*d*)	**20.** (*c*)	**21.** (*d*)	**22.** (*b*)	**23.** (*c*)	**24.** (*c*)	**25.** (*c*)	**26.** (*c*)	**27.** (*d*)
28. (*c*)	**29.** (*d*)	**30.** (*b*)	**31.** (*d*)	**32.** (*b*)	**33.** (*b*)	**34.** (*d*)	**35.** (*b*)	**36.** (*d*)
37. (*a*)	**38.** (*a*)	**39.** (*b*)	**40.** (*a*)	**41.** (*a*)	**42.** (*b*)	**43.** (*b*)	**44.** (*b*)	**45.** (*b*)
46. (*b*)	**47.** (*c*)	**48.** (*c*)	**49.** (*c*)	**50.** (*a*)	**51.** (*a*)	**52.** (*c*)	**53.** (*d*)	**54.** (*a*)
55. (*a*)	**56.** (*c*)	**57.** (*b*)	**58.** (*c*)	**59.** (*c*)	**60.** (*a*)	**61.** (*b*)	**62.** (*c*)	**63.** (*b*)
64. (*c*)	**65.** (*a*)	**66.** (*a*)	**67.** (*b*)	**68.** (*a*)	**69.** (*b*)	**70.** (*c*)	**71.** (*c*)	**72.** (*b*)
73. (*b*)	**74.** (*c*)	**75.** (*b*)	**76.** (*b*)	**77.** (*b*)	**78.** (*b*)	**79.** (*b*)	**80.** (*c*)	**81.** (*d*)
82. (*b*)	**83.** (*d*)	**84.** (*b*)	**85.** (*b*)	**86.** (*d*)	**87.** (*d*)	**88.** (*b*)	**89.** (*b*)	**90.** (*c*)
91. (*c*)	**92.** (*c*)	**93.** (*b*)	**94.** (*c*)	**95.** (*d*)	**96.** (*b*)	**97.** (*c*)	**98.** (*b*)	**99.** (*b*)
100. (*a*)	**101.** (*c*)	**102.** (*b*)	**103.** (*c*)	**104.** (*a*)	**105.** (*c*)	**106.** (*a*)	**107.** (*c*)	**108.** (*a*)
109. (*a*)	**110.** (*b*)	**111.** (*c*)	**112.** (*c*)					

SOLUTIONS

1. $3G = 54 \times 2 = 108 \Rightarrow G = 36.$
   $3P = 36 \times 2 = 72 \Rightarrow P = 24$
   $3C = 24 \times 2 = 48 \Rightarrow C = 16.$
   $\therefore$ Cost of a cricket ball = Rs. 16.

2.   S.P. = Rs. 100, gain = Rs. 15. So, C.P. = Rs. (100 – 15) = Rs. 85.
   $\therefore$ Gain % = $\left(\dfrac{15}{85} \times 100\right)$% = $17\dfrac{11}{17}$%

3.   S.P. = Rs. 100, loss = Rs. 10. So, C.P. = $\left(\dfrac{100}{90} \times 100\right)$ = Rs. $\dfrac{1000}{9}$.
   $\therefore$ Loss % = $\left(10 \times \dfrac{9}{1000} \times 100\right)$% = 9 %.

4.   Gain % = $\left(\dfrac{164.36}{2400} \times 100\right)$% = 6.84 % = 7 % approx.

5.   S.P. = Rs. 34.80, Loss = 25 %
   C.P. = Rs. $\left(\dfrac{100}{75} \times 34.80\right)$ = Rs. 46.40.

6.   S.P. = Rs. 247.50, Gain= $\dfrac{25}{2}$ %.
   $\therefore$ C.P. = Rs. $\left[\dfrac{100}{\left(100 + \dfrac{25}{2}\right)} \times 247.50\right]$ = Rs. $\left(\dfrac{200}{225} \times 247.50\right)$ = Rs. 220.

7.   C.P. = Rs. (225 + 15) = Rs 240, S.P. = Rs. 300
   $\therefore$ Gain % = $\left(\dfrac{60}{240} \times 100\right)$% = 25 %.

8.   S.P. = 125 % of Rs. 319.60 = Rs. $\left(\dfrac{125}{100} \times 319.60\right)$.
   = Rs. 399.50 = Rs. 400 (Approx).

9.   Let C.P. = x. Then, S.P.= $\dfrac{4x}{3}$. Gain = $\left(\dfrac{4x}{3} - x\right) = \dfrac{x}{3}$.
   $\therefore$ Gain % = $\left(\dfrac{x}{3} \times \dfrac{1}{x} \times 100\right)$% = $33\dfrac{1}{3}$ % .

10.   90 : 10.80 = 120 : x or $\dfrac{90}{10.80} = \dfrac{120}{x}$.
   $\therefore$ $x = \dfrac{120 \times 10.80}{90}$ = 14.40. Hence, S.P = Rs. 14.40.

11. $130 : 19.50 = 140 : x$ or $\dfrac{130}{19.50} = \dfrac{140}{x}$.

$\therefore x = \dfrac{140 \times 19.50}{130} = 21$.

S.P. to be increased = Rs. $(21 - 19.50)$ = Rs. 1.50.

12. Rate of buying = Rs. 7 per kg, Rate of selling = Rs. 10 per kg.

To gain Rs. 3, he must buy = 1 kg.

To gain Rs. 102, be must buy = $\left(\dfrac{1}{3} \times 102\right)$ kg = 34 kg.

13. Least C.P. = Rs (200×8) = Rs. 1600.

Greatest S.P. = Rs. (425×8) = Rs. 3400.

Required profit = Rs $(3400 - 1600)$ = Rs. 1800.

14. Let C.P. of each article be Re 1.

C.P. of 15 articles = Rs. 15.

S.P. of 15 articles = Rs. 20.

Profit % = $\left(\dfrac{5}{15} \times 100\right)$ % = $33\dfrac{1}{3}$ %.

15. Let C.P. of each mango be Re 1.

C.P. of 320 mangoes = Rs. 320.

S.P. of 320 mangoes = Rs.400.

$\therefore$ Gain % = $\left(\dfrac{80}{320} \times 100\right)$ % = 25 %.

16. Let C.P. of each table be Re 1.

C.P. of 16 tables = Rs. 16.

S.P. of 16 tables = Rs. 12.

Loss % = $\left(\dfrac{4}{16} \times 100\right)$ % = 25 %.

17. Let C.P. of each article be Re 1.

C.P. of 18 articles = Rs. 18.

S.P. of 18 articles = Rs. 21.

$\therefore$ Gain % = $\left(\dfrac{3}{18} \times 100\right)$ % = $16\dfrac{2}{3}$ %.

18. Gain = (S.P. of 250 chairs) – (C.P. of 250 chairs).

$\therefore$ (S.P. of 250 chairs) – (C.P. of 250 chairs) = S.P. of 50 charis.

S.P. of 200 chairs = C.P. of 250 chairs.

Let C.P. of each chair be Re 1.

C.P. of 200 chairs = Rs. 200.

S.P. of 200 chairs = Rs. 250.

Gain % = $\left(\dfrac{50}{200} \times 100\right)$ % = 25 %.

19. Let C.P. of each mango be Re 1.

C.P. of 110 mangoes = Rs. 110.

S.P. of 110 mangoes = Rs. 120.

Gain % $= \left(\dfrac{10}{110} \times 100 \right)\% = 9\dfrac{1}{11}\%$.

20. (C.P. of 36) − (S.P. of 36) = Loss = S.P. of 4.

∴ S.P. of 40 = C.P. of 36.

Let C.P. of each mango = Re 1.

C.P. of 40 mangoes = Rs 40.

S.P. of 40 mangoes = Rs. 36.

Loss % $= \left(\dfrac{4}{40} \times 100 \right)\% = 10\%$.

21. Let the C.P. be Rs. x.

Then, $x - 15 = \dfrac{x}{16} \Rightarrow x - \dfrac{x}{16} = 15 \Leftrightarrow \dfrac{15x}{16} = 15 \Leftrightarrow x = 16$.

∴ C.P. = Rs. 16.

22. S.P. = C.P. $+ \dfrac{1}{4}$ C.P. $= \dfrac{5}{4}$ C.P.

∴ $\dfrac{5}{4}$ C.P. = 375 $\Rightarrow$ C.P. $= \left(375 \times \dfrac{4}{5} \right) =$ Rs. 300.

23. Loss = (C.P. − S.P.) $\Leftrightarrow \dfrac{1}{11}$ C.P. = C.P. − 10 $\Leftrightarrow \dfrac{10}{11}$ C.P. = 10.

∴ C.P. $= \left(\dfrac{11 \times 10}{10} \right) =$ Rs 11.

24. Let the number of oranges be l.c.m. of 3, 5, 2, 4 = 60.

C.P. of 60 oranges = Rs. $\left(\dfrac{5}{3} \times 60 \right) =$ Rs. 100.

S.P. of 60 oranges = Rs. $\left(\dfrac{4}{2} \times 60 \right) =$ Rs. 120

∴ Gain % = 20 %

25. Suppose, the number of books purchased = 11 × 10 = 110.

C.P. of 110 books = Rs. $\left(\dfrac{10}{11} \times 110 \right) =$ Rs. 100.

S.P. of 110 books = Rs. $\left(\dfrac{11}{10} \times 110 \right) =$ Rs. 121.

Profit % = 21 %.

26. Suppose he bought 1 dozen oranges of each kind.

C.P. of 2 dozens = Rs. $\left(\dfrac{1}{3} \times 12 + \dfrac{1}{2} \times 12 \right) =$ Rs. 10.

Profit = 20 %.

$\therefore$ S.P. of 2 dozens = 120 % of Rs. $10 = \text{Rs}\left(\dfrac{120}{100} \times 10\right) = $ Rs. 12.

$\therefore$ S.P. per dozen = Rs. 6.

27. Suppose he buys 6 eggs of each kind.

C.P. of 12 eggs = Rs. $\left(\dfrac{1}{2} \times 6 + \dfrac{2}{3} \times 6\right) = $ Rs. 7.

S.P. of 12 eggs = Rs. $\left(\dfrac{3}{5} \times 12\right) = $ Rs. 7.20.

$\therefore$ Gain $= \left(\dfrac{0.20}{7} \times 100\right)\% = 2\dfrac{6}{7}\%$.

28. C.P. of 2 dozen oranges = Rs. $(5 + 4) = $ Rs. 9.

S.P. of 2 dozen oranges = Rs. 11.

If profit is Rs 2, oranges bought = 2 dozen.

If profit is Rs. 50, oranges bought $= \left(\dfrac{2}{2} \times 50\right)$ dozens = 50 dozens.

29. C.P. of 25 kg = Rs. $(15 \times 14.50 + 10 \times 13) = $ Rs. 347.50.

S.P. of 25 kg = Rs. $(25 \times 15) = $ Rs. 375.

$\therefore$ Gain = Rs. $(375 - 347.50) = $ Rs. 27.50.

30. Suppose he bought 5 kg and 3 kg of tea.

C.P. = Rs. $(5 \times 18 + 3 \times 20) = $ Rs. 150.

S.P. = Rs. $(8 \times 21) = $ Rs. 168.

Gain % $= \left(\dfrac{18}{150} \times 100\right)\% = 12\%$.

31. C.P. of 65 kg rice = Rs. $(35 \times 9.50 + 30 \times 10.50) = $ Rs. 647.50

S.P. of 65 kg rice = 135 % of 647.50 = Rs. $\left(\dfrac{135}{100} \times 647.50\right)$

S.P. per kg = Rs. $\left(\dfrac{135}{100} \times 647.50 \times \dfrac{1}{65}\right) = $ Rs. 13.44 = Rs. 13.50 (App.)

32. Mean price = Rs. $\left(\dfrac{100}{120} \times 96\right) = $ Rs. 80 per kg.

By the rule of alligation :

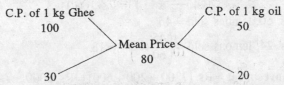

C.P. of 1 kg Ghee   C.P. of 1 kg oil
100   50
Mean Price
80
30   20

$\therefore$ Required ratio = 30 : 20 = 3 : 2.

33. C.P. of 5 kg = Rs. $(14 \times 2 + x \times 3) = $ Rs. $(28 + 3x)$.

S.P. of 5 kg = Rs. $(22 \times 5) = $ Rs. 110.

$$\therefore \quad \frac{110 - (28 + 3x)}{28 + 3x} \times 100 = 10 \Leftrightarrow \frac{82 - 3x}{28 + 3x} = \frac{1}{10} \Leftrightarrow 820 - 30x = 28 + 3x$$

$$\therefore \quad 33x = 792 \quad \text{or} \quad x = \frac{729}{33} = 24.$$

So, the C.P. of larger quantity is Rs. 24 per kg.

34. Gain $\% = \left(\frac{100}{900} \times 100\right)\% = 11\frac{1}{9}\%.$

35. Let error $= x$ gms.

Then, $\frac{x}{1000 - x} \times 100 = 6\frac{18}{47} \Leftrightarrow \frac{100x}{1000 - x} = \frac{300}{47}.$

$\therefore \quad 47x = 3(1000 - x) \quad \text{or} \quad 50x = 3000 \quad \text{or} \quad x = 60.$

$\therefore$ Weight used $= (1000 - 60) = 940$ gms.

36. Rule : Gain $\% = \frac{(100 + \text{common gain } \%)^2}{100} - 100.$

$\therefore$ Gain $\% = \left[\frac{(100 + 10)^2}{100} - 100\right]\% = \left(\frac{12100 - 10000}{100}\right)\% = 21\%.$

37. C.P. of 3 toffees = Re 1.

S.P. of 3 toffees = 150 % of Re 1 = Rs. $\frac{3}{2}$.

For Rs. $\frac{3}{2}$, toffees sold = 3.

For Re 1, toffees sold $= \left(3 \times \frac{2}{3}\right) = 2.$

38. Let S.P. of 20 toffees be Rs. x. Then,

$96 : 1 = 120 : x \quad \text{or} \quad \frac{96}{1} = \frac{120}{x} \quad \text{or} \quad x = \frac{120 \times 1}{96} = \frac{5}{4}.$

For Rs. $\frac{5}{4}$, toffees sold = 20.

For Re 1, toffees sold $= \left(20 \times \frac{4}{5}\right) = 16.$

39. Let S.P. of 45 lemons be Rs. x.

$80 : 40 = 120 : x \quad \text{or} \quad \frac{80}{40} = \frac{120}{x} \quad \text{or} \quad x = \frac{40 \times 120}{80} = 60$

For Rs. 60, lemons sold = 45

For Rs. 24, lemons sold $= \left(\frac{45}{60} \times 24\right) = 18.$

40. Total investment = Rs. $(7200 + 200 + 600)$ = Rs. 8000.

Total receipt = Rs. (330×28) = Rs. 9240.

Gain $\% = \left(\frac{1240}{8000} \times 100\right)\% = 15.5\%.$

41. Total investment = Rs. $(120 \times 80 + 280 + \dfrac{40}{100} \times 120 + 72)$.

$= $ Rs. $(9600 + 280 + 48 + 72) = $ Rs. 10000.

S.P. of 120 reams = 108 % of Rs. 10000 = Rs. 10800.

$\therefore$ S.P. per ream = Rs. $\left(\dfrac{10800}{120}\right) = $ Rs. 90.

42. $110 : x = (100 + p) : 2x$ or $\dfrac{110}{x} = \dfrac{100 + p}{2x}$ or $100 + p = 220$

$\therefore p = 120 \%$.

43. Investment = Rs. $(20 \times 8 + 10) = $ Rs. 170.

Receipt = Rs. $(30 \times 5 + 20 \times 4) = $ Rs. 230.

$\therefore$ Gain % $= \left(\dfrac{60}{170} \times 100\right) \% = 35.29 \% = 35.3 \%$.

44. 125 % of 120 % of $A = 1500 \Rightarrow \dfrac{125}{100} \times \dfrac{120}{100} A = 1500$.

$\therefore A = \left(1500 \times \dfrac{2}{3}\right) = 1000$.

45. 110 % of 90 % of 120 % of $A = 1188$.

$\therefore \dfrac{110}{100} \times \dfrac{90}{100} \times \dfrac{120}{100} A = 1188$ or $A = \dfrac{1188}{1000} A = 1188$ or $A = 1000$.

A purchased it for Rs. $(1000 - 110) = $ Rs. 890.

46. 125 % of 115 % of 110 % of $P = 1265$.

$\therefore \dfrac{125}{100} \times \dfrac{115}{100} \times \dfrac{110}{100} p = 1265$ or $\dfrac{253}{160} P = 1265$.

$\therefore P = \left(\dfrac{1265 \times 160}{253}\right) = $ Rs. 800.

47. Money spent by Kanak = Rs. 10000.

Money received by him = 110 % of Rs. 10000 = Rs. 11000

C.P. to Kanak = 90 % of 1100 = Rs. 9900.

$\therefore$ Profit earned = Rs. $(1000 + 100) = $ Rs. 1100

48. Let C.P. of a mixer be Rs. x and that of a T.V. be Rs. y.

Then, $2x + y = 7000$ and $2y + x = 9800$.

Multiplying 2nd equation by 2 and subtracting first from it, we get

$3y = 19600 - 7000 = 12600$ or $y = 4200$

$\therefore$ C.P. of a T.V. = Rs. 4200

49. Loss % $= \left(\dfrac{\text{common gain or loss } \%}{10}\right)^2 = \left(\dfrac{10}{10}\right)^2 = 1 \%$.

50. Loss % $= \left(\dfrac{5}{10}\right)^2 \% = 0.25 \%$.

51. Total S.P. = Rs. 8000 & Total C.P. = Rs. 8000.

S.P. of 1st commodity = Rs. 4000. Gain on it= 25 %.

$\therefore$ C.P. of this commodity = Rs. $\left(\dfrac{100}{125} \times 4000\right)$ = Rs. 3200.

C.P. of the other commodity = Rs. (8000 – 3200) = Rs. 4800.
S.P. of this commodity = Rs. 4000.

$\therefore$ Loss on it $= \left(\dfrac{800}{4800} \times 100\right)\% = 16\dfrac{2}{3}\%$.

52. Total S.P. = Rs. 24000.

C.P. of horse = Rs. $\left(\dfrac{100}{80} \times 12000\right)$ = Rs. 15000.

C.P. of cow = Rs. $\left(\dfrac{100}{120} \times 12000\right)$ = Rs. 10000

Total C.P. = Rs. 25000.

$\therefore$ Gain = Rs. (25000 – 24000) = Rs. 1000.

53. Let the investments be 3x and 5x.
Then, total investment = 8x.
Total receipt = (115 % of 3x + 90 % of 5x).
$\qquad$ = (3.45x + 4.5x) = 7.95x.

$\therefore$ Loss $= \left(\dfrac{0.05x}{8x} \times 100\right)\% = 0.625\%$.

54. Suppose, he must produce x items. Then,
C.P. = Rs. (40x + 3000), S.P. = Rs. 60x.

$\therefore$ 60x – (40x + 3000) = 1000 or 20x = 4000 or x = 200.

55. Let selling price be Rs x.

C.P. $= \dfrac{9}{10}x$, Receipt = 108 % of $x = \dfrac{27x}{25}$.

Gain $= \left(\dfrac{27x}{25} - \dfrac{9x}{10}\right) = \left(\dfrac{108x - 90x}{100}\right) = \dfrac{18x}{100}$.

$\therefore$ Gain % $= \left(\dfrac{18x}{100} \times \dfrac{10}{9x} \times 100\right)\% = 20\%$.

56. Let original S.P. be Rs x..

New S.P. $= \dfrac{2}{3}x$, loss = 10 %.

$\therefore$ C.P. $= \left(\dfrac{100}{90} \times \dfrac{2}{3}x\right) = \dfrac{20x}{27}$.

Now, C.P. $= \dfrac{20x}{27}$, S.P. = Rs. x. Gain $= \left(x - \dfrac{20x}{27}\right) = \dfrac{7x}{27}$.

$\therefore$ Gain % $= \left(\dfrac{7x}{27} \times \dfrac{27}{20x} \times 100\right)\% = 35\%$.

57. Let C.P. $= x$, profit $\% = x$ and S.P. $=$ Rs. 39

$$\therefore \ x = \left[\frac{100}{(100 + x)} \times 39 \right] \Rightarrow x^2 + 100x = 3900.$$

$x^2 + 130x - 30x - 3900 = 0 \Rightarrow x(x + 130) - 30(x + 130) = 0$

$\therefore \ (x + 130)(x - 30) = 0.$ So, $x = 30$

58. Let us consider a packet of rice marked 1 kg.

Its actual weight is 80% of 1000 gm = 800 gm.

Let C.P. of each gm be Re 1.

Then, C.P. of this packet = Rs. 800.

S.P. of this packet = 110 % of C.P. of 1 kg.

$$= \left(\frac{110}{100} \times 1000 \right) = \text{Rs. } 1100.$$

$$\therefore \ \text{Gain } \% = \left(\frac{300}{800} \times 100 \right) \% = 37.5 \ \%.$$

59. Let C.P. of whole be Rs x.

C.P. of $\frac{3}{4}$th = Rs. $\frac{3x}{4}$, C.P. of $\frac{1}{4}$th = Rs. $\frac{x}{4}$.

$$\therefore \ \text{Total S.P.} = \left(120 \ \% \text{ of } \frac{3x}{4} \right) + \frac{x}{4} = \left(\frac{9x}{10} + \frac{x}{4} \right) = \frac{23x}{20}.$$

$$\text{Gain} = \left(\frac{23x}{20} - x \right) = \frac{3x}{20}.$$

$$\therefore \ \text{Gain } \% = \left(\frac{3x}{20} \times \frac{1}{x} \times 100 \right) \% = 15 \ \%.$$

60. C.P. of $\frac{3}{4}$th $= \left(\frac{3}{4} \times 400 \right) =$ Rs. 300, C.P. of $\frac{1}{4}$th = Rs. 100.

$$\therefore \ \text{Total S.P.} = (90 \ \% \text{ of Rs. } 300 + 110 \ \% \text{ of } 100) = \text{Rs. } 380.$$

$$\text{Loss} = \left(\frac{20}{400} \times 100 \right) = 5 \ \%.$$

61. Let the total value be Rs. x.

Value of $\frac{2}{3}$rd $= \frac{2x}{3}$, Value of $\frac{1}{3}$rd $= \frac{x}{3}$.

Total S.P. $= \left(105 \ \% \text{ of } \frac{2x}{3} + 98 \ \% \text{ of } \frac{x}{3} \right)$

$$= \left(\frac{210x}{300} + \frac{98x}{300} \right) = \frac{308x}{300}.$$

$$\frac{308x}{300} - x = 400 \Rightarrow \frac{308x - 300x}{300} = 400$$

$$\therefore \ x = \frac{300 \times 400}{8} = 15000.$$

62. Total C.P. = Rs. (120×110) = Rs. 13200

Total S.P.

$= (30 \times 110 + 30 \times 12) + (75 \times 110 + 75 \times 14) + (15 \times 110 - 15 \times 7)$

= Rs. 14505.

Average profit = Rs. $\left(\dfrac{14505 - 13200}{120}\right)$ = Rs. $\dfrac{1305}{120}$ = Rs. 10.875.

63. Total profit required = Rs. (42×18) = Rs. 756

Profit on 22 sarees = Rs. $(460 + 144)$ = Rs. 604

Profit on 20 sarees = Rs. $(756 - 604)$ = Rs. 152

Average profit on these sarees = Rs. $\left(\dfrac{152}{20}\right)$ = Rs. 7.60.

64. Suppose, the quantity sold at a loss be x kg and let C.P. per kg be Re 1.

Total C.P. = Rs. 24.

Total S.P. = 120 % of $(24 - x)$ + 95 % of x.

$$= \frac{6}{5}(24 - x) + \frac{19x}{20} = \frac{576 - 24x + 19x}{20} = \frac{576 - 5x}{20}.$$

$\therefore \dfrac{576 - 5x}{20}$ = 110 % of 24 or $\dfrac{576 - 5x}{20} = \dfrac{264}{10}$.

or $576 - 5x = 528$ or $5x = 48$ or $x = 9.6$ kg.

65. Let the cost prices be Rs. x and Rs. $(840 - x)$.

Total S.P. = 116 % of x + 88 % of $(840 - x)$.

$$= \frac{116x}{100} + \frac{88(840 - x)}{100} = \frac{28x + 88 \times 840}{100}.$$

$\therefore \dfrac{28x + 88 \times 840}{100} = 840$ or $28x + 88 \times 840 = 840 \times 100$.

or $28x = 12 \times 840$ or $x = \dfrac{12 \times 840}{28} = 360$.

$\therefore$ Their cost prices are Rs. 360 & Rs. 480.

66. C.P. $= \dfrac{40}{100} \times$ S.P. *i.e.* S.P. $= \dfrac{5}{2}$ C.P. $= \left(\dfrac{5}{2} \times 100\right)$ % of C.P.

$\therefore$ S.P. = 250 % of C.P.

67. Let C.P. be Rs. x.

1st S.P. = 110 % of $x = \dfrac{11x}{10}$.

2nd S.P. = 90 % of $x = \dfrac{9x}{10}$.

$\dfrac{11x}{10} - \dfrac{9x}{10} = 80 \Rightarrow 2x = 800 \Rightarrow x = 400.$

68. Let C.P. be Rs. x..

(105 % of x) − (95 % of x) = 6.72 or 10 % of x = 6.72.

$\therefore \quad \dfrac{x}{10} = 6.72 \quad$ or $\quad x = 67.20.$

69. Let C.P. be Rs. x.

$(105\ \%\ \text{of}\ x) - (97\tfrac{1}{2}\ \%\ \text{of}\ x) = 6 \quad$ or $\quad 7\tfrac{1}{2}\ \%\ \text{of}\ x = 6.$

or $\dfrac{15}{2 \times 100}\, x = 6 \quad$ or $\quad x = \left(\dfrac{6 \times 2 \times 100}{15}\right) = 80.$

70. Let original C.P. be Rs. x. Its S.P. $= \dfrac{90x}{100} = \dfrac{9x}{10}.$

New C.P. $= \dfrac{80x}{100} = \dfrac{4x}{5},$ New S.P. $= \dfrac{140}{100} \times \dfrac{4x}{5} = \dfrac{28x}{25}.$

$\dfrac{28x}{25} - \dfrac{9x}{10} = 55 \quad$ or $\quad \dfrac{112x - 90x}{100} = 55 \quad$ or $\quad 22x = 55 \times 100$

$\therefore \quad x = \left(\dfrac{55 \times 100}{22}\right) = 250.$

71. Let original C.P. be Rs. x. Its S.P. $= \dfrac{105}{100}\, x = \dfrac{21x}{20}.$

New C.P. $= \dfrac{95}{100}\, x = \dfrac{19x}{20},$ New S.P. $= \dfrac{110}{100} \times \dfrac{19x}{20} = \dfrac{209x}{200}.$

$\dfrac{21x}{20} - \dfrac{209x}{200} = 1 \quad$ or $\quad x = 200.$

72. Let the total quantity be x quintals.

C.P. $=$ Rs. $150x.$

S.P. required $= \left(\dfrac{120}{100} \times 150x\right) = 180x.$

S.P. of $\dfrac{90}{100}\, x$ quintals $= 180x.$

S.P. per quintal $= \left(180x \times \dfrac{100}{90x}\right) =$ Rs. $200.$

73. Let original price per dozen be Rs. x.

New price per dozen $= \dfrac{75x}{100} = \dfrac{3x}{4}.$

Now, $96 \times \dfrac{4}{3x} - \dfrac{96}{x} = 4 \quad$ or $\quad (128 - 96) = 4x \quad$ or $\quad x = 8.$

74. Let the C.P. be Rs. x. Then,

$\dfrac{105}{100}\, x - \dfrac{95}{100}\, x = 15 \quad$ or $\quad \dfrac{10x}{100} = 15 \quad$ or $\quad x = 150$

75. Total C.P. $=$ Rs. $(12 \times 4 + 16 \times 2) =$ Rs. $80.$

S.P. of 6 dozen oranges $=$ Rs. $\left(\dfrac{120}{100} \times 80\right) =$ Rs. $96.$

S.P. per dozen $=$ Rs. $16.$

76. C.P. = Rs. (48×20) = Rs. 960.

C.P. of 8 dozen = Rs. (48×8) = Rs. 384.

C.P. of 12 dozen = Rs. $(960 - 384)$ = Rs. 576.

$\therefore$ Total S.P. $= \left(\dfrac{110}{100} \times 384 + \dfrac{120}{100} \times 576 \right)$ = Rs. 1113.60.

$\therefore$ Profit % $= \left(\dfrac{153.60}{960} \times 100 \right)\% = 16\%$.

77. Let C.P. be Rs. x. Then,

$425 - x = x - 355 \Rightarrow 2x = 780 \Rightarrow x = 390$.

78. Let C.P. be Rs. x..

$840 - x = 2\,(x - 600) \Rightarrow 3x = 2040 \Rightarrow x = 680$.

79. Let C.P. be Rs. x.

$900 - x = 2\,(x - 450) \Rightarrow 3x = 1800 \Rightarrow x = 600$.

C.P. = Rs. 600, gain required = 25 %.

$\therefore$ S.P. = Rs. $\left(\dfrac{125}{100} \times 600 \right)$ = Rs. 750.

80. Let C.P. be Rs. x.

$\dfrac{78 - x}{x} \times 100 = 2 \times \dfrac{69 - x}{x} \times 100$.

$78 - x = 138 - 2x$ or $x = 60$.

81. Let C.P. be Rs. x. Then,

$(1060 - x) = \dfrac{120}{100}\,(x - 950)$.

$106000 - 100x = 120x - 120 \times 950$.

$\therefore\ 220x = 220000 \Rightarrow x = 1000$.

$\therefore$ Desired S.P. = Rs. $\left(\dfrac{120}{100} \times 1000 \right)$ = Rs. 1200.

82. Let C.P. be Rs. x.

$2\,(x - 75) = (96 - x) \Rightarrow 3x = 246 \Rightarrow x = 82$.

83. Let C.P. be Rs. x. Then,

$(107\frac{1}{2}\% \text{ of } x - 97\frac{1}{2}\% \text{ of } x) = 100$

10% of $x = 100$ or $\dfrac{10}{100} x = 100$ or $x = 1000$.

Desired S.P. = $112\frac{1}{2}\%$ of 1000 $= \left(\dfrac{112.5}{100} \times 1000 \right) = 1125$

84. Let marked price be Rs. 100.

Then, S.P. = 80 % of 60 % of 100 $= \dfrac{80}{100} \times \dfrac{60}{100} \times 100 = 48$.

$\therefore$ Single discount = 52 %.

85. Let marked price be Rs. 100.

Then, S.P. = 90 % of 80 % of 70 % of 100

$$= \left(\frac{90}{100} \times \frac{80}{100} \times \frac{70}{100} \times 100 \right) = 50.4.$$

∴ Single discount = (100 − 50.4) % = 49.6 %

86. Let marked price be Rs. 100. Then,

$$S.P. = \frac{(100-y)}{100} \times \frac{(100-x)}{100} \times 100 = \frac{(100-x)(100-y)}{100}$$

∴ Single discount $= \left[100 - \frac{(100-x)(100-y)}{100} \right] \%$

$$= \left(x + y + \frac{xy}{100} \right) \%.$$

87. Cash price = 95% of 90% of 80% of Rs. 300.

$$= \left(\frac{95}{100} \times \frac{90}{100} \times \frac{80}{100} \times 300 \right) = Rs. 205.20.$$

88. S.P. in 1st case = 70% of 90% of 90% of Rs. 10000.

$$= \left(\frac{70}{100} \times \frac{90}{100} \times \frac{90}{100} \times 10000 \right) = Rs. 5670.$$

S.P. In 2nd case = 95% of 95% of 60% of Rs. 10000.

$$= \left(\frac{95}{100} \times \frac{95}{100} \times \frac{60}{100} \times 10000 \right) = Rs. 5415.$$

Saving = Rs. (5670 − 5415) = Rs. 255.

89. S.P. = Rs. $\left(\frac{85}{100} \times 620 \right)$ = Rs. 527.

90. Rate of discount $= \left(\frac{12}{80} \times 100 \right) = 15 \%.$

91. Let C.P. be Rs. 100. Then, marked price = Rs. 130.

S.P. $= \left(100 - \frac{25}{4} \right) \%$ of Rs 130 $= \left(\frac{375}{400} \times 130 \right) = 121.875.$

∴ Profit % $= 21.875 = \frac{21875}{1000} = 21 \frac{7}{8} \%.$

92. 1st discount = Rs. (40 % of 500) = Rs. $\left(\frac{40}{100} \times 500 \right)$ = Rs. 200.

2nd discount = (36 % of 500 + 4 % of 64 % of 500).

$$= Rs \left(\frac{36}{100} \times 500 + \frac{4}{100} \times \frac{64}{100} \times 500 \right) = Rs. 192.80.$$

Difference = Rs. (200 − 192.80) = Rs. 7.20.

93. Let C.P. = Rs. 100. Then, S.P. = Rs. 133.
Let marked price be Rs. *x*..

Then, 95 % of $x = 133 \Rightarrow \dfrac{95}{100} x = 133 \Rightarrow x = \left(133 \times \dfrac{100}{95}\right) = 140.$

∴ Marked price = 40 % above C.P.

94. Let C.P. be Rs. 100. Then, M.P. = Rs. 120.

S.P. = Rs. 108.

Discount on Rs. 120 = Rs. 12.

Discount on Rs. 100 = $\left(\dfrac{12}{120} \times 100\right) \% = 10 \%.$

95. S.P. = Rs. 660, profit = 10 %.

∴ C.P. = $\left(\dfrac{100}{110} \times 660\right) =$ Rs. 600. Let, M.P. be Rs x.

Now, 75 % of $x = 600 \Rightarrow \dfrac{75}{100} x = 600 \Rightarrow x = 800.$

96. C.P. = Rs. 153, Gain = 20 %.

∴ S.P. = $\left(\dfrac{120}{100} \times 153\right) =$ Rs. 183.60.

Let, the marked price be Rs. x.

$\dfrac{85}{100} x = 183.60 \Rightarrow x = \dfrac{183.60 \times 100}{85} = 216.$

97. S.P. after 1st discount = $\left(\dfrac{80}{100} \times 150\right) =$ Rs. 120.

Net S.P. = Rs. 108.

Discount on Rs. 120 = Rs. 12.

Discount on Rs. 100 = $\left(\dfrac{12}{120} \times 100\right) \% = 10 \%.$

98. Let, the list price be Rs. x.

$\dfrac{80}{100} x = 24 \Rightarrow x = \dfrac{24 \times 100}{80} = 30.$

Required S.P. = 70 % of Rs. 30 = Rs. 21.

99. Let the list price be Rs. z.

∴ $(100 - x) \%$ of $z = y \Rightarrow \left(\dfrac{100 - x}{100}\right) \times z = y.$

∴ $z = \left(\dfrac{100y}{100 - x}\right).$

100. Let the marked price be Rs. x.

Then, 90 % of 80 % of $x = 108.$

∴ $\dfrac{90}{100} \times \dfrac{80}{100} x = 108$ or $x = \dfrac{108 \times 100 \times 100}{90 \times 80} = 150.$

101. Final amount = 90 % of 75 % of Rs. 600.

$= \left(\dfrac{90}{100} \times \dfrac{75}{100} \times 600\right) =$ Rs. 405.

102. Let the C.P. be Rs. 100. Then, S.P. = Rs. 112.

Let the printed price be Rs. x.

Then, 90 % of $x = 112 \Rightarrow \dfrac{90}{100} x = 112$.

$\therefore x = \left(\dfrac{112 \times 100}{90}\right) = \dfrac{1120}{9}$.

$\therefore$ (C.P.) : (Printed price) $= 100 : \dfrac{1120}{9} = 900 : 1120 = 45 : 56$.

103. Let the C.P. of each article be Re. 1.

Then, C.P. of 30 = Rs. 27, S.P. of 30 = Rs. 30

$\therefore$ Gain % $= \left(\dfrac{3}{27} \times 100\right)\% = 11\dfrac{1}{9}\%$.

104. Let the original price be Rs. x.

Then, C.P. $= \left(\dfrac{80}{100}x\right) = $ Rs. $\dfrac{4x}{5}$.

$\dfrac{4x}{5} + 50 = \dfrac{150}{100} \times \dfrac{4x}{5} \Rightarrow x = 125$.

105. Let the labelled price be Rs. x.

$\therefore$ S.P. $= \dfrac{80}{100} \times x = \dfrac{4x}{5}$.

New S.P. $= \dfrac{75}{100} x = \dfrac{3x}{4}$.

$\therefore \dfrac{4x}{5} - \dfrac{3x}{4} = 500 \Rightarrow x = 10000$.

106. S.P. = Rs. 1955, gain = 15 %.

$\therefore$ C.P. $= \left(\dfrac{100}{115} \times 1955\right) = $ Rs. 1700.

Let the marked price be Rs x.

Then, 85 % of $x = 1700$

or $\dfrac{85}{100} x = 1700$ or $x = \dfrac{1700 \times 100}{85} = 2000$.

$\therefore$ Discount = Rs. (2000 – 1700) = Rs. 300.

107. Let its original price be Rs. x.

Then, $\left(x - \dfrac{70}{100}x\right) = 30$ or $x = 100$.

New S.P. = Rs. 70

108. Rs. 25 is the rebate on Rs. 100.

Rs. 40 will be the rebate on Rs. $\left(\dfrac{100}{25} \times 40\right) = $ Rs. 160.

$\therefore$ Number of shirts purchased $= \frac{160}{32} = 5.$

109. Let the marked price be Rs. 100.

Then, S.P. = Rs. $\left(\frac{90}{100} \times 100\right)$ = Rs. 90.

But, gain = 20 %

$\therefore$ C.P. = $\left(\frac{100}{120} \times 90\right)$ = Rs. 75.

New commission = Rs. 20.

New S.P. = Rs. 80.

Profit % now = $\left(\frac{5}{75} \times 100\right)\% = 6\frac{2}{3}\%$.

110. Let C.P. be Rs. 100. Then, marked price = Rs. 120.

$\therefore$ S.P. = Rs. $\left(\frac{90}{100} \times 120\right)$ = Rs. 108.

$\therefore$ Gain = 8 %.

111. C.P. = Rs. 320, profit = 15 %.

$\therefore$ S.P. = Rs. $\left(\frac{115}{100} \times 320\right)$ = Rs. 368.

$\therefore$ Marked price = Rs. (368 + 32) = Rs. 400.

Required profit = $\left(\frac{80}{320} \times 100\right)\% = 25\%$.

112. Let the marked price be Rs. x.

Then, $\frac{90}{100}x = 540 \Rightarrow x = \frac{540 \times 100}{90} = 600.$

Now, S.P. = Rs. 600 & Profit = 20 %.

$\therefore$ C.P. = $\left(\frac{100}{120} \times 600\right)$ = Rs. 500.

वस्तुनिष्ठ अंकगणित

आर० एस० अग्रवाल

(पूर्ण हल सहित)

- सभी प्रतियोगी परिक्षाओं के लिए सफलता की कुंजी
- सभी प्रकार के प्रश्नो का संक्षिप्त हल के साथ समावेश

12. Ratio & Proportion

Ratio: *The ratio of two quantities in the same units is a fraction that one quantity is of the other.*

The ratio $a : b$ represents a fraction $\frac{a}{b}$.

The first term of a ratio is called *antecedent* while the second term is known as *consequent*.

Thus, the ratio $5 : 7$ represents $\frac{5}{7}$ with antecedent 5 and consequent 7.

Rule : *The multiplication or division of each term of a ratio by a same non-zero number does not effect the ratio.*

Thus, $4 : 5 = 8 : 10 = 12 : 15 = 16 : 20 = \frac{4}{5} : 1$ etc.

Proportion : *The equality of two ratios is called proportion.*

If $a : b = c : d$, we write, $a : b :: c : d$ and we say that a, b, c, d are in proportion.

In a proportion, the first and fourth terms are known as **extremes,** while second and third terms are known as **means.**

We have, **Product of Means = Product of Extremes.**

Fourth Proportional : *If $a : b = c : d$, then d is called the fourth proportional to a, b, c.*

Third Proportional : *The third proportional to a, b is the fourth proportional to a, b, b.*

Mean Proportional : *Mean proportional between a and b is $\sqrt{ab}$.*

Comparison of Ratios : We say that $(a : b) > (c : d)$ if $\frac{a}{b} > \frac{c}{d}$.

Compounded Ratio : *The compounded ratio of the ratios*
$$(a : b), (c : d), (e : f) \text{ is } (ace : bdf).$$

Some More Definitions :

   (i) $a^2 : b^2$ is called the **duplicate ratio** of $a : b$

   (ii) $\sqrt{a} : \sqrt{b}$ is called the **sub-duplicate ratio** of $a : b$

   (iii) $a^3 : b^3$ is called the **triplicate ratio** of $a : b$.

   (iv) $a^{1/3} : b^{1/3}$ is called the **sub-triplicate ratio** of $a : b$.

   (v) If $\frac{a}{b} = \frac{c}{d}$ then $\frac{a+b}{a-b} = \frac{c+d}{c-d}$ (**componendo & dividendo**)

Variation : *We say that x is directly proportional to y if $x = ky$ for some constant k and we write, $x \propto y$.*

Also, we say that x is **inversely proportional** to y,

if $x = \dfrac{k}{y}$ for some constant k and we write, $x \propto \dfrac{1}{y}$.

SOLVED PROBLEMS

Ex. 1. *If $a : b = 5 : 9$ and $b : c = 4 : 7$, find $a : b : c$ and $a : c$.*

Sol. $a : b = 5 : 9$

$b : c = 4 : 7 = 4 \times \dfrac{9}{4} : 7 \times \dfrac{9}{4} = 9 : \dfrac{63}{4}$.

$\therefore\ a : b : c = 5 : 9 : \dfrac{63}{4} = 20 : 36 : 63$.

Also, $\dfrac{a}{c} = \dfrac{a}{b} \times \dfrac{b}{c} = \dfrac{5}{9} \times \dfrac{4}{7} = \dfrac{20}{63}$. So, $a : c = 20 : 63$.

Ex. 2. *Find :*

  (i) fourth proportional to 4, 9, 12;

  (ii) third proportional to 16 and 36;

  (iii) mean proportion between .08 and .18.

Sol.   *(i)* Let $4 : 9 : : 12 : x$.

    Then, $4x = 9 \times 12$ or $x = \left(\dfrac{9 \times 12}{4} \right) = 27$.

(ii) Let $16 : 36 : : 36 : x$.

    Then, $16x = 36 \times 36$ or $x = \left(\dfrac{36 \times 36}{16} \right) = 81$.

(iii) Mean proportion between .08 and .18

$= \sqrt{.08 \times .18} = \sqrt{\dfrac{144}{100 \times 100}} = \dfrac{12}{100} = 0.12$.

Ex. 3. *Find :*

  (i) the duplicate ratio of 3 : 7 ;

  (ii) the triplicate ratio of 2 : 5 ;

  (iii) the sub-duplicate ratio of 25 : 16 ;

  (iv) the sub-triplicate ratio of 125 : 64 ;

  (v) the compounded ratio of (2 : 5), (3 : 4) and (4 : 9).

Sol.   *(i)* Duplicate ratio of $3 : 7$ is $3^2 : 7^2 = 9 : 49$.

    (ii) Triplicate ratio of $2 : 5$ is $2^3 : 5^3 = 8 : 125$.

    (iii) The sub-duplicate ratio of $25 : 16 = \sqrt{25} : \sqrt{16} = 5 : 4$.

    (iv) The sub-triplicate ratio of $125 : 64 = (125)^{1/3} : (64)^{1/3} = 5 : 4$.

    (v) Compounded ratio of $(2 : 5), (3 : 4)$ and $(4 : 9)$

$$= \left(\dfrac{2}{5} \times \dfrac{3}{4} \times \dfrac{4}{9} \right) = \dfrac{2}{15}\ i.e.\ 2 : 15.$$

Ex. 4. *If $x : y = 3 : 4$, find $(4x + 5y) : (5x - 2y)$.*

Sol. Given : $\dfrac{x}{y} = \dfrac{3}{4}$.

$\therefore \dfrac{4x + 5y}{5x - 2y} = \dfrac{4\left(\dfrac{x}{y}\right) + 5}{5\left(\dfrac{x}{y}\right) - 2}$ [*Dividing Nr & Dr by y*]

$= \dfrac{4 \times \dfrac{3}{4} + 5}{5 \times \dfrac{3}{4} - 2} = \dfrac{8 \times 4}{7} = \dfrac{32}{7}$.

Ex. 5. *Divide Rs. 672 in the ratio 5 : 3.*

Sol. Sum of the terms of the ratio = $(5 + 3) = 8$.

$\therefore$ First part = Rs $\left(672 \times \dfrac{5}{8}\right)$ = Rs. 420.

Second part = Rs. $\left(672 \times \dfrac{3}{8}\right)$ = Rs. 252.

Ex. 6. *Divide Rs. 1162 among A, B, C in the ratio 35 : 28 : 20.*

Sol. Sum of the terms of the ratio = $(35 + 28 + 20) = 83$.

$\therefore$ A's share = Rs. $\left(1162 \times \dfrac{35}{83}\right)$ = Rs. 490.

B's share = Rs. $\left(1162 \times \dfrac{28}{83}\right)$ = Rs.392.

C's share = Rs. $[1162 - (490 + 392)]$ = Rs. 280.

Ex. 7. *A bag contains 50 paise, 25 paise and 10 paise coins in the ratio 5 : 9 : 4, amounting to Rs. 206. Find the number of coins of each type.*

Sol. Ratio of values $= \dfrac{5}{2} : \dfrac{9}{4} : \dfrac{4}{10} = 50 : 45 : 8$.

Value of 50-paise coins = Rs $\left(206 \times \dfrac{50}{103}\right)$ = Rs. 100.

Value of 25-paise coins = Rs $\left(206 \times \dfrac{45}{103}\right)$ = Rs. 90.

Value of 10-paise coins = Rs $\left(206 \times \dfrac{8}{103}\right)$ = Rs. 16.

$\therefore$ Number of 50-paise coins = $(100 \times 2) = 200$.

Number of 25-paise coins = $(90 \times 4) = 360$.

Number of 10-paise coins = $(16 \times 10) = 160$.

Ex. 8. *Which one of 2 : 3, 4 : 5, 7 : 9 and 11 : 13 is the largest ratio ?*

Sol. $2 : 3 = \dfrac{2}{3} = 0.666; 4 : 5 = \dfrac{4}{5} = 0.8;$

$7 : 9 = \dfrac{7}{9} = 0.777; \ 11 : 13 = \dfrac{11}{13} = 0.846.$

Clearly, $0.846 > 0.8 > 0.777 > 0.666$.

Hence, $11 : 13$ is the largest ratio.

Ex. 9. *A mixture contains alcohol and water in the ratio 4 : 3. If 5 litres of water is added to the mixture, the ratio becomes 4 : 5. Find the quantity of alcohol in the given mixture.*

Sol. Let the quantity of alcohol & water be $4x$ & $3x$ respectively.

Then, $\dfrac{4x}{3x + 5} = \dfrac{4}{5} \Leftrightarrow 20x = 12x + 20 \Leftrightarrow x = 2.5.$

$\therefore$ Alcohol in given mixture $= 4x$ litres $= 10$ litres.

Ex. 10. *Suppose x varies inversely as square of y and when y = 3, then x = 4. Find x, when y = 6.*

Sol. Let $x = \dfrac{k}{y^2}$, where k is a constant.

When $y = 3$, we have $x = 4$.

$\therefore \ 4 = \dfrac{k}{9}$ or $k = 36$.

$\therefore \ x = \dfrac{36}{y^2}.$

Now, when $y = 6$, we have $x = \dfrac{36}{36} = 1.$

Ex. 11. *Suppose y varies as the sum of two quantities of which one varies directly as x and the other inversely as x. If y = 6 when x = 4 and y = 3 $\frac{1}{3}$, when x = 3. Find the relation between x and y.*

Sol. Let $y = a + b$, where $a \propto x$ and $b \propto \dfrac{1}{x}$.

Let $a = k_1 x$ and $b = \dfrac{k_2}{x}$, where k_1, k_2 are constants.

Then, $y = k_1 x + \dfrac{k_2}{x}$ ...(i)

Putting $y = 6$ & $x = 4$ in (i), we get $16k_1 + k_2 = 24$ ...(ii)

Putting $y = 3\frac{1}{3}$ & $x = 3$ in (i), we get $9k_1 + k_2 = 10$ ...(iii)

Solving (ii) & (iii), we get $k_1 = 2$ and $k_2 = -8$.

Putting these values in (i), we get : $y = \left(2x - \dfrac{8}{x} \right).$

EXERCISE 12

Mark ($\sqrt{}$) against the correct answer :

1. If $A : B = 5 : 7$ and $B : C = 6 : 11$, then $A : B : C$ is :
    - (a) 55 : 77 : 66
    - (b) 30 : 42 : 77
    - (c) 35 : 49 : 42
    - (d) None of these
2. If $p : q = 3 : 4$ and $q : r = 8 : 9$, then $p : r$ is :   **(Assistant Grade 1994)**
    - (a) 1 : 3
    - (b) 3 : 2
    - (c) 2 : 3
    - (d) 1 : 2
3. If $A : B = 8 : 15$, $B : C = 5 : 8$ and $C : D = 4 : 5$, then $A : D$ is equal to :
    - (a) 2 : 7
    - (b) 4 : 15
    - (c) 8 : 15
    - (d) 15 : 4

    (Central Excise & I.Tax 1991)

4. The ratio $4^{3.5} : 2^5$ is the same as :
    - (a) 4 : 1
    - (b) 2 : 1
    - (c) 7 : 5
    - (d) 7 : 10
5. If 15% of x is the same as 20% of y, then $x : y$ is :   **(C.B.I. 1990)**
    - (a) 3 : 4
    - (b) 4 : 3
    - (c) 17 : 16
    - (d) 16 : 17
6. If $7 : x = 17.5 : 22.5$, then the value of x is :   **(Assistant grade 1993)**
    - (a) 9
    - (b) 7.5
    - (c) 6
    - (d) 5.5
7. If $\dfrac{1}{5} : \dfrac{1}{x} = \dfrac{1}{x} : \dfrac{1}{1.25}$, the value of x is :
    - (a) 1.5
    - (b) 2
    - (c) 2.5
    - (d) 3.5
8. If $0.4 : 1.4 :: 1.4 : x$, the value of x is :   **(Teacher's Exam 1991)**
    - (a) 49
    - (b) 4.9
    - (c) 0.49
    - (d) 0.4
9. The compounded ratio of $(2 : 3)$, $(6 : 11)$ and $(11 : 2)$ is :
    - (a) 1 : 2
    - (b) 2 : 1
    - (c) 11 : 24
    - (d) 36 : 121

    (Assistant Grade 1994)

10. If $2A = 3B = 4C$, then $A : B : C$ is :
    - (a) 2 : 3 : 4
    - (b) 4 : 3 : 2
    - (c) 6 : 4 : 3
    - (d) 3 : 4 : 6
11. If $\dfrac{1}{3} A = \dfrac{1}{4} B = \dfrac{1}{5} C$, then $A : B : C$ is :
    - (a) 4 : 3 : 5
    - (b) 5 : 4 : 3
    - (c) 3 : 4 : 5
    - (d) 20 : 15 : 12
12. If $A = \dfrac{1}{3} B$ and $B = \dfrac{1}{2} C$, then $A : B : C$ is :
    - (a) 1 : 3 : 6
    - (b) 3 : 1 : 2
    - (c) 2 : 3 : 6
    - (d) 3 : 2 : 6
13. If $2A = 3B$ and $4B = 5C$, then $A : C$ is :
    - (a) 4 : 3
    - (b) 8 : 15
    - (c) 15 : 8
    - (d) 3 : 4
14. If $x : y = 5 : 2$, then the value of $(8x + 9y) : (8x + 2y)$ is :
    - (a) 26 : 61
    - (b) 61 : 26
    - (c) 29 : 22
    - (d) 22 : 29
15. If $x : y = 2 : 1$, then $(x^2 - y^2) : (x^2 + y^2)$ is :
    - (a) 3 : 5
    - (b) 5 : 3
    - (c) 1 : 3
    - (d) 3 : 1
16. If $(4x^2 - 3y^2) : (2x^2 + 5y^2) = 12 : 19$, then $x : y$ is :   **(U.D.C. 1993)**

    (*a*) 2 : 3   (*b*) 1 : 2   (*c*) 3 : 2   (*d*) 2 : 1

17. The fourth proportional of 0.2, 0.12 and 0.3 is :

    (*a*) 0.13   (*b*) 0.15   (*c*) 0.18   (*d*) 0.8

18. The third proportional to 0.36 and 0.48 is :

    (*a*) 0.64   (*b*) 0.1728   (*c*) $24\sqrt{.0003}$ (*d*) None of these

19. The mean proportion between 0.32 and 0.02 is :

    (*a*) 0.8   (*b*) 0.08   (*c*) 0.008   (*d*) 0.4

20. The third proportional to $(x^2 - y^2)$ and $(x - y)$ is :

    (*a*) $\dfrac{x+y}{x-y}$ (*b*) $\dfrac{x-y}{x+y}$ (*c*) $x + y$ (*d*) $(x - y)$

(Central Excise & I.Tax 1992)

21. The ratio of third proportional to 12 and 30 and the mean proportional of 9 and 25 is :   (**C.B.I. 1993**)

    (*a*) 2 : 1   (*b*) 5 : 1   (*c*) 7 : 15   (*d*) 9 : 14

22. In a ratio which is equal to 3 : 4, if the antecedent is 12, then consequent is :

    (*a*) 9   (*b*) 16   (*c*) 20   (*d*) 24

23. If 0.4 of a number is equal to 0.06 of another number, then the ratio of the numbers is :

    (*a*) 2 : 3   (*b*) 3 : 4   (*c*) 3 : 20   (*d*) 20 : 3

24. A fraction which bears the same ratio to $\dfrac{1}{27}$ that $\dfrac{3}{11}$ does to $\dfrac{5}{9}$, is :

    (*a*) $\dfrac{1}{55}$ (*b*) 55   (*c*) $\dfrac{1}{11}$ (*d*) $\dfrac{3}{11}$

(Assistant Grade 1993)

25. If $a + b : b + c : c + a = 6 : 7 : 8$ and $a + b + c = 14$, then the value of c is :   (**C.B.I. 1993**)

    (*a*) 6   (*b*) 7   (*c*) 8   (*d*) 14

26. If $\dfrac{a}{3} = \dfrac{b}{4} = \dfrac{c}{7}$, then $\dfrac{a+b+c}{c}$ is equal to :

    (*a*) 7   (*b*) 2   (*c*) $\dfrac{1}{2}$ (*d*) $\dfrac{1}{7}$

27. If $\dfrac{x}{5} = \dfrac{y}{8}$, then $(x + 5) : (y + 8)$ is equal to :

    (*a*) 3 : 5   (*b*) 13 : 8   (*c*) 8 : 5   (*d*) 5 : 8

28. If $x : y = 6 : 5$, then $(5x + 3y) : (5x - 3y)$ is equal to :

    (*a*) 2 : 1   (*b*) 3 : 1   (*c*) 5 : 3   (*d*) 5 : 2

(Assistant Grade 1992)

29. If the ratio of A to B is 9 times the ratio of B to A, then $\dfrac{A}{B}$ could be :

    (*a*) 9   (*b*) 3   (*c*) $\dfrac{1}{3}$ (*d*) $\dfrac{1}{9}$

30. What is the ratio whose terms differ by 40 and the measure of which is $\frac{2}{7}$?
    (a) 16 : 56   (b) 10 : 50   (c) 20 : 70   (d) 36 : 76

31. If $x^2 + 4y^2 = 4xy$, then $x : y$ is :   **(Assistant Grade 1993)**
    (a) 2 : 1   (b) 1 : 2   (c) 1 : 1   (d) 1 : 4

32. If $5x^2 - 13xy + 6y^2 = 0$, then $x : y$ is :
    (a) 5 : 3 or 1 : 2   (b) 3 : 5 or 2 : 1
    (c) 2 : 1 only   (d) 3 : 5 only

33. Two numbers are in the ratio 3 : 5. If each number is increased by 10, the ratio becomes 5 : 7. The numbers are :
    (a) 3, 5   (b) 12, 20   (c) 15, 25   (d) 18, 30

34. What same number must be added to each term of the ratio 7 : 13 so that the ratio becomes 2 : 3 ?
    (a) 1   (b) 2   (c) 3   (d) 5

35. What number should be subtracted from both the terms of the ratio 15 : 19 so as to make it as 3 : 4 ?   **(Assistant Grade 1994)**
    (a) 3   (b) 5   (c) 6   (d) 9

36. The least whole number which when subtracted from both the terms of the ratio 6 : 7 to give a ratio less than 16 : 21, is :
    (a) 2   (b) 3   (c) 4   (d) 6
    (Central Excise & I.Tax 1992)

37. The ratio between two numbers is 3 : 4. If each number is increased by 6, the ratio becomes 4 : 5. The difference between the numbers is :
    (a) 1   (b) 3   (c) 6   (d) 8

38. What number should be added to each of the numbers 8, 21, 13 and 31 so that the resulting numbers, in this order form a proportion ?
    (a) 2   (b) 3   (c) 5   (d) 7
    (U.D.C. 1993)

39. What number should be subtracted from each of the numbers 23, 30, 57 and 78 so that the remainders may be proportional ?
    (a) 4   (b) 5   (c) 6   (d) 7

40. Which of the following ratios is the greatest ?
    (a) 7 : 15   (b) 15 : 23   (c) 17 : 25   (d) 21 : 29

41. Two whole numbers whose sum is 72 cannot be in the ratio :
    (a) 5 : 7   (b) 3 : 5   (c) 4 : 5   (d) 3 : 4

42. If a carton containing a dozen mirrors is dropped, which of the following cannot be the ratio of broken mirrors to unbroken mirrors ?
    (a) 2 : 1   (b) 3 : 1   (c) 3 : 2   (d) 7 : 5
    (Bank P.O. 1991)

43. The ratio of two numbers is 3 : 4 and their sum is 420. The greater of the two numbers is : **(Railways 1991)**
    (a) 175   (b) 200   (c) 240   (d) 315

44. The ratio between two numbers is 3 : 4 and their l.c.m is 180. The first number is :
    (a) 60   (b) 45   (c) 20   (d) 15

45. The L.C.M. and H.C.F. of two numbers x and y are l and h repectively. Then,
    (a) $l : h = x : y$ (b) $x : h = l : y$ (c) $x : l = y : h$ (d) $x : h = y : l$

46. A and B together have Rs. 1210 with them. If $\dfrac{4}{15}$ of A's amount is equal to $\dfrac{2}{5}$ of B's amount, how much amount does B have ?
    (a) Rs. 466   (b) Rs. 484   (c) Rs. 550   (d) Rs. 664

47. Five bananas and four apples cost as much as three bananas and seven apples. The ratio of the cost of one banana to that of one apple is :
    (a) 3 : 2   (b) 4 : 3   (c) 3 : 4   (d) 1 : 3

48. The salaries of $A, B,$ and C are in the ratio of 1 : 2 : 3. The salary of B and C together is Rs. 6000. By what percent is the salary of C more than that of A ? **(Bank P.O. 1992)**
    (a) 100%   (b) 200%   (c) 300%   (d) 600%

49. The average age of three boys is 25 years and their ages are in the proportion 3 : 5 : 7.The age of the youngest boy is :
    (a) 21 years   (b) 18 years   (c) 15 years   (d) 9 years

50. An amount of Rs. 2430 is divided among A, B and C such that if their shares be reduced by Rs. 5, Rs. 10 and Rs. 15 respectively, the remainders shall be in the ratio 3 : 4 : 5. The share of B is :
    (a) Rs. 605   (b) Rs. 790   (c) Rs. 800   (d) Rs. 810

51. An amount of Rs. 735 was divided between A, B and C. If each of them had received Rs. 25 less, their shares would have been in the ratio of 1 : 3 : 2. The money received by C was :
    (a) Rs. 195   (b) Rs. 200   (c) Rs. 225   (d) Rs. 245

52. An amount of money is to be distributed among P, Q and R in the ratio 3 : 5 : 7. If Q's share is Rs. 1500, what is the difference between P's and R's shares ? **(Bank P.O. 1994)**
    (a) Rs. 1200   (b) Rs. 1500   (c) Rs. 1600   (d) Rs. 1900

53. A sum of money is to the divided among P, Q and R in the ratio of 2 : 3 : 5. If the total share of P and R together is Rs 400 more than that of Q, what is R's share in it ? **(Bank P.O. 1991)**
    (a) Rs. 400   (b) Rs. 500   (c) Rs. 600   (d) Rs. 750

54. X, Y and Z share a sum of money in the ratio 7 : 8 : 16. If Z receives Rs. 27 more than X, then the total money shared was :

(a) Rs. 48   (b) Rs. 93   (c) Rs. 279   (d) Rs. 558
(Central Excise & I.Tax 1991)

55. A profit of Rs. 30000 is to be distributed among A, B, C in the proportion 3 : 5 : 7. What will be the difference between B's and C's shares ?
(a) Rs. 2000   (b) Rs. 4000   (c) Rs. 10000   (d) Rs. 14000
(Bank P.O. 1993)

56. Rs. 407 are to be divided among A, B and C so that their shares are in the ratio of $\frac{1}{4} : \frac{1}{5} : \frac{1}{6}$. The respective shares of A, B, C are :
(a) Rs. 165, Rs, 132, Rs. 110   (b) Rs. 165, Rs, 110, Rs. 132
(c) Rs. 132, Rs. 110, Rs. 165   (d) Rs. 110, Rs. 132, Rs. 165
(Assistant Grade 1994)

57. If Rs 1066 are divided among A, B, C and D such that $A : B = 3 : 4$, $B : C = 5 : 6$ and $C : D = 7 : 5$, who will get the maximum ?
(a) B (b) A (c) C (d) D

58. A certain amount was divided between Salim and Rahim in the ratio of 4 : 3. If Rahim's share was Rs. 2400, the total amount was :
(a) Rs. 5600   (b) Rs. 3200   (c) Rs. 9600   (d) Rs. 16800
(Bank P.O. 1988)

59. The ratio of the ages of mother and son is 7 : 3. If the sum of their ages is 60 years, what is the difference in their ages ?
(a) 42 years   (b) 24 years   (c) 18 years   (d) 4 years

60. The speeds of three cars are in the ratio 5 : 4 : 6. The ratio between the times taken by them to travel the same distance is :
(a) 5 : 4 : 6   (b) 6 : 4 : 5   (c) 10 : 12 : 15   (d) 12 : 15 : 10

61. The sides of a triangle are in the ratio $\frac{1}{2} : \frac{1}{3} : \frac{1}{4}$ and its perimeter is 104 cm. The length of longest side is :
(a) 52 cm   (b) 48 cm   (c) 32 cm   (d) 26 cm

62. In a college, the ratio of the number of boys to girls is 8 : 5. If there are 160 girls, the total number of students in the college is :
(a) 100   (b) 250   (c) 260   (d) 416
(Central Excise & I.Tax 1992)

63. The prices of a scooter and T.V. are in the ratio of 5 : 4. If the scooter costs Rs. 4000 more than the T.V. set, the price of a T.V. set (in rupees) is :
(a) 12000   (b) 14000   (c) 16000   (d) 20000

64. Pencils, Pens and Exercise books in a shop are in the ratio of 10 : 2 : 3. If there are 120 pencils, the number of exercise books in the shop is :
(a) 36   (b) 48   (c) 72   (d) 400
(Assistant Grade 1993)

65. In a factory, the ratio of male workers to female workers was 5 : 3. If the number of female workers was less by 40, what was the total number of workers in the factory ?

    (*a*) 100   (*b*) 160   (*c*) 200   (*d*) 500

66. An alloy is to contain copper and zinc in the ratio 9 : 4. The zinc required (in kg) to be melted with 24 kg of copper, is ? **(Assistant Grade 1994)**

    (*a*) $10\frac{2}{3}$ (*b*) $10\frac{1}{3}$ (*c*) $9\frac{2}{3}$ (*d*) 9

67. The ratio of income of *A* to that of *B* is 5 : 4 and the expenditure of *A* to that of *B* is 3 : 2. If at the end of the year, each saves Rs. 800, the income of *A* is : **(Assistant Grade 1994)**

    (*a*) Rs. 1600   (*b*) Rs. 1800   (*c*) Rs. 2000   (*d*) Rs. 2200

68. A dog takes 3 leaps for every 5 leaps of a hare. If one leap of the dog is equal to 3 leaps of the hare, the ratio of the speed of the dog to that of the hare is : **(U.D.C. 1993)**

    (*a*) 8 : 5   (*b*) 9 : 5   (*c*) 8 : 7   (*d*) 9: 7

69. 60 kg of an alloy *A* is mixed with 100 kg of alloy *B*. If alloy *A* has lead and tin in the ratio 3 : 2 and alloy *B* has tin and copper in the ratio 1 : 4, then the amount of tin in the new alloy is :

    (*a*) 36 kg   (*b*) 44 kg   (*c*) 53 kg   (*d*) 80 kg

70. 94 is divided into two parts in such a way that fifth part of first and the eighth part of the second are in the ratio 3 : 4. The first part is :

    (*a*) 27   (*b*) 30   (*c*) 36   (*d*) 48

71. $33\frac{1}{3}\%$ of a man's output is equal to 50% of a second man's daily output. If the second man turns out 1500 screws daily, then the first man's output in terms of making screws is : **(I.Tax 1991)**

    (*a*) 500   (*b*) 1000   (*c*) 2000   (*d*) 2250

72. The sum of three numbers is 98. If the ratio of the first to the second is 2 : 3 and that of second to the third is 5 : 8, then the second number is :

    (*a*) 20   (*b*) 30   (*c*) 48   (*d*) 58

73. If three numbers in the ratio 3 : 2 : 5 be such that the sum of their squares is 1862, the middle number will be : **(Teacher's Exam. 1991)**

    (*a*) 7   (*b*) 14   (*c*) 21   (*d*) 35

74. Some money is divided among three persons *A*, *B*, *C* in such a way that 5 times *A*'s share, 3 times *B*'s share and 2 times *C*'s share are all equal. The ratio between *A*, *B* and *C*'s shares is :

    (*a*) 5 : 3 : 2   (*b*) 2 : 2 : 5   (*c*) 15 : 10 : 6 (*d*) 6 : 10 : 15

75. A sum of Rs. 427 is to be divided among *A*, *B* and *C* such that 3 times *A*'s share, 4 times *B*'s share and 7 times *C*'s share are all equal. The share of *C* is : **(Assistant Grade 1994)**

    (*a*) Rs. 84   (*b*) Rs. 147   (*c*) Rs. 196   (*d*) Rs. 240

76. If Rs. 1540 be divided amongst A, B, C in such a way that the share of B is equal to $\frac{3}{11}$ of what A and C together receive. Then, B's share will be :   **(Central Excise & I.Tax 1993)**

  (a) Rs. 330   (b) Rs. 420   (c). Rs. 880   (d) Rs. 1210

77. Rs. 1870 are divided into three parts in such a way that half of the first part, one-third of the second part and one-sixth of the third part are equal. The third part is :

  (a) Rs. 510   (b) Rs. 680   (c) Rs. 850   (d) Rs. 1020

78. Rs. 2040 are divided among A, B, C such that A gets $\frac{2}{3}$ of what B gets and B gets $\frac{1}{4}$ of what C gets. Then B's share is :

  (a) Rs. 180   (b) Rs. 240   (c) Rs. 360   (d) Rs. 480

79. A sum of money is divided among A, B, C such that to each rupee A gets, B gets 65 paise and C gets 35 paise. If C's share is Rs. 28, the sum is :

  (a) Rs. 120   (b) Rs. 140   (c) Rs. 160   (d) Rs. 180

80. Rs. 730 were divided among A, B, C in such a way that if A gets Rs. 3, then B gets Rs. 4 and if B gets Rs. 3.50 then C gets Rs. 3. The share of B exceeds that of C by :   **(Central Excise & I.Tax 1990)**

  (a) Rs. 30   (b) Rs. 40   (c) Rs. 70   (d) Rs. 210

81. Rs. 53 are divided among three persons A, B, C in such a way that A gets Rs 7 more than what B gets and B gets Rs. 8 more than what C gets. The ratio of their shares is :

  (a) 16 : 9 : 18   (b) 25 : 18 : 10

  (c) 18 : 25 : 10   (d) 15 : 8 : 30

82. Rs. 120 are divided among A, B, C such that A's share is Rs. 20 more than B's and Rs. 20 less than C's. What is B's share ?   **(Railways 1991)**

  (a) Rs. 10   (b) Rs. 15   (c) Rs. 20   (d) Rs. 25

83. A sum of Rs. 1300 is divided among P, Q, R and S such that :

$$\frac{P\text{'s share}}{Q\text{'s share}} = \frac{Q\text{'s share}}{R\text{'s share}} = \frac{R\text{'s share}}{S\text{'s share}} = \frac{2}{3}.$$

What is P's share ?

  (a) Rs. 320   (b) Rs. 240   (c) Rs. 160   (d) Rs. 140

84. Rs. 600 are divided among A, B, C so that Rs. 40 more than $\frac{2}{5}$ th of A's share, Rs. 20 more than $\frac{2}{7}$th of B's share and Rs. 10 more than $\frac{9}{17}$ th of C's share may all be equal. What is A's share ?

  (a) Rs. 150   (b) Rs. 170   (c) Rs. 200   (d) Rs. 280

85. Rs. 180 contained in a box consists of one rupee, 50-paise and 25-paise coins in the proportion of 2 : 3 :4. What is the number of 50-paise coins ?   **(Hotel Management 1992)**

    (*a*) 120   (*b*) 150   (*c*) 180   (*d*) 240

86. A box contains Rs. 56 in the form of coins of one rupee, 50-paise and 25-paise. The number of 50-paise coins is double the number of 25 paise coins and four times the number of one rupee coins. How many 50 paise coins are there in the box ?   **(Bank P.O. 1994)**

    (*a*) 64   (*b*) 32   (*c*) 16   (*d*) Data inadequate

87. In a cash bag there are currency notes in denominations of Rs. 20, Rs. 10 and Rs. 5 in the ratio 3 : 4 : 5. If the total amount in the bag is Rs. 1000, the number of five-rupee notes is : **(Excise & I. Tax 1991)**

    (*a*) 40   (*b*) 36   (*c*) 30   (*d*) 25

88. A purse contains one-rupee, 50-paise, 25-paise and 20-paise coins in the ratio of 1 : 2 : 4 : 5. If the total value of coins is Rs. 400, then the number of 20-paise coins exceeding those of 25-paise coins is :

    (*a*) 100   (*b*) 200   (*c*) 400   (*d*) 500

89. In a school, 10% of the boys are same in number as $\frac{1}{4}$ th of the girls and 10% of the girls are same in number as $\frac{1}{25}$ th of the boys. What is the ratio of boys to girls in that school ?   **(Bank P.O. 1992)**

    (*a*) 3 : 2   (*b*) 5 : 2   (*c*) 2 : 1   (*d*) 4 ; 3

90. The incomes of *A, B, C* are in the ratio of 7 : 9 : 12 and their spendings are in the ratio of 8 : 9 : 15. If *A* saves $\frac{1}{4}$ th of his income, then the savings of *A, B, C* are in the ratio of :

    (*a*) 56 : 99 : 69   (*b*) 99 : 56 : 69 (*c*) 69 : 56 : 99 (*d*) 99 : 69 : 56

91. If 76 is divided into four parts proportional to 7, 5, 3, 4, the smallest part is :   **(Assistant Grade 1993)**

    (*a*) 12   (*b*) 15   (*c*) 16   (*d*) 19

92. Ramlal divides two sums of money among his four sons Anil, Rahul, Deepak and Sanjeev. The first sum is divided in the ratio 4 : 3 : 2 : 1 and second in the ratio 5 : 6 : 7 : 8. If the second sum is twice the first, the largest total is received by :

    (*a*) Anil   (*b*) Rahul   (*c*) Deepak   (*d*) Sanjeev

93. An ornament weighs 12.5 gms of which 2.5 gm is pure silver and the rest alloy. The ratio of pure silver to alloy is : **(Assistant Grade 1992)**

    (*a*) 1 : 4   (*b*) 1 : 5   (*c*) 4 : 1   (*d*) 4 : 5

94. The marks obtained by Praveen and Vijay are in the ratio of 4 : 5 and those obtained by Vijay and Suresh are in the ratio of 3 : 2. The marks obtained by Praveen and Suresh are in the ratio of : **(Bank P.O. 1991)**

    (*a*) 2 : 1   (*b*) 5 : 3   (*c*) 6 : 5   (*d*) 5 : 6

95. Anshul got twice as many marks in English as in Science. His total marks in English, Science and Maths are 180. If the proportion of his marks in English and Maths is 2 : 3, what are his marks in Science ?

(a) 15   (b) 30   (c) 60   (d) 90

96. Two numbers are in the ratio 3 : 4 and the product of their L.C.M. and H.C.F. is 10800. The sum of the numbers is :

(a) 180   (b) 210   (c) 225   (d) 240

97. The ages of X and Y are in the ratio of 3 : 1. Fifteen years hence, the ratio will be 2 : 1. Their present ages (in years) are :

(a) 30, 10   (b) 45, 15   (c) 21, 7   (d) 60, 20

(**Assistant Grade 1994**)

98. The ratio of the number of boys and girls in a school is 3 : 2. If 20% of the boys and 25% of the girls are scholarship holders, the percentage of the school students who are not scholarship holders, is :

(a) 56   (b) 70   (c) 78   (d) 80

99. Gold is 19 times as heavy as water and copper is 9 times as heavy as water. In what ratio should these be mixed to get an alloy 15 times as heavy as water ? (**Central Excise & I. Tax 1992**)

(a) 1 : 1   (b) 2 : 3   (c) 1 : 2   (d) 3 : 2

100. 85 kg of a mixture contains milk and water in the ratio 27 : 7. How much more water is to be added to get a new mixture containing milk and water in the ratio 3 : 1 ?

(a) 5 kg   (b) 6.5 kg   (c) 7.25 kg   (d) 8 kg

101. 15 litres of a mixture contains 20% alcohol and the rest water. If 3 litres of water be mixed in it, the percentage of alcohol in the new mixture will be :

(a) 15   (b) $16\frac{2}{3}$ (c) 17   (d) $18\frac{1}{2}$

102. 20 litres of a mixture contains milk and water in the ratio 5 : 3. If 4 litres of this mixture are replaced by 4 litres of milk, the ratio of milk to water in the new mixture will become :

(a) 2 : 1   (b) 7 : 3   (c) 8 : 3   (d) 4 : 3

103. A and B are two alloys of gold and copper prepared by mixing metals in the ratio 7 : 2 and 7 : 11 respectively. If equal quantities of the alloys are melted to form a third alloy C, the ratio of gold and copper in C will be :

(a) 5 : 9   (b) 5 : 7   (c) 7 : 5   (d) 9 : 5

104. A mixture contains milk and water in the ratio 5 : 1. On adding 5 litres of water, the ratio of milk to water becomes 5 : 2. The quantity of milk in the original mixture is :

(a) 16 litres   (b) 25 litres   (c) 22.75 litres   (d) 32.5 litres

105. Two equal glasses are respectively $\frac{1}{3}$ and $\frac{1}{4}$ full of milk. They are then filled with water and the contents mixed in a tumbler. The ratio of milk and water in the tumbler is :

(a) 7 : 5   (b) 7 : 17   (c) 9 : 21   (d) 11 : 23

106. Three bottles are filled with a mixture of milk and water in the ratio 4 : 3, 5 : 4 and 7 : 6 respectively. If the contents of three bottles are poured into a single vessel, then the ratio of milk to water in the new vessel is :

(a) $\left(\dfrac{4}{3} + \dfrac{5}{4} + \dfrac{7}{6} : \dfrac{3}{4} + \dfrac{4}{5} + \dfrac{6}{7}\right)$

(b) $\left(\dfrac{4}{7} + \dfrac{5}{9} + \dfrac{7}{13} : \dfrac{3}{7} + \dfrac{4}{9} + \dfrac{6}{13}\right)$

(c) $\left(\dfrac{4}{3} + \dfrac{5}{4} + \dfrac{7}{6} : 1 + 1 + 1\right)$

(d) $\left(1 + 1 + 1 : \dfrac{3}{4} + \dfrac{4}{5} + \dfrac{6}{7}\right)$

ANSWERS

1. (b)	2. (c)	3. (b)	4. (a)	5. (b)	6. (a)	7. (c)	8. (b)	9. (b)
10. (c)	11. (c)	12. (a)	13. (c)	14. (c)	15. (a)	16. (c)	17. (c)	18.(a)
19. (b)	20. (b)	21. (b)	22. (b)	23. (c)	24. (a)	25. (a)	26. (b)	27. (d)
28. (b)	29. (b)	30. (a)	31. (a)	32. (b)	33. (c)	34. (d)	35. (a)	36. (b)
37. (c)	38. (c)	39. (c)	40. (d)	41. (d)	42. (c)	43. (c)	44. (b)	45. (b)
46. (b)	47. (a)	48. (b)	49. (c)	50. (d)	51. (c)	52. (a)	53. (b)	54. (b)
55. (b)	56. (a)	57. (c)	58. (a)	59. (b)	60. (d)	61. (b)	62. (d)	63. (c)
64. (a)	65. (b)	66. (a)	67. (c)	68. (b)	69. (b)	70. (b)	71. (d)	72. (b)
73. (b)	74. (d)	75. (a)	76. (a)	77. (d)	78. (c)	79. (c)	80. (b)	81. (b)
82. (c)	83. (c)	84. (a)	85. (a)	86. (a)	87. (a)	88. (a)	89. (b)	90. (a)
91. (a)	92. (a)	93. (a)	94. (c)	95. (b)	96. (b)	97. (b)	98. (c)	99. (d)
100. (a)	101. (b)	102. (b)	103. (c)	104. (b)	105. (b)	106. (b)		

SOLUTIONS

1. $A : B = 5 : 7$

$B : C = 6 : 11 = 6 \times \dfrac{7}{6} : 11 \times \dfrac{7}{6} = 7 : \dfrac{77}{6}$.

$\therefore\ A : B : C = 5 : 7 : \dfrac{77}{6} = 30 : 42 : 77$.

2. $\dfrac{p}{r} = \left(\dfrac{p}{q} \times \dfrac{q}{r}\right) = \dfrac{3}{4} \times \dfrac{8}{9} = \dfrac{2}{3}$. So, $p : r = 2 : 3$.

3. $\dfrac{A}{D} = \left(\dfrac{A}{B} \times \dfrac{B}{C} \times \dfrac{C}{D}\right) = \left(\dfrac{8}{15} \times \dfrac{5}{8} \times \dfrac{4}{5}\right) = \dfrac{4}{15}$. So, $A : D = 4 : 15$.

4. $4^{3.5} : 2^5 = (2^2)^{7/2} : 2^5 = 2^7 : 2^5 = 2^2 : 1 = 4 : 1$.

[Dividing each term by 2^5]

5. 15% of $x = 20\%$ of $y \Leftrightarrow \dfrac{15x}{100} = \dfrac{20y}{100} \Leftrightarrow \dfrac{x}{y} = \dfrac{4}{3}$.

6. $7 \times 22.5 = x \times 17.5 \Leftrightarrow x = \dfrac{7 \times 22.5}{17.5} \Leftrightarrow x = 9.$

7. $\dfrac{1}{5} \times \dfrac{1}{1.25} = \dfrac{1}{x^2} \Leftrightarrow x^2 = 5 \times 1.25 \Leftrightarrow x^2 = 6.25 \Leftrightarrow x = 2.5.$

8. $0.4 \times x = 1.4 \times 1.4 \Leftrightarrow x = \dfrac{1.4 \times 1.4}{0.4} = \dfrac{14 \times 14}{40} = 4.9.$

9. Required ratio $= \dfrac{2}{3} \times \dfrac{6}{11} \times \dfrac{11}{2} = \dfrac{2}{1}$, *i.e.* $2 : 1.$

10. Let $2A = 3B = 4C = k.$

Then, $A = \dfrac{k}{2}, B = \dfrac{k}{3}$ and $C = \dfrac{k}{4}.$

$\therefore A : B : C = \dfrac{k}{2} : \dfrac{k}{3} : \dfrac{k}{4} = 6 : 4 : 3.$

11. $\dfrac{1}{3}A = \dfrac{1}{4}B = \dfrac{1}{5}C = k.$ Then, $A = 3k, B = 4k$ and $C = 5k.$

$\therefore A : B : C = 3k : 4k : 5k = 3 : 4 : 5.$

12. $\dfrac{A}{B} = \dfrac{1}{3}$ and $\dfrac{B}{C} = \dfrac{1}{2}.$

$\therefore A : B = 1 : 3$ and $B : C = 1 : 2 = 3 : 6.$

$\therefore A : B : C = 1 : 3 : 6.$

13. $\dfrac{A}{B} = \dfrac{3}{2}$ and $\dfrac{B}{C} = \dfrac{5}{4}.$

$\therefore \dfrac{A}{C} = \dfrac{A}{B} \times \dfrac{B}{C} = \dfrac{3}{2} \times \dfrac{5}{4} = \dfrac{15}{8}.$ So, $A : C = 15 : 8.$

14. Given : $\dfrac{x}{y} = \dfrac{5}{2}.$

$\therefore \dfrac{8x + 9y}{8x + 2y} = \dfrac{8\left(\dfrac{x}{y}\right) + 9}{8\left(\dfrac{x}{y}\right) + 2} = \dfrac{8 \times \dfrac{5}{2} + 9}{8 \times \dfrac{5}{2} + 2} = \dfrac{29}{22}.$

15. $\dfrac{x}{y} = \dfrac{2}{1} \Rightarrow \dfrac{x^2}{y^2} = \dfrac{4}{1}.$

$\therefore \dfrac{x^2 - y^2}{x^2 + y^2} = \dfrac{4 - 1}{4 + 1} = \dfrac{3}{5} \qquad \text{[by componendo \& dividendo]}$

16. $\dfrac{4x^2 - 3y^2}{2x^2 + 5y^2} = \dfrac{12}{19} \Leftrightarrow 19\,(4x^2 - 3y^2) = 12\,(2x^2 + 5y^2)$

$\Leftrightarrow (76x^2 - 24x^2) = (60y^2 + 57y^2)$

$\Leftrightarrow 52x^2 = 117y^2 \Leftrightarrow 4x^2 = 9y^2$

$$\Leftrightarrow \frac{x^2}{y^2} = \frac{9}{4} \Leftrightarrow \frac{x}{y} = \frac{3}{2}.$$

17. Let $0.2 : 0.12 = 0.3 : x$.

Then, $0.2x = 0.12 \times 0.3$ or $x = \dfrac{0.12 \times 0.3}{0.2} = 0.18$.

18. Let $0.36 : 0.48 = 0.48 : x$.

Then, $0.36x = 0.48 \times 0.48$ or $x = \dfrac{0.48 \times 0.48}{0.36} = 0.64$.

19. Required mean proportion $= \sqrt{0.32 \times 0.02} = \sqrt{\dfrac{64}{10000}} = \dfrac{8}{100} = .08$.

20. Let $(x^2 - y^2) : (x - y) = (x - y) : z$.

Then, $z = \dfrac{(x - y)(x - y)}{(x^2 - y^2)} = \dfrac{(x - y)}{(x + y)}$.

21. Let $12 : 30 = 30 : x$. Then, $x = \dfrac{30 \times 30}{12} = 75$.

Also, $y = \sqrt{9 \times 25} = 15$.

$\therefore$ Required ratio $= x : y = 75 : 15 = 5 : 1$.

22. $\dfrac{3}{4} = \dfrac{12}{x} \Leftrightarrow 3x = 48 \Leftrightarrow x = 16$.

23. $0.4A = 0.06B \Leftrightarrow \dfrac{A}{B} = \dfrac{0.06}{0.4} = \dfrac{6}{40} = \dfrac{3}{20}$.

24. $x : \dfrac{1}{27} = \dfrac{3}{11} : \dfrac{5}{9} \Leftrightarrow \dfrac{5}{9} x = \dfrac{1}{27} \times \dfrac{3}{11}$.

$\therefore \dfrac{5}{9} x = \dfrac{1}{99}$ or $x = \left(\dfrac{1}{99} \times \dfrac{9}{5} \right) = \dfrac{1}{55}$.

25. Let $(a + b) = 6k$, $b + c = 7k$ and $c + a = 8k$.

Then, $2(a + b + c) = 21k$ or $2 \times 14 = 21k$ or $k = \dfrac{4}{3}$.

$\therefore a + b = \left(6 \times \dfrac{4}{3} \right) = 8$. So, $c = (a + b + c) - (a + b) = (14 - 8) = 6$.

26. $\dfrac{a}{3} = \dfrac{b}{4} = \dfrac{c}{7} = k$. Then, $a = 3k$, $b = 4k$ and $c = 7k$.

$\therefore \dfrac{a + b + c}{c} = \dfrac{3k + 4k + 7k}{7k} = \dfrac{14k}{7k} = 2$.

27. Let $\dfrac{x}{5} = \dfrac{y}{8} = k$. Then, $x = 5k$ and $y = 8k$.

$\therefore \dfrac{x + 5}{y + 8} = \dfrac{5k + 5}{8k + 8} = \dfrac{5(k + 1)}{8(k + 1)} = \dfrac{5}{8}$.

28. Given : $\dfrac{x}{y} = \dfrac{6}{5}$.

$$\therefore \frac{5x+3y}{5x-3y} = \frac{5\left(\dfrac{x}{y}\right)+3}{5\left(\dfrac{x}{y}\right)-3} = \frac{5\times\dfrac{6}{5}+3}{5\times\dfrac{6}{5}-3} = \frac{9}{3} = \frac{3}{1}.$$

29. $\dfrac{A}{B} = \dfrac{9B}{A} \Leftrightarrow \dfrac{A^2}{B^2} = \dfrac{9}{1} \Leftrightarrow \dfrac{A}{B} = \dfrac{3}{1}.$

30. $\dfrac{x}{x+40} = \dfrac{2}{7} \Leftrightarrow 7x = 2x + 80 \Leftrightarrow x = 16.$

$\therefore$ The ratio is $16 : 56.$

31. $x^2 + 4y^2 = 4xy \Leftrightarrow x^2 - 4xy + 4y^2 = 0 \Leftrightarrow (x-2y)^2 = 0$

$$\Leftrightarrow x - 2y = 0 \Leftrightarrow x = 2y \Leftrightarrow \frac{x}{y} = \frac{2}{1}.$$

32. $5x^2 - 13xy + 6y^2 = 0 \Leftrightarrow 5x^2 - 10xy - 3xy + 6y^2 = 0$

$\Leftrightarrow 5x(x-2y) - 3y(x-2y) = 0$

$\Leftrightarrow (x-2y)(5x-3y) = 0$

$\Leftrightarrow x - 2y = 0$ or $5x - 3y = 0$

$\Leftrightarrow x = 2y$ or $5x = 3y$

$\Leftrightarrow x : y = 2 : 1$ or $x : y = 3 : 5.$

33. Let the numbers be $3x$ and $5x$.

$\dfrac{3x+10}{5x+10} = \dfrac{5}{7} \Leftrightarrow 7(3x+10) = 5(5x+10) \Leftrightarrow x = 5.$

So, the numbers are **15 and 25.**

34. Let x be added.

Then, $\dfrac{7+x}{13+x} = \dfrac{2}{3} \Leftrightarrow 3(7+x) = 2(13+x) \Leftrightarrow x = 5.$

35. Let x be subtracted. Then,

$\dfrac{15-x}{19-x} = \dfrac{3}{4} \Leftrightarrow 4(15-x) = 3(19-x) \Leftrightarrow x = 3.$

36. Let x be subtracted. Then,

$\dfrac{6-x}{7-x} < \dfrac{16}{21} \Leftrightarrow 21(6-x) < 16(7-x) \Leftrightarrow 5x > 14 \Leftrightarrow x > 2.8.$

$\therefore$ Least such number is **3.**

37. Let the numbers be $3x$ and $4x$. Then,

$\dfrac{3x+6}{4x+6} = \dfrac{4}{5} \Leftrightarrow 5(3x+6) = 4(4x+6) \Leftrightarrow x = 6.$

So, the numbers are **18 and 24.**

$\therefore$ Difference between the numbers $= (24 - 18) = 6.$

38. Let $\dfrac{8+x}{21+x} = \dfrac{13+x}{31+x}.$

Then, $(8+x)(31+x) = (13+x)(21+x)$

or $39x + 248 = 34x + 273$ or $5x = 25$ or $x = 5.$

39. Let $\dfrac{23-x}{30-x}=\dfrac{57-x}{78-x}$.

    $\therefore (23-x)(78-x)=(57-x)(30-x)$

    or $-101x+1794=1710-87x \Leftrightarrow 14x=84 \Leftrightarrow x=6$.

40. $\dfrac{7}{15}=0.466$, $\dfrac{15}{23}=0.652$, $\dfrac{17}{25}=0.68$ & $\dfrac{21}{29}=0.724$.

    Clearly, 0.724 is greatest and hence 21 : 29 is greatest.

41. The sum of the ratio terms must divide 72.

    So, the ratio cannot be 3 : 4.

42. For dividing 12 into two whole numbers, the sum of the terms of the ratio must be a factor of 12.

    So, they cannot be in the ratio 3 : 2.

43. Required number $=\left(420 \times \dfrac{4}{7}\right)=240$.

44. Let the numbers be $3x$ and $4x$.

    Then, their l.c.m. $= 12x$.

    Now, $12x=180 \Leftrightarrow x=15$.

    $\therefore$ First number $=45$.

45. Product of numbers = Product of their H.C.F. & L.C.M.

    $\therefore xy=lh \Leftrightarrow \dfrac{x}{h}=\dfrac{l}{y} \Leftrightarrow x:h=l:y$.

46. $\dfrac{4}{15}A=\dfrac{2}{5}B \Rightarrow \dfrac{A}{B}=\left(\dfrac{2}{5}\times\dfrac{15}{4}\right)=\dfrac{3}{2}$. Thus, $A:B=3:2$.

    $\therefore$ B's share = Rs. $\left(1210\times\dfrac{2}{5}\right)$ = Rs. 484.

47. Let the cost of each banana be x paise and that of each apple be y paise. Then,

    $5x+4y=3x+7y \Leftrightarrow 2x=3y \Leftrightarrow \dfrac{x}{y}=\dfrac{3}{2}$.

    $\therefore$ Required ratio is 3 : 2.

48. Let the salaries of A, B, C be x, $2x$ and $3x$ respectively.

    Then, $2x+3x=6000 \Rightarrow x=1200$.

    $\therefore$ A's salary = Rs. 1200, B's salary = Rs. 2400, and C's salary = Rs. 3600.

    $\therefore$ Excess of C's salary over A's $=\left(\dfrac{2400}{1200}\times 100\right)\%=200\%$.

49. Total age of 3 boys $=(25 \times 3)$ years $= 75$ years.

    $\therefore$ Age of the youngest $=\left(75\times\dfrac{3}{15}\right)=15$ years.

50. Remainder = Rs. $[2430-(5+10+15)]$ = Rs. 2400.

$\therefore B$'s share = Rs. $\left[\left(2400 \times \dfrac{4}{12}\right) + 10\right]$ = Rs. 810.

51. Remainder = Rs. $(735 - (25 \times 3))$ = Rs. 660.

$\therefore$ Money received by C = Rs. $\left[\left(660 \times \dfrac{2}{6}\right) + 25\right]$ = Rs. 225.

52. Let $P = 3x$, $Q = 5x$ and $R = 7x$.

Then, $5x = 1500 \Leftrightarrow x = 300$.

$\therefore P = 900$, $Q = 1500$ and $R = 2100$.

Hence, $(R - P) = (2100 - 900) = 1200$.

53. Let $P = 2x$, $Q = 3x$ and $R = 5x$.

Now $P + R - Q = 400 \Leftrightarrow 2x + 5x - 3x = 400 \Leftrightarrow x = 100$.

$\therefore R = 5x = 500$.

54. Let $X = 7x$, $Y = 8x$ & $Z = 16x$.

Then, total money = $31x$.

Now, $Z - X = 27 \Leftrightarrow 16x - 7x = 27 \Leftrightarrow x = 3$.

$\therefore$ Total money = $31x$ = Rs. 93.

55. B's share = Rs. $\left(30000 \times \dfrac{5}{15}\right)$ = Rs. 10000.

C's share = Rs. $\left(30000 \times \dfrac{7}{15}\right)$ = Rs. 14000.

$\therefore$ Difference in B's & C's shares = Rs. 4000.

56. $A : B : C = \dfrac{1}{4} : \dfrac{1}{5} : \dfrac{1}{6} = 15 : 12 : 10$.

A's share = Rs. $\left(407 \times \dfrac{15}{37}\right)$ = Rs.165,

B's share = Rs. $\left(407 \times \dfrac{12}{37}\right)$ = Rs. 132,

C's share = Rs. $[407 - (165 + 132)]$ = Rs. 110.

57. $A : B = 3 : 4$, $B : C = 5 : 6 = 5 \times \dfrac{4}{5} : 6 \times \dfrac{4}{5} = 4 : \dfrac{24}{5}$.

$\therefore A : B : C = 3 : 4 : \dfrac{24}{5} = 15 : 20 : 24$ & $C : D = 7 : 5$

or $A : B : C = 15 : 20 : 24$ & $C : D = \dfrac{24}{7} \times 7 : \dfrac{24}{7} \times 5$

or $A : B : C = 15 : 20 : 24$ & $C : D = 24 : \dfrac{120}{7}$.

$\therefore A : B : C : D = 15 : 20 : 24 : \dfrac{120}{7} = 105 : 140 : 168 : 120$.

Clearly, C will get the maximum amount.

58. Let $S = 4x$ and $R = 3x$. Total amount = $7x$.

Then, $3x = 2400 \Leftrightarrow x = 800$.

$\therefore$ Total amount $= 7x =$ Rs. 5600

59. Mother's age $= \left(60 \times \dfrac{7}{10}\right) = 42$ years.

Son's age $= (60 - 42)$ years $= 18$ years.
Difference of their ages $= (42 - 18)$ years $= 24$ years.

60. Ratio of times taken $= \dfrac{1}{5} : \dfrac{1}{4} : \dfrac{1}{6} = 12 : 15 : 10$.

61. Ratio of sides $= \dfrac{1}{2} : \dfrac{1}{3} : \dfrac{1}{4} = 6 : 4 : 3$.

Largest side $= \left(104 \times \dfrac{6}{13}\right)$ cm $= 48$ cm.

62. Let the number of boys and girls be $8x$ and $5x$.
Then, total number of students $= 13x$.
Now, $5x = 160 \Leftrightarrow x = 32$.
$\therefore$ Total number of students $= 13x = 13 \times 32 = 416$.

63. Let the costs of scooter & T.V. be $5x$ and $4x$.
Then, $5x - 4x = 4000 \Leftrightarrow x = 4000$.
$\therefore$ Cost of a T.V. $= 4x =$ Rs. 16000.

64. Let Pencils $= 10x$, Pens $= 2x$ & Exercise books $= 3x$.
Now, $10x = 120 \Leftrightarrow x = 12$.
$\therefore$ Number of exercise books $= 3x = 36$.

65. Let males $= 5x$ and females $= 3x$. Then, total $= 8x$.
Now, $5x - 3x = 40 \Leftrightarrow x = 20$.
$\therefore$ Total number of workers in the factory $= 8x = 160$.

66. $9 : 4 :: 24 : x \Leftrightarrow 9x = 4 \times 24 \Leftrightarrow x = \dfrac{4 \times 24}{9} = 10\dfrac{2}{3}$ kg.

67. Let the incomes of A and B be $5x$ & $4x$ and the expenditures of A and B be $3y$ and $2y$. Then,
$5x - 3y = 800$ and $4x - 2y = 800$.
On solving we get : $x = 400$.
$\therefore$ A's income $= 5x =$ Rs. 2000.

68. Dog : Hare $= (3 \times 3)$ leaps of hare : 5 leaps of hare $= 9 : 5$.

69. Tin in 60 kg. of $A = \left(60 \times \dfrac{2}{5}\right) = 24$ kg.

Tin in 100 kg of $B = \left(100 \times \dfrac{1}{5}\right) = 20$ kg.

$\therefore$ Amount of tin in new alloy $= (24 + 20)$ kg $= 44$ kg.

70. $\dfrac{(A/5)}{(B/8)} = \dfrac{3}{4} \Leftrightarrow \dfrac{A}{5} \times \dfrac{8}{B} = \dfrac{3}{4} \Leftrightarrow \dfrac{A}{B} = \dfrac{3}{4} \times \dfrac{5}{8} = \dfrac{15}{32}$.

Thus, $A : B = 15 : 32$.

$$\therefore \quad \text{First part} = \left(94 \times \frac{15}{47}\right) = 30.$$

71. $\dfrac{100}{3 \times 100} A = \dfrac{50}{100} B \Leftrightarrow \dfrac{1}{3} A = \dfrac{1}{2} B.$

$B = 1500.$ So, $\dfrac{1}{3} A = \dfrac{1}{2} \times 1500 = 750.$

$\therefore \quad A = (3 \times 750) = 2250.$

72. Let the numbers be A, B and C.

Then, $A : B = 2 : 3$ and $B : C = 5 : 8 = \dfrac{3}{5} \times 5 : \dfrac{3}{5} \times 8 = 3 : \dfrac{24}{5}.$

$\therefore \quad A : B : C = 2 : 3 : \dfrac{24}{5} = 10 : 15 : 24.$

$$\text{Second number} = \left(98 \times \frac{15}{49}\right) = 30.$$

73. Let the numbers be $3x$, $2x$ and $5x$. Then,

$9x^2 + 4x^2 + 25x^2 = 1862 \Leftrightarrow 38x^2 = 1862 \Leftrightarrow x^2 = 49 \Leftrightarrow x = 7.$

$\therefore \quad$ Second number $= 2x = 14.$

74. $5A = 3B = 2C = k.$ Then, $A = \dfrac{k}{5},\ B = \dfrac{k}{3}$ & $C = \dfrac{k}{2}.$

$\therefore \quad A : B : C = \dfrac{k}{5} : \dfrac{k}{3} : \dfrac{k}{2} = \dfrac{1}{5} : \dfrac{1}{3} : \dfrac{1}{2} = 6 : 10 : 15.$

75. $3A = 4B = 7C = k.$ Then, $A = \dfrac{k}{3},\ B = \dfrac{k}{4}$ and $C = \dfrac{k}{7}.$

$\therefore \quad A : B : C = \dfrac{k}{3} : \dfrac{k}{4} : \dfrac{k}{7} = 28 : 21 : 12.$

$\therefore \quad C\text{'s share} = \text{Rs.} \left(427 \times \dfrac{12}{61}\right) = \text{Rs. } 84.$

76. $B = \dfrac{3}{11}(A + C).$ So, $B : (A + C) = 3 : 11.$

$\therefore \quad B\text{'s share} = \text{Rs.} \left(1540 \times \dfrac{3}{14}\right) = \text{Rs. } 330.$

77. $\dfrac{A}{2} = \dfrac{B}{3} = \dfrac{C}{6} = k.$ Then $A = 2k,\ B = 3k$ and $C = 6k.$

$\therefore \quad A : B : C = 2k : 3k : 6k = 2 : 3 : 6.$

$\therefore \quad$ Third part $= \text{Rs.} \left(1870 \times \dfrac{6}{11}\right) = \text{Rs. } 1020.$

78. Suppose C gets Re 1. Then, B gets Re $\dfrac{1}{4}.$

A gets $= \dfrac{2}{3}$ of Re $\dfrac{1}{4} = $ Re $\dfrac{1}{6}.$

$$\therefore \ A:B:C=\frac{1}{6}:\frac{1}{4}:1=2:3:12.$$

$$\therefore \ B\text{'s share} = \text{Rs.} \left(2040 \times \frac{3}{17}\right) = \text{Rs. } 360.$$

79. $A:B:C=100:65:35=20:13:7.$

$$\therefore \ 7:40=28:x \ \text{ or } \ x=\frac{40 \times 28}{7}=160.$$

$$\therefore \ \text{Sum} = \text{Rs. } 160.$$

80. $A:B=3:4 \text{ and } B:C=\dfrac{7}{2}:3=\dfrac{8}{7} \times \dfrac{7}{2}:\dfrac{8}{7} \times 3=4:\dfrac{24}{7}$

$$\therefore \ A:B:C=3:4:\frac{24}{7}=21:28:24.$$

$$\therefore \ B\text{'s share} = \text{Rs.} \left(730 \times \frac{28}{73}\right) = \text{Rs. } 280.$$

$$C\text{'s share} = \text{Rs.} \left(730 \times \frac{24}{73}\right) = \text{Rs. } 240.$$

$$\therefore \ \text{Difference of their shares} = \text{Rs. } 40.$$

81. Let $C=x.$ Then, $B=(x+8) \ \& \ A=(x+15)$

$$\therefore \ x+x+8+x+15=53 \ \text{ or } \ x=10.$$

$$\therefore \ A:B:C=25:18:10.$$

82. Let $C=x.$ Then, $A=(x-20)$ and $B=(x-40).$

$$\therefore \ x+x-20+x-40=120 \ \text{ or } \ x=60.$$

$$\therefore \ A:B:C=40:20:60=2:1:3.$$

$$B\text{'s share} = \text{Rs.} \left(120 \times \frac{1}{6}\right) = \text{Rs. } 20.$$

83. $P:Q=2:3, \ Q:R=2:3=\dfrac{3}{2} \times 2:\dfrac{3}{2} \times 3=3:\dfrac{9}{2}.$

$$\therefore \ P:Q:R=2:3:\frac{9}{2}=4:6:9$$

And, $R:S=2:3=\dfrac{9}{2} \times 2:\dfrac{9}{2} \times 3=9:\dfrac{27}{2}$

$$\therefore \ P:Q:R:S=4:6:9:\frac{27}{2}=8:12:18:27.$$

$$\therefore \ P\text{'s share} = \text{Rs.} \left(1300 \times \frac{8}{65}\right) = \text{Rs. } 160.$$

84. $\dfrac{2}{5}A+40=\dfrac{2}{7}B+20=\dfrac{9}{17}C+10=x.$

$$\therefore \ A=\frac{5}{2}(x-40), B=\frac{7}{2}(x-20) \text{ and } C=\frac{17}{9}(x-10).$$

$$\therefore \ \frac{5}{2}(x-40)+\frac{7}{2}(x-20)+\frac{17}{9}(x-10)=600 \ \text{ or } \ x=100.$$

$\therefore$ A's share = Rs. $\left[\dfrac{5}{2}(100-40)\right]$ = Rs. 150.

85. Ratio of values = $\dfrac{2}{1} : \dfrac{3}{2} : \dfrac{4}{4} = 2 : \dfrac{3}{2} : 1 = 4 : 3 : 2.$

Value of 50-paise coins = Rs. $\left(180 \times \dfrac{3}{9}\right)$ = Rs. 60.

Number of 50-paise coins = $(60 \times 2) = 120.$

86. Let rupee coins = x, 50-paise coins = $4x$ and 25-paise coins = $2x$.

$\therefore$ Ratio of these coins $x : 4x : 2x = 1 : 4 : 2.$

Ratio of their values = $\dfrac{1}{1} : \dfrac{4}{2} : \dfrac{2}{4} = 4 : 8 : 2 = 2 : 4 : 1.$

$\therefore$ Value of 50-paise coins = Rs. $\left(56 \times \dfrac{4}{7}\right)$ = Rs. 32.

Number of 50-paise coins = 64.

87. Ratio of the number of Rs. 20, Rs. 10, Rs. 5 notes = $3 : 4 : 5.$

Ratio of their values = $60 : 40 : 25 = 12 : 8 : 5.$

Value of five-rupee notes = Rs. $\left(1000 \times \dfrac{5}{25}\right)$ = Rs. 200.

Number of five-rupee notes = $\left(\dfrac{200}{5}\right) = 40.$

88. Ratio of values = $\dfrac{1}{1} : \dfrac{2}{2} : \dfrac{4}{4} : \dfrac{5}{5} = 1 : 1 : 1 : 1.$

Value of 20 paise coins = Rs. $\left(400 \times \dfrac{1}{4}\right)$ = Rs. 100.

Number of 20 paise coins = $(100 \times 5) = 500.$

Value of 25 paise coins = Rs. $\left(400 \times \dfrac{1}{4}\right)$ = Rs. 100.

Number of 25-paise coins = $(100 \times 4) = 400.$

Difference in number of 20-paise & 25-paise coins = 100.

89. $\dfrac{10}{100} B = \dfrac{1}{4} G$ and $\dfrac{10}{100} G = \dfrac{1}{25} B$

$2B - 5G = 0$ and $5G - 2B = 0.$

$\therefore$ $2B = 5G$ or $\dfrac{B}{G} = \dfrac{5}{2}.$

90. Let their incomes be $7x$, $9x$ and $12x$ and their spendings be $8y$, $9y$ and $15y$.

Then, their savings are $(7x - 8y)$, $(9x - 9y)$ & $(12x - 15y)$.

Now, $7x - 8y = \dfrac{7x}{4}$ or $21x = 32y$ or $\dfrac{x}{y} = \dfrac{32}{21}.$

$$\therefore \frac{7x-8y}{9x-9y} = \frac{7\left(\dfrac{x}{y}\right)-8}{9\left(\dfrac{x}{y}\right)-9} = \frac{7 \times \dfrac{32}{21}-8}{9 \times \dfrac{32}{21}-9} = \frac{8}{3} \times \frac{7}{33} = \frac{56}{99}.$$

$$\frac{9x-9y}{12x-15y} = \frac{9\left(\dfrac{x}{y}\right)-9}{12\left(\dfrac{x}{y}\right)-15} = \frac{9 \times \dfrac{32}{21}-9}{12 \times \dfrac{32}{21}-15} = \frac{33}{23} = \frac{99}{69}.$$

∴ Ratio of savings = 56 : 99 : 69.

91. Given Ratio is 7 : 5 : 3 : 4.

∴ Smallest part $= \left(76 \times \dfrac{3}{19}\right) = 12.$

92. Let their parts in first sum be $4x$, $3x$, $2x$ and x and let their parts in second sum be $5y$, $6y$, $7y$ and $8y$.

∴ $2(4x + 3x + 2x + x) = (5y + 6y + 7y + 8y)$

or $20x = 26y$ or $x = \dfrac{13}{10}y.$

∴ $A = 4x + 5y = 4 \times \dfrac{13}{10}y + 5y = \dfrac{102y}{10} = 10.2y,$

$R = 3x + 6y = 3 \times \dfrac{13}{10}y + 6y = \dfrac{99y}{10} = 9.9y,$

$D = 2x + 7y = 2 \times \dfrac{13}{10}y + 7y = \dfrac{96y}{10} = 9.6y,$

$S = x + 8y = \dfrac{13}{10}y + 8y = \dfrac{93y}{10} = 9.3y.$

So, Anil received the largest total.

93. Pure silver : Alloy = 2.5 : (12.5 − 2.5) = 2.5 : 10 = 1 : 4.

94. $P : V = 4 : 5$ and $V : S = 3 : 2$

$\dfrac{P}{V} = \dfrac{4}{5}$ and $\dfrac{V}{S} = \dfrac{3}{2}$. So, $\dfrac{P}{S} = \dfrac{P}{V} \times \dfrac{V}{S} = \dfrac{4}{5} \times \dfrac{3}{2} = \dfrac{6}{5}.$

95. $E = 2S$, $E + S + M = 180 \Leftrightarrow E + \dfrac{1}{2}E + M = 180$

∴ $3E + 2M = 360$ and $\dfrac{E}{M} = \dfrac{2}{3}$ or $M = \dfrac{3}{2}E.$

∴ $3E + 2 \times \dfrac{3}{2}E = 360$ or $E = 60.$

∴ $S = \dfrac{1}{2}E = \dfrac{1}{2} \times 60 = 30.$

96. Let the numbers be $3x$ and $4x$. Then,

$3x \times 4x = 10800 \Leftrightarrow 12x^2 = 10800 \Leftrightarrow x^2 = 900 \Leftrightarrow x = 30.$

∴ Sum of numbers $= 7x = 7 \times 30 = 210$.

97. Let the ages of X and Y be $3x$ and x.

$$\frac{3x+15}{x+15} = \frac{2}{1} \quad \text{or} \quad 3x+15 = 2x+30 \quad \text{or} \quad x = 15.$$

∴ Present ages of X and Y are 45 years and 15 years respectively.

98. Let boys $= 3x$ & girls $= 2x$.

Number of those who are not scholarship holders

$= 80\%$ of $3x + 75\%$ of $2x$

$$= \left(\frac{80}{100} \times 3x + \frac{75}{100} \times 2x \right) = \frac{39x}{10}.$$

$$= \frac{78}{100} \times (5x) = 78\% \text{ of the total.}$$

99. Let 1 gm of gold be mixed with x gm of copper to give $(1+x)$ gm of alloy.

Now, $1\,G = 19\,W$, $1C = 9W$ & Alloy $= 15\,W$

1 gm gold $+ x$ gm Copper $= (1+x)$ gm alloy.

∴ $19\,W + 9Wx = (1+x) \times 15W$

or $x = \dfrac{4W}{6W} = \dfrac{2}{3}$.

So, the ratio of gold and copper is $1 : \dfrac{2}{3}$ or $3 : 2$.

100. Milk in 85 kg $= \left(85 \times \dfrac{27}{34} \right) \text{kg} = \dfrac{135}{2} \text{ kg.}$

Water in 85 kg $= \left(85 - \dfrac{135}{2} \right) \text{kg} = \dfrac{35}{2} \text{ kg.}$

Let x kg of water be added.

$$\frac{\text{Milk}}{\text{Water}} = \frac{3}{1} \Leftrightarrow \frac{\dfrac{135}{2}}{\dfrac{35}{2}+x} = \frac{3}{1}$$

or $\dfrac{135}{35+2x} = \dfrac{3}{1}$ or $6x + 105 = 135$ or $x = 5$ kg.

101. Alcohol in 15 litres $= \left(\dfrac{20}{100} \times 15 \right)$ litres $= 3$ litres.

Percentage of alcohol in new mix. $= \left(\dfrac{3}{15+3} \times 100 \right) \% = 16\dfrac{2}{3}\%$.

102. Milk in 16 litres $= \left(16 \times \dfrac{5}{8} \right)$ litres $= 10$ litres.

Water in 16 litres $= (16 - 10)$ litres $= 6$ litres.

∴ Ratio of milk in new mixture $= (10+4) = 14$ litres.

Milk in new mixture $= (10+4) = 14$ litres.

∴ Ratio of milk and water in new mix. $= 14 : 6 = 7 : 3$.

103. Gold in $C = \left(\dfrac{7}{9} + \dfrac{7}{18}\right) = \dfrac{7}{6}$.

Copper in $C = \left(\dfrac{2}{9} + \dfrac{11}{18}\right) = \dfrac{5}{6}$.

Gold : Copper $= \dfrac{7}{6} : \dfrac{5}{6} = 7 : 5$.

104. Let milk $= 5x$ and water $= x$. Then,

$\dfrac{5x}{x+5} = \dfrac{5}{2}$ or $10x = 5x + 25$ or $x = 5$.

∴ Quantity of milk in given mix. $= 25$ litres.

105. First glass contains Milk $= \dfrac{1}{3}$, Water $= \dfrac{2}{3}$

Second glass contains Milk $= \dfrac{1}{4}$, Water $= \dfrac{3}{4}$.

New tumbler contains :

Milk $= \left(\dfrac{1}{3} + \dfrac{1}{4}\right) = \dfrac{7}{12}$,

Water $= \left(\dfrac{2}{3} + \dfrac{3}{4}\right) = \dfrac{17}{12}$ ..

∴ Ratio of Milk & Water $= \dfrac{7}{12} : \dfrac{17}{12}$.

106. In new vessel, we have :

Milk $= \left(\dfrac{4}{7} + \dfrac{5}{9} + \dfrac{7}{13}\right)$

Water $= \left(\dfrac{3}{7} + \dfrac{4}{9} + \dfrac{6}{13}\right)$

∴ Milk : Water $= \left(\dfrac{4}{7} + \dfrac{5}{9} + \dfrac{7}{13}\right) : \left(\dfrac{3}{7} + \dfrac{4}{9} + \dfrac{6}{13}\right)$.

13. Partnership

Partnership : *When two or more than two persons run a business jointly, they are called partners and the deal is known as partnership.*

Ratio of Division of Gains :

(i) *When investments of all the partners are for the same time, the gain or loss is distributed among the partners in the ratio of their investments.*

(ii) *When investments are for different time, then equivalent capitals are calculated for a unit of time by taking (capital × number of units of time). Now gain or loss is divided in the ratio of these capitals.*

Working & sleeping Partners : *A partner who manages the business is known as a working partner and the one who simply invests the money is a sleeping partner.*

Solved Problems

Ex. 1. *Manoj and Vinod started a business by investing Rs. 120000 and Rs. 135000 respectively. Find the share of each, out of an annual profit of Rs. 35700.*

Sol. Ratio of their shares = 120000 : 135000 = 8 : 9

$\therefore$ Manoj's share = Rs. $\left(35700 \times \dfrac{8}{17}\right)$ = Rs. 16800.

Vinod's share = Rs. $\left(35700 \times \dfrac{9}{17}\right)$ = Rs. 18900.

Ex. 2. *Sanjeev started a business by investing Rs. 36000. After 3 months Rajeev joined him by investing Rs. 36000. Out of an annual profit of Rs. 37100, find the share of each.*

Sol. Ratio of their capitals = 36000 × 12 : 36000 × 9 = 4 : 3.

Sanjeev's share = Rs. $\left(37100 \times \dfrac{4}{7}\right)$ = Rs. 21200.

Rajeev's share = Rs. $\left(37100 \times \dfrac{3}{7}\right)$ = Rs. 15900.

Ex. 3. *A, B and C start a business each investing Rs. 20000. After 5 months A withdrew Rs. 5000, B withdrew Rs. 4000 and C invests Rs. 6000 more. At the end of the year, a total profit of Rs. 69900 was recorded. Find the share of each.*

Sol. Ratio of the capitals of *A, B* and *C*

= 20000 × 5 + 15000 × 7 : 20000 × 5 + 16000 × 7 : 20000 × 5 + 26000 × 7

= 205000 : 212000 : 282000 = 205 : 212 : 282

$$\therefore \ A's \ share = Rs. \left(69900 \times \frac{205}{699} \right) = Rs. \ 20500,$$

$$B's \ share = Rs. \left(69900 \times \frac{212}{699} \right) = Rs. \ 21200,$$

$$C's \ share = Rs. \left(69900 \times \frac{282}{699} \right) = Rs. \ 28200.$$

Ex. 4. *A started a business with Rs. 21000 and is joined afterwards by B with Rs. 36000. After how many months did B join, if the profits at the end of the year are divided equally ?*

Sol. Suppose B joined after x months.

Then, B's money was invested for $(12 - x)$ months.

$\therefore \ 21000 \times 12 = 36000 \times (12 - x) \Leftrightarrow 36x = 180 \Leftrightarrow x = 5.$

So, B joined after 5 months.

EXERCISE 13

Mark ($\sqrt{}$) **against the correct answer :**

1. Three partners A, B, C invest Rs. 36000, Rs. 45000 and Rs. 54000 respectively in a business. Out of a total profit of Rs. 37500, C's share is :

    (a) Rs. 12500   (b) Rs. 15000   (c) Rs. 10000   (d) Rs. 15500

2. Kavita and Sunita are partners in a business. Kavita invests Rs. 35000 for 8 months and Sunita invests Rs. 42000 for 10 months. Out of a profit of Rs. 31570, Kavita's share is :

    (a) Rs. 18942   (b) Rs. 12628   (c) Rs. 9471   (d) Rs. 18040

3. Jayant opened a shop investing Rs. 30000. Madhu joined him 2 months later, investing Rs. 45000. They earned a profit of Rs. 54000 after completion of one year. What will be Madhu's share of profit ?

    (a) Rs. 27000   (b) Rs. 24000   (c) Rs. 30000   (d) Rs. 36000

    (Bank P.O. 1993)

4. Alok started a business investing Rs. 90000. After 3 months Shabir joined him with a capital of Rs. 120000. If at the end of 2 years, the total profit made by them was Rs. 96000, what will be the difference between their shares ?   **(Bank P.O. 1994)**

    (a) Rs. 20000   (b) Rs. 24000   (c) Rs. 8000   (d) none of these

5. Nirmal and Kapil started a business investing Rs. 9000 and Rs. 12000 respectively. After 6 months, Kapil withdrew half of his investment. If after a year, the total profit was Rs. 4600, what was Kapil's share in it ?   **(Bank P.O. 1993)**

    (a) Rs. 2000   (b) Rs. 2600   (c) Rs. 1900   (d) Rs. 2300

6. *A, B* and *C* enter into a partnership. *A* initially invests Rs. 25 lakhs and adds another Rs. 10 lakhs after one year. *B* initially invests Rs. 35 lakhs and withdraws Rs. 10 lakhs after 2 years and *C* invests Rs. 30 lakhs. In what ratio should the profits be divided at the end of 3 years ?
    (a) 20 : 19 : 18   (b) 10 : 10 : 9
    (c) 20 : 20 : 19   (d) none of these
                                    (Hotel Management 1993)

7. Yogesh started a business investing Rs. 45000. After 3 months, Pranab joined him with a capital of Rs. 60000. After another 6 months, Atul joined them with a capital of Rs. 90000. At the end of the year, they made a profit of Rs. 20000. What would be Atul's share in it ?
    (a) Rs. 4000   (b) Rs. 4500   (c) Rs. 6000   (d) Rs. 8000
                                    (Bank P.O. 1993)

8. Mohinder and Surinder entered into a partnership investing Rs. 12000 and Rs. 9000 respectively. After 3 months, Sudhir joined them with an investment of Rs. 15000. What is the share of Sudhir in a half yearly profit of Rs. 9500 ?   **(Hotel Management 1992)**
    (a) Rs. 3500   (b) Rs. 3000   (c) Rs. 2500   (d) Rs. 4000

9. *A* and *B* entered into a partnership investing Rs. 16000 and Rs. 12000 respectively. After 3 months, A withdrew Rs. 5000 while *B* invested Rs. 5000 more. After 3 more months *C* joins the business with a capital of Rs. 21000. The share of *B* exceeds that of *C*, out of a total profit of Rs. 26400 after one year by :   **(Central Excise & I.Tax 1989)**
    (a) Rs. 2400   (b) Rs. 3000   (c) Rs. 3600   (d) Rs. 4800

10. *X* and *Y* invested in a business. They earned some profit which they divided in the ratio of 2 : 3. If *X* invested Rs. 40000, the amount invested by *Y* is :
    (a) Rs. 50000   (b) Rs. 60000   (c) Rs. 80000   (d) Rs. 45000

11. Manoj received Rs. 6000 as his share out of the total profit of Rs. 9000 which he and Ramesh earned at the end of one year. If Manoj invested Rs. 20000 for 6 months, whereas Ramesh invested his amount for the whole year, what was the amount invested by **Ramesh** ?
    (a) Rs. 6000   (b) Rs. 10000   (c) Rs. 4000   (d) Rs. 5000
                                    (Bank P.O. 1991)

12. Three partners *A, B, C* start a business. Twice *A*'s capital is equal to thrice *B*'s capital and *B*'s capital is four times *C*'s capital. Out of a total profit of Rs. 16500 at the end of the year, *B*'s share is :
    (a) Rs. 4000   (b) Rs. 6000   (c) Rs. 7500   (d) Rs. 6600

13. *A, B, C* subscribe Rs. 50000 for a business. *A* subscribes Rs. 4000 more than *B* and *B* Rs. 5000 more than *C*. Out of a total profit of Rs. 35000, *A* receives :
    (a) Rs. 11900   (b) Rs. 8400   (c) Rs. 14700   (d) Rs. 13600

14. Rs. 700 is divided among *A*, *B*, *C* so that A receives half as much as
B and *B* half as much as *C*. Then *C*'s share is :   **(C.B.I. 1991)**
  (*a*) Rs. 200   (*b*) Rs. 300   (*c*) Rs. 400   (*d*) Rs. 600

15. If 4 (*A's* capital) = 6 (*B's* capital) = 10 (*C's* capital), then out of a profit
of Rs. 4650, *C* will receive :
  (*a*) Rs. 2250   (*b*) Rs. 1550   (*c*) Rs. 900   (*d*) Rs. 465

16. *A*, *B*, *C* hire a meadow for Rs. 1095. If *A* puts in 10 cows for 20 days;
B 30 cows for 8 days and *C* 16 cows for 9 days, then the rent paid by
C is :
  (*a*) Rs. 270   (*b*) Rs. 320   (*c*) Rs. 450   (*d*) Rs. 285

17. Four milkmen rented a pasture. *A* grazed 24 cows for 3 months; *B* 10
cows for 5 months, *C* 35 cows for 4 months and *D* 21 cows for 3 months.
If *A*'s share of rent is Rs. 720, the total rent of the field is :
  (*a*) Rs. 3000   (*b*) Rs. 3200   (*c*) Rs. 3250   (*d*) Rs. 3300

18. *A*, *B*, *C* start a business jointly. *A* invests 3 times as much as *B* invests
and *B* invests two-third of what *C* invests. At the end of the year, the
profit earned is Rs. 660. Out of it, *B*'s share is :
  (*a*) Rs. 220   (*b*) Rs. 120   (*c*) Rs. 180   (*d*) Rs. 240

19. *A*, *B* and *C* enter into partnership. *A* invests some money at the
beginning, *B* invests double the amount after 6 months and *C* invests
thrice the amount after 8 months. If the annual profit be Rs. 27000, *C*'s
share is :
  (*a*) Rs. 9000   (*b*) Rs. 11250   (*c*) Rs. 10800   (*d*) Rs. 8625

20. *A* and *B* started a business jointly. *A*'s investment was thrice the
investment of *B* and the period of his investment was two times the
period of investment of *B*. If *B* received Rs. 4000 as profit, then their
total profit is :   **(Bank P.O. 1990)**
  (*a*) Rs. 16000   (*b*) Rs. 24000   (*c*) Rs. 20000   (*d*) Rs. 28000

21. *A*, *B* and *C* started a shop by investing Rs. 27000, Rs, 72000 and
Rs. 81000 respectively. At the end of the year the profits were
distributed among them. If *C*'s share of profit be Rs. 36000, then the
total profit was :
  (*a*) Rs. 80000   (*b*) Rs. 116000 (*c*) Rs. 108000 (*d*) Rs. 9560

22. *A* and *B* start a business jointly. *A* invests Rs. 16000 for 8 months and
B remains in the business for 4 months. Out of total profit, *B* claims
$\frac{2}{7}$ of the profit. How much money was contributed by *B* ?
  (*a*) Rs. 10500   (*b*) Rs. 11900   (*c*) Rs. 12800   (*d*) Rs. 13600

23. *A* and *B* started a business with initial investments in the ratio 14 : 15
and their annual profits were in the ratio 7 : 6. If *A* invested the money
for 10 months, for how many months did *B* invest his money ?
  (*a*) 8   (*b*) 9   (*c*) 6   (*d*) 7

24. A, B, C enter into a partnership and their capitals are in the proportion 20 : 15 : 12. A withdraws half his capital at the end of 4 months. Out of a total annual profit of Rs. 847, A's share is :
    (a) Rs. 252   (b) Rs. 280   (c) Rs. 315   (d) Rs. 412

25. In a partnership, A invests $\frac{1}{6}$ of the capital for $\frac{1}{6}$ of the time, B invests $\frac{1}{3}$ of the capital for $\frac{1}{3}$ of the time and C, the rest of the capital for the whole time. Out of a profit of Rs. 4600, B's share is :
    (a) Rs. 650   (b) Rs. 800   (c) Rs. 960   (d) Rs. 1000

26. A, B and C enter into a partnership in the ratio $\frac{7}{2} : \frac{4}{3} : \frac{6}{5}$. After 4 months, A increases his share by 50%. If the total profit at the end of one year be Rs. 21600, then B's share in the profit is :
    (a) Rs. 2100   (b) Rs 2400   (c) Rs. 3600   (d) Rs. 4000

27. A and B invest in a business in the ratio 3 : 2. If 5% of the total profit goes to charity and A's share is Rs. 855, the total profit is :
    (a) Rs. 1425   (b) Rs. 1500   (c) Rs. 1537.50   (d) Rs. 1576

28. A is a working and B, a sleeping partner in a business. A puts in Rs. 12000 and B Rs. 20000. A receives 10% of the profits for managing, the rest being divided in proportion to their capitals. Out of a total profit of Rs. 9600, the money received by A is :
    (a) Rs. 3240   (b) Rs. 3600   (c) Rs. 4200   (d) Rs. 4500

29. A invested Rs. 76000 in a business. After few months B joined him with Rs. 57000. At the end of the year, the total profit was divided between them in the ratio 2 : 1. After how many months did B join ?
    (a) 3   (b) 4   (c) 5   (d) 7

30. A, B, C started a business with their investments in the ratio 1 : 3 : 5. After 4 months, A invested the same amount as before and B as well as C withdrew half of their investments. The ratio of their profits at the end of the year is :
    (a) 5 : 6 : 10   (b) 6 : 5 : 10   (c) 10 : 5 : 6   (d) 4 : 3 : 5

31. A, B and C contract a work for Rs. 1100. A and B together are to do $\frac{7}{11}$ of the work. C's share is :
    (a) Rs. 366.66   (b) Rs. 400   (c) Rs. 600   (d) Rs. 800

32. A and B start a business with initial investments in the ratio 12 : 7 and their annual profits were in the ratio 4 : 3. If A invested the money for 7 months, then B invested his money for :
    (a) 8 months   (b) 9 months   (c) 10 months   (d) 5 months

33. A and B entered into partnership with capitals in the ratio 4 : 5. After 3 months A withdrew $\frac{1}{4}$ of his capital and B withdrew $\frac{1}{5}$ of his capital. The gain at the end of 10 months was Rs. 760. A's share in this profit is :

(a) Rs. 330   (b) Rs. 360   (c) Rs. 380   (d) Rs. 430

34. A, B, C hired a car for Rs. 520 and used it for 7,8 and 11 hours respectively. Hire charges paid by B were :

(a) Rs. 140   (b) Rs. 160   (c) Rs. 180   (d) Rs. 220

35. A, B and C enter into a partnership with a capital in which A's contribution is Rs. 10000. If out of a total profit of Rs. 1000, A gets Rs. 500 and B gets Rs. 300, then C's capital is :

(a) Rs. 4000   (b) Rs. 5000   (c) Rs. 6000   (d) Rs. 9000

36. A, B, C invest Rs. 20000, Rs. 30000, Rs. 40000 in a business. After one year, A removed his money but B and C continued for one more year. If the net profit after 2 years be Rs. 32000, then A's share in the profit is :

(a) Rs. 4000   (b) Rs. 6000   (c) Rs. 8000   (d) Rs. 10000

ANSWERS

1. (b)	**2.** (b)	**3.** (c)	**4.** (d)	**5.** (d)	**6.** (d)	**7.** (a)	**8.** (c)	**9.** (c)
10. (b)	**11.** (d)	**12.** (c)	**13.** (c)	**14.** (c)	**15.** (c)	**16.** (a)	**17.** (c)	**18.** (b)
19. (a)	**20.** (d)	**21.** (a)	**22.** (c)	**23.** (a)	**24.** (b)	**25.** (b)	**26.** (d)	**27.** (b)
28. (c)	**29.** (b)	**30.** (a)	**31.** (b)	**32.** (b)	**33.** (a)	**34.** (b)	**35.** (a)	**36.** (a)

SOLUTIONS

1. $A : B : C = 36000 : 45000 : 54000 = 4 : 5 : 6$

$C's$ share $=$ Rs. $\left(37500 \times \dfrac{6}{15}\right) =$ Rs. 15000.

2. Ratio of their shares $= 35000 \times 8 : 42000 \times 10 = 2 : 3$

Kavita's share $=$ Rs. $\left(31570 \times \dfrac{2}{5}\right) =$ Rs. 12628.

3. Jayant : Madhu $= 30000 \times 12 : 45000 \times 10 = 4 : 5$.

Madhu's share $=$ Rs. $\left(54000 \times \dfrac{5}{9}\right) =$ Rs. 30000.

4. Alok : Shabir $= 90000 \times 24 : 120000 \times 21 = 6 : 7$.

Difference of their shares

$=$ Rs. $\left(96000 \times \dfrac{7}{13} - 96000 \times \dfrac{6}{13}\right) =$ Rs. $\left(\dfrac{96000}{13}\right) =$ Rs. 7384.62.

5. Nirmal : Kapil $= 9000 \times 12 : 12000 \times 6 + 6000 \times 6 = 1 : 1$.

$\therefore$ Kapil's share $=$ Rs. $\left(4600 \times \dfrac{1}{2}\right) =$ Rs. 2300.

6. Ratio of their shares

$= (25 \text{ lakhs} \times 1) + (35 \text{ lakhs} \times 2) : (35 \text{ lakhs} \times 2 + 25 \text{ lakhs} \times 1)$

$: (30 \text{ lakhs} \times 3)$

$= 95 \text{ lakhs} : 95 \text{ lakhs} : 90 \text{ lakhs} = 19 : 19 : 18.$

7. Yogesh : Pranab : Atul
    $= 45000 \times 12 : 60000 \times 9 : 90000 \times 3 = 2 : 2 : 1.$

    $\therefore$ Atul's share $= $ Rs. $\left(20000 \times \dfrac{1}{5}\right) = $ Rs. 4000.

8. Mohinder : Surinder : Sudhir $= 12000 \times 6 : 9000 \times 6 : 15000 \times 3$
    $$= 8 : 6 : 5$$

    Sudhir's share $= $ Rs. $\left(9500 \times \dfrac{5}{19}\right) = $ Rs.2500.

9. $A : B : C = 16000 \times 3 + 11000 \times 9 : 12000 \times 3 + 17000 \times 9 : 21000 \times 6$
    $$= 147 : 189 : 126 = 7 : 9 : 6$$
    Difference of B and C's shares

    $= $ Rs. $\left(26400 \times \dfrac{9}{22} - 26400 \times \dfrac{6}{22}\right) = $ Rs. 3600.

10. Suppose Y invested Rs. y. Then,

    $\dfrac{2}{3} = \dfrac{40000}{y}$ or $y = \left(\dfrac{40000 \times 3}{2}\right) = 60000.$

11. Suppose Ramesh invested Rs. x. Then,
    Manoj : Ramesh $= 20000 \times 6 : x \times 12.$

    $\therefore \dfrac{120000}{12x} = \dfrac{6000}{3000}$ or $x = \dfrac{120000}{24} = 5000.$

12. Let $C = x$. Then, $B = 4x$ and $2A = 3 \times 4x = 12x$ or $A = 6x.$
    $\therefore A : B : C = 6x : 4x : x = 6 : 4 : 1.$

    $\therefore B$'s capital $= $ Rs. $\left(16500 \times \dfrac{4}{11}\right) = $ Rs. 6000.

13. Let $C = x$. Then $B = x + 5000$ and $A = x + 5000 + 4000 = x + 9000$
    $\therefore x + x + 5000 + x + 9000 = 50000 \Leftrightarrow x = 12000.$
    $\therefore A : B : C = 21000 : 17000 : 12000 = 21 : 17 : 12$

    $\therefore A$'s share $= $ Rs. $\left(35000 \times \dfrac{21}{50}\right) = $ Rs. 14700.

14. Let $C = x$. Then, $B = \dfrac{x}{2}$ and $A = \dfrac{x}{4}.$

    $\therefore A : B : C = \dfrac{x}{4} : \dfrac{x}{2} : x = 1 : 2 : 4.$

    $\therefore C$'s share $= $ Rs. $\left(700 \times \dfrac{4}{7}\right) = $ Rs. 400.

15. $4A = 6B = 10C = k \Leftrightarrow A = \dfrac{k}{4}, B = \dfrac{k}{6}$ and $C = \dfrac{k}{10}.$

$$\therefore \ A:B:C=\frac{k}{4}:\frac{k}{6}:\frac{k}{10}=15:10:6$$

$$\therefore \ C\text{'s share} = \text{Rs.}\left(4650\times\frac{6}{31}\right)=\text{Rs. 900.}$$

16. $A:B:C=10\times20:30\times8:16\times9=200:240:144=25:30:18.$

$$\therefore \ C\text{'s rent} = \text{Rs.}\left(1095\times\frac{18}{73}\right)=\text{Rs. 270.}$$

17. $A:B:C:D=24\times3:10\times5:35\times4:21\times3=72:50:140:63$
     Let total rent be Rs. x. Then,

$$A\text{'s share} = \text{Rs.}\left(x\times\frac{72}{325}\right)$$

$$\therefore \ \frac{72x}{325}=720 \Leftrightarrow x=\frac{720\times325}{72}=3250.$$

18. Let $C=x$. Then, $B=\frac{2}{3}x$ & $A=3\times\frac{2}{3}x=2x.$

$$\therefore \ A:B:C=2x:\frac{2}{3}x:x=6:2:3.$$

$$B\text{'s share} = \text{Rs.}\left(660\times\frac{2}{11}\right)=\text{Rs. 120.}$$

19. Let $A=x\times12$. Then, $B=2x\times6$ & $C=3x\times4.$
     $\therefore \ A:B:C=12x:12x:12x=1:1:1.$

$$\therefore \ C\text{'s share} = \text{Rs.}\left(27000\times\frac{1}{3}\right)=\text{Rs. 9000.}$$

20. Suppose B invested Rs. x for y months.
     Then A invested Rs. $3x$ for $2y$ months.
     $\therefore \ A:B=3x\times2y:x\times y=6:1.$
     $\therefore \ B$'s profit : Total profit $=1:7.$

$$\therefore \ \frac{1}{7}=\frac{4000}{z} \ \text{ or } \ z=28000.$$

     Hence, total profit $=$ Rs. 28000.

21. $A:B:C=27000:72000:81000=3:8:9.$
     $\therefore \ C$'s share : Total profit $=9:20.$

$$\therefore \ \frac{9}{20}=\frac{36000}{z} \ \text{ or } \ z=\frac{36000\times20}{9}=80000.$$

22. Let the total profit be Rs. x.

$$\therefore \ B=\frac{2}{7}x \ \text{ and } \ A=\left(x-\frac{2x}{7}\right)=\frac{5x}{7}.$$

$$\therefore \ A:B=\frac{5x}{7}:\frac{2x}{7}=5:2.$$

     Now $\dfrac{16000\times8}{y\times4}=\dfrac{5}{2}$ or $y=\dfrac{16000\times8\times2}{5\times4}=12800.$

23. Let A invested Rs. $14x$ for 10 months and B invested $15x$ for y months.
    Then,
    $$\frac{14x \times 10}{15x \times y} = \frac{7}{6} \Leftrightarrow y = \frac{840}{105} = 8.$$
    Hence B invested the money for 8 months.

24. Let their initial investments be $20x$, $15x$ and $12x$.
    $$A : B : C = 20x \times 4 + 10x \times 8 : 15x \times 12 : 12x \times 12 = 160 : 180 : 144$$
    $$= 40 : 45 : 36.$$
    $\therefore$ A's share $= $ Rs. $\left(847 \times \dfrac{40}{121}\right) = $ Rs. 280.

25. Suppose A invests $\dfrac{x}{6}$ for $\dfrac{y}{6}$ months.

    B invests $\dfrac{x}{3}$ for $\dfrac{y}{3}$ months.

    C invests $\left[x - \left(\dfrac{x}{6} + \dfrac{x}{3}\right)\right]$ i.e. $\dfrac{x}{2}$ for y months.

    $\therefore$ $A : B : C = \dfrac{x}{6} \times \dfrac{y}{6} : \dfrac{x}{3} \times \dfrac{y}{3} : \dfrac{x}{2} \times y = \dfrac{1}{36} : \dfrac{1}{9} : \dfrac{1}{2} = 1 : 4 : 18.$

    $\therefore$ B's share $= $ Rs. $\left(4600 \times \dfrac{4}{23}\right) = $ Rs. 800.

26. Ratio of initial investments $= 105 : 40 : 36$.
    Let the initial investments be $105x$, $40x$ & $36x$.
    $\therefore$ $A : B : C = 105x \times 4 + \dfrac{150}{100} \times 105x \times 8 : 40x \times 12 : 36x \times 12$
    $$= 1680x : 480x : 432x = 35 : 10 : 9$$
    $\therefore$ B's share $= $ Rs. $\left(21600 \times \dfrac{10}{54}\right) = $ Rs. 4000.

27. Let the total profit be Rs. 100.
    After paying to charity, A's share $= $ Rs. $\left(95 \times \dfrac{3}{5}\right) = $ Rs. 57.
    $\therefore$ $57 : 100 = 855 : x$ or $x = \dfrac{100 \times 855}{57} = 1500.$

28. For managing, A receives $= $ Rs. 960.
    Balance $= $ Rs. $(9600 - 960) = $ Rs. 8640.
    Ratio of their investments $= 12000 : 20000 = 3 : 5$.
    $\therefore$ A's share $= $ Rs. $\left(8640 \times \dfrac{3}{8}\right) = $ Rs. 3240.
    $\therefore$ A receives $= $ Rs. $(3240 + 960) = $ Rs. 4200.

29. Suppose B joined after x months.
    Then, B remained in the business for $(12 - x)$ months.

$$\therefore \ \frac{76000 \times 12}{57000 \times (12 - x)} = \frac{2}{1} \Leftrightarrow x = 4.$$

Hence B joined after 4 months.

30. Let their initial investments be $x, 3x, 5x$. Then,

$$A : B : C = x \times 4 + 2x \times 8 : 3x \times 4 + \frac{3x}{2} \times 8 : 5x \times 4 + \frac{5x}{2} \times 8$$

$$= 20x : 24x : 40x = 5 : 6 : 10.$$

31. $(A + B) : C = \dfrac{7}{11} : \dfrac{4}{11} = 7 : 4.$

$$\therefore \ C\text{'s share} = \text{Rs.} \left(1100 \times \frac{4}{11} \right) = \text{Rs. } 400.$$

32. Let A invested $12x$ for 7 months and B invested $7x$ for y months. Then,

$$\frac{12x \times 7}{7x \times y} = \frac{4}{3} \Leftrightarrow y = 9 \text{ months.}$$

33. $A : B = 4x \times 3 + \left(4x - \dfrac{1}{4} \times 4x \right) \times 7 : 5x \times 3 + \left(5x - \dfrac{1}{5} \times 5x \right) \times 7.$

$$= 12x + 21x : 15x + 28x = 33x : 43x = 33 : 43$$

$$\therefore \ A\text{'s share} = \text{Rs.} \left(760 \times \frac{33}{76} \right) = \text{Rs. } 330.$$

34. $A : B : C = 7 : 8 : 11.$

Hire charges paid by $B = \text{Rs.} \left(520 \times \dfrac{8}{26} \right) = \text{Rs. } 160.$

35. $A : B : C = 500 : 300 : 200 = 5 : 3 : 2.$

Let their capitals be $5x, 3x$ and $2x$.

Then, $5x = 10000 \Leftrightarrow x = 2000.$

$\therefore \ C$'s capital $= 2x = \text{Rs. } 4000.$

36. $A : B : C = 20000 \times 12 : 30000 \times 24 : 40000 \times 24$

$$= 24 : 72 : 96 = 1 : 3 : 4.$$

A's share $= \text{Rs.} \left(32000 \times \dfrac{1}{8} \right) = \text{Rs. } 4000.$

14. Chain Rule

Direct Proportion : *Two quantities are said to be directly proportional if on the increase (or decrease) of the one, the other increases (or decreases) to the same extent.*

Ex. 1. *The cost of articles is directly proportional to the number of articles.*

(More articles, More cost) & (Less articles, less cost).

Ex. 2. *The work done is directly proportional to the number of men working at it.*

(More Men, More work) & (Less Men, Less work)

Indirect Proportion : *Two quantities are said to be indirectly proportional if on the increase of the one, the other decreases to the same extent and vice versa.*

Ex. 1. *Time taken to cover a distance is inversely proportional to the speed of the car.*

(More speed, Less is the time taken to cover a distance)

Ex. 2. *Time taken to finish a work is inversely proportional to the number of persons working at it.*

(More persons, Less is the time taken to finish a job)

Remark : *In solving questions on chain rule, we make repeated use of finding the fourth proportional. We compare every item with the term to be found out.*

Solved Problems

Ex. 1. *If 15 toys cost Rs. 234, what do 35 toys cost ?*

Sol. More toys, More cost (Direct proportion)

Let the required cost be Rs. x.

Then $15 : 35 :: 234 : x$

or $15 \times x = 35 \times 234$.

$\therefore x = \left(\dfrac{35 \times 234}{15} \right) = 546.$

$\therefore$ Cost of 35 toys = Rs. 546.

Ex. 2. *If 36 men can do a certain piece of work in 25 days, in how many days will 15 men do it ?*

Sol. Less men, More days (Indirect proportion)

Let the required number of days be x.

So, inverse ratio of men is equal to ratio of time taken

$\therefore 15 : 36 :: 25 : x$ or $15 \times x = 36 \times 25.$

$$\therefore \ x = \left(\frac{36 \times 25}{15}\right) = 60.$$

Hence, the required number of days = 60.

Ex. 3. *If 20 men can build a wall 56 metres long in 6 days, what length of a similar wall can be built by 35 men in 3 days ?*

Sol. Since the length is to be found out, we compare each item with the length as shown below.

More men, More length built (Direct)

Less days, Less length built (Direct)

$$\left.\begin{array}{ll}\text{Men} & 20:35 \\ \text{Days} & 6:3\end{array}\right\} :: 56 : x$$

$$\therefore \ 20 \times 6 \times x = 35 \times 3 \times 56 \ \text{ or } \ x = \left(\frac{35 \times 3 \times 56}{20 \times 6}\right) = 49.$$

Hence, the required length = 49 metres.

Ex. 4. *If 15 men working 9 hours a day can reap a field in 16 days, in how many days will 18 men reap the field, working 8 hours a day ?*

Sol. Since the number of days is to be found out, we compare each item with the number of days.

More men, Less days (Indirect)

Less working hours, More days (Indirect)

$$\left.\begin{array}{ll}\text{Men} & 18:15 \\ \text{Working Hrs.} & 8:9\end{array}\right\} :: 16 : x$$

$$\therefore \ 18 \times 8 \times x = 15 \times 9 \times 16 \ \text{ or } \ x = \left(\frac{15 \times 9 \times 16}{18 \times 8}\right) = 15.$$

$\therefore$ Required number of days = 15.

Ex. 5. *If 8 men working 9 hours a day can build a wall 18 m long, 2 m wide and 12 m high in 10 days, how many men will be required to build a wall 32 m long, 5 m wide and 9m high, working 6 hours a day in 8 days?*

Sol. We shall compare each item with the number of men.

Less working hours, More men	(Indirect)
More length, More men	(Direct)
More breadth, More men	(Direct)
Less height, Less men	(Direct)
Less days, More men	(Indirect)

$$\left.\begin{array}{ll}\text{Working hours} & 6:9 \\ \text{Length} & 18:32 \\ \text{Breadth} & 2:5 \\ \text{Height} & 12:9 \\ \text{Days} & 8:10\end{array}\right\} :: 8 : x$$

$$\therefore \ 6 \times 18 \times 2 \times 12 \times 8 \times x = 9 \times 32 \times 5 \times 9 \times 10 \times 8$$

$$\therefore \ x = \left\{\frac{9 \times 32 \times 5 \times 9 \times 10 \times 8}{6 \times 18 \times 2 \times 12 \times 8}\right\} = 50.$$

$\therefore$ Required number of men = 50.

Ex. 6. *If 9 engines consume 24 metric tonnes of coal, when each is working 8 hours a day ; how much coal will be required for 8 engines, each running 13 hours a day, it being given that 3 engines of the former type consume as much as 4 engines of latter type.*

Sol. We shall compare each item with the quantity of coal.

Less engines, less coal consumed   (Direct)

More working hours, More coal consumed   (Direct)

If 3 engines of former type consume 1 unit, then 1 engine will consume $\frac{1}{3}$ unit.

If 4 engines of latter type consume 1 unit, then 1 engine will consume $\frac{1}{4}$ unit.

Less rate of consumption, Less coal consumed (Direct)

$$\therefore \left.\begin{array}{ll} \text{Number of Engines} & 9:8 \\ \text{Working hours} & 8:13 \\ \text{Rate of consumption} & \frac{1}{3}:\frac{1}{4} \end{array}\right\} ::24:x$$

$$9 \times 8 \times \frac{1}{3} \times x = 8 \times 13 \times \frac{1}{4} \times 24$$

or $24x = 48 \times 13$ or $x = \dfrac{48 \times 13}{24} = 26.$

$\therefore$ Required consumption of coal = 26 metric tonnes.

Ex. 7. *A contract is to be completed in 46 days and 117 men were set to work, each working 8 hours a day. After 33 days $\frac{4}{7}$ of the work is completed. How many additional men may be employed so that the work may be completed in time, each man now working 9 hours a day ?*

Sol. Remaining work $= \left(1 - \dfrac{4}{7}\right) = \dfrac{3}{7}.$

Remaining period $= (46 - 33)$ days $= 13$ days.

$$\left\{\begin{array}{ll} \text{Less work, Less men} & (Direct) \\ \text{Less days, More men} & (Indirect) \\ \text{More Hrs/Day, Less men} & (Indirect) \end{array}\right.$$

$$\therefore \left.\begin{array}{ll} \text{Work} & \frac{4}{7}:\frac{3}{7} \\ \text{Days} & 13:33 \\ \text{Hrs/Day} & 9:8 \end{array}\right\} ::117:x.$$

$\therefore \dfrac{4}{7} \times 13 \times 9 \times x = \dfrac{3}{7} \times 33 \times 8 \times 117$ or $x = \left(\dfrac{3 \times 33 \times 8 \times 117}{4 \times 13 \times 9}\right) = 198.$

$\therefore$ Additional men to be employed $= (198 - 117) = 81.$

Ex. 8. *A garrison of 3300 men had provisions for 32 days, when given at the rate of 850 gms per head. At the end of 7 days, a reinforcement arrives and it was found that the provisions will last 17 days more, when given at the rate of 825 gms per head. What is the strength of the reinforcement ?*

Sol. *The problem becomes :*

3300 men taking 850 gms per head have provisions for (32 – 7) or 25 days. How many men taking 825 gms each have provisions for 17 days ?

Less ration per head, more men   (Indirect)

Less days, More men   (Indirect)

$$\left.\begin{array}{l}\text{.Ration}\quad 825:850\\ \text{Days}\qquad 17:25\end{array}\right\} :: 3300 : x$$

$\therefore\ 825 \times 17 \times x = 850 \times 25 \times 3300$ or $x = \dfrac{850 \times 25 \times 3300}{825 \times 17} = 5000.$

$\therefore$ Strength of reinforcement = (5000 – 3300) = 1700.

EXERCISE 14

Mark ($\sqrt{}$) against the correct answer in each of the following :

1.   The price of 357 mangoes is Rs. 1517.25. What will be the approximate price of 49 dozens of such mangoes ?   **(Bank P.O. 1993)**
     (*a*) Rs. 3000   (*b*) Rs. 3500   (*c*) Rs. 4000   (*d*) Rs. 2500

2.   The price of 438 oranges is Rs. 1384.08. What will be the approximate price of 8 dozens of oranges ?   **(Bank P.O. 1994)**
     (*a*) Rs. 300   (*b*) Rs. 400   (*c*) Rs. 500   (*d*) Rs. 250

3.   If 11.25 m of a uniform iron rod weighs 42.75 kg, what will be the weight of 6 m of the same rod ?
     (*a*) 22.8 kg   (*b*) 25.6 kg   (*c*) 28 kg   (*d*) 26.5 kg

4.   On a scale of a map, 0.6 cm represents 6.6 km. If the distance between two points on the map is 80.5 cm, the actual distance between these points is :
     (*a*) 9 km   (*b*) 72.5 km   (*c*) 190.75 km (*d*) 885.5 km

5.   If 20 men working together can finish a job in 20 days, then the number of days taken by 25 men of the same capacity to finish the job is :
     (*a*) 25   (*b*) 20   (*c*) 16   (*d*) 12

     (U.D.C. 1993)

6.   If 10 men can reap a field in 8 days, then 8 men will reap the same field in :   **(Central Excise & I. Tax 1992)**
     (*a*) 5 days   (*b*) 4 days   (*c*) 10 days   (*d*) 20 days

7.   14 pumps of equal capacity can fill a tank in 6 days. If the tank has to be filled in 4 days, the number of extra pumps needed is :

(a) 7   (b) 14   (c) 21   (d) 28

(U.D.C. 1993)

8. If 16 men working 7 hours a day can plough a field in 48 days, in how many days will 14 men working 12 hours a day plough the same field ? **(C.B.I. 1993)**

     (a) 46   (b) 35   (c) 32   (d) 30

9. If 80 lamps can be lighted 5 hours per day for 10 days for Rs. 21.25, then the number of lamps which can be lighted 4 hours daily for 30 days for Rs. 76.50, is : **(C.B.I. 1993)**

     (a) 100   (b) 120   (c) 150   (d) 160

10. If 12 carpenters, working 6 hours a day can make 460 chairs in 24 days, how many chairs will 18 carpenters make in 36 days, each working 8 hours a day ? **(Hotel Management 1992)**

     (a) 1260   (b) 1320   (c) 920   (d) 1380

11. 400 persons working 9 hours per day complete $\frac{1}{4}$ th of the work in 10 days. The number of additional persons, working 8 hours per day required to complete the remaining work in 20 days, is :

     (a) 675   (b) 275   (c) 250   (d) 225

(Assistant Grade 1994)

12. Some persons can do a piece of work in 12 days. Two times the number of such persons will do half of that work in : **(Assistant Grade 1994)**

     (a) 6 days   (b) 4 days   (c) 12 days   (d) 3 days

13. If 18 persons can build a wall 140 m long in 42 days, the number of days that 30 persons will take to complete a similar wall 100 m long, is : **(Central Excise & I. Tax 1993)**

     (a) 18   (b) 21   (c) 24   (d) 28

14. If it takes 10 days to dig a trench 100 m long, 50 m broad and 10 m deep, what length of trench, 25 m broad and 15 m deep can be dug in 30 days ? **(Hotel Management 1992)**

     (a) 400 m   (b) 200 m   (c) 100 m   (d) $88\frac{8}{9}$ m

15. A certain number of men can finish a piece of work in 100 days. If however, there were 10 men less, it would take 10 days more for the work to be finished. How many men were there originally ?

     (a) 75   (b) 82   (c) 100   (d) 110

(Hotel Management 1992)

16. A certain number of men could do a piece of work in 60 days. If there were 8 more men, it could be finished in 10 days less. The number of men in the beginning were :

     (a) 30   (b) 35   (c) 40   (d) 45

17. If 18 binders bind 900 books in 10 days, how many binders will be required to bind 660 books in 12 days ?   **(Bank P.O. 1988)**

   (a) 22   (b) 14   (c) 13   (d) 11

18. If 300 men can do a piece of work in 16 days, how many men would do $\frac{1}{5}$ of the work in 15 days ?

   (a) 56   (b) 60   (c) 64   (d) 72

19. If 6 men working 8 hours a day earn Rs. 840 per week, then 9 men working 6 hours a day will earn how much per week ?   **(I. Tax 1988)**

   (a) Rs. 840   (b) Rs. 945   (c) Rs. 1620   (d) Rs. 1680

20. If 17 labourers can dig a ditch 26 m long in 18 days, working 8 hours a day ; how many more labourers should be engaged to dig a similar ditch 39 m long in 6 days, each labourer working 9 hours a day ?

   (a) 34   (b) 51   (c) 68   (d) 85

21. 20 men complete one-third of a piece of work in 20 days. How many more men should be employed to finish the rest of the work in 25 more days ?

   (a) 10   (b) 12   (c) 15   (d) 20

22. If 18 pumps can raise 2170 tonnes of water in 10 days, working 7 hours a day ; in how many days will 16 pumps raise 1736 tonnes of water, working 9 hours a day ?

   (a) 6 days   (b) 7 days   (c) 8 days   (d) 9 days

23. If 9 examiners can examine a certain number of answer books in 12 days by working 5 hours a day ; for how many hours a day would 4 examiners have to work in order to examine twice the number of answer books in 30 days ?

   (a) 6   (b) 8   (c) 9   (d) 10

24. If 54 kg of corn would feed 35 horses for 21 days, in how many days would 72 kg of it feed 28 horses ?

   (a) 35   (b) 28   (c) 42   (d) $31\frac{1}{2}$

25. A rope makes 70 rounds of the circumference of a cylinder whose radius of the base is 14 cm. How many times can it go round a cylinder with radius 20 cm ?

   (a) 40   (b) 49   (c) 100   (d) None of these

26. If $\frac{3}{5}$ of a cistern is filled in 1 minute, how much more time will be required to fill the rest of it ?

   (a) 30 sec   (b) 40 sec   (c) 36 sec   (d) 24 sec

27. Ten pipes through which water flows at the same rate can fill a tank in 28 minutes. If three pipes go out of order, how long will the remaining pipes take to fill the tank ?

(a) 40 min.   (b) 8 min 24 sec
(c) 25 min 12 sec   (d) 32 min. 36 sec

28. If 21 cows eat that much as 15 buffaloes, how many cows will eat that much as 105 buffaloes ?

(a) 75   (b) 147   (c) 63   (d) None of these

29. 95 men had provisions for 200 days. After 5 days, 30 men died due to an epidemic. The remaining food will last for how many days ?

(a) $136\frac{16}{19}$ days   (b) 180 days   (c) 285 days   (d) None of these

30. A garrison of 500 men had provisions for 27 days. After 3 days, a reinforcement of 300 men arrived. The remaining food will now last for how many days ?

(a) 15   (b) 16   (c) $17\frac{1}{2}$ (d) 18

31. A garrison had provisions for a certain number of days. After 10 days $\frac{1}{5}$ th of the men desert and it is found that the provisions will now last just as long as before. How long was that ?

(a) 15 days   (b) 25 days   (c) 35 days   (d) 50 days

32. If a certain number of workmen can do a piece of work in 25 days, in what time will another set of an equal number of men do a piece of work twice as great, supposing that 2 men of the first set can do as much work in an hour as 3 men of the second set can do in an hour ?

(a) 60 days   (b) 75 days   (c) 90 days   (d) 105 days

33. If x men working x hours per day can do x units of a work in x days, then y men working y hours per day would be able to complete how many units of work in y days.

(a) $\dfrac{x^2}{y^3}$ (b) $\dfrac{x^3}{y^2}$ (c) $\dfrac{y^2}{x^3}$ (d) $\dfrac{y^3}{x^2}$

34. If 9 men working $7\frac{1}{2}$ hours a day can finish a piece of work in 20 days, then how many days will be taken by 12 men, working 6 hours a day to finish the work, it being given that 2 men of latter type work as much as 3 men of the former type ?

(a) $9\frac{1}{2}$ (b) 11   (c) $12\frac{1}{2}$ (d) 13

35. If 5 engines consume 6 metric tonnes of coal when each is running 9 hours a day, how much coal (in metric tonnes) will be needed for 8 engines, each running 10 hours a day, it being given that 3 engines of the former type consume as much as 4 engines of latter type ?

(a) $3\frac{1}{8}$ (b) 8   (c) $8\frac{8}{9}$ (d) $6\frac{12}{25}$

36. 15 men take 21 days of 8 hours each to do a piece of work. How many days of 6 hours each would 21 women take, if 3 women do as much work as 2 men ?

(a) 18   (b) 20   (c) 25   (d) 30

37. A contractor undertook to do a certain piece of work in 9 days. He employed certain number of men, but 6 of them being absent from the very first day, the rest could finish the work in 15 days. The number of men originally employed were :

(a) 12   (b) 15   (c) 18   (d) 24

38. A contractor undertakes to do a piece of work in 40 days. He engages 100 men at the beginning and 100 more after 35 days and completes the work in stipulated time. If he had not engaged the additional men, how many days behind schedule would it be finished ?

(a) 3   (b) 5   (c) 6   (d) 9

39. A contractor employed 30 men to do a piece of work in 38 days. After 25 days, he employed 5 men more and the work was finished one day earlier. How many days he would have been behind, if he had not employed additional men ?

(a) 1   (b) $1\frac{1}{4}$ (c) $1\frac{3}{4}$ (d) $1\frac{1}{2}$

40. If 3 men or 6 boys can do a piece of work in 10 days, working 7 hours a day ; how many days will it take to complete a piece of work twice as large with 6 men and 2 boys working together for 8 hours a day ?

(a) 6   (b) $7\frac{1}{2}$ (c) $8\frac{1}{2}$ (d) 9

41. 2 men and 7 boys can do a piece of work in 14 days ; 3 men and 8 boys can do the same in 11 days. Then, 8 men and 6 boys can do three times the amount of this work in :

(a) 18 days   (b) 21 days   (c) 24 days   (d) 36 days

42. 12 men and 18 boys working $7\frac{1}{2}$ hours a day can do a work in 60 days. If 1 man works equal to 2 boys, then the number of boys required to help 21 men to do twice the work in 50 days, working 9 hours a day, will be :   **(Central Excise & I. Tax 1990)**

(a) 30   (b) 42   (c) 48   (d) 90

43. A wheel rotates 10 times every minute and moves 20 cm during each rotation. How many cms does the wheel move in 1 hour ?

(a) 2000   (b) 600   (c) 1200   (d) 12000

(Assistant Grade 1994)

ANSWERS

1. (*d*)	**2.** (*a*)	**3.** (*a*)	**4.** (*d*)	**5.** (*c*)	**6.** (*c*)	**7.** (*a*)	**8.** (*c*)	**9.** (*b*)
10. (*d*)	**11.** (*b*)	**12.** (*d*)	**13.** (*a*)	**14.** (*a*)	**15.** (*d*)	**16.** (*c*)	**17.** (*d*)	**18.** (*c*)
19. (*b*)	**20.** (*b*)	**21.** (*b*)	**22.** (*b*)	**23.** (*c*)	**24.** (*a*)	**25.** (*b*)	**26.** (*b*)	**27.** (*a*)
28. (*b*)	**29.** (*c*)	**30.** (*a*)	**31.** (*d*)	**32.** (*b*)	**33.** (*d*)	**34.** (*c*)	**35.** (*b*)	**36.** (*d*)
37. (*b*)	**38.** (*b*)	**39.** (*a*)	**40.** (*b*)	**41.** (*b*)	**42.** (*b*)	**43.** (*d*)		

SOLUTIONS

1. More mangoes, more cost (Direct)

$357 : 49 \times 12 : : 1517.25 : x$

or $375 \times x = 49 \times 12 \times 1517.25$.

$\therefore x = \left(\dfrac{49 \times 12 \times 1517.25}{357} \right) = 2499$.

$\therefore$ Approximate cost = Rs. 2500.

2. Less oranges, less cost (Direct)

$438 : 96 : : 1384.08 : x$ or $x = \dfrac{96 \times 1384.08}{438} = 303.36$

$\therefore$ Approximate cost = Rs. 300.

3. Less length, less weight (Direct)

$\therefore 11.25 : 6 : : 42.75 : x$ or $x = \left(\dfrac{6 \times 42.75}{11.25} \right) = 22.8$.

$\therefore$ Weight of 6 m long rod = 22.8 kg.

4. More distance on the map, more actual distance (Direct)

$0.6 : 80.5 : : 6.6 : x$

or $0.6\, x = 80.5 \times 6.6$ or $x = \left(\dfrac{80.5 \times 6.6}{0.6} \right) = 885.5$ km.

Hence, actual distance = 885.5 km.

5. More men, less days (Indirect)

$25 : 20 : : 20 : x$ or $25x = 20 \times 20$ or $x = \left(\dfrac{20 \times 20}{25} \right) = 16$.

$\therefore$ Required number of days = 16.

6. Less men, more days (Indirect)

$8 : 10 : : 8 : x$ or $8x = 10 \times 8$ or $x = \left(\dfrac{10 \times 8}{8} \right) = 10$.

$\therefore$ Required number of days = 10.

7. Less days, more pumps (Indirect)

$4 : 6 : : 14 : x$ or $4x = 6 \times 14$ or $x = \left(\dfrac{6 \times 14}{4} \right) = 21$.

$\therefore$ Extra pumps needed = (21 − 14) = 7.

8. Less men, more days   (Indirect)
More hrs/day, less days   (Indirect)

$$\left.\begin{array}{ll}\text{Men} & 14:16 \\ \text{Hrs/Day} & 12:7\end{array}\right\}::48:x$$

$\therefore$ $14 \times 12 \times x = 16 \times 7 \times 48$ or $x = \left(\dfrac{16 \times 7 \times 48}{14 \times 12}\right) = 32$.

$\therefore$ Required number of days = 32.

9. Less hours per day, more lamps (Indirect)
More money, more lamps (Direct)
More days, less lamps (Indirect)

$$\left.\begin{array}{ll}\text{Hrs/Day} & 4:5 \\ \text{Money} & 21.25:76.50 \\ \text{Days} & 30:10\end{array}\right\}::80:x$$

$\therefore$ $4 \times 21.25 \times 30 \times x = 5 \times 76.50 \times 10 \times 80$

or $x = \left(\dfrac{5 \times 76.50 \times 10 \times 80}{4 \times 21.25 \times 30}\right) = 120$.

$\therefore$ Required number of lamps = 120.

10. More carpenters, more chairs   (Direct)
More hrs/day, more chairs   (Direct)
More Days, more chairs   (Direct)

$$\left.\begin{array}{ll}\text{Carpenters} & 12:18 \\ \text{Hrs/Day} & 6:8 \\ \text{Days} & 24:36\end{array}\right\}::460:x$$

$12 \times 6 \times 24 \times x = 18 \times 8 \times 36 \times 460$ or $x = \left(\dfrac{18 \times 8 \times 36 \times 460}{12 \times 6 \times 24}\right) = 1380$.

$\therefore$ Required number of chairs = 1380.

11. Work done $= \dfrac{1}{4}$, Remaining work $= \left(1 - \dfrac{1}{4}\right) = \dfrac{3}{4}$.

Less hours/day, more men required (Indirect)
More work, more men required   (Direct)
More days, less men required   (Indirect)

$$\left.\begin{array}{ll}\text{Hrs/Day} & 8:9 \\ \text{Work} & \dfrac{1}{4}:\dfrac{3}{4} \\ \text{Days} & 20:10\end{array}\right\}::400:x$$

$\therefore$ $8 \times \dfrac{1}{4} \times 20 \times x = 9 \times \dfrac{3}{4} \times 10 \times 400$ or $x = \left(\dfrac{9 \times 3 \times 10 \times 400}{8 \times 20}\right) = 675$.

$\therefore$ Additional men $= (675 - 400) = 275$.

12. Let x men can do the work in 12 days.
More men, less days (Indirect)
Less work, less days (Direct)

.Men $2x : x$
Work $1 : \dfrac{1}{2}$ $\Bigg\} :: 12 : y$

$\therefore \ 2x \times 1 \times y = x \times \dfrac{1}{2} \times 12 \ $ or $ \ y = 3.$

Hence, the required number of days = 3.

13. Less length, less days (Direct)
More persons, less days (Indirect)
.Length $140 : 100$
Persons $30 : 18$ $\Bigg\} :: 42 : x$

$\therefore \ 140 \times 30 \times x = 100 \times 18 \times 42 \ $ or $ \ x = \left(\dfrac{100 \times 18 \times 42}{140 \times 30} \right) = 18.$

$\therefore$ Required number of days = 18.

14. More days, more length   (Direct)
Less breadth, more length   (Indirect)
More depth, less length   (Indirect)
.Days $10 : 30$
Breadth $25 : 50$ $\Bigg\} :: 100 : x$
Depth $15 : 10$

$\therefore \ 10 \times 25 \times 15 \times x = 30 \times 50 \times 10 \times 100$

or $x = \left(\dfrac{30 \times 50 \times 10 \times 100}{10 \times 25 \times 15} \right) = 400.$

$\therefore$ Required length = 400 m.

15. Originally let there be x men.
Less men, more days (Indirect)

$\therefore \ (x - 10) : x :: 100 : 110 \ $ or $ \ \dfrac{x - 10}{x} = \dfrac{100}{110}$

or $11x - 110 = 10x \ $ or $ \ x = 110.$
So, originally there were 110 men.

16. Let x men can finish the work in 60 days.
Then, $(x + 8)$ men can finish it in 50 days.
More men, less days (Indirect)

$\therefore \ x + 8 : x = 60 : 50 \ $ or $ \ \dfrac{x + 8}{x} = \dfrac{60}{50} \ $ or $ \ 50 (x + 8) = 60x \ $ or $ \ x = 40.$

$\therefore$ Number of men in the beginning = 40.

17. Less books, less binders (Direct)
More days, less binders (Indirect)
.Books $900 : 660$
Days $12 : 10$ $\Bigg\} :: 18 : x$

$\therefore \ 900 \times 12 \times x = 660 \times 10 \times 18 \ $ or $ \ x = \left(\dfrac{660 \times 10 \times 18}{900 \times 12} \right) = 11.$

$\therefore$ Required number of binders = 11.

18. Less work, less men (Direct)
    Less days, more men (Indirect)

    $$\left.\begin{array}{l} \text{Work} \quad 1:\dfrac{1}{5} \\ \text{Days} \quad 15:16 \end{array}\right\} :: 300:x$$

    $$\therefore \; 1 \times 15 \times x = \frac{1}{5} \times 16 \times 300 \quad \text{or} \quad x = \left(\frac{16 \times 60}{15}\right) = 64.$$

    ∴ Required number of men = 64.

19. More men, more earning (Direct)
    Less hrs/day, less earning (Direct)

    $$\left.\begin{array}{l} \text{Men} \qquad 6:9 \\ \text{Hrs/Day} \quad 8:6 \end{array}\right\} :: 840:x$$

    $$\therefore \; 6 \times 8 \times x = 9 \times 6 \times 840 \quad \text{or} \quad x = \left(\frac{9 \times 6 \times 840}{6 \times 8}\right) = 945.$$

    ∴ Required earning = Rs. 945.

20. More length, more labourers (Direct)
    Less days, more labourers (Indirect)
    More hrs/day, less labourers (Indirect)

    $$\left.\begin{array}{l} \text{Length} \quad 26:39 \\ \text{Days} \qquad 6:18 \\ \text{Hrs/Day} \quad 9:8 \end{array}\right\} :: 17:x$$

    $$\therefore \; 26 \times 6 \times 9 \times x = 39 \times 18 \times 8 \times 17 \quad \text{or} \quad x = \left(\frac{39 \times 18 \times 8 \times 17}{26 \times 6 \times 9}\right) = 68.$$

    ∴ Number of more labourers = (68 − 17) = 51.

21. Work done = $\dfrac{1}{3}$, Remaining work = $\left(1 - \dfrac{1}{3}\right) = \dfrac{2}{3}$.

    More work, more men   (Direct)
    More days, less men   (Indirect)

    $$\left.\begin{array}{l} \text{Work} \quad \dfrac{1}{3}:\dfrac{2}{3} \\ \text{Days} \quad 25:20 \end{array}\right\} :: 20:x$$

    $$\therefore \; \frac{1}{3} \times 25 \times x = \frac{2}{3} \times 20 \times 20 \quad \text{or} \quad x = \left(\frac{2 \times 20 \times 20}{25}\right) = 32.$$

    ∴ More men to be employed = (32 − 20) = 12.

22. Less pumps, more days   (Indirect)
    Less water, less days   (Direct)
    More hrs/day, less days   (Indirect)

    $$\left.\begin{array}{l} \text{Pumps} \qquad 16:18 \\ \text{Water} \quad 2170:1736 \\ \text{Hrs/Day} \qquad 9:7 \end{array}\right\} :: 10:x$$

    $$\therefore \; 16 \times 2170 \times 9 \times x = 18 \times 1736 \times 7 \times 10$$

or $x = \left(\dfrac{18 \times 1736 \times 7 \times 10}{16 \times 2170 \times 9} \right) = 7.$

∴ Required number of days = 7.

23. Less examiners, more hours per day   (Indirect)
More days, less hours per day   (Indirect)
More answer books, more hours per day   (Direct)

$\left. \begin{array}{ll} \text{Examiners} & 4:9 \\ \text{Days} & 30:12 \\ \text{Ans. Books} & 1:2 \end{array} \right\} :: 5 : x$

∴ $4 \times 30 \times 1 \times x = 9 \times 12 \times 2 \times 5$

or $x = \left(\dfrac{9 \times 12 \times 2 \times 5}{4 \times 30 \times 1} \right) = 9.$

∴ New set of examiners will have to work 9 hrs per day.

24. More corn, more days   (Direct)
Less horses, more days   (Indirect)

$\left. \begin{array}{ll} \text{Corn} & 54:72 \\ \text{Horses} & 28:35 \end{array} \right\} :: 21 : x$

∴ $54 \times 28 \times x = 72 \times 35 \times 21$

or $x = \left(\dfrac{72 \times 35 \times 21}{54 \times 28} \right) = 35.$

∴ Required number of days = 35.

25. More Radius, less rounds (Indirect)

$20 : 14 :: 70 : x$ or $20x = 14 \times 70$ or $x = \left(\dfrac{14 \times 70}{20} \right) = 49.$

∴ Required number of rounds = 49.

26. Remaining part $= \left(1 - \dfrac{3}{5} \right) = \dfrac{2}{5}.$

Less part, less time (Direct)

$\dfrac{3}{5} : \dfrac{2}{5} :: 60 : x$ or $\dfrac{3}{5}x = \dfrac{2}{5} \times 60$ or $x = 40$ sec.

∴ Rest of the cistern will be filled in 40 sec.

27. Less pipes, more time (Indirect)

∴ $7 : 10 :: 28 : x$ or $7x = 10 \times 28$ or $x = \dfrac{10 \times 28}{7} = 40.$

∴ Remaining pipes will fill the tank in 40 min.

28. 15 buffaloes ≡ 21 cows

105 buffaloes ≡ $\left(\dfrac{21}{15} \times 105 \right)$ cows = 147 cows.

29. The remaining food is sufficient for 95 men for 195 days.
But, now remaining men = (95 − 30) = 65.
Less men, More days (Indirect)

$\therefore \ 65:95::195:x$ or $65x = 95 \times 195$ or $x = \dfrac{95 \times 195}{65} = 285.$

Hence, the remaining food will last for 285 days.

30. The remaining food is sufficient for 500 men for 24 days.

But, now the number of men $= (500 + 300) = 800.$

More men, less days (Indirect)

$800 : 500 :: 24 : x$ or $800x = 500 \times 24$ or $x = \dfrac{500 \times 24}{800} = 15.$

$\therefore$ The food will now last for 15 days.

31. Initially, let there be x men having food for y days.

After 10 days, x men had food for $(y - 10)$ days.

i.e. $\left(x - \dfrac{x}{5}\right)$ or $\dfrac{4x}{5}$ men had food for y days.

$\therefore \ x\,(y - 10) = \left(\dfrac{4x}{5}\right)y$ or $xy - 50x = 0$

or $x\,(y - 50) = 0.$ So, $y = 50$ [$\because \ x \neq 0$]

32. Speeds of working of 1st and 2nd type of men are $\dfrac{1}{2} \ \& \ \dfrac{1}{3}.$

Now, More work, More time (Direct)
Less speed, More time (Indirect)

$\left.\begin{array}{l} \text{Work} \quad 1:2 \\[2mm] \text{Speed} \quad \dfrac{1}{3}:\dfrac{1}{2} \end{array}\right\} :: 25 : x$

$\therefore \ 1 \times \dfrac{1}{3} \times x = 2 \times \dfrac{1}{2} \times 25$ or $x = 75$ days.

$\therefore$ Required number of days = 75.

33. More men, More work (Direct)
More working hrs., More work (Direct)
More days, More work (Direct)

$\left.\begin{array}{ll} \text{Men} & x:y \\ \text{Hrs/Day} & x:y \\ \text{Days} & x:y \end{array}\right\} :: x : z$ or $z = \left(\dfrac{y \times y \times y \times x}{x \times x \times x \times x}\right) = \dfrac{y^3}{x^2}.$

$\therefore$ Required number of units $= \dfrac{y^3}{x^2}.$

34. More men, Less days (Indirect)
Less Hrs/Day, More days (Indirect)
Less Speed, More days (Indirect)

$$\left.\begin{array}{l} \text{Men} \qquad 12:9 \\ \text{Hrs/Day} \quad 6:\dfrac{15}{2} \\ \text{Speed} \qquad \dfrac{1}{2}:\dfrac{1}{3} \end{array}\right\} :: 20:x$$

$\therefore\ 12 \times 6 \times \dfrac{1}{2} \times x = 9 \times \dfrac{15}{2} \times \dfrac{1}{3} \times 20$ or $x = 12\dfrac{1}{2}$ days.

$\therefore$ Required number of days $= 12\dfrac{1}{2}$.

35. More engine, More coal (Direct)
    More hrs/day, More coal (Direct)
    More rate, More coal (Direct)

$$\left.\begin{array}{l} \text{Engines} \quad 5:8 \\ \text{Hrs/Day} \quad 9:10 \\ \text{Rate} \qquad \dfrac{1}{3}:\dfrac{1}{4} \end{array}\right\} :: 6:x$$

$\therefore\ 5 \times 9 \times \dfrac{1}{3} \times x = 8 \times 10 \times \dfrac{1}{4} \times 6$ or $x = 8$ metric tonnes.

$\therefore$ Required quantity of coal $= 8$ metric tonnes.

36. 3 women $\equiv 2$ men. So, 21 women $\equiv 14$ men.
    Less men, More days (Indirect)
    Less hrs/day, More days (Indirect)

$$\left.\begin{array}{l} \text{Men} \qquad 14:15 \\ \text{Hrs/Day} \ 6:8 \end{array}\right\} :: 21:x \text{ or } x = \left(\dfrac{15 \times 8 \times 21}{14 \times 6}\right) = 30 \text{ days.}$$

$\therefore$ Required number of days $= 30$.

37. Let there be x men at the beginning.
    Now, less men would take more days.
    $\therefore\ 15:9::x:(x-6)$ or $15(x-6) = 9x$ or $x = 15$ men.

38. $[(100 \times 35) + (200 \times 5)]$ men working for 1 day can finish the work.
    $\therefore$ 4500 men can finish the work in 1 day
    100 men can finish it in $\left(\dfrac{4500}{100}\right)$ days $= 45$ days.
    i.e. 5 days behind schedule.

39. After 25 days, 35 men complete the work in 12 days.
    35 men can finish the remaining work in 12 days
    $\therefore$ 30 men can do it in $\left(\dfrac{12 \times 35}{30}\right) = 14$ days, i.e. 1 day behind.

40. 3 men $\equiv 6$ boys. So, (6 men $+ 2$ boys) $\equiv 14$ boys.
    More work, More days (Direct)
    More boys, Less days (Indirect)
    More Hrs/day, Less days (Indirect)

$$\left.\begin{array}{ll}\text{Work} & 1:2 \\ \text{Boys} & 14:6 \\ \text{Hrs/Day} & 8:7\end{array}\right\}:10:x \text{ or } x=\left(\frac{2\times6\times7\times10}{1\times14\times8}\right)=7\frac{1}{2} \text{ days.}$$

41. (2×14) men $+(7\times14)$ boys $\equiv(3\times11)$ men $+(8\times11)$ boys

∴ 5 men $\equiv$ 10 boys or 1 man $\equiv$ 2 boys.

∴ 2 men + 7 boys $\equiv$ 11 boys & 8 men + 6 boys $\equiv$ 22 boys.

More boys, Less days (Indirect)

More work, More days (Direct)

$$\left.\begin{array}{ll}.\text{Boys} & 22:11 \\ \text{Work} & 1:3\end{array}\right\}::14:x \text{ or } x=\left(\frac{11\times3\times14}{22\times1}\right)=21 \text{ days.}$$

42. 1 man $\equiv$ 2 boys, 12 men + 18 boys $\equiv$ 42 boys.

Less days, More boys (Indirect)

More hrs/day, Less boys (Indirect)

More work, More boys (Direct)

$$\left.\begin{array}{ll}.\text{Days} & 50:60 \\ \text{Hrs/Day} & 9:\dfrac{15}{2} \\ \text{Work} & 1:2\end{array}\right\}::42:x$$

∴ $50\times9\times1\times x=60\times\dfrac{15}{2}\times2\times42$ or $x=82$.

Now 82 boys $\equiv$ 21 men + 42 boys.

∴ Number of boys required = 42.

43. Number of times wheel moves in 1 hour $=(10\times60)=600$.

∴ Distance moved $=(600\times20)$ cms $=12000$ cms.

S.S.C. Clerk's Grade Kit

By : R. S. Aggarwal

¤ *A comprehensive study of all topics included in latest syllabus.*

¤ *A whole lot of fully solved questions on General Intelligence, English Language and Quantitative Aptitude.*

¤ *Previous year's questions fully solved.*

15. Time & Work

General Rules :

(*i*) If *A* can do a piece of work in *n* days, then *A*'s 1 day's work = $\dfrac{1}{n}$.

(*ii*) If *A*'s 1 day's work = $\dfrac{1}{n}$, then *A* can finish the work in *n* days.

(*iii*) If *A* is thrice as good a workman as *B*, then :

Ratio of work done by *A* and *B* = 3 : 1,

Ratio of times taken by *A* & *B* to finish a work = 1 : 3.

Solved Problems

Ex. 1. *A can do a piece of work in 10 days which B alone can do in 12 days. In how many days will they finish the work, both working together ?*

Sol. *A*'s 1 day's work = $\dfrac{1}{10}$, *B*'s 1 day's work = $\dfrac{1}{12}$.

$(A + B)$'s 1 day's work = $\left(\dfrac{1}{10} + \dfrac{1}{12}\right) = \dfrac{11}{60}$.

∴ Both will finish the work in $\dfrac{60}{11} = 5\dfrac{5}{11}$ days.

Ex. 2. *Two persons A and B working together can dig a trench in 8 hours while A alone can dig it in 12 hours. In how many hours B alone can dig such a trench ?*

Sol. $(A + B)$'s 1 hour's work = $\dfrac{1}{8}$, *A*'s 1 hour's work = $\dfrac{1}{12}$.

∴ *B*'s 1 hour's work = $\left(\dfrac{1}{8} - \dfrac{1}{12}\right) = \dfrac{1}{24}$.

Hence *B* alone can dig the trench in 24 hours.

Ex.3. *A and B can do a piece of work in 12 days ; B and C can do it in 15 days ; A and C can do it in 20 days. In how many days will A, B and C finish it, working all together ?*

Also ,find the number of days taken by each to finish it working alone.

Sol. $(A + B)$'s 1 day's work = $\dfrac{1}{12}$; $(B + C)$'s 1 day's work = $\dfrac{1}{15}$

and $(A + C)$'s 1 day's work = $\dfrac{1}{20}$.

Adding, we get : $2(A + B + C)$'s 1 day's work = $\left(\dfrac{1}{12} + \dfrac{1}{15} + \dfrac{1}{20}\right) = \dfrac{1}{5}$.

$\therefore$ $(A + B + C)$'s 1 day's work $= \dfrac{1}{10}$.

Thus, A, B and C together can finish the work in 10 days.

Now, A's 1 day's work

$$= [(A + B + C)\text{'s 1 day's work}] - [(B + C)\text{'s 1 day's work}]$$

$$= \left(\dfrac{1}{10} - \dfrac{1}{15}\right) = \dfrac{1}{30}.$$

$\therefore$ A alone can finish the work in 30 days.

Similarly, B's 1 day's work $= \left(\dfrac{1}{10} - \dfrac{1}{20}\right) = \dfrac{1}{20}$.

$\therefore$ B alone can finish the work in 20 days.

And, C's 1 day's work $= \left(\dfrac{1}{10} - \dfrac{1}{12}\right) = \dfrac{1}{60}$.

$\therefore$ C alone can finish the work in 60 days.

Ex. 4. *3 men can complete a piece of work in 6 days. Two days after they started the work, 3 more men joined them. How many days will they take to complete the remaining work ?*   **(Bank P.O. 1993)**

Sol. Work done by 3 men in 2 days $= \left(\dfrac{1}{6} \times 2\right) = \dfrac{1}{3}$.

Remaining work $= \left(1 - \dfrac{1}{3}\right) = \dfrac{2}{3}$.

Now 3 men's 1 day's work $= \dfrac{1}{6}$

1 man's 1 day's work $= \dfrac{1}{18}$

6 men's 1 day's work $= \left(6 \times \dfrac{1}{18}\right) = \dfrac{1}{3}$.

Now, $\dfrac{1}{3}$ work is done by them in 1 day.

$\therefore$ $\dfrac{2}{3}$ work is done by them in $\left(3 \times \dfrac{2}{3}\right) = 2$ days.

Ex. 5. *2 men and 3 boys can do a piece of work in 10 days while 3 men and 2 boys can do the same work in 8 days. In how many days can 2 men and 1 boy do the work ?*   **(I. Tax 1992)**

Sol. Let 1 man's 1 day's work $= x$ & 1 boy's 1 day's work $= y$.

Then, $2x + 3y = \dfrac{1}{10}$ and $3x + 2y = \dfrac{1}{8}$

Solving, we get : $x = \dfrac{7}{200}$ and $y = \dfrac{1}{100}$.

$\therefore$ (2 men + 1 boy)'s 1 day's work $= \left(2 \times \dfrac{7}{200} + 1 \times \dfrac{1}{100}\right) = \dfrac{16}{200} = \dfrac{2}{25}$.

So, 2 men & 1 boy together can finish the work in $\frac{25}{2} = 12\frac{1}{2}$ days.

Ex. 6. *A is twice as good a workman as B and together they finish a piece of work in 18 days. In how many days will A alone finish the work ?*

Sol. (*A*'s 1 day's work) : (*B*'s 1 day's work) = 2 : 1.

$(A + B)$'s 1 day's work $= \frac{1}{18}$.

Divide $\frac{1}{18}$ in the ratio 2 : 1.

$\therefore$ A's 1 day's work $= \left(\frac{1}{18} \times \frac{2}{3}\right) = \frac{1}{27}$.

Hence, *A* alone can finish the work in 27 days.

Ex.7. *A and B undertake to do a piece of work for Rs. 600. A alone can do it in 6 days while B alone can do it in 8 days. With the help of C, they finish it in 3 days. Find the share of each.*

Sol. C's 1 day's work $= \frac{1}{3} - \left(\frac{1}{6} + \frac{1}{8}\right) = \frac{1}{24}$.

$\therefore$ $A : B : C$ = Ratio of their 1 day's work $= \frac{1}{6} : \frac{1}{8} : \frac{1}{24} = 4 : 3 : 1$.

$\therefore$ A's share $= \text{Rs}\left(600 \times \frac{4}{8}\right) = \text{Rs. } 300$,

B's share $= \text{Rs.}\left(600 \times \frac{3}{8}\right) = \text{Rs. } 225$.

C's share $= \text{Rs. } [600 - (300 + 225)] = \text{Rs. } 75$.

EXERCISE 15

Mark ($\sqrt{}$) against the correct answer :

1. A can do a piece of work in 30 days while *B* alone can do it in 40 days. In how many days can *A* and *B* working together do it ?

   (a) $17\frac{1}{7}$ (b) $27\frac{1}{7}$ (c) $42\frac{3}{4}$ (d) 70

   (Railways 1990)

2. *A* and *B* together can complete a piece of work in 35 days while *A* alone can complete the same work in 60 days. *B* alone will be able to complete the same work in :   **(Assistant Grade 1994)**

   (a) 42 days   (b) 72 days   (c) 84 days   (d) 96 days

3. A can do a piece of work in 7 days of 9 hours each and *B* can do it in 6 days of 7 hours each. How long will they take to do it, working together $8\frac{2}{5}$ hours a day ?   **(Central Excise & I.Tax 1992)**

(a) 3 days   (b) 4 days   (c) $4\frac{1}{2}$ days   (d) None of these

4. A can do a piece of work in 15 days and B alone can do it in 10 days. B works at it for 5 days and then leaves. A alone can finish the remaining work in :   **(Assistant Grade 1993)**

     (a) $6\frac{1}{2}$ days   (b) $7\frac{1}{2}$ days   (c) 8 days   (d) 9 days

5. A can do $\frac{1}{3}$ of the work in 5 days and B can do $\frac{2}{5}$ of the work in 10 days. In how many days both A and B together can do the work ?

     (a) $7\frac{3}{4}$ (b) $8\frac{4}{5}$ (c) $9\frac{3}{8}$ (d) 10

                                        (Railways 1991)

6. A can do a piece of work in 80 days. He works at it for 10 days and then B alone finishes the remaining work in 42 days. The two together could complete the work in :   **(U.D.C. 1991)**

     (a) 24 days   (b) 25 days   (c) 30 days   (d) 35 days

7. A and B can together finish a work in 30 days. They worked at it for 20 days and then B left. The remaining work was done by A alone in 20 more days. A alone can finish the work in :

     (a) 48 days   (b) 50 days   (c) 54 days   (d) 60 days

                            (Central Excise & I.Tax 1988)

8. A and B can do a piece of work in 45 days and 40 days respectively. They began to do the work together but A leaves after some days and then B completed the remaining work in 23 days. The number of days after which A left the work was :   **(Central Excise & I. Tax 1992)**

     (a) 6   (b) 8   (c) 9   (d) 12

9. A does half as much work as B in three-fourth of the time. If together they take 18 days to complete the work, how much time shall B take to do it ?   **(L.I.C. 1988)**

     (a) 30 days   (b) 35 days   (c) 40 days   (d) none of these

10. A can do a certain job in 12 days. B is 60% more efficient than A. The number of days, it takes B to do the same piece of work, is :

     (a) 6   (b) $6\frac{1}{4}$ (c) $7\frac{1}{2}$ (d) 8

                                      (C.B.I. 1990)

11. A can do a certain job in 25 days which B alone can do in 20 days. A started the work and was joined by B after 10 days. The number of days taken in completing the work was :

(a) $12\frac{1}{2}$ (b) $14\frac{2}{9}$ (c) 15   (d) $16\frac{2}{3}$

12. A is twice as good a workman as B and together they finish a piece of work in 14 days. The number of days taken by A alone to finish the work, is :
    (a) 11   (b) 21   (c) 28   (d) 42

13. A is thrice as good a workman as B and takes 10 days less to do a piece of work than B takes. B alone can do the whole work in :
    (a) 12 days   (b) 15 days   (c) 20 days   (d) 30 days

14. A can do a piece of work in 14 days which B can do in 21 days. They begin together but 3 days before the completion of the work, A leaves off. The total number of days to complete the work is :
    (a) $6\frac{3}{5}$ (b) $8\frac{1}{2}$ (c) $10\frac{1}{5}$ (d) $13\frac{1}{2}$

15. If Ramesh, Suresh and Harish can do a piece of work in 15 days, 10 days and 6 days respectively, how long will they take to do it, if all the three work at it together ?   **(Central Excise & I. Tax 1990)**

    (a) 3 days   (b) $3\frac{1}{2}$ days   (c) $3\frac{9}{20}$ days   (d) $3\frac{3}{20}$ days

16. A and B can do a piece of work in 72 days ; B and C can do it in 120 days ; A and C can do it in 90 days. In what time can A alone do it ?
    (a) 150 days   (b) 120 days   (c) 100 days   (d) 80 days
    (Assistant Grade 1993)

17. A and B can do a piece of work in 5 days ; B and C can do it in 7 days; A and C can do it in 4 days. Who among these will take the least time if put to do it alone ?   **(Hotel Management 1993)**
    (a) A   (b) B   (c) C   (d) Data inadequate

18. If A, B and C together can finish a piece of work in 4 days ; A alone can do it in 12 days and B in 18 days, then C alone can do it in :
    (a) 21 days   (b) 16 days   (c) 14 days   (d) 9 days
    (C.D.S. 1993)

19. A and B can do a piece of work in 18 days ; B and C can do it in 24 days ; A and C can do it in 36 days. In how many days can they do it all working together ?
    (a) 12   (b) 13   (c) 16   (d) 26

20. A and B together can do a piece of work in 12 days, which B and C together can do in 16 days. After A has been working at it for 5 days and B for 7 days, C finishes in 13 days. In how many days C alone will do the work ?   **(Central Excise & I. Tax 1993)**
    (a) 16   (b) 24   (c) 36   (d) 48

21. A is twice as good a workman as *B* and together they complete a work in 15 days. In how many days can the work be completed by *B* alone ?

(Assistant Grade 1994)

(*a*) $22\frac{1}{2}$ (*b*) 30   (*c*) $37\frac{1}{2}$ (*d*) 45

22. 45 men can complete a work in 16 days. Six days after they started working, 30 more men joined them. How many days will they now take to complete the remaining work ?

(Bank P.O. 1994)

(*a*) 4   (*b*) 5   (*c*) 6   (*d*) 8

23. 12 men can complete a work in 18 days. Six days after they started working, 4 men joined them. How many days will all of them take to finish the remaining work ?

(Central Excise & I. Tax 1993)

(*a*) 9   (*b*) 10   (*c*) 12   (*d*) 15

24. Twelve men can complete a work in 8 days. Three days after they started the work, 3 more men joined. In how many days will all of them together complete the remaining work ?

(L.I.C. 1990)

(*a*) 2   (*b*) 4   (*c*) 5   (*d*) 6

25. A, B and C are employed to do a piece of work for Rs. 529. A and C are supposed to finish $\frac{19}{23}$ of the work together. How much shall be paid to *B* ?

(Central Excise & I. Tax 1993)

(*a*) Rs. 82   (*b*) Rs. 92   (*c*) Rs. 300   (*d*) Rs. 437

26. A job is completed by 10 men in 20 days and by 20 women in 15 days. How many days will it take for 5 men and 10 women to finish that work ?

(Bank P.O. 1992)

(*a*) $17\frac{1}{2}$ (*b*) $17\frac{1}{7}$ (*c*) 17   (*d*) $17\frac{1}{120}$

27. A piece of work can be done by 6 men and 5 women in 6 days or 3 men and 4 women in 10 days. It can be done by 9 men and 15 women in :

(Assistant Grade 1994)

(*a*) 1 day   (*b*) 2 days   (*c*) 3 days   (*d*) 4 days

28. 4 men and 6 women finish a job in 8 days, while 3 men and 7 women finish it in 10 days. In how many days will 10 women working together finish it ?

(*a*) 24   (*b*) 32   (*c*) 36   (*d*) 40

29. 12 children take 16 days to complete a work which can be completed by 8 adults in 12 days. 16 adults started working and after 3 days 10 adults left and 4 children joined them. How many days will it take them to complete the remaining work ?

(Bank P.O. 1991)

(*a*) 6   (*b*) 8   (*c*) 4   (*d*) 3

30. Ram can do a piece of work in 8 days which Shyam can finish in 12 days. If they work at it on alternate days with Ram beginning, in how many days, the work will be finished ? **(Central Excise & I. Tax 1994)**

(a) $9\dfrac{1}{3}$ (b) $9\dfrac{1}{2}$ (c) $9\dfrac{1}{24}$ (d) $10\dfrac{1}{3}$

31. A and B working separately can do a piece of work in 9 and 12 days respectively. If they work for a day alternately, A beginning, in how many days the work will be completed ?

(a) $10\dfrac{1}{2}$ (b) $10\dfrac{1}{3}$ (c) $10\dfrac{1}{4}$ (d) $10\dfrac{2}{3}$

32. A, B and C can do a piece of work in 11 days, 20 days and 55 days respectively, working alone. How soon can the work be done if A is assisted by B and C on alternate days ?   **(Assistant Grade 1993)**

(a) 7 days   (b) 8 days   (c) 9 days   (d) 10 days

33. Machines A and B produce 8000 clips in 4 and 6 hours respectively. If they work alternately for 1 hour, A starting first, then 8000 clips will be produced in :   **(Assistant Grade 1994)**

(a) $4\dfrac{1}{3}$ hours   (b) $4\dfrac{2}{3}$ hrs   (c) $5\dfrac{1}{3}$ hrs   (d) $5\dfrac{2}{3}$ hrs

34. A father can do a job as fast as his two sons working together. If one son does the job in 3 hours and the other in 6 hours, how many hours does it take the father to do the job ?   **(Assistant Grade 1994)**

(a) 1   (b) 2   (c) 3   (d) 4

35. A sum of money is sufficient to pay A's wages for 21 days and B's wages for 28 days. The same money is sufficient to pay the wages of both for :

(a) 12 days   (b) 14 days   (c) $12\dfrac{1}{4}$ days   (d) $24\dfrac{1}{2}$ days

36. A alone can finish a piece of work in 10 days which B alone can finish in 15 days. If they work together and finish it, then out of total wages of Rs. 225, the amount (in rupees) that A will get, is :

(a) 90   (b) 112.50   (c) 135   (d) 150

37. A can do a piece of work in 6 days and B alone can do it in 8 days. A and B undertook to do it for Rs. 640. With the help of C, they finished it in 3 days. How much is paid to C ?

(a) Rs. 75   (b) Rs. 80   (c) Rs. 120   (d) Rs. 160

38. A, B and C together earn Rs. 300 per day, while A and C together earn Rs. 188 and B and C together earn Rs. 152. The daily earning of C is :

(a) Rs. 150   (b) Rs. 112   (c) Rs. 68   (d) Rs. 40

39. Sunil can complete a work in 4 days whereas Dinesh can complete it in 6 days. Ramesh works $1\frac{1}{2}$ times as fast as Sunil. How many days will it take for the three together to complete the work ?

    (a) $\frac{7}{12}$ (b) $1\frac{5}{7}$ (c) $1\frac{5}{12}$ (d) None of these

40. If 10 men or 18 boys can do a piece of work in 15 days, then 25 men and 15 boys together will do twice the work in :   **(Assistant Grade 1993)**

    (a) $4\frac{1}{2}$ days   (b) 9 days   (c) 8 days   (d) 36 days

41. A certain number of men complete a piece of work in 60 days. If there were 8 men more, the work could be finished in 10 days less. How many men were originally there ?

    (a) 30   (b) 32   (c) 36   (d) 40

42. The rates of working of A and B are in the ratio 5 : 6. The number of days taken by them to finish the work are in the ratio :

    (a) 5 : 6   (b) 25 : 36   (c) 6 : 5   (d) None of these

43. If 1 man or 2 women or 3 boys can do a piece of work in 44 days, then the same piece of work will be done by 1 man, 1 woman and 1 boy in :

    (a) 21 days   (b) 24 days   (c) 26 days   (d) 33 days

44. 8 men can dig a pit in 20 days. If a man works half as much again as a boy, then 4 men and 9 boys can dig a similar pit in :

    (a) 10 days   (b) 12 days   (c) 15 days   (d) 16 days

45. A does half as much work as B and C does half as much work as A and B together. If C alone can finish the work in 40 days, then together all will finish the work in :   **(Central Excise & I. Tax 1990)**

    (a) $13\frac{1}{3}$ days   (b) 15 days   (c) 20 days   (d) 30 days

46. A and B can separately do a piece of work in 20 and 15 days respectively. They worked together for 6 days, after which B was replaced by C. If the work was finished in next 4 days, then the number of days in which C alone could do the work will be :   **(Central Excise & I. Tax 1990)**

    (a) 60   (b) 40   (c) 35   (d) 30

47. A, B and C can do a piece of work in 36, 54 and 72 days respectively. They started the work but A left 8 days before the completion of the work while B left 12 days before the completion. The number of days for which C worked is :   **(Central Excise & I. Tax 1991)**

    (a) 4   (b) 8   (c) 12   (d) 24

ANSWERS

1. (*a*)	**2.** (*c*)	**3.** (*a*)	**4.** (*b*)	**5.** (*c*)	**6.** (*c*)	**7.** (*d*)	**8.** (*c*)	**9.** (*a*)
10. (*c*)	**11.** (*d*)	**12.** (*b*)	**13.** (*b*)	**14.** (*c*)	**15.** (*a*)	**16.** (*b*)	**17.** (*a*)	**18.** (*d*)
19. (*c*)	**20.** (*b*)	**21.** (*d*)	**22.** (*c*)	**23.** (*a*)	**24.** (*b*)	**25.** (*b*)	**26.** (*b*)	**27.** (*c*)
28. (*d*)	**29.** (*a*)	**30.** (*b*)	**31.** (*c*)	**32.** (*b*)	**33.** (*b*)	**34.** (*b*)	**35.** (*a*)	**36.** (*c*)
37. (*b*)	**38.** (*d*)	**39.** (*d*)	**40.** (*b*)	**41.** (*d*)	**42.** (*c*)	**43.** (*b*)	**44.** (*d*)	**45.** (*a*)
46. (*b*)	**47.** (*d*)							

SOLUTIONS

1. A's 1 day's work $= \dfrac{1}{30}$ & B's 1 day's work $= \dfrac{1}{40}$.

$\therefore$ $(A + B)$'s 1 day's work $= \left(\dfrac{1}{30} + \dfrac{1}{40}\right) = \dfrac{7}{120}$.

$\therefore$ Both together will finish the work in $\dfrac{120}{7} = 17\dfrac{1}{7}$ days.

2. $(A + B)$'s 1 day's work $= \dfrac{1}{35}$ & A's 1 day's work $= \dfrac{1}{60}$.

$\therefore$ B's 1 day's work $= \left(\dfrac{1}{35} - \dfrac{1}{60}\right) = \dfrac{5}{420} = \dfrac{1}{84}$.

Hence B alone will finish the work in 84 days.

3. A can complete the work in (7×9) hrs = 63 hrs.
B can complete the work in (6×7) hrs = 42 hrs.

$\therefore$ A's 1 hour's work $= \dfrac{1}{63}$ & B's 1 hour's work $= \dfrac{1}{42}$.

$(A + B)$'s 1 hour's work $= \left(\dfrac{1}{63} + \dfrac{1}{42}\right) = \dfrac{5}{126}$.

$\therefore$ Both will finish the work in $\left(\dfrac{126}{5}\right)$ hrs.

Number of days of $8\dfrac{2}{5}$ hrs each $= \left(\dfrac{126}{5} \times \dfrac{5}{42}\right) = 3$ days.

4. B's 5 day's work $= \left(\dfrac{1}{10} \times 5\right) = \dfrac{1}{2}$.

Remaining work $= \left(1 - \dfrac{1}{2}\right) = \dfrac{1}{2}$.

A can do $\dfrac{1}{2}$ work in $7\dfrac{1}{2}$ days.

5. Whole work will be done by A in $(5 \times 3) = 15$ days.

Whole work will be done by B in $\left(10 \times \dfrac{5}{2}\right) = 25$ days.

A's 1 day's work $= \dfrac{1}{15}$ & B's 1 day's work $= \dfrac{1}{25}$.

$(A + B)$'s 1 day's work $= \left(\dfrac{1}{15} + \dfrac{1}{25}\right) = \dfrac{8}{75}$.

So, both together can finish it in $\dfrac{75}{8} = 9\dfrac{3}{8}$ days.

6. Work done by A in 10 days $= \left(\dfrac{1}{80} \times 10\right) = \dfrac{1}{8}$.

Remaining work $= \left(1 - \dfrac{1}{8}\right) = \dfrac{7}{8}$.

Now, $\dfrac{7}{8}$ work is done by B in 42 days

Whole work will be done by B in $\left(42 \times \dfrac{8}{7}\right) = 48$ days.

$\therefore$ A's 1 day's work $= \dfrac{1}{80}$ & B's 1 day's work $= \dfrac{1}{48}$.

$\therefore$ $(A + B)$'s 1 day's work $= \left(\dfrac{1}{80} + \dfrac{1}{48}\right) = \dfrac{8}{240} = \dfrac{1}{30}$.

Hence, both will finish the work in 30 days.

7. Work done by A and B in 20 days $= \left(\dfrac{1}{30} \times 20\right) = \dfrac{2}{3}$.

Remaining work $= \left(1 - \dfrac{2}{3}\right) = \dfrac{1}{3}$.

Now, $\dfrac{1}{3}$ work is done by A in 20 days

$\therefore$ Whole work will be done by A in $(20 \times 3) = 60$ days.

8. $(A + B)$'s 1 day's work $= \left(\dfrac{1}{45} + \dfrac{1}{40}\right) = \dfrac{17}{360}$.

Work done by B in 23 days $= \left(\dfrac{1}{40} \times 23\right) = \dfrac{23}{40}$.

Remaining work $= \left(1 - \dfrac{23}{40}\right) = \dfrac{17}{40}$.

Now, $\dfrac{17}{360}$ work was done by $(A + B)$ in 1 day

$\dfrac{17}{40}$ work was done by $(A + B)$ in $\left(1 \times \dfrac{360}{17} \times \dfrac{17}{40}\right) = 9$ days.

$\therefore$ A left after 9 days.

9. Suppose B takes x days to do the work.

$\therefore$ *A* takes $\left(2 \times \dfrac{3}{4} x\right) = \dfrac{3x}{2}$ days to do it.

$(A + B)$'s 1 day's work $= \dfrac{1}{18}$.

$\therefore \dfrac{1}{x} + \dfrac{2}{3x} = \dfrac{1}{18}$ or $x = 30$.

10. Ratio of times taken by *A* and *B* = 160 : 100 = 8 : 5.

$8 : 5 :: 12 : x$ or $8x = 5 \times 12$ or $x = 7\dfrac{1}{2}$ days.

11. Work done by *A* in 10 days $= \left(\dfrac{1}{25} \times 10\right) = \dfrac{2}{5}$.

Remaining work $= \left(1 - \dfrac{2}{5}\right) = \dfrac{3}{5}$.

$(A + B)$'s 1 day's work $= \left(\dfrac{1}{25} + \dfrac{1}{20}\right) = \dfrac{9}{100}$.

Now, $\dfrac{9}{100}$ work is done by them in 1 day.

$\therefore \dfrac{3}{5}$ work will be done by them in $\left(\dfrac{100}{9} \times \dfrac{3}{5}\right) = \dfrac{20}{3}$ days.

Total time taken $= \left(10 + \dfrac{20}{3}\right) = 16\dfrac{2}{3}$ days.

12. (A's 1 day's work) : (B's 1 day's work) = 2 : 1

$(A + B)$'s 1 day's work $= \dfrac{1}{14}$.

Divide $\dfrac{1}{14}$ in the ratio 2 : 1.

$\therefore$ *A*'s 1 day's work $= \left(\dfrac{1}{14} \times \dfrac{2}{3}\right) = \dfrac{1}{21}$.

Hence, *A* alone can finish the work in 21 days.

13. Ratio of times taken by *A* & *B* = 1 : 3.
If difference of time is 2 days, *B* takes 3 days.

If difference of time is 10 days, *B* takes $\left(\dfrac{3}{2} \times 10\right) = 15$ days.

14. *B*'s 3 day's work $= \left(\dfrac{1}{21} \times 3\right) = \dfrac{1}{7}$.

Remaining work $= \left(1 - \dfrac{1}{7}\right) = \dfrac{6}{7}$.

$(A + B)$'s 1 day's work $= \left(\dfrac{1}{14} + \dfrac{1}{21}\right) = \dfrac{5}{42}$.

Now, $\dfrac{5}{42}$ work is done by A & B in 1 day.

$\therefore$ $\dfrac{6}{7}$ work in done by A & B in $\left(\dfrac{42}{5} \times \dfrac{6}{7}\right) = \dfrac{36}{5}$ days.

$\therefore$ Total time taken $= \left(3 + \dfrac{36}{5}\right)$ days $= 10\dfrac{1}{5}$ days.

15. (Ramesh + Suresh + Harish)'s 1 day's work

$$= \left(\dfrac{1}{15} + \dfrac{1}{10} + \dfrac{1}{6}\right) = \dfrac{10}{30} = \dfrac{1}{3}.$$

So, all the three will finish the work in 3 days.

16. $(A + B)$'s 1 day's work $= \dfrac{1}{72}$, $(B + C)$'s 1 day's work $= \dfrac{1}{120}$,

$(A + C)$'s 1 day's work $= \dfrac{1}{90}$.

Adding 2 $(A + B + C)$'s 1 day's work $= \left(\dfrac{1}{72} + \dfrac{1}{120} + \dfrac{1}{90}\right) = \dfrac{12}{360} = \dfrac{1}{30}.$

$\therefore$ $(A + B + C)$'s 1 day's work $= \dfrac{1}{60}.$

A's 1 day's work $= \left(\dfrac{1}{60} - \dfrac{1}{120}\right) = \dfrac{1}{120}.$

$\therefore$ A alone can finish the work in 120 days.

17. $(A + B)$'s 1 day's work $= \dfrac{1}{5}$; $(B + C)$'s 1 day's work $= \dfrac{1}{7}$

and $(A + C)$'s 1 day's work $= \dfrac{1}{4}.$

2 $(A + B + C)$'s 1 day's work $= \left(\dfrac{1}{5} + \dfrac{1}{7} + \dfrac{1}{4}\right) = \dfrac{83}{140}.$

$(A + B + C)$'s 1 day's work $= \dfrac{83}{280}.$

C's 1 day's work $= \left(\dfrac{83}{280} - \dfrac{1}{5}\right) = \dfrac{27}{280}.$

A's 1 day's work $= \left(\dfrac{83}{280} - \dfrac{1}{7}\right) = \dfrac{43}{280}.$

B's 1 day's work $= \left(\dfrac{83}{280} - \dfrac{1}{4}\right) = \dfrac{13}{280}.$

Thus time taken by A, B, C is $\dfrac{280}{43}$ days, $\dfrac{280}{13}$ days, $\dfrac{280}{27}$ days

respectively.

Clearly, the time taken by A is least.

18. $(A+B+C)$'s 1 day's work $=\dfrac{1}{4}$

$(A+B)$'s 1 day's work $=\left(\dfrac{1}{12}+\dfrac{1}{18}\right)=\dfrac{5}{36}$.

C's 1 day's work $=\left(\dfrac{1}{4}-\dfrac{5}{36}\right)=\dfrac{4}{36}=\dfrac{1}{9}$.

$\therefore$ C alone can finish the work in 9 days.

19. $(A+B)$'s 1 day's work $=\dfrac{1}{18}$, $(B+C)$'s 1 day's work $=\dfrac{1}{24}$

and $(A+C)$'s 1 day's work $=\dfrac{1}{36}$.

$\therefore$ $2(A+B+C)$'s 1 day's work $=\left(\dfrac{1}{18}+\dfrac{1}{24}+\dfrac{1}{36}\right)=\dfrac{9}{72}=\dfrac{1}{8}$.

$\therefore$ $(A+B+C)$'s 1 day's work $=\dfrac{1}{16}$.

Hence, all working together can do the work in 16 days.

20. $(A+B)$'s 5 days' work $+ (B+C)$'s 2 day's work
$$+ \ C\text{'s 11 day's work} = 1.$$

$\dfrac{5}{12}+\dfrac{2}{16}+C$'s 11 day's work $= 1$

C's 11 day's work $=\dfrac{11}{24}$

C's 1 day's work $=\left(\dfrac{11}{24}\times\dfrac{1}{11}\right)=\dfrac{1}{24}$.

$\therefore$ C alone can finish it in 24 days.

21. $(A$'s 1 day's work$)$: $(B$'s 1 day's work$)$ = 2 : 1.

$(A+B)$'s 1 day's work $=\dfrac{1}{15}$.

Divide $\dfrac{1}{15}$ in the ratio 2 : 1.

B's 1 day's work $=\left(\dfrac{1}{15}\times\dfrac{1}{3}\right)=\dfrac{1}{45}$.

$\therefore$ B alone can finish the work in 45 days.

22. (45×16) men can complete the work in 1 day.

$\therefore$ 1 man's 1 day's work $=\dfrac{1}{720}$.

45 men's 6 day's work $=\left(\dfrac{1}{16}\times 6\right)=\dfrac{3}{8}$.

Remaining work $=\left(1-\dfrac{3}{8}\right)=\dfrac{5}{8}$.

75 men's 1 day's work $= \dfrac{75}{720} = \dfrac{5}{48}$.

Now $\dfrac{5}{48}$ work is done by them in 1 day.

$\therefore \dfrac{5}{8}$ work is done by them in $\left(\dfrac{48}{5} \times \dfrac{5}{8}\right) = 6$ days.

23. (12×18) men can complete the work in 1 day.

$\therefore$ 1 man's 1 day's work $= \dfrac{1}{216}$.

12 men's 6 day's work $= \left(\dfrac{1}{18} \times 6\right) = \dfrac{1}{3}$.

Remaining work $= \left(1 - \dfrac{1}{3}\right) = \dfrac{2}{3}$.

16 men's 1 day's work $= \dfrac{16}{216} = \dfrac{2}{27}$.

$\dfrac{2}{27}$ work is done by them in 1 day.

$\dfrac{2}{3}$ work is done by them in $\left(\dfrac{27}{2} \times \dfrac{2}{3}\right) = 9$ days.

24. 1 man's 1 day's work $= \dfrac{1}{96}$.

12 men's 3 day's work $= \left(\dfrac{1}{8} \times 3\right) = \dfrac{3}{8}$.

Remaining work $= \left(1 - \dfrac{3}{8}\right) = \dfrac{5}{8}$.

15 men's 1 day's work $= \dfrac{15}{96}$.

Now, $\dfrac{15}{96}$ work is done by them in 1 day

$\therefore \dfrac{5}{8}$ work is done by them in $\left(\dfrac{96}{15} \times \dfrac{5}{8}\right) = 4$ days.

25. Work done by $B = \left(1 - \dfrac{19}{23}\right) = \dfrac{4}{23}$.

$\therefore (A + C) : B = \dfrac{19}{23} : \dfrac{4}{23} = 19 : 4$.

$\therefore B$'s share $=$ Rs. $\left(529 \times \dfrac{4}{23}\right) =$ Rs. 92.

26. Let 1 man's 1 day's work $= x$ & 1 woman's 1 day's work $= y$.

Then, $10x = \dfrac{1}{20}$ and $20y = \dfrac{1}{15}$. So, $x = \dfrac{1}{200}$ and $y = \dfrac{1}{300}$.

$\therefore$ (5 men + 10 women)'s 1 day's work $= \left(\dfrac{5}{200} + \dfrac{10}{300} \right) = \dfrac{7}{120}$.

So, they will finish the work in $\dfrac{120}{7} = 17\dfrac{1}{7}$ days.

27. Let 1 man's 1 day's work $= x$ & 1 woman's 1 day's work $= y$.

Then, $6x + 5y = \dfrac{1}{6}$, $3x + 4y = \dfrac{1}{10}$.

On solving, we get $x = \dfrac{1}{54}$ and $y = \dfrac{1}{90}$.

(9 men + 15 women)'s 1 day's work $= \left(\dfrac{9}{54} + \dfrac{15}{90} \right) = \dfrac{1}{3}$.

$\therefore$ They will finish the work in 3 days.

28. Let 1 man's 1 day's work $= x$ & 1 woman's 1 day's work $= y$.

Then, $4x + 6y = \dfrac{1}{8}$ and $3x + 7y = \dfrac{1}{10}$.

Solving, we get : $y = \dfrac{1}{400}$.

10 women's 1 day' work $= \dfrac{10}{400} = \dfrac{1}{40}$.

$\therefore$ 10 women will finish the work in 40 days.

29. Let 1 child's 1 day's work $= x$ & 1 adult's 1 day's work $= y$.

Then, $12x = \dfrac{1}{16}$ or $x = \dfrac{1}{192}$ and $8y = \dfrac{1}{12}$ or $y = \dfrac{1}{96}$.

Work done in 3 days $= \left(16 \times \dfrac{1}{96} \times 3 \right) = \dfrac{1}{2}$.

Work left $= \left(1 - \dfrac{1}{2} \right) = \dfrac{1}{2}$.

(6 adults + 4 children)'s 1 day's work $= \left(\dfrac{6}{96} + \dfrac{4}{192} \right) = \dfrac{1}{12}$.

$\dfrac{1}{12}$ work is done by them in 1 day.

$\dfrac{1}{2}$ work is done by them in $\left(12 \times \dfrac{1}{2} \right) = 6$ days.

30. (Ram + Shyam)'s 2 days work $= \left(\dfrac{1}{8} + \dfrac{1}{12} \right) = \dfrac{5}{24}$.

Their 8 day's work $= \left(\dfrac{5}{24} \times 4 \right) = \dfrac{5}{6}$.

Their 9 day's work $= \left(\dfrac{5}{6} + \dfrac{1}{8} \right) = \dfrac{23}{24}$.

Remaining work $= \left(1 - \dfrac{23}{24}\right) = \dfrac{1}{24}.$

Now it is Shyam's turn.

$\dfrac{1}{12}$ work is done by him in 1 day.

$\dfrac{1}{24}$ work is done by him in $\left(12 \times \dfrac{1}{24}\right) = \dfrac{1}{2}$ day.

$\therefore$ Total time taken $= 9\dfrac{1}{2}$ days.

31. $(A + B)$'s 2 day's work $= \left(\dfrac{1}{9} + \dfrac{1}{12}\right) = \dfrac{7}{36}.$

Work done in 5 pairs of days $= \left(5 \times \dfrac{7}{36}\right) = \dfrac{35}{36}.$

Remaining work $= \left(1 - \dfrac{35}{36}\right) = \dfrac{1}{36}.$

On 11th day, it is A's turn.

$\dfrac{1}{9}$ work is done by him in 1 day.

$\dfrac{1}{36}$ work is done by him in $\left(9 \times \dfrac{1}{36}\right) = \dfrac{1}{4}$ day.

$\therefore$ Total time taken $= 10\dfrac{1}{4}$ days.

32. $(A + B)$'s 1 day's work $= \left(\dfrac{1}{11} + \dfrac{1}{20}\right) = \dfrac{31}{220}.$

$(A + C)$'s 1 day's work $= \left(\dfrac{1}{11} + \dfrac{1}{55}\right) = \dfrac{6}{55}.$

Work done in 2 days $= \left(\dfrac{31}{220} + \dfrac{6}{55}\right) = \dfrac{55}{220} = \dfrac{1}{4}.$

Now, $\dfrac{1}{4}$ work is done in 2 days.

$\therefore$ Whole work will be done in $(4 \times 2) = 8$ days.

33. $(A + B)$'s 2 hour's work $= \left(\dfrac{1}{4} + \dfrac{1}{6}\right) = \dfrac{5}{12}.$

$(A + B)$'s 4 hour's work $= \left(\dfrac{5}{12} \times 2\right) = \dfrac{10}{12} = \dfrac{5}{6}.$

Remaining work $= \left(1 - \dfrac{5}{6}\right) = \dfrac{1}{6}.$

Now, it is A's turn.

$\dfrac{1}{4}$ work is done by A in 1 hour

$\dfrac{1}{6}$ work is done by A in $\left(4 \times \dfrac{1}{6}\right) = \dfrac{2}{3}$ hours.

Total time taken $= 4\dfrac{2}{3}$ hours.

34. Father's 1 hour's work $= \left(\dfrac{1}{3} + \dfrac{1}{6}\right) = \dfrac{1}{2}$.

$\therefore$ Time taken by father to complete the work $= 2$ hours.

35. Let total money be Rs. x.

A's 1 day's wages $= \dfrac{x}{21}$, B's 1 day's wages $= \dfrac{x}{28}$.

$\therefore$ $(A+B)$'s 1 day's wages $= \left(\dfrac{x}{21} + \dfrac{x}{28}\right) = \dfrac{x}{12}$.

$\therefore$ Money is sufficient to pay the wages of both for 12 days.

36. A's wages : B's wages $= A$'s 1 day's work : B's 1 day's work

$$= \dfrac{1}{10} : \dfrac{1}{15} : 3 : 2.$$

$\therefore$ A's wages $=$ Rs. $\left(225 \times \dfrac{3}{5}\right) =$ Rs. 135.

37. C's 1 day's work $= \dfrac{1}{3} - \left(\dfrac{1}{6} + \dfrac{1}{8}\right) = \left(\dfrac{1}{3} - \dfrac{7}{24}\right) = \dfrac{1}{24}$.

$\therefore$ $A : B : C = \dfrac{1}{6} : \dfrac{1}{8} : \dfrac{1}{24} = 4 : 3 : 1$.

$\therefore$ C's share $=$ Rs. $\left(640 \times \dfrac{1}{8}\right) =$ Rs. 80.

38. B's daily earning $=$ Rs. $(300 - 188) =$ Rs. 112.

A's daily earning $=$ Rs. $(300 - 152) =$ Rs. 148.

C's daily earning $=$ Rs. $[300 - (112 + 148)] =$ Rs. 40.

39. Time taken by Ramesh alone $= \left(\dfrac{2}{3} \times 4\right) = \dfrac{8}{3}$ days.

Their 1 day's work $= \left(\dfrac{1}{4} + \dfrac{1}{6} + \dfrac{3}{8}\right) = \dfrac{19}{24}$.

$\therefore$ Three together can finish the work in $\dfrac{24}{19} = 1\dfrac{5}{19}$ days.

40. 10 men $\equiv$ 18 boys $\Leftrightarrow$ 1 man $\equiv \dfrac{18}{10}$ boys.

$\therefore$ 25 men + 15 boys $\equiv \left(25 \times \dfrac{18}{10} + 15\right)$ boys $= 60$ boys.

Now, more work, more days

More boys, less days

$$\left.\begin{array}{l} \text{.Work} \quad 1:2 \\ \text{Boys} \quad 60:18 \end{array}\right\} :: 15:x$$

$$\therefore \ 1 \times 60 \times x = 2 \times 18 \times 15 \ \text{ or } \ x = \left(\frac{2 \times 18 \times 15}{60}\right) = 9 \text{ days.}$$

41. Originally, let there be x men.

More men, Less days

$$\therefore \ (x+8):x :: 60:50$$

So, $\dfrac{x+8}{x} = \dfrac{60}{50}$ or $x = 40$.

Hence, there were 40 men, originally.

42. Ratio of number of days $= \dfrac{1}{5} : \dfrac{1}{6} = 6 : 5$.

43. 1 woman $\equiv \dfrac{1}{2}$ man & 1 boy $\equiv \dfrac{1}{3}$ man.

$$\therefore \ (1 \text{ man} + 1 \text{ woman} + 1 \text{ boy}) \equiv \left(1 + \frac{1}{2} + \frac{1}{3}\right) \text{men}$$

Now, 1 man can do the work in 44 days

$$\therefore \ \frac{11}{6} \text{ men can do it in } \left(44 \times \frac{6}{11}\right) = 24 \text{ days.}$$

44. 1 man $\equiv \dfrac{3}{2}$ boys. So, (4 men + 9 boys) $\equiv$ 15 boys.

Also, 8 men $\equiv \left(\dfrac{3}{2} \times 8\right)$ boys $= 12$ boys.

More boys, less days.

$$15 : 12 :: 20 : x$$

$$\therefore \ x = \left(\frac{12 \times 20}{15}\right) = 16.$$

45. C alone can finish the work in 40 days.

$$\therefore \ (A+B) \text{ can do it in 20 days.}$$

$$\therefore \ (A+B)\text{'s 1 day's work} = \frac{1}{20}.$$

A's 1 day's work : B's 1 day's work $= \dfrac{1}{2} : 1 = 1 : 2$.

$$\therefore \ A\text{'s 1 day's work} = \left(\frac{1}{20} \times \frac{1}{3}\right) = \frac{1}{60}. \left[\text{Divide } \frac{1}{20} \text{ in the ratio } 1:2\right]$$

$$B\text{'s 1 day's work} = \left(\frac{1}{20} \times \frac{2}{3}\right) = \frac{1}{30}.$$

$$(A+B+C)\text{'s 1 day's work} = \left(\frac{1}{60} + \frac{1}{30} + \frac{1}{40}\right) = \frac{9}{120} = \frac{3}{40}.$$

∴ All the three together will finish it in $\frac{40}{3} = 13\frac{1}{3}$ days.

46. $(A + B)$'s 6 day's work $= 6\left(\frac{1}{20} + \frac{1}{15}\right) = \frac{7}{10}$.

$(A + C)$'s 4 day's work $= \frac{3}{10}$. $(A + C)$'s 1 day's work $= \frac{3}{40}$

A's 1 day's work $= \frac{1}{20}$

∴ C's 1 day's work $= \left(\frac{3}{40} - \frac{1}{20}\right) = \frac{1}{40}$.

Hence, C alone can finish the work in 40 days.

47. Suppose the work was finished in x days.

Then A's $(x - 8)$ day's work $+ B$'s $(x - 12)$ day's work
$+ C$'s x day's work $= 1$

$\frac{(x - 8)}{36} + \frac{(x - 12)}{54} + \frac{x}{72} = 1 \Leftrightarrow 6(x - 8) + 4(x - 12) + 3x = 216$

∴ $13x = 312 \Leftrightarrow x = 24$.

16. Pipes & Cisterns

General Results :

Inlet : A pipe connected with a tank or a cistern or a reservoir, that fills it, is known as an inlet.

Outlet : A pipe connected with a tank or a cistern or a reservoir, emptying it, is known as an outlet.

Formulae :

(*i*) If a pipe can fill a tank in x hours, then :

$$\text{part filled in 1 hour} = \frac{1}{x}.$$

(*ii*) If a pipe can empty a full tank in y hours, then :

$$\text{part emptied in 1 hour} = \frac{1}{y}.$$

(*iii*) If a pipe can fill a tank in x hours and another pipe can empty the full tank in y hours (where $y > x$), then on opening both the pipes, the net part filled in 1 hour $= \left(\frac{1}{x} - \frac{1}{y} \right)$.

Solved Problems

Ex. 1. *Two pipes A and B can fill a tank in 36 hours and 45 hours respectively. If both the pipes are opened simultaneously, how much time will be taken to fill the tank ?*

Sol. Part filled by A in 1 hour $= \frac{1}{36}$.

Part filled by B in 1 hour $= \frac{1}{45}$.

Part filled by $(A + B)$ in 1 hour $= \left(\frac{1}{36} + \frac{1}{45} \right) = \frac{9}{180} = \frac{1}{20}$.

Hence, both the pipes together will fill the tank in 20 hours.

Ex. 2. *A pipe can fill a tank in 16 hours. Due to a leak in the bottom, it is filled in 24 hours. If the tank is full, how much time will the leak take to empty it ?*

Sol. Work done by the leak in 1 hour $= \left(\frac{1}{16} - \frac{1}{24} \right) = \frac{1}{48}$.

∴ Leak will empty the full cistern in 48 hours.

Ex. 3. *A cistern is filled by pipe A in 10 hours and the full cistern can be leaked out by an exhaust pipe B in 12 hours. If both the pipes are opened, in what time the cistern is full ?*

Sol. Work done by the inlet in 1 hour $= \dfrac{1}{10}$.

Work done by the outlet in 1 hour $= \dfrac{1}{12}$.

Net part filled in 1 hour $= \left(\dfrac{1}{10} - \dfrac{1}{12}\right) = \dfrac{1}{60}$.

∴ The cistern will be full in 60 hours.

Ex. 4. *Two pipes can fill a cistern in 14 hours and 16 hours respectively. The pipes are opened simultaneously and it is found that due to leakage in the bottom, 32 minutes extra are taken for the cistern to be filled up. When the cistern is full, in what time will the leak empty it ?*

Sol. Work done by the two pipes in 1 hour $= \left(\dfrac{1}{14} + \dfrac{1}{16}\right) = \dfrac{15}{112}$.

∴ Time taken by these pipes to fill the tank $= \dfrac{112}{15}$ hours

$$= (7 \text{ hrs. } 28 \text{ min.})$$

Due to leakage, time taken $= (7 \text{ hrs } 28 \text{ min.}) + 32 \text{ min.} = 8 \text{ hrs.}$

∴ Work done by (two pipes + leak) in 1 hour $= \dfrac{1}{8}$.

Work done by the leak in 1 hour $= \left(\dfrac{15}{112} - \dfrac{1}{8}\right) = \dfrac{1}{112}$.

∴ Leak will empty the full cistern in 112 hours.

Ex. 5. *Pipes A and B can fill a tank in 20 hours and 30 hours respectively and pipe C can empty the full tank in 40 hours. If all the pipes are opened together, how much time will be needed to make the tank full ?*

Sol. Net part filled in 1 hour $= \left(\dfrac{1}{20} + \dfrac{1}{30} - \dfrac{1}{40}\right) = \dfrac{7}{120}$.

∴ The tank will be full in $\dfrac{120}{7} = 17\dfrac{1}{7}$ hours.

Ex. 6. *Two pipes A and B can fill a tank in 24 min. and 32 min. respectively. If both the pipes are opened simultaneously, after how much time B should be closed so that the tank is full in 18 minutes ?*

Sol. Let B be closed after x minutes. Then,

part filled by $(A + B)$ in x min. + part filled by A in $(18 - x)$ min. $= 1$.

∴ $x\left(\dfrac{1}{24} + \dfrac{1}{32}\right) + (18 - x) \times \dfrac{1}{24} = 1$ or $\dfrac{7x}{96} + \dfrac{18 - x}{24} = 1$

∴ $7x + 4(18 - x) = 96$ or $x = 8$.

Hence, B must be closed after 8 minutes.

Ex. 7. *Two pipes A and B can fill a tank in 36 min. and 45 min. respectively. A water pipe C can empty the tank in 30 min. First A and B are opened. After 7 minutes, C is opened. In how much time, the tank is full ?*

Sol. Part filled in 7 min. $= 7\left(\dfrac{1}{36} + \dfrac{1}{45}\right) = \dfrac{7}{20}$.

Remaining part $= \left(1 - \dfrac{7}{20}\right) = \dfrac{13}{20}$.

Net part filled in 1 min. when A, B and C are opened

$$= \left(\dfrac{1}{36} + \dfrac{1}{45} - \dfrac{1}{30}\right) = \dfrac{1}{60}.$$

Now, $\dfrac{1}{60}$ part is filled in 1 min.

$\dfrac{13}{20}$ part is filled in $\left(60 \times \dfrac{13}{20}\right) = 39$ min.

Total time taken to fill the tank $= (39 + 7)$ min. $= 46$ min.

EXERCISE 16

Mark ($\surd$) against the correct answer :

1. Two taps A and B can fill a tank in 10 hours and 15 hours respectively. If both the taps are opened together, the tank will be full in :

   (a) 5 hrs   (b) 6 hrs   (c) $12\dfrac{1}{2}$ hrs   (d) $7\dfrac{1}{2}$ hrs

2. To fill a cistern, pipes A, B and C take 20 minutes, 15 minutes and 12 minutes respectively. The time in minutes that the three pipes together will take to fill the cistern, is :   **(Assistant Grade 1994)**

   (a) 5   (b) 10   (c) 12   (d) $15\dfrac{2}{3}$

3. Two pipes can fill a tank in 10 hours and 12 hours respectively while a third pipe empties the full tank in 20 hours. If all the three pipes operate simultaneously, in how much time the tank will be filled ?

   (a) 7 hrs   (b) 8 hrs

   (c) 7 hrs 30 min.   (d) 8 hrs. 30 min.

   (Central Excise & I. Tax 1991)

4. A cistern can be filled in 9 hours but it takes 10 hours due to a leak in its bottom. If the cistern is full, then the time that the leak will take to empty it, is :   **(U.D.C. 1993)**

   (a) 60 hrs   (b) 70 hrs   (c) 80 hrs   (d) 90 hrs

5. An electric pump can fill a tank in 3 hours. Because of a leak in the tank, it took $3\dfrac{1}{2}$ hours to fill the tank. The leak can drain out all the water of the tank in :   **(Assistant Grade 1993)**

   (a) $10\dfrac{1}{2}$ hrs   (b) 12 hrs   (c) 21hrs   (d) 24 hrs

6. Taps *A* and *B* can fill a bucket in 12 minutes and 15 minutes respectively. If both are opened and *A* is closed after 3 minutes, how much further time would it take for *B* to fill the bucket ?
   (*a*) 7 min. 45 sec.   (*b*) 7 min. 15 sec.
   (*c*) 8 min. 5 sec.   (*d*) 8 min. 15 sec.
   (**Central Excise & I. Tax 1991**)

7. A tank can be filled by a tap in 20 minutes and by another tap in 60 minutes. Both the taps are kept open for 10 minutes and then the first tap is shut off. After this, the tank will be completely filled in :
   (*a*) 10 min.   (*b*) 12 min.   (*c*) 15 min.   (*d*) 20 min.
   (**Central Excise & I. Tax 1993**)

8. If two pipes function simultaneously, the reservoir will be filled in 12 hours. One pipe fills the reservoir 10 hours faster than the other. How many hours it takes the second pipe to fill the reservoir ?
   (*a*) 25 hrs   (*b*) 28 hrs   (*c*) 30 hrs   (*d*) 35 hrs

9. One tap can fill a cistern in 2 hours and another tap can empty the cistern in 3 hours. How long will they take to fill the cistern if both the taps are opened ?   (**Railways 1989**)
   (*a*) 5 hrs   (*b*) 6 hrs   (*c*) 7 hrs   (*d*) 8 hrs

10. 12 buckets of water fill a tank when the capacity of each bucket is 13.5 litres. How many buckets will be needed to fill the same tank, if the capacity of each bucket is 9 litres ?   (**Bank P.O. 1991**)
    (*a*) 8   (*b*) 16   (*c*) 15   (*d*) 18

11. Bucket *P* has thrice the capacity as bucket *Q*. It takes 60 turns for bucket *P* to fill the empty drum. How many turns it will take for both the buckets *P* and *Q*, having each turn together to fill the empty drum ?
    (*a*) 30   (*b*) 40   (*c*) 45   (*d*) 90
    (**Bank P.O. 1989**)

12. Two pipes *A* and *B* fill a tank in 15 hours and 20 hours respectively while a third pipe *C* can empty the full tank in 25 hours. All the three pipes are opened in the beginning. After 10 hours, *C* is closed. In how much time, will the tank be full ?
    (*a*) 12 hrs   (*b*) 13 hrs   (*c*) 16 hrs   (*d*) 18 hrs

13. Two pipes *A* and *B* can fill a cistern in 12 minutes and 15 minutes respectively but a third pipe *C* can empty the full tank in 6 minutes. *A* and *B* are kept open for 5 minutes in the beginning and then *C* is also opened. In what time is the cistern emptied ?
    (*a*) 30 min.   (*b*) 33 min.   (*c*) $37\frac{1}{2}$ min.   (*d*) 45 min.

14. Three pipes *A*, *B* and *C* can fill a tank in 6 hours. After working at it together for 2 hours, *C* is closed and *A* and *B* can fill the remaining part in 7 hours. The number of hours taken by *C* alone to fill the cistern, is :

(a) 10   (b) 12   (c) 14   (d) 16

15. A leak in the bottom of a tank can empty the full tank in 8 hours. An inlet pipe fills water at the rate of 6 litres a minute. When the tank is full, the inlet is opened and due to the leak, the tank is empty in 12 hours. How many litres does the cistern hold ?

     (a) 7580   (b) 7960   (c) 8290   (d) 8640

16. A leak in the bottom of a tank can empty the full tank in 6 hours. An inlet pipe fills water at the rate of 4 litres a minute. When the tank is full, the inlet is opened and due to the leak the tank is empty in 8 hours. The capacity of the tank (in litres) is :

     (a) 5260   (b) 5760   (c) 5846   (d) 6970

17. A tap can fill a tank in 16 minutes and another can empty it in 8 minutes. If the tank is already half full and both the tanks are opened together, the tank will be :

     (a) filled in 12 min.   (b) emptied in 12 min.
     (c) filled in 8 min.   (d) emptied in 8 min.

18. A cistern has two taps which fill it in 12 min. and 15 min. respectively. There is also a waste pipe in the cistern. When all the three are opened, the empty cistern is full in 20 minutes. How long will the waste pipe take to empty the full cistern ?

     (a) 8 min.   (b) 10 min.   (c) 12 min.   (d) 16 min.

19. Two pipes A and B can fill a cistern in 12 minutes and 16 minutes respectively. If both the pipes are opened together, then after how much time B should be closed so that the tank is full in 9 minutes ?

     (a) $3\frac{1}{2}$ min.   (b) 4 min.   (c) $4\frac{1}{2}$ min.   (d) $4\frac{3}{4}$ min.

20. Two pipes A and B can fill a tank in 6 hours and 4 hours respectively. If they are opened on alternate hours and if pipe A is opened first, in how many hours, the tank shall be full ?

     (a) 4   (b) 5   (c) $4\frac{1}{2}$ (d) $5\frac{1}{2}$

ANSWERS

1. (b)   **2.** (a)   **3.** (c)   **4.** (d)   **5.** (c)   **6.** (d)   **7.** (d)   **8.** (c)   **9.** (b)
10. (d)   **11.** (c)   **12.** (a)   **13.** (d)   **14.** (c)   **15.** (d)   **16.** (b)   **17.** (d)   **18.** (b)
19. (b)   **20.** (b)

SOLUTIONS

1. A's 1 hour's work = $\frac{1}{10}$, B's 1 hour's work = $\frac{1}{15}$.

$(A + B)$'s 1 hour's work $= \left(\dfrac{1}{10} + \dfrac{1}{15}\right) = \dfrac{5}{30} = \dfrac{1}{6}$.

∴ Both the taps can fill the tank in 6 hours.

2. Part filled by $(A + B + C)$ in 1 min. $= \left(\dfrac{1}{20} + \dfrac{1}{15} + \dfrac{1}{12}\right) = \dfrac{12}{60} = \dfrac{1}{5}$.

∴ All the three pipes together will fill the tank in 5 min.

3. Net part filled in 1 hour $= \left(\dfrac{1}{10} + \dfrac{1}{12} - \dfrac{1}{20}\right) = \dfrac{8}{60} = \dfrac{2}{15}$.

∴ The tank will be full in $\dfrac{15}{2}$ hrs = 7 hrs 30 min.

4. Work done by the leak in 1 hour $= \left(\dfrac{1}{9} - \dfrac{1}{10}\right) = \dfrac{1}{90}$.

∴ Leak will empty the full cistern in 90 min.

5. Work done by the leak in 1 hour $= \left(\dfrac{1}{3} - \dfrac{2}{7}\right) = \dfrac{1}{21}$.

∴ Leak will empty the tank in 21 hours.

6. Part filled in 3 min. $= 3\left(\dfrac{1}{12} + \dfrac{1}{15}\right) = \left(3 \times \dfrac{9}{60}\right) = \dfrac{9}{20}$.

Remaining part $= \left(1 - \dfrac{9}{20}\right) = \dfrac{11}{20}$.

Part filled by B in 1 min. $= \dfrac{1}{15}$.

$\dfrac{1}{15} : \dfrac{11}{20} = 1 : x$ or $x = \left(\dfrac{11}{20} \times 1 \times \dfrac{15}{1}\right) = 8$ min. 15 sec.

∴ Remaining part is filled by B in 8 min. 15 sec.

7. Part filled in 10 min. $= 10\left(\dfrac{1}{20} + \dfrac{1}{60}\right) = \left(10 \times \dfrac{4}{60}\right) = \dfrac{2}{3}$.

Remaining part $= \left(1 - \dfrac{2}{3}\right) = \dfrac{1}{3}$.

Part filled by second tap in 1 min. $= \dfrac{1}{60}$.

$\dfrac{1}{60} : \dfrac{1}{3} :: 1 : x$ or $x = \left(\dfrac{1}{3} \times 1 \times 60\right) = 20$ min.

Hence, the remaining part will be filled in 20 min.

8. Let the reservoir be filled by first pipe in x hours.
Then, second pipe will fill it in $(x + 10)$ hours.

∴ $\dfrac{1}{x} + \dfrac{1}{x + 10} = \dfrac{1}{12} \Leftrightarrow \dfrac{x + 10 + x}{x(x + 10)} = \dfrac{1}{12}$

$\Leftrightarrow x^2 - 14x - 120 = 0 \Leftrightarrow (x - 20)(x + 6) = 0 \Leftrightarrow x = 20$.

$\therefore$ Second pipe takes 30 hrs to fill the reservoir.

9. Net part filled in 1 hour $= \left(\dfrac{1}{2} - \dfrac{1}{3}\right) = \dfrac{1}{6}$.

    $\therefore$ Cistern will be full in 6 hours.

10. Capacity of the tank $= (12 \times 13.5)$ litres $= 162$ litres.
    Capacity of each bucket $= 9$ litres

    Number of buckets needed $= \left(\dfrac{162}{9}\right) = 18$.

11. Let capacity of P be x litres. Then, capacity of $Q = \dfrac{x}{3}$ litres.

    Capacity of the drum $= 60\,x$ litres.

    Required number of turns $= \dfrac{60x}{\left(x + \dfrac{x}{3}\right)} = \left(60 \times \dfrac{3}{4x}\right) = 45$.

12. Part filled in 10 hours $= 10\left(\dfrac{1}{15} + \dfrac{1}{20} - \dfrac{1}{25}\right) = \dfrac{23}{30}$.

    Remaining part $= \left(1 - \dfrac{23}{30}\right) = \dfrac{7}{30}$.

    $(A + B)$'s 1 hour's work $= \left(\dfrac{1}{15} + \dfrac{1}{20}\right) = \dfrac{7}{60}$.

    $\dfrac{7}{60} : \dfrac{7}{30} :: 1 : x$ or $x = \left(\dfrac{7}{30} \times 1 \times \dfrac{60}{7}\right) = 2$ hours.

    $\therefore$ The tank will be full in $(10 + 2)$ hrs $= 12$ hrs.

13. Part filled in 5 min. $= 5\left(\dfrac{1}{12} + \dfrac{1}{15}\right) = \left(5 \times \dfrac{9}{60}\right) = \dfrac{3}{4}$.

    Part emptied in 1 min., when all the pipes are opened

    $= \dfrac{1}{6} - \left(\dfrac{1}{12} + \dfrac{1}{15}\right) = \left(\dfrac{1}{6} - \dfrac{3}{20}\right) = \dfrac{1}{60}$.

    Now, $\dfrac{1}{60}$ part is emptied in 1 min.

    $\therefore \dfrac{3}{4}$ part will be emptied on $\left(60 \times \dfrac{3}{4}\right) = 45$ min.

14. Part filled in 2 hours $= \dfrac{2}{6} = \dfrac{1}{3}$, Remaining part $= \left(1 - \dfrac{1}{3}\right) = \dfrac{2}{3}$.

    $\therefore (A + B)$'s 7 hour's work $= \dfrac{2}{3}$

    $(A + B)$'s 1 hour's work $= \dfrac{2}{21}$.

    $\therefore C$'s 1 hour's work

    $= [(A + B + C)\text{'s 1 hour's work}] - (A + B)\text{'s 1 hour's work} = \left(\dfrac{1}{6} - \dfrac{2}{21}\right) = \dfrac{1}{14}$.

∴ *C* alone can fill the tank in 14 hours.

15. Work done by the inlet in 1 hour $=\left(\dfrac{1}{8}-\dfrac{1}{12}\right)=\dfrac{1}{24}.$

Work done by the inlet in 1 min. $=\left(\dfrac{1}{24}\times\dfrac{1}{60}\right)=\dfrac{1}{1440}.$

∴ Volume of $\dfrac{1}{1440}$ part = 6 litres

∴ Volume of whole = (1440×6) litres = 8640 litres.

16. Work done by the inlet in 1 hour $=\left(\dfrac{1}{6}-\dfrac{1}{8}\right)=\dfrac{1}{24}.$

Work done by the inlet in 1 min. $=\left(\dfrac{1}{24}\times\dfrac{1}{60}\right)=\dfrac{1}{1440}.$

Volume of $\dfrac{1}{1440}$ part = 4 litres.

Volume of whole = (1440×4) litres = 5760 litres.

17. Rate of waste pipe being more, the tank will be emptied when both the pipes are opened.

Net emptying work done by both in 1 min. $=\left(\dfrac{1}{8}-\dfrac{1}{16}\right)=\dfrac{1}{16}.$

Now, full tank will be emptied by them in 16 min.

∴ Half full tank will be emptied in 8 min.

18. Work done by waste pipe in 1 min.

$=\dfrac{1}{20}-\left(\dfrac{1}{12}+\dfrac{1}{15}\right)=-\dfrac{1}{10}$ [– *ve sign means emptying*]

∴ Waste pipe will empty the full cistern in 10 min.

19. Let *B* be closed after *x* minutes. Then,

Part filled by $(A+B)$ in *x* min. + Part filled by *A* in $(9-x)$ min. = 1

∴ $x\left(\dfrac{1}{12}+\dfrac{1}{16}\right)+(9-x)\cdot\dfrac{1}{12}=1$ or $\dfrac{7x}{48}+\dfrac{9-x}{12}=1$

or $7x+36-4x=48$ or $x=4.$

So, *B* must be closed after 4 minutes.

20. *A*'s work in 1 hour $=\dfrac{1}{6}$, *B*'s work in 1 hour $=\dfrac{1}{4}.$

$(A+B)$'s 2 hour's work when opened alternately $=\left(\dfrac{1}{6}+\dfrac{1}{4}\right)=\dfrac{5}{12}.$

$(A+B)$'s 4 hour's work when opened alternately $=\dfrac{10}{12}=\dfrac{5}{6}.$

Remaining part $=\left(1-\dfrac{5}{6}\right)=\dfrac{1}{6}.$

Now, it is *A*'s turn and $\dfrac{1}{6}$ part is filled by *A* in 1 hour.

∴ Total time taken to fill the tank = $(4+1)$ hrs. = 5 hrs.

17. Time And Distance

FORMULAE :

(*i*) Speed $= \left(\dfrac{\text{distance}}{\text{time}}\right)$, Time $= \left(\dfrac{\text{distance}}{\text{speed}}\right)$.

(*ii*) Distance $=$ (Speed $\times$ Time).

(*iii*) 1 km/hour $= \dfrac{5}{18}$ m/sec.

(*iv*) 1 m/sec. $= \dfrac{18}{5}$ km/hr.

(*v*) If the ratio of the speeds of A and B is $a : b$, then the ratio of the times taken by them to cover the same distance is $\dfrac{1}{a} : \dfrac{1}{b}$ or $b : a$.

(*vi*) Suppose a man covers a certain distance at x kmph and an equal distance at y kmph. Then, the average speed during the whole journey is $\left(\dfrac{2xy}{x+y}\right)$ kmph.

Solved Problems

Ex. 1. *A scooterist covers a certain distance at 36 kmph. How many metres does he cover in 2 minutes ?*

Sol. Speed $= 36$ kmph $= \left(36 \times \dfrac{5}{18}\right)$ m/sec. $= 10$ m/sec.

$\therefore$ Distance covered in 2 min. $= (10 \times 2 \times 60)$ m $= 1200$ m.

Ex. 2. *If a man runs at 3 metres per second, how many kilometres does he run in 1 hour 40 minutes.*

Sol. Speed of the man $= \left(3 \times \dfrac{18}{5}\right)$ km/hr $= \dfrac{54}{5}$ km/hr.

Distance covered in $\dfrac{5}{3}$ hours $= \left(\dfrac{54}{5} \times \dfrac{5}{3}\right)$ km $= 18$ km.

Ex. 3. *There are two towns A and B. Anil goes from A to B at 40 kmph and comes back to the starting point at 60 kmph. What is his average speed during the whole journey ?*

Sol. Average Speed $= \left(\dfrac{2xy}{x+y}\right)$ kmph $= \dfrac{(2 \times 40 \times 60)}{(40 + 60)}$ kmph $= 48$ kmph.

Ex. 4. *If a man walks at the rate of 5 kmph, he misses a train by only 7 minutes. However, if he walks at the rate of 6 kmph, he reaches the station 5 minutes before the arrival of the train. Find the distance covered by him to reach the station.* (U.D.C. Exam 1993)

Sol. Let the required distance be x km.

Difference in the times taken at two speeds = 12 min. = $\dfrac{1}{5}$ hr.

$\therefore \dfrac{x}{5} - \dfrac{x}{6} = \dfrac{1}{5}$ or $6x - 5x = 6$ or $x = 6$ km.

Hence, the required distance is 6 km.

Ex. 5. *A man travels for 5 hrs 15 min. If he covers the first half of the journey at 60 kmph and the rest at 45 kmph. Find the total distance travelled by him.*

Sol. Let the total distance be x km. Then,

$\dfrac{(x/2)}{60} + \dfrac{(x/2)}{45} = \dfrac{21}{4}$ or $\dfrac{x}{120} + \dfrac{x}{90} = \dfrac{21}{4}$

or $3x + 4x = 21 \times 90$ or $x = 270$.

$\therefore$ Required distance = 270 km.

Ex. 6. *A and B are two stations 330 km apart. A train starts from A at 8 a.m. and travels towards B at 60 kmph. Another train starts from B at 9. a.m. and travels towards A at 75 kmph. At what time do they meet ?*

Sol. Suppose they meet x hrs after 8 a.m. Then,

(Distance moved by first in x hrs)

+ [Distance moved by second in $(x-1)$ hrs] = 330

$\therefore \ 60x + 75\,(x - 1) = 330$ or $x = 3$.

So, they meet at 11 a.m.

Ex. 7. *A goods train leaves a station at a certain time and at a fixed speed. After 6 hours, an express train leaves the same station and moves in the same direction at a uniform speed of 90 kmph. This train catches up the goods train in 4 hours. Find the speed of the goods train.*

Sol. Let the speed of the goods train be x kmph.

Distance covered by goods train in 10 hours

= Distance covered by the express train in 4 hours.

$\therefore \ 10x = 4 \times 90$ or $x = 36$.

$\therefore$ Speed of goods train = 36 kmph.

Ex. 8. *Walking $\dfrac{5}{6}$ of its usual speed, a train is 10 minutes too late. Find its usual time to cover the journey.*

Sol. New speed = $\dfrac{5}{6}$ of the usual speed.

$\therefore$ New time taken = $\dfrac{6}{5}$ of the usual time.

$$\therefore \left(\frac{6}{5} \text{ of the usual time}\right) - (\text{usual time}) = 10 \text{ min.}$$

$$\therefore \frac{1}{5} \text{ of the usual time} = 10 \text{ min. or usual time} = 50 \text{ min.}$$

Ex. 9. *Two bicyclists cover the same distance at 15 kmph and 16 kmph respectively. Find the distance travelled by each, if one takes 16 minutes longer than the other.*

Sol. Let the required distance be x km. Then,

$$\frac{x}{15} - \frac{x}{16} = \frac{16}{60} \text{ or } 16x - 15x = 64 \text{ or } x = 64.$$

Hence, the required distance = 64 km.

Ex. 10. *A thief is spotted by a policeman from a distance of 200 m. When the policeman starts the chase, the thief also starts running. If the speed of the thief be 10 km/hr and that of policeman 12 km/hr, how far the thief will have run before he is overtaken ?*

Sol. Relative speed of the policeman = 2 kmph.

Time taken by policeman to cover 200 m = $\left(\frac{200}{1000} \times \frac{1}{2}\right)$ hrs = $\frac{1}{10}$ hrs.

In $\frac{1}{10}$ hrs, the thief covers a distance of $\left(10 \times \frac{1}{10}\right)$ km = 1 km.

EXERCISE 17

Mark ($\sqrt{}$) against the correct answer :

1. Walking at the rate of 4 kmph a man covers a certain distance in 2 hours 45 min. Running at a speed of 16.5 kmph, the man will cover the same distance in :

    (a) 40 min.   (b) 45 min.   (c) 100 min.   (d) 41 min. 15 sec.

2. A car can finish a certain journey in 10 hours at a speed of 48 kmph. In order to cover the same distance in 8 hours, the speed of the car must be increased by :   **(Assistant Grade 1993)**

    (a) 6 km/hr   (b) 7.5 km/hr   (c) 12 km/hr   (d) 15 km/hr

3. A train covers a certain distance in 50 minutes, if it runs at a speed of 48 kmph on an average. The speed at which the train must run to reduce the time of journey to 40 minutes, will be :   **(C.B.I. 1993)**

    (a) 50 km/hr   (b) 55 km/hr   (c) 60 km/hr   (d) 70 km/hr

4. A car takes 6 hours to cover a journey at a speed of 45 kmph. At what speed must it travel in order to complete the journey in 5 hours ?

    (a) 55 km/hr   (b) 54 km/hr   (c) 53 km/hr   (d) 52 km/hr
                                                    (Assistant Grade 1994)

5. If a man running at 15 kmph crosses a bridge in 5 minutes, then the length of the bridge is :   **(Central Excise & I. Tax 1993)**

    (*a*) 1333.33 m   (*b*) 1000 m   (*c*) 7500 m   (*d*) 1250 m

6.   Ravi runs at 15.6 kmph. How many metres does he run in 2 minutes ?   **(Bank P.O. 1989)**

    (*a*) 260 m   (*b*) 312 m   (*c*) 520 m   (*d*) 1040 m

7.   If the speed of a train be 92.4 kmph, how many metres would it cover in 20 minutes ?

    (*a*) 61600 m   (*b*) 30800 m   (*c*) 15400 m   (*d*) None

8.   Deepak can cover a distance of 5 km in 20 minutes. The distance covered by him in 50 minutes is :

    (*a*) 10.5 km   (*b*) 12 km   (*c*) 12.5 km   (*d*) 13.5 km

9.   Vikas can cover a certain distance in 1 hr 24 min. by covering two–third of the distance at 4 kmph and the rest at 5 kmph. The total distance is :

    (*a*) 5 km   (*b*) 6 km   (*c*) 8 km   (*d*) 9.2 km

10. A man travels for 14 hours 40 minutes. He covers half of the journey by train at the rate of 60 kmph and the rest half by road at the rate of 50 kmph. The distance travelled by him is :

    (*a*) 720 km   (*b*) 800 km   (*c*) 960 km   (*d*) 1000 km

11. Walking at $\frac{3}{4}$ of his usual speed, a man is late by $2\frac{1}{2}$ hours. The usual time would have been :   **(Assistant Grade 1994)**

    (*a*) $7\frac{1}{2}$ hrs   (*b*) $3\frac{1}{2}$ hrs   (*c*) $3\frac{1}{4}$ hrs   (*d*) $\frac{7}{8}$ hrs

12. Walking at $\frac{6}{7}$ of his usual speed, a man is 25 min. too late. His usual time is :

    (*a*) $1\frac{1}{2}$ hrs   (*b*) $2\frac{1}{2}$ hrs   (*c*) $1\frac{6}{7}$ hrs   (*d*) $2\frac{4}{5}$ hrs.

13. If a boy walks from his house to school at the rate of 4 kmph, he reaches the school 10 minutes earlier than the scheduled time. However, if he walks at the rate of 3 kmph, he reaches 10 minutes late. The distance of the school from his house is :   **(Assistant Grade 1994)**

    (*a*) 6 km   (*b*) 4.5 km   (*e*) 4 km   (*d*) 3 km

14. If a student walks from his house to school at 5 kmph, he is late by 30 minutes. However, if he walks at 6 kmph, he is late by 5 minutes only. The distance of his school from his house is :

    (*a*) 2.5 km   (*b*) 3.6 km   (*c*) 5.5 km   (*d*) 12.5 km

15. A man covers a certain distance on scooter. Had he moved 3 kmph faster, he would have taken 40 minutes less. If he had moved 2 kmph slower, he would have taken 40 minutes more. The distance (in km) is :

    (*a*) 20   (*b*) 36   (*c*) 37.5   (*d*) 40

16. If a train runs at 40 kmph, it reaches its destination late by 11 minutes but if it runs at 50 kmph, it is late by 5 minutes only. The correct time for the train to complete its journey is :

    (a) 13 min.   (b) 15 min.   (c) 19 min.   (d) 21 min.

17. A car travels a distance of 715 km at a uniform speed. If the speed of the car is 10 kmph more, it takes 2 hours less to cover the same distance. The original speed was :

    (a) 45 kmph   (b) 55 kmph   (c) 60 kmph   (d) 65 kmph

18. Excluding stoppages, the speed of a bus is 54 kmph and including stoppages, it is 45 kmph. For how many minutes does the bus stop per hour ?

    (a) 9   (b) 10   (c) 12   (d) 20

19. Two men starting from the same place walk at the rate of 5 kmph and 5.5 kmph respectively. What time will they take to be 8.5 km apart, if they walk in the same direction ?

    (a) 2 hrs 55 min. (b) 4 hrs 15 min.   (c) 17 hours   (d) None

20. Two cyclists start from the same place in opposite directions. One goes towards north at 18 kmph and the other goes towards south at 20 kmph. What time will they take to be 47.5 km apart ?

    (a) $2\frac{1}{4}$ hrs   (b) $1\frac{1}{4}$ hrs   (c) 2 hrs 23 min.   (d) $23\frac{1}{4}$ hrs.

21. Two trains starting at the same time from two stations 200 km apart and going in opposite directions cross each other at a distance of 110 km from one of the stations. What is the ratio of their speeds ?

    (Hotel Management 1993)

    (a) 11 : 20   (b) 9 : 20   (c) 11 : 9   (d) None

22. Two trains start from stations A and B and travel towards each other at speeds of 50 kmph and 60 kmph respectively. At the time of their meeting the second train has travelled 120 km more than the first. The distance between A and B is :   **(Central Excise & I. Tax 1993)**

    (a) 990 km   (b) 1200 km   (c) 1320 km   (d) 1440 km

23. A walks at 4 kmph and 4 hours after his start, B cycles after him at 10 kmph. How far from the start does B catch up with A ?

    (Central Excise & I. Tax 1993)

    (a) 16.7 km   (b) 18.6 km   (c) 21.5 km   (d) 26.7 km

24. A thief steals a car at 2.30 p.m. and drives it at 60 kmph. The theft is discovered at 3 p.m. and the owner sets off in another car at 75 kmph. When will he overtake the thief ?

    (a) 4.30 p.m.   (b) 4.45 p.m.   (c) 5 p.m.   (d) 5.15 p.m.

25. In covering a certain distance, the speeds of A and B are in the ratio of 3 : 4. A takes 30 min. more than B to reach the destination. The time taken by A to reach the destination, is :   **(Assistant Grade 1994)**

(a) $1\frac{1}{4}$ hrs   (b) $1\frac{1}{3}$ hrs   (c) 2 hrs   (d) $2\frac{1}{2}$ hrs

26. A train starts from station X at the rate of 60 kmph and reaches station Y in 45 minutes. If the speed is reduced by 6 kmph, how much more time will the train take to return from station Y to station X ?

(Bank P.O. 1990)

(a) 5 min   (b) $7\frac{1}{2}$ min.   (c) 6 min.   (d) 4 min.

27. Bombay Express left Delhi for Bombay at 14.30 hrs, travelling at a speed of 60 kmph and Rajdhani Express left Delhi for Bombay on the same day at 16.30 hrs, travelling at a speed of 80 kmph. How far away from Delhi will the two trains meet ?   **(Central Excise & I. Tax 1991)**

(a) 120 km   (b) 360 km   (c) 480 km   (d) 500 km

28. A motorist covers a distance of 39 km in 45 minutes by moving at a speed of x kmph for the first 15 minutes, then moving at double the speed for the next 20 minutes and then again moving at his original speed for the rest of the journey. Then, x is equal to :   **(I. Tax 1991)**

(a) 31.2   (b) 36   (c) 40   (d) 52

29. A man goes uphill with an average speed of 24 kmph and comes down with an average speed of 36 kmph. The distance travelled in both the cases being the same, the average speed for the entire journey is :

(a) 30 km/hr   (b) 28.8 km/hr (c) 32.6 km/hr (d) None

30. A and B are two towns. Mr. Faruqui covers the distance from A to B on cycle at 17 kmph and returns to A by a tonga running at a uniform speed of 8 kmph. His average speed during the whole journey is :

(a) 12.5 km/hr   (b) 5.44 km/hr (c) 10.88 km/hr   (d) None

31. A man drives 150 km from A to B in 3 hours 20 min. and returns to A in 4 hours 10 min. Then, average speed from A to B exceeds the average speed for the entire trip by :   **(Central Excise & I. Tax. 1993)**

(a) 5 km/hr   (b) 4.5 km/hr   (c) 4 km/hr   (d) 2.5 km/hr

32. Two buses travel to a place at 45 km/hr and 60 km/hr respectively. If the second bus takes $5\frac{1}{2}$ hours less than the first for the journey, the length of the journey is :

(a) 900 km   (b) 945 km   (c) 990 km   (d) 1350 km

33. A car covers four successive 3 km stretches at speeds of 10 kmph, 20 kmph, 30 kmph and 60 kmph respectively. Its average speed over this distance is :

(a) 20 km/hr   (b) 25 km/hr,   (c) 30 km/hr   (d) 15 km/hr

34. A car completes a certain journey in 8 hours. It covers half the distance at 40 kmph and the rest at 60 kmph. The total distance of the journey is :   **(Central Excise & I.Tax 1992)**

(a) 350 km   (b) 384 km   (c) 400 km   (d) 420 km

5×6 + 4×12 =
30 + 48 = 88.

35. A person walks at 5 kmph for 6 hours and at 4 kmph for 12 hours. The average speed of the man is : **(C.D.S. 1993)**

   (a) 4 km/hr   (b) $4\frac{1}{3}$ km/hr   (c) $4\frac{1}{2}$ km/hr   (d) $4\frac{2}{3}$ km/hr

36. An aeroplane travels distances 2500 km, 1200 km and 500 km at the rate of 500 km/hr, 400 km/hr and 250 km/hr respectively. The average speed (in kmph) is : **(N.D.A. 1993)**

   (a) 405   (b) 410   (c) 420   (d) 575

37. A bullock cart has to cover a distance of 80 km in 10 hours. If it covers half of the journey in $\frac{3}{5}$ th time, what should be its speed to cover the remaining distance in the time left ? **(Bank P.O. 1988)**

   (a) 8 km/hr   (b) 6.4 km/hr   (c) 10 km/hr   (d) 20 km/hr

38. In covering a certain distance, the speeds of A and B are in the ratio of 3 : 4. If A takes 20 minutes more than B to reach the destination, the time taken by A to reach the destination is : **(Assistant Grade 1994)**

   (a) $1\frac{1}{4}$ hrs   (b) $1\frac{1}{3}$ hrs   (c) 2 hrs   (d) $2\frac{1}{2}$ hrs

39. The ratio between the speeds of A and B is 2 : 3 and therefore A takes 10 minutes more than the time taken by B to reach a destination. If A had walked at double the speed, he would have covered the distance in :

   (a) 30 min.   (b) 25 min   (c) 20 min   (d) 15 min.

40. A is twice as fast as B and B is thrice as fast as C is. The journey covered by C in 54 minutes will be covered by B in :

   (a) 18 min.   (b) 27 min   (c) 38 min   (d) 9 min.

41. The ratio between the rates of walking of A and B is 3 : 4. If the time taken by B to cover a certain distance is 36 minutes, the time taken by A to cover that much distance is :

   (a) 27 min.   (b) 48 min   (c) $15\frac{3}{7}$ min.   (d) None

42. A boy goes to school from his village at 3 kmph and returns back at 2 kmph. If he takes 5 hours in all, the distance between the village and the school is :

   (a) 6 km   (b) 7 km   (c) 8 km   (d) 9 km

43. Ramesh covers two–third of a certain distance at 4 kmph and the remaining at 5 kmph. If he takes 42 minutes in all, the distance is :

   (a) 2.5 km   (b) 3 km   (c) 4 km   (d) 4.6 km

44. A man performs $\frac{3}{5}$ of the total journey by rail, $\frac{17}{20}$ by bus and the remaining 6.5 km on foot. His total journey is :

   (a) 100 km   (b) 120 km   (c) 130 km   (d) 65 km

45. Vivek travelled 1200 km by air which formed $\frac{2}{5}$ of his trip. One–third of the whole trip, he travelled by car and the rest of the journey he performed by train. The distance travelled by train was :
    (a) 480 km　　(b) 800 km　　(c) 1600 km　(d) 1800 km
    (Hotel Management 1991)

46. Two men start together to walk to a certain destination, one at 3 kmph and another at 3.75 kmph. The latter arrives half an hour before the former. The distance is :
    (a) 6 km　　(b) 7.5 km　　(c) 8 km　　(d) 9.5 km

47. A train M leaves Meerut at 5 a.m. and reaches Delhi at 9 a.m. Another train N leaves Delhi at 7 a.m. and reaches Meerut at 10.30 a.m. At what time do the two trains cross one another ?
    (a) 8.26 a.m.　　(b) 8 a.m.　　(c) 7.36 a.m.　(d) 7.56 a.m.

48. A and B travel the same distance at 9 kmph and 10 kmph respectively. If A takes 36 minutes longer than B, the distance travelled by each is :
    (a) 48 km　　(b) 54 km　　(c) 60 km　　(d) 125 km

49. A man riding a cycle at 12 kmph can reach a town in 4 hours 30 min. If he is delayed by 1 hour 30 min. at the start, then in order to reach his destination in time, he should ride with a speed of :
    (a) 15 kmph　　(b) 16 kmph　　(c) 18 kmph　(d) 20 kmph

50. A man takes 5 hours 45 min. in walking to a certain place and riding back. He would have gained 2 hours by riding both ways. The time he would take to walk both ways, is :
    (a) 3 hrs 45 min.　　　　　　(b) 7 hrs 30 min
    (c) 7 hrs 45 min　　　　　　(d) 11 hrs 45 min

51. The ratio between the rates of walking of A and B is 3 : 4. If the time taken by B to cover a distance is 24 minutes, the time taken by A to cover that much distance is :
    (a) 18 min　　(b) 32 min　　(c) $10\frac{6}{7}$ min　(d) $13\frac{5}{7}$ min.

52. Two buses travel to a place at 45 kmph and 60 kmph respectively. If the second bus takes $5\frac{1}{2}$ hours less than the first for the same journey, the length of journey is :
    (a) 900 km　　(b) 945 km　　(c) 990 km　　(d) 1350 km

ANSWERS

1. (a)	**2.** (c)	**3.** (c)	**4.** (b)	**5.** (d)	**6.** (c)	**7.** (b)	**8.** (c)	**9.** (b)
10. (b)	**11.** (a)	**12.** (b)	**13.** (c)	**14.** (d)	**15.** (d)	**16.** (c)	**17.** (b)	**18.** (b)
19. (c)	**20.** (b)	**21.** (c)	**22.** (c)	**23.** (d)	**24.** (c)	**25.** (c)	**26.** (a)	**27.** (c)
28. (b)	**29.** (b)	**30.** (c)	**31.** (a)	**32.** (c)	**33.** (a)	**34.** (b)	**35.** (b)	**36.** (c)
37. (c)	**38.** (b)	**39.** (d)	**40.** (a)	**41.** (b)	**42.** (a)	**43.** (b)	**44.** (c)	**45.** (b)
46. (b)	**47.** (d)	**48.** (b)	**49.** (c)	**50.** (c)	**51.** (b)	**52.** (c)		

SOLUTIONS

1. Distance = (time × speed) = $\left(\dfrac{11}{4} \times 4\right)$ km = 11 km .

Now, distance = 11 km & new speed = 16.5 kmph.

∴ Time = $\left(\dfrac{\text{distance}}{\text{speed}}\right) = \left(\dfrac{11}{16.5}\right)$ hrs. = $\left(\dfrac{11}{16.5} \times 60\right)$ min. = 40 min.

2. Time = 10 hours, Speed = 48 kmph.

∴ Distance = (Speed × Time) = (48 × 10) km = 480 km.

Now, distance = 480 km, New time = 8 hours.

New speed = $\left(\dfrac{\text{Distance}}{\text{Time}}\right) = \left(\dfrac{480}{8}\right)$ kmph = 60kmph.

∴ Increase in speed = (60 − 48) kmph = 12 kmph.

3. Time = $\left(\dfrac{50}{60}\right)$ hr = $\dfrac{5}{6}$ hr , Speed = 48 kmph.

∴ Distance = $\left(48 \times \dfrac{5}{6}\right)$ km = 40 km.

Now, distance = 40 km & time = $\left(\dfrac{40}{60}\right)$ hr = $\dfrac{2}{3}$ hr.

∴ New speed = $\left(40 \times \dfrac{3}{2}\right)$ km/hr = 60 km/hr.

4. Time = 6 hours, speed = 45 kmph.

∴ Distance = (45 × 6) km = 270 km.

New time taken = 5 hours.

∴ New speed = $\left(\dfrac{270}{5}\right)$ km/hr = 54 km/hr.

5. Speed = $\left(15 \times \dfrac{5}{18}\right)$ m/sec. = $\dfrac{25}{6}$ m/sec.

Distance covered in 5 min. = $\left(\dfrac{25}{6} \times 5 \times 60\right)$ m = 1250 m.

6. Speed = $\left(15.6 \times \dfrac{5}{18}\right)$ m/sec. = $\left(\dfrac{13}{3}\right)$ m/sec.

Distance = (Speed × Time) = $\left(\dfrac{13}{3} \times 2 \times 60\right)$ m = 520 m.

7. Speed = $\left(92.4 \times \dfrac{5}{18}\right)$ m/sec = $\left(\dfrac{77}{3}\right)$ m/sec.

Distance covered in 20 min. = $\left(\dfrac{77}{3} \times 20 \times 60\right)$ m = 30800 m.

8.   Distance covered in 50 min. $= \left(\dfrac{5}{20} \times 50\right)$ km $= 12.5$ km.

9.   Let the total distance be x km. Then,

$$\dfrac{\frac{2}{3}x}{4} + \dfrac{\frac{1}{3}x}{5} = \dfrac{7}{5} \quad \text{or} \quad \dfrac{x}{6} + \dfrac{x}{15} = \dfrac{7}{5}$$

or $5x + 2x = 42$ or $x = 6$ km.

10. Let the total distance be x km. Then,

$$\dfrac{(x/2)}{60} + \dfrac{(x/2)}{50} = \dfrac{44}{3} \quad \text{or} \quad \dfrac{x}{120} + \dfrac{x}{100} = \dfrac{44}{3}$$

or $5x + 6x = 8800$ or $x = 800$ km.

11. New speed is $\dfrac{3}{4}$ of the usual speed.

∴ New time taken is $\dfrac{4}{3}$ of the usual time.

∴ $\left(\dfrac{4}{3} \text{ of the usual time}\right) - (\text{usual time}) = \dfrac{5}{2}$

or $\dfrac{1}{3}$ of the usual time $= \dfrac{5}{2}$

or usual time $= \left(\dfrac{5}{2} \times 3\right)$ hrs. $= 7\dfrac{1}{2}$ hrs.

12. New speed $= \dfrac{6}{7}$ of the usual speed.

New time taken $= \dfrac{7}{6}$ of the usual time.

$\left(\dfrac{7}{6} \text{ of usual time}\right) - (\text{usual time}) = 25$ min.

$\dfrac{1}{6}$ of usual time $= 25$ min.

∴ Usual time $= 150$ min. $= 2\dfrac{1}{2}$ hrs.

13. Let the distance be x km.

Difference in timings $= 20$ min. $= \dfrac{1}{3}$ hour.

∴ $\dfrac{x}{3} - \dfrac{x}{4} = \dfrac{1}{3}$ or $4x - 3x = 4$ or $x = 4$ km.

14. Let the distance be x km.

Difference in timings $= 25$ min. $= \dfrac{25}{60}$ hr $= \dfrac{5}{12}$ hr.

∴ $\dfrac{x}{5} - \dfrac{x}{6} = \dfrac{5}{12}$ or $12x - 10x = 25$ or $x = 12.5$ km.

15. Let distance $= x$ km & usual rate $= y$ kmph.

$\dfrac{x}{y} - \dfrac{x}{y+3} = \dfrac{40}{60}$ or $2y\,(y+3) = 9x$ ...(i)

And, $\dfrac{x}{y-2} - \dfrac{x}{y} = \dfrac{40}{60}$ or $y\,(y-2) = 3x$ ...(ii)

On dividing (i) by (ii), we get $x = 40$.

16. Let the correct time to complete the journey be x min.

Distance covered in $(x+11)$ min. at 40 kmph.

$\qquad\qquad\qquad$ = distance covered in $(x+5)$ min. at 50 kmph.

$\therefore\ \dfrac{(x+11)}{60} \times 40 = \dfrac{(x+5)}{60} \times 50 \Leftrightarrow x = 19$ min.

17. Let original speed be x kmph. Then,

$\dfrac{715}{x} - \dfrac{715}{(x+10)} = 2$ or $\dfrac{1}{x} - \dfrac{1}{x+10} = \dfrac{2}{715}$

or $\dfrac{x+10-x}{x\,(x+10)} = \dfrac{2}{715}$ or $x^2 + 10x - 3575 = 0$

or $(x+65)\,(x-55) = 0$.   So, $x = 55$ kmph.

18. Due to stoppages, it covers 9 km less.

Time taken to cover 9 km $= \left(\dfrac{9}{54} \times 60\right)$ min. $= 10$ min.

19. To be 0.5 km apart, they take 1 hour.

To be 8.5 km apart, they take $\left(\dfrac{1}{0.5} \times 8.5\right)$ hrs $= 17$ hrs.

20. To be $(18+20)$ km apart, they take 1 hour

To be 47.5 km apart, they take $\left(\dfrac{1}{38} \times 47.5\right)$ hrs $= 1\dfrac{1}{4}$ hrs.

21. In the same time, they cover 110 km & 90 km respectively.

$\therefore$ Ratio of their speeds $= 110 : 90 = 11 : 9$.

22. At the time of meeting, let the distance travelled by the first train be x km. Then, distance covered by the second train is $(x+120)$ km.

$\therefore\ \dfrac{x}{50} = \dfrac{x+120}{60}$ or $60x = 50x + 6000$ or $x = 600$.

$\therefore$ Distance between A & $B = (x + x + 120) = 1320$ km.

23. Suppose after x km from the start B catches up with A. Then, the difference in the time taken by A to cover x km and that taken by B to cover x km is 4 hours.

$\therefore\ \dfrac{x}{4} - \dfrac{x}{10} = 4$ or $x = 26.7$ km.

24. Suppose the thief is overtaken x hrs after 2.30 p.m. Then, distance covered by the thief in x hrs

= distance covered by the owner in $\left(x - \dfrac{1}{2}\right)$ hrs.

$\therefore \;\; 60\,x = 75\left(x - \dfrac{1}{2}\right)$ or $15x = \dfrac{75}{2}$ or $x = \dfrac{5}{2}$ hrs.

i.e. He is overtaken at 5 p.m.

25. Ratio of speeds = 3 : 4.

Ratio of times taken = 4 : 3.

Suppose A takes $4x$ hrs & B takes $3x$ hrs to reach the destination. Then,

$$4x - 3x = \dfrac{30}{60} = \dfrac{1}{2} \quad \text{or} \quad x = \dfrac{1}{2}.$$

$\therefore \;\;$ Time taken by $A = 4x$ hrs $= \left(4 \times \dfrac{1}{2}\right)$ hrs $= 2$ hrs.

26. Distance $XY = \left(60 \times \dfrac{45}{60}\right)$ km = 45 km.

New speed = $(60 - 6)$ kmph = 54 kmph.

Time taken = $\left(\dfrac{45}{54} \times 60\right)$ min. = 50 min.

$\therefore \;\;$ Extra time taken = $(50 - 45)$ min. = 5 min.

27. Suppose they meet x hrs after 14.30 hrs.

Then, $60x = 80\,(x - 2)$ or $x = 8$.

$\therefore \;\;$ Required distance = (60×8) km = 480 km.

28. $x \times \dfrac{15}{60} + 2x \times \dfrac{20}{60} + x \times \dfrac{10}{60} = 39 \;\Rightarrow\; \dfrac{x}{4} + \dfrac{2x}{3} + \dfrac{x}{6} = 39$

$\therefore \;\; 3x + 8x + 2x = 468$ or $x = 36$.

29. Average Speed = $\left(\dfrac{2xy}{x+y}\right)$ km/hr

$\qquad = \left(\dfrac{2 \times 24 \times 36}{24 + 36}\right)$ km/hr = 28.8 km/hr.

30. Average Speed = $\left(\dfrac{2xy}{x+y}\right)$ km/hr.

$\qquad = \left(\dfrac{2 \times 17 \times 8}{25}\right)$ km/hr = 10.88 km/hr.

31. Average Speed from A to B = $\left(150 \times \dfrac{3}{10}\right)$ km/hr = 45 km/hr.

Average Speed from B to A = $\left(150 \times \dfrac{6}{25}\right)$ km/hr = 36 km/hr.

$\therefore \;\;$ Average Speed for the entire trip = $\left(\dfrac{2 \times 45 \times 36}{45 + 36}\right)$ km/hr.

$\therefore \;\;$ Required difference = 5 km/hr.

32. Let the length of the journey be x km. Then,

$\dfrac{x}{45} - \dfrac{x}{60} = \dfrac{11}{2}$ or $4x - 3x = 990$ or $x = 990$ km.

33. Total distance covered = (3×4) km = 12 km.

Total time taken = $\left(\dfrac{3}{10} + \dfrac{3}{20} + \dfrac{3}{30} + \dfrac{3}{60}\right)$ hr = $\dfrac{3}{5}$ hr.

$\therefore$ Required average speed = $\left(12 \times \dfrac{5}{3}\right)$ km/hr = 20 km/hr.

34. Let the total journey be x km. Then,

$\dfrac{(x/2)}{40} + \dfrac{(x/2)}{60} = 8$ or $\dfrac{x}{80} + \dfrac{x}{120} = 8$

or $3x + 2x = 240 \times 8$ or $x = 384$.

35. Total distance covered = $(5 \times 6 + 4 \times 12)$ km = 78 km.
Total time taken = $(6 + 12)$ hrs = 18 hours.

$\therefore$ Average Speed = $\left(\dfrac{78}{18}\right)$ km/hr = $4\dfrac{1}{3}$ km/hr.

Total distance covered = $(2500 + 1200 + 500)$ km = 4200 km.

36. Total time taken = $\left(\dfrac{2500}{500} + \dfrac{1200}{400} + \dfrac{500}{250}\right)$ hrs. = 10 hrs.

$\therefore$ Average Speed = $\left(\dfrac{4200}{10}\right)$ km/hr = 420 km/hr.

37. Distance covered = $\left(\dfrac{1}{2} \times 80\right)$ km = 40 km.

Time elapsed = $\left(\dfrac{3}{5} \times 10\right)$ hrs = 6 hrs.

Distance left = 40 km, Time left = 4 hrs.

$\therefore$ Speed required = $\left(\dfrac{40}{4}\right)$ km/hr = 10 km/hr.

38. Ratio of Speeds = 3 : 4.
Ratio of time taken = 4 : 3.
Let the time taken by A and B be $4x$ hrs and $3x$ hrs respectively.

Then, $4x - 3x = \dfrac{20}{60}$ or $x = \dfrac{1}{3}$.

$\therefore$ Time taken by $A = 4x$ hrs = $\left(4 \times \dfrac{1}{3}\right)$ hrs = $1\dfrac{1}{3}$ hrs.

39. Ratio of times taken by A and B = 3 : 2.
Suppose B takes x minutes, then A takes $(x + 10)$ minutes.

$\therefore$ $(x + 10) : x = 3 : 2$ or $\dfrac{x + 10}{x} = \dfrac{3}{2}$ or $x = 20$.

Thus, A takes $(x + 10)$ min. i.e. 30 min.

At double the speed, A will take 15 min.

40. Let C's speed $= x$ km/hr. Then,

B's Speed $= 3x$ km/hr & A's Speed $= 6x$ km/hr.

$\therefore$ Ratio of Speeds of $A, B, C = 6x : 3x : x = 6 : 3 : 1$.

Ratio of times taken $= \dfrac{1}{6} : \dfrac{1}{3} : 1 = 1 : 2 : 6$.

If C takes 6 min., then B takes 2 min.

If C takes 54 min, then B takes $\left(\dfrac{2}{6} \times 54\right)$ min. $= 18$ min.

41. Ratio of speeds of A and $B = 3 : 4$.

Ratio of times taken $= \dfrac{1}{3} : \dfrac{1}{4} = 4 : 3$.

If B takes 3 min, A takes 4 min.

If B takes 36 min, A takes $\left(\dfrac{4}{3} \times 36\right)$ min. $= 48$ min.

42. Let the required distance be x km.

Then, $\dfrac{x}{3} + \dfrac{x}{2} = 5$ or $2x + 3x = 30$ or $x = 6$ km.

43. Let the distance be x km. Then,

$\dfrac{\left(\dfrac{2x}{3}\right)}{4} + \dfrac{\left(\dfrac{x}{3}\right)}{5} = \dfrac{42}{60}$ or $\dfrac{x}{6} + \dfrac{x}{15} = \dfrac{7}{10}$

or $5x + 2x = 21$ or $x = 3$ km.

44. Let the total journey be x km.

Then, $\dfrac{3x}{5} + \dfrac{7x}{20} + 6.5 = x$

or $12x + 7x + 20 \times 6.5 = 20x$ or $x = 130$ km.

45. Let the total trip be x km. Then,

$\dfrac{2}{5} x = 1200$ or $x = \left(1200 \times \dfrac{5}{2}\right) = 3000$ km.

Distance travelled by car $= \left(\dfrac{1}{3} \times 3000\right)$ km $= 1000$ km.

Journey by train $= [\, 3000 - (1200 + 1000)\,]$ km $= 800$ km.

46. Let the distance be x km. Then,

$\dfrac{x}{3} - \dfrac{x}{3.75} = \dfrac{1}{2}$ or $2.5x - 2x = 3.75$

or $0.5x = 3.75$ or $x = \dfrac{3.75}{0.50} = \dfrac{375}{50} = \dfrac{15}{2} = 7.5$ km.

47. Let the distance between Meerut and Delhi be x km and let the trains meet y hours after 7 a.m.

Clearly, M covers x km. in 4 hrs and N covers x km in $(7/2)$ hrs.

$\therefore$ Speed of $M = \dfrac{x}{4}$ kmph, Speed of $N = \dfrac{2x}{7}$ kmph.

Distance covered by M in $(y + 2)$ hrs + Distance covered by N in y hrs $= x$.

$\therefore \dfrac{x}{4}(y + 2) + \dfrac{2x}{7}(y) = x$ or $\dfrac{(y + 2)}{4} + \dfrac{2y}{7} = 1$

$\therefore y = \dfrac{14}{15}$ hrs $= \left(\dfrac{14}{15} \times 60\right)$ min. $= 56$ min.

Hence, the trains meet at 7.56 a.m.

48. Let the distance be x km. Then,

$\dfrac{x}{9} - \dfrac{x}{10} = \dfrac{36}{60}$ or $\dfrac{x}{9} - \dfrac{x}{10} = \dfrac{3}{5}$ or $10x - 9x = 54$ or $x = 54$ km.

49. Distance = (Speed × Time) $= \left(12 \times \dfrac{9}{2}\right)$ km $= 54$ km.

Time left now = 3 hours.

New Speed $= \left(\dfrac{54}{3}\right)$ km/hr $= 18$ km/hr.

50. (Time taken to walk x km) + (Time taken to ride x km) $= \dfrac{23}{4}$ hrs.

(Time taken to walk $2x$ km) + (Time taken to ride $2x$ km) $= \dfrac{23}{2}$ hrs.

But, time taken to ride $2x$ km $= \dfrac{15}{4}$ hrs.

$\therefore$ Time taken to walk $2x$ km $= \left(\dfrac{23}{2} - \dfrac{15}{4}\right)$ hrs $= \dfrac{31}{4}$ hrs.

$\qquad\qquad\qquad\qquad\qquad\qquad\qquad\qquad = 7$ hrs 45 min.

51. Ratio of speeds $= 3 : 4$.

Ratio of time taken $= \dfrac{1}{3} : \dfrac{1}{4} = 4 : 3$.

$\therefore \dfrac{4}{3} = \dfrac{x}{24}$ or $3x = 96$ or $x = 32$ min.

52. Let the length of journey be x km.

Then, $\dfrac{x}{45} - \dfrac{x}{60} = \dfrac{11}{2}$ or $x = 990$ km.

18. Problems On Trains

Important Points :

1. *Time taken by a train x metres long in passing a signal post or a pole or a standing man = Time taken by the train to cover x metres.*

2. *Time taken by a train x metres long in passing a stationary object of length y metres = Time taken by the train to cover (x + y) metres.*

3. Suppose two trains or two bodies are moving in the same direction at u kmph and v kmph such that $u > v$, then
   their relative speed = (u − v) kmph.

4. If two trains of length x km and y km are moving in the same direction at u kmph and v kmph, where $u > v$, then *time taken by faster train to cross the slower train*
   $$= \left(\frac{x+y}{u-v}\right) hrs.$$

5. Suppose two trains or two bodies are moving in opposite directions at u kmph and v kmph. Then, *their relative speed = (u + v) kmph.*

6. If two trains of length x km and y km are moving in opposite directions at u kmph and v kmph, then : *time taken by the trains to cross each other*
   $$= \left(\frac{x+y}{u+v}\right) hrs.$$

7. If two trains start at the same time from two points A and B towards each other and after crossing they take a and b hours in reaching B and A respectively.
   Then, A's speed : B's speed $= (\sqrt{b} : \sqrt{a})$.

8. x kmph $= \left(x \times \dfrac{5}{18}\right)$ m/sec.

9. y metres/sec. $= \left(y \times \dfrac{18}{5}\right)$ km/hr.

$$\boxed{\textbf{Solved Problems}}$$

Ex. 1. *Find the time taken by a train 180 m long, running at 72 kmph, in crossing an electric pole.*

Sol. Speed of the train $= \left(72 \times \dfrac{5}{18}\right)$ m/sec = 20 m/sec.

Distance moved in passing the pole = 180 m.

Required time taken $= \left(\dfrac{180}{20}\right)$ sec $= 9$ sec.

Ex. 2. *A train 140 m long is running at 60 kmph. In how much time will it pass a platform 260 m long ?*

Sol. Speed of the train $= \left(60 \times \dfrac{5}{18}\right)$ m/sec $= \dfrac{50}{3}$ m/sec.

Distance covered in passing the platform $= (140 + 260)$ m $= 400$ m

∴ Time taken $= \left(400 \times \dfrac{3}{50}\right)$ sec $= 24$ sec.

Ex. 3. *A man is standing on a railway bridge which is 180 m long. He finds that a train crosses the bridge in 20 seconds but himself in 8 seconds. Find the length of the train and its speed.*

Sol. Let the length of the train be x metres.

Then, the train covers x metres in 8 seconds and $(x + 180)$ metres in 20 seconds.

∴ $\dfrac{x}{8} = \dfrac{x + 180}{20} \Leftrightarrow 20x = 8\,(x + 180) \Leftrightarrow x = 120$.

∴ Length of train $= 120$ m.

Speed of the train $= \left(\dfrac{120}{8}\right)$ m/sec $= 15$ m/sec $= \left(15 \times \dfrac{18}{5}\right)$ kmph

$= 54$ kmph.

Ex. 4. *A train 150 m long is running with a speed of 68 kmph. In what time will it pass a man who is running at 8 kmph in the same direction in which the train is going ?*

Sol. Speed of the train relative to man $= (68 - 8)$ kmph

$= \left(60 \times \dfrac{5}{18}\right)$ m/sec $= \left(\dfrac{50}{3}\right)$ m/sec.

Time taken by the train to cross the man

$=$ Time taken by it to cover 150 m at $\left(\dfrac{50}{3}\right)$ m/sec

$= \left(150 \times \dfrac{3}{50}\right)$ sec $= 9$ sec.

Ex. 5. *A train 220 m long is running with a speed of 59 kmph. In what time will it pass a man who is running at 7 kmph in the direction opposite to that in which the train is going ?*

Sol. Speed of the train relative to man $= (59 + 7)$ kmph

$= \left(66 \times \dfrac{5}{18}\right)$ m/sec $= \left(\dfrac{55}{3}\right)$ m/sec.

Time taken by the train to cross the man

= Time taken by it to cover 220 m at $\left(\dfrac{55}{3}\right)$ m/sec

$= \left(220 \times \dfrac{3}{55}\right)$ sec = 12 sec.

Ex. 6. *Two trains 137 metres and 163 metres in length are running towards each other on parallel lines, one at the rate of 42 kmph and another at 48 kmph. In what time will they be clear of each other from the moment they meet ?*

Sol. Relative speed of the trains = (42 + 48) kmph = 90 kmph

$$= \left(90 \times \dfrac{5}{18}\right) \text{ m/sec} = 25 \text{ m/sec.}$$

Time taken by the trains to pass each other
= Time taken to cover (137 + 163) m at 25 m/sec

$= \left(\dfrac{300}{25}\right)$ sec = 12 seconds.

Ex. 7. *A train 100 metres long takes 6 seconds to cross a man walking at 5 kmph in a direction opposite to that of the train. Find the speed of the train.*

Sol. Let the speed of the train be x kmph.

Speed of the train relative to man = $(x + 5)$ kmph.

$$= (x + 5) \times \dfrac{5}{18} \text{ m/sec.}$$

$\therefore \quad \dfrac{100}{(x + 5) \times \dfrac{5}{18}} = 6 \Leftrightarrow 30 (x + 5) = 1800 \Leftrightarrow x = 55.$

$\therefore$ Speed of the train is 55 kmph.

Ex. 8. *A train running at 54 kmph takes 20 seconds to pass a platform. Next it takes 12 seconds to pass a man walking at 6 kmph in the same direction in which the train is going. Find the length of the train and the length of the platform.*

Sol. Let the length of train be x metres & length of platform be y metres.

Speed of the train relative to man = (54 − 6) kmph = 48 kmph

$$= \left(48 \times \dfrac{5}{18}\right) \text{ m/sec} = \dfrac{40}{3} \text{ m/sec.}$$

In passing a man, the train covers its own length with relative speed.

$\therefore$ Length of train = (Relative speed × Time)

$$= \left(\dfrac{40}{3} \times 12\right) \text{ m} = 160 \text{ m.}$$

Also, speed of the train = $\left(54 \times \dfrac{5}{18}\right)$ m/sec = 15 m/sec.

$\therefore \dfrac{x+y}{15} = 20$ or $x + y = 300$ or $y = (300 - 160)$ m $= 140$ m.

$\therefore$ Length of the platform $= 140$ m.

Ex. 9. *A man sitting in a train which is travelling at 50 kmph observes that a goods train, travelling in opposite direction, takes 9 seconds to pass him. If the goods train is 150 m long, find its speed.*

Sol. Relative speed $= \left(\dfrac{150}{9}\right)$ m/sc $= \left(\dfrac{150}{9} \times \dfrac{18}{5}\right)$ kmph $= 60$ kmph.

$\therefore$ Speed of goods train $= (60 - 50)$ kmph $= 10$ kmph.

EXERCISE 18

Mark ($\sqrt{}$) against the correct answer :

1. A train moves with a speed of 108 kmph. Its speed in metres per second is :
   - (a) 38.8
   - (b) 18
   - (c) 30
   - (d) 10.8

2. A speed of 14 metres per second is the same as :
   - (a) 50.4 km/hr
   - (b) 28 km/hr
   - (c) 70 km/hr
   - (d) 46.6 km/hr

3. A man on riding crosses a bridge in 5 minutes when riding is being done at 15 kmph. The length of the bridge is :
   - (a) 125 m
   - (b) 250 m
   - (c) 1250 m
   - (d) 2500 m

4. A train 150 m long is running at a speed of 90 kmph. Time taken by the train to cross a tree is :   **(U.D.C. 1993)**
   - (a) 3 sec
   - (b) 4 sec
   - (c) 6 sec
   - (d) 8 sec

5. A train 280 m long, running with a speed of 63 km/hr will pass an electric pole in :
   - (a) 20 sec
   - (b) 16 sec
   - (c) 15 sec
   - (d) 18 sec

6. A train is moving at a speed of 132 kmph. If the length of the train is 110 metres, how long will it take to cross a railway platform 165 m long ?   **(Assistant Grade 1993)**
   - (a) 5 sec
   - (b) 7.5 sec
   - (c) 10 sec
   - (d) 15 sec

7. A train 280 m long is moving at 60 kmph. The time taken by the train to cross a tunnel 220 m long, is :   **(Railways 1989)**
   - (a) 20 sec
   - (b) 25 sec
   - (c) 30 sec
   - (d) 35 sec

8. With a speed of 60 kmph a train crosses a pole in 30 seconds. The length of the train is :   **(Assistant Grade 1994)**
   - (a) 1000 m
   - (b) 900 m
   - (c) 750 m
   - (d) 500 m

9. A train travelling at a speed of 90 kmph, crosses a pole in 10 seconds. The length of the train is :   **(Bank P.O. 1993)**
   - (a) 250 m
   - (b) 150 m
   - (c) 900 m
   - (d) 100 m

10. A train 120 m long crosses a standing man in 15 seconds. The speed of the train is :
    (*a*) 32 km/hr   (*b*) 36.5 km/hr   (*c*) 28.8 km/hr   (*d*) 40 km/hr

11. A train 700 m long is running at 72 kmph. If it crosses a tunnel in 1 minute, the length of the tunnel is :
    (*a*) 700 m   (*b*) 600 m   (*c*) 550 m   (*d*) 500 m

12. The length of a bridge which a train 130 m long and travelling at 45 kmph can cross in 30 seconds, is :   **(Assistant Grade 1993)**
    (*a*) 200 m   (*b*) 225 m   (*c*) 245 m   (*d*) 250 m

13. If a 200 m long train crosses a platform of the same length as that of the train in 20 seconds, then the speed of the train is :   **(N.D.A. 1992)**
    (*a*) 50 km/hr   (*b*) 60 km/hr   (*c*) 72 km/hr   (*d*) 80 km/hr

14. A train 60 m long passes a platform 90 m long in 10 seconds. The speed of the train is :
    (*a*) 10 km/hr   (*b*) 15 km/hr   (*c*) 54 km/hr   (*d*) 48 km/hr

15. A train 300 m long crossed a platform 900 m long in 1 minute 12 seconds. The speed of the train (in km/hr) is :   **(C.B.I. 1990)**
    (*a*) 45   (*b*) 50   (*c*) 54   (*d*) 60

16. A train crosses a platform 100 m long in 60 seconds at a speed of 45 kmph. The time taken by the train to cross an electric pole is :
    (*a*) 8 sec   (*b*) 52 sec   (*c*) 1 minute   (*d*) data inadequate
                                                      (Bank P.O. 1990)

17. A train of length 150 m takes 40.5 seconds to cross a tunnel of length 300 m. The speed of the train (in km/hr) is :
    (*a*) 13.33   (*b*) 26.67   (*c*) 40   (*d*) 400
                             (Central Excise & I. Tax 1991)

18. A train 150 m long takes 20 seconds to cross a platform 450 m long. The speed of the train (in m/sec) is :   **(Assistant Grade 1994)**
    (*a*) 22.5   (*b*) 30   (*c*) 45   (*d*) 96

19. A train speeds past a pole in 15 seconds and a platform 100 m long in 25 seconds. Its length is :   **(Bank P.O. 1992)**
    (*a*) 200 m   (*b*) 150 m   (*c*) 50 m   (*d*) data inadequate

20. A train takes 18 seconds to pass completely through a station 162 m long and 15 seconds through another station 120 m long. The length of the train is :   **(C.D.S. 1993)**
    (*a*) 70 m   (*b*) 80 m   (*c*) 90 m   (*d*) 100 m

21. If a train 110 m long passes a telegraph pole in 3 seconds, then the time taken by it to cross a railway platform 165 m long, is :   **(N.D.A. 1994)**
    (*a*) 3 sec   (*b*) 4 sec   (*c*) 5 sec   (*d*) 7.5 sec

22. A train 110 m long is travelling at a speed of 58 kmph. The time in which it will pass a passer by, walking at 4 kmph in the same direction, is : **(Assistant Grade 1994)**

(*a*) 6 sec   (*b*) $7\frac{1}{2}$ sec   (*c*) $7\frac{1}{3}$ sec   (*d*) $7\frac{1}{3}$ min

23. A train 150 m long moving at a speed of 25 metres per second overtakes a man moving at 5 metres/sec in opposite direction. The train will pass the man in : **(Hotel Management 1992)**

(*a*) 5 sec   (*b*) 6 sec   (*c*) $4\frac{2}{7}$ sec   (*d*) 8 sec

24. Two trains 200 m and 150 m long are running on parallel rails at the rate of 40 kmph and 45 kmph respectively. In how much time will they cross each other, if they are running in the same direction ?

(*a*) 72 sec   (*b*) 132 sec   (*c*) 192 sec   (*d*) 252 sec

25. Two trains 126 m and 114 m long are running in opposite directions, one at the rate of 30 kmph and another one at 42 kmph. From the moment they meet will cross each other in :

(*a*) 10 sec   (*b*) 11 sec   (*c*) 12 sec   (*d*) 13 sec

26. A train 270 m long is moving at a speed of 24 kmph. It will cross a man coming from the opposite direction at a speed of 3 kmph, in :

(*a*) 24 sec   (*b*) 28 sec   (*c*) 32 sec   (*d*) 36 sec

27. A train 125 m long passes a man, running at 5 kmph in the same direction in which the train is going, in 10 seconds. The speed of the train is :

(*a*) 50 km/hr   (*b*) 45 km/hr   (*c*) 55 km/hr   (*d*) 54 km/hr

28. A train 110 m long passes a man, running at 6 kmph in the direction opposite to that of the train, in 6 seconds. The speed of the train is :

(*a*) 60 km/hr   (*b*) 66 km/hr   (*c*) 54 km/hr   (*d*) 72 km/hr

29. Two trains are moving in the same direction at 65 kmph and 45 kmph. The faster train crosses a man in slower train in 18 seconds. The length of the faster train is : **(Central Excise & I. Tax 1992)**

(*a*) 120 m   (*b*) 180 m   (*c*) 100 m   (*d*) 145 m

30. A train 108 m long moving at a speed of 50 km/hr crosses a train 112 m long coming from opposite direction in 6 seconds. The speed of the second train is :

(*a*) 48 kmph   (*b*) 54 kmph   (*c*) 66 kmph   (*d*) 82 kmph

31. A train *B* speeding with 120 kmph crosses another train *C*, running in the same direction in 2 minutes. If the lengths of the trains *B* and *C* be 100 m and 200 m respectively, what is the speed of the train *C* ?

(*a*) 111 kmph   (*b*) 127 kmph   (*c*) 123 kmph   (*d*) 129 kmph

(Bank P.O. 1992)

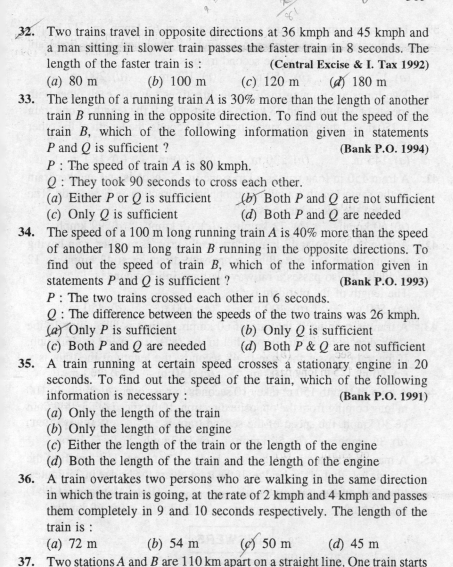

32. Two trains travel in opposite directions at 36 kmph and 45 kmph and a man sitting in slower train passes the faster train in 8 seconds. The length of the faster train is :   **(Central Excise & I. Tax 1992)**

(*a*) 80 m   (*b*) 100 m   (*c*) 120 m   (*d*) 180 m

33. The length of a running train *A* is 30% more than the length of another train *B* running in the opposite direction. To find out the speed of the train *B*, which of the following information given in statements *P* and *Q* is sufficient ?   **(Bank P.O. 1994)**

P : The speed of train *A* is 80 kmph.

Q : They took 90 seconds to cross each other.

(*a*) Either *P* or *Q* is sufficient   (*b*) Both *P* and *Q* are not sufficient

(*c*) Only *Q* is sufficient   (*d*) Both *P* and *Q* are needed

34. The speed of a 100 m long running train *A* is 40% more than the speed of another 180 m long train *B* running in the opposite directions. To find out the speed of train *B*, which of the information given in statements *P* and *Q* is sufficient ?   **(Bank P.O. 1993)**

P : The two trains crossed each other in 6 seconds.

Q : The difference between the speeds of the two trains was 26 kmph.

(*a*) Only *P* is sufficient   (*b*) Only *Q* is sufficient

(*c*) Both *P* and *Q* are needed   (*d*) Both *P* & *Q* are not sufficient

35. A train running at certain speed crosses a stationary engine in 20 seconds. To find out the speed of the train, which of the following information is necessary :   **(Bank P.O. 1991)**

(*a*) Only the length of the train

(*b*) Only the length of the engine

(*c*) Either the length of the train or the length of the engine

(*d*) Both the length of the train and the length of the engine

36. A train overtakes two persons who are walking in the same direction in which the train is going, at the rate of 2 kmph and 4 kmph and passes them completely in 9 and 10 seconds respectively. The length of the train is :

(*a*) 72 m   (*b*) 54 m   (*c*) 50 m   (*d*) 45 m

37. Two stations *A* and *B* are 110 km apart on a straight line. One train starts from *A* at 7 a.m. and travels towards *B* at 20 kmph. Another train starts from *B* at 8 a.m. and travels towards *A* at a speed of 25 kmph. At what time will they meet ?   **(Railways 1989)**

(*a*) 9 a.m.   (*b*) 10 a.m.   (*c*) 11 a.m.   (*d*) 10.30 a.m.

38. A train *X* starts from Meerut at 4 P.M. and reaches Ghaziabad at 5 P.M. while another train *Y* starts from Ghaziabad at 4 P.M. and reaches Meerut at 5.30 P.M. The two trains will cross each other at :

(*a*) 4.36 p.m.   (*b*) 4.42 p.m.   (*c*) 4.48 p.m.   (*d*) 4.50 p.m.

39. Two trains running in the same direction at 65 kmph and 47 kmph, completely pass one another in 1 minute. If the length of the first train is 125 m, the length of the second train is :
    (*a*) 125 m   (*b*) 150 m   (*c*) 175 m   (*d*) 200 m

40. Two trains are running in opposite directions towards each other with speeds of 54 kmph and 48 kmph respectively. If the length of one train is 250 m and they cross each other in 18 seconds, the length of the other train is :
    (*a*) 145 m   (*b*) 230 m   (*c*) 260 m   (*d*) 180 m

41. A train 150 m long passes a km stone in 15 seconds and another train of the same length travelling in opposite direction in 8 seconds. The speed of the second train is :
    (*a*) 60 kmph   (*b*) 72 kmph   (*c*) 66 kmph   (*d*) 99 kmph

42. A train travelling at 48 kmph completely crosses another train having half its length and travelling in opposite direction at 42 kmph, in 12 seconds. It also passes a railway platform in 45 seconds.
The length of the platform is :
    (*a*) 560 m   (*b*) 400 m   (*c*) 600 m   (*d*) 450 m

43. A train is running at the rate of 60 kmph. A man is also going in the same direction on a track parallel to the rails at a speed of 45 kmph. If the train crosses the man in 48 seconds, the length of the train is :
    (*a*) 50 m   (*b*) 100 m   (*c*) 150 m   (*d*) 200 m

44. A train of length 150 m takes 10 seconds to pass over another train 100 m long coming from the opposite direction. If the speed of the first train be 30 kmph, the speed of the second train is :   **(Railways 1991)**
    (*a*) 36 kmph   (*b*) 54 kmph   (*c*) 60 kmph   (*d*) 72 kmph

45. A man sees a train passing over a bridge 1 km long. The length of the train is half that of the bridge. If the train clears the bridge in 2 minutes, the speed of the train is :   **(Hotel Management 1991)**
    (*a*) 30 km/hr   (*b*) 45 km/hr   (*c*) 50 km/hr   (*d*) 60 km/hr

ANSWERS

1. (*c*)	**2.** (*a*)	**3.** (*c*)	**4.** (*c*)	**5.** (*b*)	**6.** (*b*)	**7.** (*c*)	**8.** (*d*)	**9.** (*a*)
10. (*c*)	**11.** (*d*)	**12.** (*c*)	**13.** (*c*)	**14.** (*c*)	**15.** (*d*)	**16.** (*b*)	**17.** (*c*)	**18.** (*b*)
19. (*b*)	**20.** (*c*)	**21.** (*d*)	**22.** (*c*)	**23.** (*a*)	**24.** (*d*)	**25.** (*c*)	**26.** (*d*)	**27.** (*a*)
28. (*a*)	**29.** (*c*)	**30.** (*d*)	**31.** (*a*)	**32.** (*d*)	**33.** (*b*)	**34.** (*a*)	**35.** (*d*)	**36.** (*c*)
37. (*b*)	**38.** (*a*)	**39.** (*c*)	**40.** (*c*)	**41.** (*d*)	**42.** (*b*)	**43.** (*d*)	**44.** (*c*)	**45.** (*b*)

SOLUTIONS

1. $108 \text{ kmph} = \left(108 \times \dfrac{5}{18}\right) \text{m/sec} = 30 \text{ m/sec.}$

2. $14 \text{ m/sec} = \left(14 \times \dfrac{18}{5}\right) \text{km/hr} = 50.4 \text{ km/hr.}$

3. $\text{Speed} = \left(15 \times \dfrac{5}{18}\right) \text{m/sec} = \dfrac{25}{6} \text{ m/sec.}$

    $\text{Time} = (5 \times 60) \text{ sec} = 300 \text{ sec.}$

    $\therefore \text{ Length of bridge} = (\text{speed} \times \text{Time}) = \left(\dfrac{25}{6} \times 300\right) \text{m} = 1250 \text{ m.}$

4. $\text{Speed} = \left(90 \times \dfrac{5}{18}\right) \text{m/sec} = 25 \text{ m/sec.}$

    $\text{Time taken} = \left(\dfrac{150}{25}\right) \text{sec} = 6 \text{ sec.}$

5. $\text{Speed} = \left(63 \times \dfrac{5}{18}\right) \text{m/sec} = \dfrac{35}{2} \text{ m/sec.}$

    $\text{Time taken} = \left(280 \times \dfrac{2}{35}\right) \text{sec} = 16 \text{ sec.}$

6. $\text{Speed} = \left(132 \times \dfrac{5}{18}\right) \text{m/sec} = \left(\dfrac{110}{3}\right) \text{m/sec.}$

    $\text{Total distance covered} = (110 + 165) \text{ m} = 275 \text{ m.}$

    $\therefore \text{ Required time} = \left(275 \times \dfrac{3}{110}\right) \text{sec} = 7.5 \text{ seconds.}$

7. $\text{Speed} = \left(60 \times \dfrac{5}{18}\right) \text{m/sec} = \left(\dfrac{50}{3}\right) \text{m/sec.}$

    $\text{Distance covered} = (280 + 220) \text{ m} = 500 \text{ m}$

    $\therefore \text{ Required time} = \left(500 \times \dfrac{3}{50}\right) \text{sec} = 30 \text{ seconds.}$

8. $\text{Speed} = \left(60 \times \dfrac{5}{18}\right) \text{m/sec} = \left(\dfrac{50}{3}\right) \text{m/sec.}$

    $\text{Length of the train} = (\text{speed} \times \text{Time}) = \left(\dfrac{50}{3} \times 30\right) \text{m} = 500 \text{ m.}$

9. $\text{Speed} = \left(90 \times \dfrac{5}{18}\right) \text{m/sec} = 25 \text{ m/sec.}$

    $\text{Length of the train} = (\text{Speed} \times \text{Time}) = (25 \times 10) \text{ m} = 250 \text{ m.}$

Quantitative Aptitude

10. Speed $= \left(\dfrac{120}{15}\right)$ m/sec $= \left(8 \times \dfrac{18}{5}\right)$ kmph $= 28.8$ kmph.

11. Speed $= \left(72 \times \dfrac{5}{18}\right)$ m/sec $= 20$ m/sec.

    Time $= 60$ sec.

    $\therefore \dfrac{700 + x}{20} = 60 \Leftrightarrow 700 + x = 1200 \Leftrightarrow x = 500$ m.

12. Speed $= \left(45 \times \dfrac{5}{18}\right)$ m/sec $= \left(\dfrac{25}{2}\right)$ m/sec, Time $= 30$ sec.

    Let the length of bridge be x metres.

    Then, $\dfrac{130 + x}{30} = \dfrac{25}{2} \Leftrightarrow 2\,(130 + x) = 750 \Leftrightarrow x = 245$ m.

13. Total distance covered $= (200 + 200)$ m $= 400$ m.
    Time taken $= 20$ sec.

    $\therefore$ Speed $= \left(\dfrac{400}{20}\right)$ m/sec $= \left(20 \times \dfrac{18}{5}\right)$ km/hr $= 72$ km/hr.

14. Total distance covered $= (60 + 90)$ m $= 150$ m.
    Time taken $= 10$ sec.

    $\therefore$ Speed $= \left(\dfrac{150}{10}\right)$ m/sec $= \left(15 \times \dfrac{18}{5}\right)$ km/hr $= 54$ km/hr.

15. Total distance covered $= (300 + 900)$ m $= 1200$ m.
    Time taken $= 1$ min. 12 sec $= 72$ sec.

    Speed $= \left(\dfrac{1200}{72}\right)$ m/sec $= \left(\dfrac{1200}{72} \times \dfrac{18}{5}\right)$ km/hr $= 60$ km/hr.

16. Speed $= \left(45 \times \dfrac{5}{18}\right)$ m/sec $= \left(\dfrac{25}{2}\right)$ m/sec.

    Let the length of the train be x metres.

    Then, $\dfrac{x + 100}{\left(\dfrac{25}{2}\right)} = 60$ or $x = 650$ m.

    $\therefore$ Time taken by the train to cross an electric pole

    $= \left(650 \times \dfrac{2}{25}\right)$ sec $= 52$ sec.

17. Total distance covered $= (150 + 300)$ m $= 450$ m.

    Time taken $= \left(\dfrac{81}{2}\right)$ seconds.

    Speed $= \left(450 \times \dfrac{2}{81}\right)$ m/sec $= \left(450 \times \dfrac{2}{81} \times \dfrac{18}{5}\right)$ kmph $= 40$ kmph.

18. Total distance covered $= (150 + 450)$ m $= 600$ m.

Time taken $= 20$ Seconds.

Speed $= \left(\dfrac{600}{20}\right)$ m/sec $= 30$ m/sec.

19. Let the length of train be x metres and its speed be y metres/sec.

Then, $\dfrac{x}{y} = 15 \Rightarrow y = \dfrac{x}{15}$.

$\dfrac{x + 100}{25} = \dfrac{x}{15} \Rightarrow x = 150$ m.

20. Let the length of the train be x metres.

$\therefore \ \dfrac{x + 162}{18} = \dfrac{x + 120}{15} \Rightarrow 15\,(x + 162) = 18\,(x + 120) \Leftrightarrow x = 90$ m.

21. Speed $= \left(\dfrac{110}{3}\right)$ m/sec.

Time taken to cross railway platform $= \left[(110 + 165) \times \dfrac{3}{110}\right]$ sec.

$= \left(275 \times \dfrac{3}{110}\right)$ sec. $= 7.5$ sec.

22. Speed of train relative to man $= (58 - 4)$ kmph $= 54$ kmph.

$= \left(54 \times \dfrac{5}{18}\right)$ m/sec $= 15$ m/sec.

$\therefore$ Time taken to pass the man $= \left(\dfrac{110}{15}\right)$ sec $= 7\dfrac{1}{3}$ sec.

23. Speed of train relative to man $= (25 + 5)$ m/sec $= 30$ m/sec.

Time taken to pass the man $= \left(\dfrac{150}{30}\right)$ sec $= 5$ sec.

24. Relative speed $= (45 - 40)$ kmph $= 5$ kmph.

$= \left(5 \times \dfrac{5}{18}\right)$ m/sec $= \left(\dfrac{25}{18}\right)$ m/sec.

Total distance covered $=$ Sum of lengths of trains $= 350$ m.

$\therefore$ Time taken $= \left(350 \times \dfrac{18}{25}\right)$ sec $= 252$ sec.

25. Relative speed $= (30 + 42)$ kmph $= 72$ kmph.

$= \left(72 \times \dfrac{5}{18}\right)$ m/sec $= 20$ m/sec.

Distance covered in crossing each other $= (126 + 114)$ m $= 240$ m.

Required time $= \left(\dfrac{240}{20}\right)$ sec $= 12$ Seconds.

26. Relative speed $= (24 + 3)$ km/hr $= \left(27 \times \dfrac{5}{18}\right)$ m/sec $= \left(\dfrac{15}{2}\right)$ m/sec

Distance covered $= 270$ m.

Time taken $= \left(270 \times \dfrac{2}{15}\right)$ sec $= 36$ sec.

27. Speed of the train relative to man $= \left(\dfrac{125}{10}\right)$ m/sec $= \left(\dfrac{25}{2}\right)$ m/sec.

$$= \left(\dfrac{25}{2} \times \dfrac{18}{5}\right) \text{kmph} = 45 \text{ kmph}.$$

Let the speed of the train be x kmph.

Then, relative speed $= (x - 5)$ kmph.

$\therefore$ $x - 5 = 45$ or $x = 50$ kmph.

28. Speed of the train relative to man $= \left(\dfrac{110}{6}\right)$ m/sec.

$$= \left(\dfrac{110}{6} \times \dfrac{18}{5}\right) \text{kmph} = 66 \text{ kmph}.$$

Let the speed of the train be x kmph.

Then, relative speed $= (x + 6)$ kmph.

$\therefore$ $x + 6 = 66$ or $x = 60$ kmph.

29. Relative speed $= (65 - 45)$ kmph $= \left(20 \times \dfrac{5}{18}\right)$ m/sec $= \left(\dfrac{50}{9}\right)$ m/sec.

Distance covered in 18 sec. at this speed $= \left(\dfrac{50}{9} \times 18\right)$ m $= 100$ m.

$\therefore$ Length of the train $= 100$ m.

30. Let the speed of the second train be x kmph.

Relative speed $= (x + 50)$ kmph $= \left[(x + 50) \times \dfrac{5}{18}\right]$ m/sec.

$$= \left(\dfrac{250 + 5x}{18}\right) \text{m/sec.}$$

Distance covered $= (108 + 112) = 220$ m.

$\therefore$ $\dfrac{220}{\left(\dfrac{250 + 5x}{18}\right)} = 6$ or $250 + 5x = 660$ or $x = 82$ kmph.

Hence, the speed of the second train is 82 kmph.

31. Let the speed of train C be x kmph.

Speed of B relative to $C = (120 - x)$ kmph.

$$= \left[(120 - x) \times \dfrac{5}{18}\right] \text{m/sec} = \left(\dfrac{600 - 5x}{18}\right) \text{m/sec.}$$

Distance covered $= (100 + 200)$ m $= 300$ m.

$\therefore \ \dfrac{300}{\left(\dfrac{600-5x}{18}\right)} = 120 \Leftrightarrow 5400 = 120\ (600 - 5x) \Leftrightarrow x = 111.$

Hence, the speed of train C is 111 kmph.

32. Relative speed $= (36 + 45)$ km/hr $= \left(81 \times \dfrac{5}{18}\right)$ m/sec $= \left(\dfrac{45}{2}\right)$ m/sec.

Length of train $= \left(\dfrac{45}{2} \times 8\right)$ m $= 180$ m.

33. Let the length of train A be x metres.

Length of train $B = \left(\dfrac{130}{100}\ x\right)$ metres $= \dfrac{13x}{10}$ metres.

Let the speed of B be y kmph. Speed of $A = 80$ kmph.

Relative speed $= \left[(y + 80) \times \dfrac{5}{18}\right]$ m/sec $= \left(\dfrac{5y + 400}{18}\right)$ m/sec.

$\therefore$ Time taken by the trains to cross each other is given by

$90 = \dfrac{\left(x + \dfrac{13x}{10}\right)}{\left(\dfrac{5y + 400}{18}\right)}.$

To find y, clearly x is also needed.

So, both P and Q are not sufficient.

34. Let speed of B be x kmph.

Then, speed of $A = \left(\dfrac{140}{100}\ x\right)$ kmph $= \left(\dfrac{7x}{5}\right)$ kmph.

Relative speed $= \left(x + \dfrac{7x}{5}\right)$ kmph $= \left(\dfrac{12x}{5} \times \dfrac{5}{18}\right)$ m/sec $= \left(\dfrac{2x}{3}\right)$ m/sec.

Time taken to cross each other $= \left[(100 + 180) \times \dfrac{3}{2x}\right]$ sec. $= \left(\dfrac{420}{x}\right)$ sec.

Now, $\dfrac{420}{x} = 6 \Leftrightarrow x = 70$ kmph.

Thus, only P is sufficient.

35. Since the sum of the lengths of the train and the engine is needed, so both the lengths must be known.

36. 2 kmph $= = \left(2 \times \dfrac{5}{18}\right)$ m/sec $= \dfrac{5}{9}$ m/sec & 4 kmph $= \dfrac{10}{9}$ m/sec.

Let the length of the train be x metres & its speed be y m/sec.

Then, $\dfrac{x}{\left(y-\dfrac{5}{9}\right)}=9$ and $\dfrac{x}{\left(y-\dfrac{10}{9}\right)}=10.$

$\therefore$ $9y-5=x$ and $10\,(9y-10)=9x$

$\therefore$ $9y-x=5$ and $90y-9x=100.$

On solving we get : $x=50.$

$\therefore$ Length of the train is 50 m.

37. Suppose they meet x hours after 7 a.m.

Distance covered by A in x hours $=20x$ km.

Distance covered by B in $(x-1)$ hours $=25\,(x-1)$ km.

$\therefore$ $20x+25\,(x-1)=110$ or $45x=135$ or $x=3.$

So, they meet at 10 a.m.

38. Suppose the distance between Meerut & Ghaziabad is x km.

Time taken by X to cover x km $=1$ hour.

Time taken by Y to cover x km $=\dfrac{3}{2}$ hours.

$\therefore$ Speed of $X=x$ kmph, Speed of $Y=\left(\dfrac{2x}{3}\right)$ kmph.

Let them meet y hours after 4 a.m. Then,

$xy+\dfrac{2xy}{3}=x \Leftrightarrow y\left(1+\dfrac{2}{3}\right)=1$ or $y=\dfrac{3}{5}$ hours.

$\therefore$ $y=\left(\dfrac{3}{5}\times 60\right)$ min $=36$ min.

So, the two trains meet at 4.36 p.m.

39. Relative speed $=(65-47)$ kmph $=\left(18\times\dfrac{5}{18}\right)$ m/sec $=5$ m/sec.

Let the length of second train be x metres.

Then $\dfrac{125+x}{5}=60 \Leftrightarrow 125+x=300 \Leftrightarrow x=175.$

$\therefore$ Length of second train $=175$ m.

40. Relative speed $=(54+48)$ kmph $=\left(102\times\dfrac{5}{18}\right)$ m/sec $=\left(\dfrac{85}{3}\right)$ m/sec.

Let the length of the other train be x metres.

Then, $(250+x)\times\dfrac{3}{85}=18$ or $750+3x=1530$ or $x=260$m.

$\therefore$ The length of the other train is 260 m.

41. Speed of first train $=\left(\dfrac{150}{15}\right)$ m/sec $=10$ m/sec.

Let the speed of second train be x metres per sec.

Relative speed $=(10+x)$ m/sec.

$$\therefore \frac{300}{10+x} = 8 \quad \text{or} \quad 300 = 80 + 8x \quad \text{or} \quad x = \frac{220}{8} = \frac{55}{2} \text{ m/sec.}$$

$$\therefore \text{ Speed of second train} = \left(\frac{55}{2} \times \frac{18}{5}\right) \text{kmph} = 99 \text{ kmph.}$$

42. Let the length of first train be x metres.

    Then, the length of second train is $(x/2)$ metres.

    Relative speed $= (48 + 42)$ kmph $= \left(90 \times \dfrac{5}{18}\right)$ m/sec $= 25$ m/sec.

$$\therefore \qquad \frac{\left(x + \dfrac{x}{2}\right)}{25} = 12 \quad \text{or} \quad \frac{3x}{2} = 300 \quad \text{or} \quad x = 200.$$

    $\therefore$ Length of first train $= 200$ m.

    Let the length of platform be y metres.

    Speed of the first train $= \left(48 \times \dfrac{5}{18}\right)$ m/sec $= \dfrac{40}{3}$ m/sec.

$$\therefore (200 + y) \times \frac{3}{40} = 45 \Leftrightarrow 600 + 3y = 1800 \Leftrightarrow y = 400 \text{ m.}$$

43. Let the length of the first train be x metres.

    Relative speed $= (60 - 45)$ kmph $= \left(15 \times \dfrac{5}{18}\right)$ m/sec $= \dfrac{25}{6}$ m / sec.

$$\therefore x \times \frac{6}{25} = 48 \quad \text{or} \quad x = 200 \text{ m.}$$

44. Let the speed of second train be x kmph.

    Relative speed $= (30 + x)$ kmph $= (30 + x) \times \dfrac{5}{18}$ m / sec.

$$(150 + 100) \times \frac{18}{5(30 + x)} = 10 \Leftrightarrow x = 60.$$

45. Length of bridge $= 1000$ m, Length of train $= 500$ m.

    Total distance covered in clearing the bridge $= 1500$ m.

    Time taken $= 120$ seconds.

$$\therefore \text{ Speed} = \left(\frac{1500}{120}\right) \text{m/sec} = \left(\frac{25}{2} \times \frac{18}{5}\right) \text{kmph} = 45 \text{ kmph.}$$

19. Problems On Boats & Streams

Important Points :

1. In water, the direction along the stream is called **downstream.** And, the direction against the stream is called **upstream.**

2. If speed of a boat in still water is u km/hr and the speed of the stream is v km/hr, then :

    Speed downstream $= (u + v)$ *km/hr.*
    Speed upstream $= (u - v)$ *km/hr.*

3. If the speed downstream is a km/hr and the speed upstream is b km/hr, then :

    Speed in still water $= \dfrac{1}{2}(a + b)$ *km/hr.*

    Rate of stream $= \dfrac{1}{2}(a - b)$ *km/hr.*

Solved Problems

Ex. 1. *A man can row upstream at 7 kmph and downstream at 10 kmph. Find man's rate in still water and the rate of current.*

Sol. Rate in still water $= \dfrac{1}{2}(10 + 7)$ km/hr $= 8.5$ km/hr.

Rate of current $= \dfrac{1}{2}(10 - 7)$ km/hr $= 1.5$ km/hr.

Ex. 2. *A man rows downstream 27 km and upstream 18 km, taking 3 hours each time. What is the velocity of the current ?*

Sol. Rate downstream $= \left(\dfrac{27}{3}\right)$ km/hr $= 9$ km/hr.

Rate upstream $= \left(\dfrac{18}{3}\right)$ km/hr $= 6$ km/hr.

$\therefore$ Velocity of current $= \dfrac{1}{2}(9 - 6)$ km/hr $= 1.5$ km/hr.

Ex. 3. *A man can row 12 kmph in still water. If takes him twice as long to row up as to row down the river. Find the rate of stream.*

Sol. Let man's rate upstream be x kmph.
Then, his rate downstream $= 2x$ kmph.

$\therefore$ Rate in still water $= \dfrac{1}{2}(2x + x)$ kmph $= \dfrac{3x}{2}$ kmph.

$\therefore \dfrac{3x}{2} = 12$ or $x = 8$.

∴   Rate upstream = 8 km/hr.

Rate downstream = 16 km/hr.

∴   Rate of stream = $\frac{1}{2}$ (16 – 8) km/hr = 4 km/hr.

Ex. 4. *A man can row 8 kmph in still water and the river is running at 2 kmph. If the man takes 1 hour to row to a place and back, how far is the place ?*

Sol. Man's rate downstream = (8 + 2) kmph = 10 kmph.

Man's rate upstream = (8 – 2) kmph = 6 kmph.

Let the required distance be x km.

Then, $\frac{x}{10} + \frac{x}{6} = 1 \Leftrightarrow 3x + 5x = 30 \Leftrightarrow x = 3.75$ km.

Hence, the required distance is 3.75 km.

Ex. 5. *In a stream running at 2 kmph, a motorboat goes 6 km upstream and back again to the starting point in 33 minutes. Find the speed of the motorboat in still water.*

Sol. Let the speed of the motorboat in still water be x kmph.

Then, speed downstream = $(x + 2)$ kmph.

Speed upstream = $(x - 2)$ kmph.

∴ $\frac{6}{x+2} + \frac{6}{x-2} = \frac{33}{60}$ or $11x^2 - 240x - 44 = 0$.

∴ $11x^2 - 242x + 2x - 44 = 0$ or $11x (x - 22) + 2 (x - 22) = 0$.

or $(x - 22) (11x + 2) = 0$ or $x = 22$.

∴   Speed of motorboat in still water = 22 kmph.

Ex. 6. *A man can row 40 km upstream and 55 km downstream in 13 hours. Also, he can row 30 km upstream and 44 km downstream in 10 hours. Find the speed of the man in still water and the speed of the current.*

Sol. Let, rate upstream = x km/hr & rate downstream = y km/hr.

Then, $\frac{40}{x} + \frac{55}{y} = 13$ ...(i)   and $\frac{30}{x} + \frac{44}{y} = 10$ ...(ii)

or $40u + 55v = 13$ ...(iii)   and $30u + 44v = 10$ ...(iv)

where $u = \frac{1}{x}$ and $v = \frac{1}{y}$.

On solving (iii) and (iv) we get : $u = \frac{1}{5}$ and $v = \frac{1}{11}$.

∴ $x = 5$ and $y = 11$.

∴   Rate in still water = $\frac{1}{2}$ (11 + 5) kmph = 8 kmph.

Rate of current = $\frac{1}{2}$ (11 – 5) kmph = 3 kmph.

EXERCISE 19

1. If a man can swim downstream at 6 kmph and upstream at 2 kmph, his speed in still water is :   **(Assistant Grade 1994)**
   (a) 4 km/hr   (b) 2 km/hr   (c) 3 km/hr   (d) 2.5 km/hr

2. A man can row upstream at 8 kmph and downstream at 13 kmph. The speed of the stream is :
   (a) 5 km/hr   (b) 2.5 km/hr   (c) 10.5 km/hr   (d) 4.2 km/hr

3. If Anshul rows 15 km upstream and 21 km downstream taking 3 hours each time, then the speed of the stream is :   **(C.B.I. 1993)**
   (a) 1 km/hr   (b) 1.5 km/hr   (c) 2 km/hr   (d) 12 km/hr

4. A man rows 750 m in 675 seconds against the stream and returns in $7\frac{1}{2}$ minutes. His rowing speed in still water is : **(Assistant Grade 1993)**
   (a) 3 km/hr   (b) 4 km/hr   (c) 5 km/hr   (d) 6 km/hr

5. A man rows 13 km upstream in 5 hours and also 28 km downstream in 5 hours. The velocity of the stream is :   **(Assistant Grade 1994)**
   (a) 1.5 km/hr   (b) 2 km/hr   (c) 2.5 km/hr   (d) 3 km/hr

6. If a boat goes 7 km upstream in 42 minutes and the speed of the stream is 3 kmph, then the speed of the boat in still water is :   **(C.B.I. 1993)**
   (a) 4.2 km/hr   (b) 9 km/hr   (c) 13 km/hr   (d) 21 km/hr

7. A man can row $9\frac{1}{3}$ kmph in still water and finds that it takes him thrice as much time to row up than as to row down the same distance in the river. The speed of the current is :   **(Central Excise & I. Tax 1992)**
   (a) $3\frac{1}{3}$ km/hr   (b) $3\frac{1}{9}$ km/hr   (c) $4\frac{2}{3}$ km/hr   (d) 14 km/hr

8. A man can row a boat at 10 kmph in still water. If the speed of the stream is 6 kmph, the time taken to row a distance of 80 km down the stream is :   **(Central Excise & I. Tax 1991)**
   (a) 8 hours   (b) 5 hours   (c) 10 hours   (d) 20 hours

9. A boat takes 4 hours for travelling downstream from point A to point B and coming back to point A upstream. If the velocity of the stream is 2 kmph and the speed of the boat in still water is 4 kmph, what is the distance between A and B ?   **(Bank P.O. 1991)**
   (a) 4 kms   (b) 6 km   (c) 8 km   (d) 9 km

10. If a man rows at 6 kmph in still water and 4.5 kmph against the current, then his rate along the current is :
    (a) 9.5 km/hr   (b) 7.5 km/hr   (c) 7 km/hr   (d) 5.25 km/hr

11. If a man's rate with the current is 11 kmph and the rate of the current is 1.5 kmph, then the man's rate against the current is :

(a) 8 km/hr   (b) 9.5 km/hr   (c) 9 km/hr   (d) 6.25 km/hr

12. Speed of a boat in standing water is 9 kmph and the speed of the stream is 1.5 kmph. A man rows to a place at a distance of 10.5 km and comes back to the starting point. The total time taken by him is :

    (a) 16 hours   (b) 18 hours   (c) 20 hours   (d) 24 hours

13. A boat moves upstream at the rate of 1 km in 10 minutes and downstream at the rate of 1 km in 6 minutes. The speed of the current is :

    (a) 1 km/hr   (b) 1.5 km/hr   (c) 2 km/hr   (d) 2.5 km/hr

14. River is running at 2 kmph. If takes a man twice as long to row up as to row down the river. The rate of the man in still water is :

    (a) 6 km/hr   (b) 4 km/hr   (c) 10 km/hr   (d) 8 km/hr

15. A man rows to a place 48 km distant and back in 14 hours. He finds that he can row 4 km with the stream in the same time as 3 km against the stream. The rate of the stream is :

    (a) 1 km/hr   (b) 1.8 km/hr   (c) 3.5 km/hr   (d) 1.5 km/hr

16. The current of stream runs at 1 kmph. A motor boat goes 35 km upstream and back again to the starting point in 12 hours. The speed of the motor boat in still water is :

    (a) 6 km/hr   (b) 7 km/hr   (c) 8 km/hr   (d) 8.5 km/hr

17. A boat covers 24 km upstream and 36 km downstream in 6 hours while it covers 36 km upstream and 24 km downstream in $6\frac{1}{2}$ hours. The velocity of the current is :

    (a) 1 km/hr   (b) 1.5 km/hr   (c) 2 km/hr   (d) 2.5 km/hr

18. A man can row three-quarters of a kilometre against the stream in $11\frac{1}{4}$ minutes and returns in $7\frac{1}{2}$ minutes. The speed of the man is still water is :

    (a) 2 km/hr   (b) 3 km/hr   (c) 4 km/hr   (d) 5 km/hr

19. The speed of a boat in still water is 15 km/hr and the rate of current is 3 km/hr. The distance travelled downstream in 12 minutes is :

    (a) 3.6 km   (b) 2.4 km   (c) 1.2 km   (d) 1.8 km

20. A man can row 5 kmph in still water. If the river is running at 1 kmph, it takes him 75 minutes to row to a place and back. How far is the place ?

    (a) 3 km   (b) 2.5 km   (c) 4 km   (d) 5 km

21. If a man rows at the rate of 5 kmph in still water and his rate against the current is 3.5 kmph, then the man's rate along the current is :

    (a) 4.25 kmph   (b) 6 kmph   (c) 6.5 kmph   (d) 8.5 kmph

ANSWERS

1. (*a*)   **2.** (*b*)   **3.** (*a*)   **4.** (*c*)   **5.** (*a*)   **6.** (*c*)   **7.** (*c*)   **8.** (*b*)   **9.** (*b*)
10. (*b*)   **11.** (*a*)   **12.** (*d*)   **13.** (*c*)   **14.** (*a*)   **15.** (*a*)   **16.** (*a*)   **17.** (*c*)   **18.** (*d*)
19. (*a*)   **20.** (*a*)   **21.** (*c*)

SOLUTIONS

1. Speed in still water $= \frac{1}{2}$ (6 + 2) kmph = 4 kmph.

2. Speed of stream $= \frac{1}{2}$ (13 – 8) kmph = 2.5 kmph.

3. Rate upstream $= \left(\frac{15}{3}\right)$ kmph = 5 kmph.

Rate downstream $= \left(\frac{21}{3}\right)$ kmph = 7 kmph.

∴ Speed of stream $= \frac{1}{2}$ (7 – 5) kmph = 1 kmph.

4. Rate upstream $= \left(\frac{750}{675}\right)$ m/sec $= \frac{10}{9}$ m/sec.

Rate downstream $= \left(\frac{750}{450}\right)$ m/sec $= \frac{5}{3}$ m/sec.

Rate in still water $= \frac{1}{2}\left(\frac{10}{9} + \frac{5}{3}\right)$ m/sec $= \frac{25}{18}$ m/sec.

$= \left(\frac{25}{18} \times \frac{18}{5}\right)$ kmph = 5 kmph.

5. Speed upstream $= \frac{13}{5}$ kmph.

Speed downstream $= \frac{28}{5}$ kmph.

Velocity of stream $= \frac{1}{2}\left(\frac{28}{5} - \frac{13}{5}\right)$ kmph = 1.5 kmph.

6. Rate upstream $= \left(\frac{7}{42} \times 60\right)$ kmph = 10 kmph.

Speed of stream = 3 kmph.
Let speed in still water be x km/hr.
Then, speed upstream = $(x - 3)$ km/hr.
∴ $x - 3 = 10$ or $x = 13$ kmph.

7. Let speed upstream be x kmph.
Then, speed downstream $= 3x$ kmph.

$\therefore$ Speed in still water $= \dfrac{1}{2}(3x + x)$ kmph $= 2x$ kmph.

$\therefore$ $2x = \dfrac{28}{3}$ $\Rightarrow$ $x = \dfrac{14}{3}$.

$\therefore$ Speed upstream $= \dfrac{14}{3}$ km/hr, Speed downstream $= 14$ km/hr.

$\therefore$ Speed of the current $= \dfrac{1}{2}\left(14 - \dfrac{14}{3}\right)$ km/hr $= \dfrac{14}{3}$ km/hr $= 4\dfrac{2}{3}$ km/hr.

8. Speed downstream $= (10 + 6)$ km/hr $= 16$ km/hr.
Time taken to cover 80 km downstream $= \left(\dfrac{80}{16}\right)$ hrs $= 5$ hrs.

9. Let the distance between A and B be x km.
Speed downstream $= 6$ kmph, speed upstream $= 2$ kmph.

$\therefore$ $\dfrac{x}{6} + \dfrac{x}{2} = 4$ $\Leftrightarrow$ $4x = 24$ $\Leftrightarrow$ $x = 6$.

$\therefore$ Distance $AB = 6$ km.

10. Let the rate of the stream be x kmph.
Then, rate against the current $= (6 - x)$ kmph.
$\therefore$ $6 - x = 4.5$ or $x = 1.5$.
$\therefore$ Rate of current $= 1.5$ kmph.
Rate along the current $= (6 + 1.5)$ kmph $= 7.5$ kmph.

11. Man's rate in still water $= (11 - 1.5)$ kmph $= 9.5$ kmph.
Man's rate against the current $= (9.5 - 1.5)$ kmph $= 8$ kmph.

12. Speed upstream $= 7.5$ kmph, speed downstream $= 10.5$ kmph.

$\therefore$ Total time taken $= \left(\dfrac{105}{7.5} + \dfrac{105}{10.5}\right)$ hrs $= 24$ hours.

13. Rate upstream $= \left(\dfrac{1}{10} \times 60\right)$ km/hr $= 6$ km/hr.

Rate downstream $= \left(\dfrac{1}{6} \times 60\right)$ km/hr $= 10$ km/hr.

Rate of the current $= \dfrac{1}{2}(10 - 6)$ km/hr $= 2$ km/hr.

14. Let rate upstream be x kmph.
Then, rate downstream $= 2x$ kmph.

Rate of current $= \dfrac{1}{2}(2x - x)$ kmph $= \dfrac{x}{2}$ kmph.

$\therefore$ $\dfrac{x}{2} = 2$ or $x = 4$.

$\therefore$ Rate upstream $= 4$ kmph, Rate downstream $= 8$ kmph.

Rate in still water $= \frac{1}{2}(8+4)$ kmph $= 6$ kmph.

15. Suppose he moves 4 km downstream in x hours. Then, speed downstream $= \left(\frac{4}{x}\right)$ km/hr, speed upstream $= \left(\frac{3}{x}\right)$ km/hr.

∴ $\frac{48}{(4/x)} + \frac{48}{(3/x)} = 14$ or $x = \frac{1}{2}$.

∴ Speed downstream = 8 km/hr, speed upstream = 6 km/hr.

Rate of the stream $= \frac{1}{2}(8-6)$ km/hr = 1 km/hr.

16. Let the speed in still water be x kmph.
Then, speed upstream $= (x-1)$ kmph,
speed downstream $= (x+1)$ kmph.

∴ $\frac{35}{x-1} + \frac{35}{x+1} = 12 \Leftrightarrow 6x^2 - 35x - 6 = 0$

∴ $(x-6)(6x+1) = 0$ or $x = 6$.

Hence, the speed in still water = 6 kmph.

17. Let rate upstream $= x$ kmph and rate downstream $= y$ kmph.

Then $\frac{24}{x} + \frac{36}{y} = 6$ ...(i) and $\frac{36}{x} + \frac{24}{y} = \frac{13}{2}$ ...(ii)

Adding (i) and (ii), $60\left(\frac{1}{x} + \frac{1}{y}\right) = \frac{25}{2}$ or $\frac{1}{x} + \frac{1}{y} = \frac{5}{24}$ ...(iii)

Subtracting (i) from (ii), $12\left(\frac{1}{x} - \frac{1}{y}\right) = \frac{1}{2}$ or $\frac{1}{x} - \frac{1}{y} = \frac{1}{24}$ ...(iv)

Adding (iii) and (iv), we get $\frac{2}{x} = \frac{6}{24}$ or $x = 8$.

$\frac{1}{8} + \frac{1}{y} = \frac{5}{24} \Leftrightarrow \frac{1}{y} = \left(\frac{5}{24} - \frac{1}{8}\right) = \frac{1}{12} \Leftrightarrow y = 12$.

∴ Speed upstream = 8 kmph, speed downstream = 12 kmph.

∴ Rate of the current $= \frac{1}{2}(12-8)$ kmph = 2 kmph.

18. Speed upstream $= \left(\frac{3}{4} \times \frac{4}{45} \times 60\right)$ kmph = 4 kmph.

Speed downstream $= \left(\frac{3}{4} \times \frac{2}{15} \times 60\right)$ kmph = 6 kmph.

Speed in still water $= \frac{1}{2}(6+4)$ kmph = 5 kmph.

19. Speed downstream = $(15 + 3)$ kmph = 18 kmph.

Distance travelled = $\left(18 \times \dfrac{12}{60}\right)$ km = 3.6 km.

20. Speed downstream = $(5 + 1)$ km/hr = 6 km/hr.

Speed upstream = $(5 - 1)$ km/hr = 4 km/hr.

Let the required distance be x km.

Then, $\dfrac{x}{6} + \dfrac{x}{4} = \dfrac{75}{60}$ or $2x + 3x = 15$ or $x = 3$.

∴ Required distance = 3 km.

21. Let the rate along the current be x kmph.

Then, $\dfrac{1}{2}(x + 3.5) = 5$ or $x = 6.5$ kmph.

---

20. Alligation or Mixture

Alligation : It is the rule that enables us to find the ratio in which two or more ingredients at the given price must be mixed to produce a mixture at a given price.

Mean Price : The cost price of a unit quantity of the mixture is called the mean price.

Rule of Alligation : If two ingredients are mixed, then :

$$\left(\frac{\text{Quantity of cheaper}}{\text{Quantity of dearer}}\right) = \frac{\text{(C.P. of dearer)} - \text{(Mean price)}}{\text{(Mean price)} - \text{(C.P. of cheaper)}}$$

We represent as under :

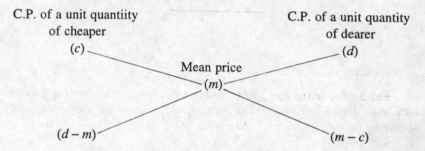

C.P. of a unit quantiity of cheaper
(c)

C.P. of a unit quantity of dearer
(d)

Mean price
(m)

(d – m)

(m – c)

∴ **(Cheaper quantity) : (Dearer quantity)** $= (d - m) : (m - c)$.

Solved Problems

Ex. 1. *In what ratio must tea at Rs. 62 per kg be mixed with tea at Rs. 72 per kg so that the mixture must be worth Rs. 64.50 per kg ?*

Sol. By the rule of alligation, we have :

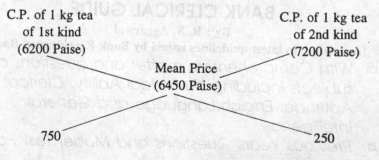

C.P. of 1 kg tea of 1st kind
(6200 Paise)

C.P. of 1 kg tea of 2nd kind
(7200 Paise)

Mean Price
(6450 Paise)

750

250

∴ (Tea of 1st kind) : (Tea of 2nd king) = 750 : 250 = 3 : 1.

Ex. 2. *In what ratio must water be mixed with milk to gain 20% by selling the mixture at cost price ?*

Sol. Let C.P. of milk be Re 1. per litre.

Then, S.P. of 1 litre of mixture = Re. 1.

Gain obtained = 20%

$\therefore$ C.P. of 1 litre of mix. $= \left(\dfrac{100}{120} \times 1\right) =$ Re. $\dfrac{5}{6}$.

By the rule of alligation, we have :

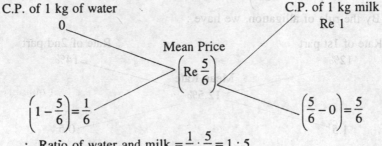

C.P. of 1 kg of water   C.P. of 1 kg milk
0   Re 1

Mean Price

$\left(\text{Re } \dfrac{5}{6}\right)$

$\left(1 - \dfrac{5}{6}\right) = \dfrac{1}{6}$ $\left(\dfrac{5}{6} - 0\right) = \dfrac{5}{6}$

$\therefore$ Ratio of water and milk $= \dfrac{1}{6} : \dfrac{5}{6} = 1 : 5$.

Ex. 3. *How many kgs. of rice costing Rs. 8.00 per kg must be mixed with 36 kg of rice costing Rs. 5.40 per kg so that 20% gain may be obtained by selling the mixture at Rs. 7.20 per kg ?*

Sol. S.P. of 1 kg mix. = Rs. 7.20, Gain = 20%.

$\therefore$ C.P. of 1 kg mix. = Rs. $\left(7.20 \times \dfrac{100}{120}\right)$ = Rs. 6.

By the rule of alligation, we have :

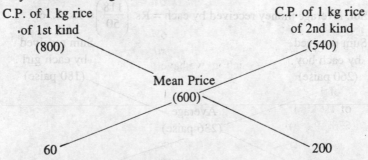

C.P. of 1 kg rice   C.P. of 1 kg rice
of 1st kind   of 2nd kind
(800)   (540)

Mean Price
(600)

60   200

Rice of 1st kind : Rice of 2nd kind = 60 : 200 = 3 : 10.

Let x kg of rice of 1st kind be mixed with 36 kg of rice of 2nd kind. Then,

     $3 : 10 = x : 36$ or $10x = 3 \times 36$ or $x = 10.8$ kg.

Ex. 4. *A man lent out Rs. 9600 partly at 12% and partly at 14% simple interest. His total income after $1\frac{1}{2}$ years was Rs. 1800. Find the sum lent at different rates.*

Sol. Total interest on Rs. 9600 for $1\frac{1}{2}$ years = Rs. 1800.

$$\therefore \text{ Rate} = \left(\frac{100 \times 1800}{9600 \times \frac{3}{2}}\right)\% = 12.5\%$$

By the rule of alligation, we have :

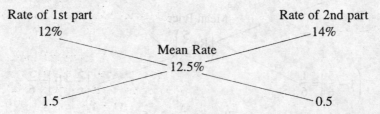

Rate of 1st part
12%

Rate of 2nd part
14%

Mean Rate
12.5%

1.5   0.5

$\therefore$ 1st part : 2nd part = 1.5 : 0.5 = 15 : 5 = 3 : 1.

$\therefore$ First part = Rs. $\left(9600 \times \frac{3}{4}\right)$ = Rs. 7200.

Second part = Rs. (9600 – 7200) = Rs. 2400.

Ex. 5. *A sum of Rs. 118 was divided among 50 boys and girls such that each boy received Rs. 2.60 and each girl Rs. 1.80. Find the number of boys and girls.*

Sol. Average money received by each = Rs. $\left(\frac{118}{50}\right)$ = Rs. 2.36.

Sum received
by each boy
(260 paise)

Sum received
by each girl
(180 paise)

Average
(236 paise)

56   24

$\therefore$ Ratio of number of boys and girls = 56 : 24 = 7 : 3.

$\therefore$ Number of boys = $\left(50 \times \frac{7}{10}\right)$ = 35.

Number of girls = (50 – 35) = 15.

Ex. 6. *A man travelled a distance of 90 km in 9 hours partly on foot at 8 kmph and partly on bicycle at 17 kmph. Find the distance travelled on foot.*

Sol. Average distance covered in 1 hour $= \left(\dfrac{90}{9}\right)$ km = 10 km.

By the rule of alligation, we have :

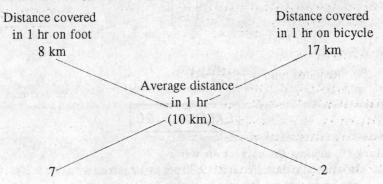

Distance covered
in 1 hr on foot
8 km

Distance covered
in 1 hr on bicycle
17 km

Average distance
in 1 hr
(10 km)

7   2

∴ Ratio of times taken = 7 : 2

Thus, out of 9 hours, he took 7 hours on foot.

∴ Distance covered on foot = (8 × 7) km = 56 km.

Ex. 7. *Two vessels A and B contain spirit and water mixed in the ratio 5 : 2 and 7 : 6 respectively. Find the ratio in which these mixtures be mixed to obtain a new mixture in vessel C containing spirit and water in the ratio 8 : 5.*

Sol. Let the C.P. of spirit be Re 1 per litre.

Spirit in 1 litre mix. of $A = \dfrac{5}{7}$ litre.

Spirit in 1 litre mix. of $B = \dfrac{7}{13}$ litre

Spirit in 1 litre mix. of $C = \dfrac{8}{13}$ litre

∴ C.P. of 1 lit. mix. in $A =$ Re $\dfrac{5}{7}$

C.P. of 1 lit. mix. in $B =$ Re $\dfrac{7}{13}$

Mean Price = Re $\dfrac{8}{13}$

By the rule of alligation, we have :

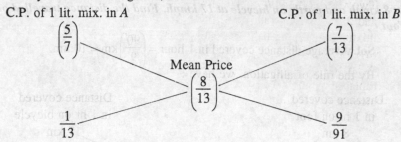

C.P. of 1 lit. mix. in A
$$\left(\frac{5}{7}\right)$$

C.P. of 1 lit. mix. in B
$$\left(\frac{7}{13}\right)$$

Mean Price
$$\left(\frac{8}{13}\right)$$

$\dfrac{1}{13}$

$\dfrac{9}{91}$

∴ Required ratio $= \dfrac{1}{13} : \dfrac{9}{91} = 7 : 9$.

EXERCISE 20

Mark (√) against the correct answer :

1. In what ratio must rice at Rs. 9.30 per kg be mixed with rice at Rs. 10.80 per kg so that the mixture be worth Rs. 10 per kg ?
    (*a*) 7 : 8   (*b*) 8 : 7   (*c*) 31 : 36   (*d*) 36 : 31

2. In what ratio must wheat at Rs. 3.20 per kg be mixed with wheat at Rs. 2.90 per kg so that the mixture be worth Rs. 3.08 per kg ?
    (*a*) 4 : 3   (*b*) 3 : 4   (*c*) 2 : 3   (*d*) 3 : 2

3. How many kilograms of sugar costing Rs. 9 per kg must be mixed with 27 kg of sugar costing Rs. 7 per kg so that there may be a gain of 10% by selling the mixture at Rs. 9.24 per kg ?
    (*a*) 54 kg   (*b*) 63 kg   (*c*) 36 kg   (*d*) 42 kg

4. In what ratio must water be mixed with milk to gain $16\frac{2}{3}\%$ on selling the mixture at cost price ?
    (*a*) 2 : 3   (*b*) 4 : 3   (*c*) 6 : 1   (*d*) 1 : 6

5. Two vessels A and B contain milk and water mixed in the ratio 8 : 5 and 5 : 2 respectively. The ratio in which these two mixtures be mixed to get a new mixture containing milk and water in the ratio 9 : 4 ?
    (*a*) 2 : 7   (*b*) 5 : 2   (*c*) 3 : 5   (*d*) 5 : 7

6. In what ratio must water be mixed with milk costing Rs. 12 per litre to obtain a mixture worth of Rs. 8 per litre ?
    (*a*) 3 : 2   (*b*) 2 : 3   (*c*) 1 : 2   (*d*) 2 : 1

7. A sum of Rs. 4000 is lent out in two parts, one at 8% simple interest and the other at 10% simple interest. If the annual interest is Rs. 352, the sum lent at 8% is :
    (*a*) Rs. 1600   (*b*) Rs. 2400   (*c*) Rs. 1800   (*d*) Rs. 2800

8. A merchant has 1000 kg of sugar, part of which he sells at 8% profit and the rest at 18% profit. He gains 14% on the whole. The quantity sold at 18% pforit is :

(a) 640 kg   (b) 560 kg   (c) 600 kg   (d) 400 kg

9. Two vessels A and B contain milk and water mixed in the ratio 4 : 3 and 2 : 3. In what ratio must these mixtures be mixed to form a new mixture containing half milk and half water ?

(a) 7 : 5   (b) 1 : 2   (c) 2 : 1   (d) 6 : 5

10. A jar full of whisky contains 40% alcohol. A part of this whisky is replaced by another containing 19% alcohol and now the percentage of alcohol was found to be 26%. The quantity of whisky replaced is :

(a) $\dfrac{1}{3}$ (b) $\dfrac{2}{3}$ (c) $\dfrac{2}{5}$ (d) $\dfrac{3}{5}$

(Hotel Management 1991)

11. 729 ml of mixture contains milk and water in the ratio 7 : 2. How much more water is to be added to get a new mixture containing milk and water in the ratio 7 : 3 ? **(Railways 1992)**

(a) 79 ml   (b) 81 ml   (c) 72 ml   (d) 91 ml

12. A sum of Rs. 312 was divided among 100 boys and girls in such a way that each boy gets Rs. 3.60 and each girl Rs. 2.40. The number of girls is :

(a) 40   (b) 60   (c) 35   (d) 65

13. A man covered a distance of 2000 km in 18 hours partly by bus at 72 kmph and partly by train at 160 kmph. The distance covered by bus is :

(a) 1280 km   (b) 720 km   (c) 860 km   (d) 640 km

14. A sum of Rs. 36.90 is made up of 180 coins which are either 10 paise coins or 25 paise coins. The number of 10 paise coins is :

(a) 126   (b) 54   (c) 120   (d) 60

15. A dishonest milkman professes to sell his milk at cost price but he mixes it with water and thereby gains 25%. The percentage of water in the mixture is :

(a) 25%   (b) 20%   (c) $6\dfrac{1}{4}$%   (d) 4%

16. A mixture of 20 kg of spirit and water contains 10% water. How much water must be added to this mixture to raise the percentage of water to 25% ?

(a) 4 kg   (b) 5 kg   (c) 8 kg   (d) 30 kg

17. A container contains 40 kg of milk. From this container 4 kg of milk was taken out and replaced by water. This process was repeated further two times. How much milk is now contained by the container ?

(a) 27.36 kg   (b) 29.16 kg   (c) 28 kg   (d) 26.34 kg

18. A can contains a mixture of two liquids A and B in the ratio 7 : 5. When 9 litres of mixture are drawn off and the can is filled with B, the ratio of A and B becomes 7 : 9. How many litres of liquid A was contained by the can initially ? **(Railways 1988)**

(a) 25   (b) 21   (c) 20   (d) 10

ANSWERS

1. (b)   **2.** (d)   **3.** (b)   **4.** (d)   **5.** (a)   **6.** (c)   **7.** (b)   **8.** (c)   **9.** (a)
10. (b)   **11.** (b)   **12.** (a)   **13.** (b)   **14.** (b)   **15.** (b)   **16.** (a)   **17.** (b)   **18.** (b)

SOLUTIONS

1.   By the rule of alligation :

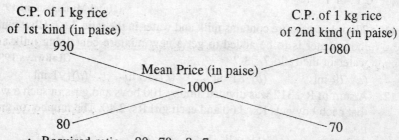

∴ Required ratio = 80 : 70 = 8 : 7.

2.   By the rule of alligation :

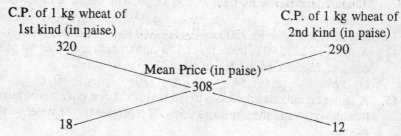

∴ Required ratio = 18 : 12 = 3 : 2.

3.   S.P. of 1 kg mix. = Rs. 9.24, Gain = 10%.

∴ C.P. of 1 kg mix. = Rs. $\left(\dfrac{100}{110} \times 9.24\right)$ = Rs. 8.40.

By the rule of alligation :

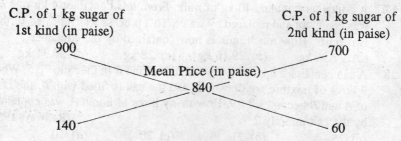

∴ Ratio of quantities of 1st & 2nd kind = 140 : 60 = 7 : 3.

Let x kg of sugar of 1st kind be mixed with 27 kg of the second kind. Then : $7 : 3 :: x : 27$ or $x = \left(\dfrac{7 \times 27}{3} \right) = 63$ kg.

4. Let C.P. of 1 litre milk be Re 1.

S.P. of 1 litre of mix. = Re. 1, Gain = $\dfrac{50}{3}$ %.

$\therefore$ C.P. of 1 litre of mix. = $\left(100 \times \dfrac{3}{350} \times 1 \right) = $ Re $\dfrac{6}{7}$.

C.P. of 1 litre   C.P. of 1 litre
of water (in Rs.)   of milk (in Rs.)

```
      0                                              1
        \        Mean Price (in Rs.)        /
          \            6                  /
            \          7                /
      1                                        6
      7                                        7
```

$\therefore$ Ratio of water and milk = $\dfrac{1}{7} : \dfrac{6}{7} = 1 : 6$.

5. Milk in 1 litre of $A = \dfrac{8}{13}$.

Milk in 1 litre of $B = \dfrac{5}{7}$

Milk in 1 litre of final mix. = $\dfrac{9}{13}$.

Let cost of 1 litre milk be Re. 1.

C.P. of 1 litre mix. in $A = $ Re $\dfrac{8}{13}$

C.P. of 1 litre mix. in $B = $ Re $\dfrac{5}{7}$

Mean Price = Re $\dfrac{9}{13}$.

$\therefore$ By the rule of alligation, we have :

C.P. of 1 litre mix. in A C.P. of 1 litre mix. in B

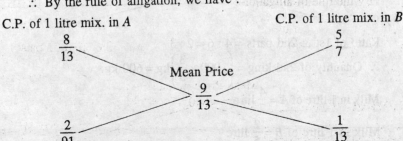

$\therefore$ Required ratio $= \dfrac{2}{91} : \dfrac{1}{13} = 2 : 7$.

6. By the rule of alligation, we have :

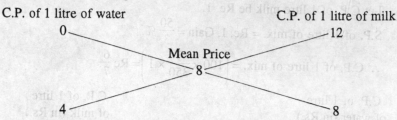

C.P. of 1 litre of water

C.P. of 1 litre of milk

0

12

Mean Price

8

4

8

$\therefore$ Water : Milk $= 4 : 8 = 1 : 2$.

7. Total interest on Rs. 4000 in 1 year = Rs. 352.

$\therefore$ Average rate $= \left(\dfrac{352 \times 100}{4000 \times 1} \right) = 8.8\%$

$\therefore$ By the rule of alligation, we have :

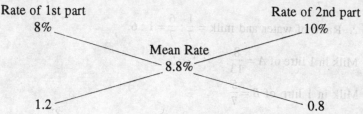

Rate of 1st part

Rate of 2nd part

8%

10%

Mean Rate

8.8%

1.2

0.8

$\therefore$ Rate of 1st & 2nd parts $= 1.2 : 0.8 = 3 : 2$.

$\therefore$ First part $= $ Rs. $\left(4000 \times \dfrac{3}{5} \right) = $ Rs. 2400.

8.

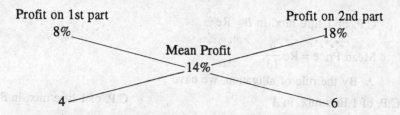

Profit on 1st part

Profit on 2nd part

8%

18%

Mean Profit

14%

4

6

Ratio of 1st & 2nd parts $= 4 : 6 = 2 : 3$.

$\therefore$ Quantity of 2nd king $= \left(1000 \times \dfrac{3}{5} \right)$ kg $= 600$ kg.

9. Milk in 1 litre of $A = \dfrac{4}{7}$ litre,

Milk in 1 litre of $B = \dfrac{2}{5}$ litre

Milk in 1 litre of final mix. $= \dfrac{1}{2}$ litre.

Let cost of 1 litre of milk be Re 1.

C.P. of 1 litre of $A =$ Re $\dfrac{4}{7}$

C.P. of 1 litre of $B =$ Re $\dfrac{2}{5}$

Mean price $=$ Re $\dfrac{1}{2}$.

By the rule of alligation :

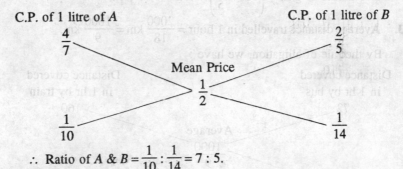

C.P. of 1 litre of A C.P. of 1 litre of B

$\dfrac{4}{7}$ $\dfrac{2}{5}$

Mean Price

$\dfrac{1}{2}$

$\dfrac{1}{10}$ $\dfrac{1}{14}$

$\therefore$ Ratio of A & $B = \dfrac{1}{10} : \dfrac{1}{14} = 7 : 5.$

10.

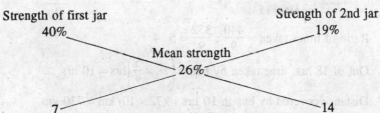

Strength of first jar   Strength of 2nd jar

40%   19%

Mean strength

26%

7   14

$\therefore$ Ratio of 1st & 2nd qualities $= 7 : 14 = 1 : 2.$

$\therefore$ Required quantity replaced $= \dfrac{2}{3}.$

11.   Milk $= \left(729 \times \dfrac{7}{9}\right)$ ml $= 567$ ml., Water $= (729 - 567)$ ml $= 162$ ml.

Let water to be added be x ml.

$\therefore \dfrac{567}{162 + x} = \dfrac{7}{3}$ or $1701 = 1134 + 7x$ or $x = 81$ ml.

12.   Average money received by each $=$ Rs. $\left(\dfrac{292}{100}\right) =$ Rs. 2.92.

By rule of alligation :

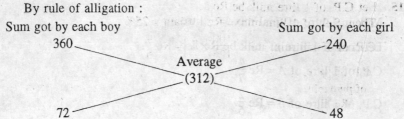

Sum got by each boy   Sum got by each girl
        360   240

                            Average
                             (312)

        72   48

∴ Ratio of boys and girls = 72 : 48 = 3 : 2.

∴ Number of girls = $\left(100 \times \dfrac{2}{5}\right)$ = 40.

13. Average distance travelled in 1 hour = $\dfrac{2000}{18}$ km = $\dfrac{1000}{9}$ km.

By the rule of alligation, we have :

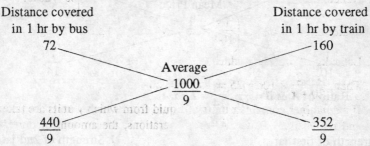

Distance covered   Distance covered
in 1 hr by bus   in 1 hr by train
        72   160

                            Average
                             $\dfrac{1000}{9}$

        $\dfrac{440}{9}$ $\dfrac{352}{9}$

Ratio of times taken = $\dfrac{440}{9} : \dfrac{352}{9}$ = 5 : 4

Out of 18 hrs, time taken by bus = $\left(18 \times \dfrac{5}{9}\right)$ hrs = 10 hrs.

Distance covered by bus in 10 hrs = (72 × 10) km = 720 km.

14. Average value of one coin = $\dfrac{3690}{180}$ paise = $\dfrac{41}{2}$ paise

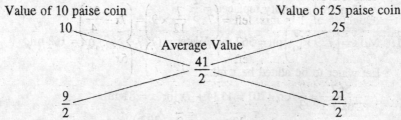

Value of 10 paise coin   Value of 25 paise coin
        10   25

                        Average Value
                             $\dfrac{41}{2}$

        $\dfrac{9}{2}$ $\dfrac{21}{2}$

∴ Ratio of 10 paise & 25 paise coins = $\dfrac{9}{2} : \dfrac{21}{2}$ = 3 : 7.

Number of 10 paise coins = $\left(180 \times \dfrac{3}{10}\right)$ = 54.

15. Let C.P. of 1 litre milk be Re 1.

Then, S.P. of 1 litre mix. = Re 1, Gain = 25%

C.P. of 1 litre mix. $= \text{Re}\left(\dfrac{100}{125} \times 1\right) = \text{Re } \dfrac{4}{5}$.

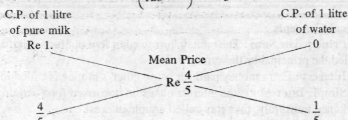

C.P. of 1 litre
of pure milk
Re 1.

C.P. of 1 litre
of water
0

Mean Price

Re $\dfrac{4}{5}$

$\dfrac{4}{5}$

$\dfrac{1}{5}$

$\therefore$ Milk : Water $= \dfrac{4}{5} : \dfrac{1}{5} = 4 : 1$.

Hence, percentage of water in the mix. $= \left(\dfrac{1}{5} \times 100\right)\% = 20\%$.

16. Water in given mix. $= \left(\dfrac{10}{100} \times 20\right)$ kg $= 2$ kg & spirit $= 18$ kg.

Let x kg of water be added.

Then, $\dfrac{x+2}{20+x} \times 100 = 25 \Rightarrow 4x + 8 = 20 + x$ or $x = 4$ kg.

17. If a container contains x units of liquid from which y units are taken out and replaced by water. After n operations, the amount of pure liquid

$$= \left[x\left(1 - \dfrac{y}{x}\right)^{n}\right] \text{ units.}$$

$\therefore$ Amount of milk left $= 40\left(1 - \dfrac{4}{40}\right)^{3}$ kg $= \left(40 \times \dfrac{9}{10} \times \dfrac{9}{10} \times \dfrac{9}{10}\right)$ kg.

$= 29.16$ kg.

18. Suppose the can initially contains $7x$ and $5x$ litres of mixtures A and B respectively.

Quantity of A in mix. left $= \left(7x - \dfrac{7}{12} \times 9\right) = \left(7x - \dfrac{21}{4}\right)$

Quantity of B in mix. left $= \left(5x - \dfrac{5}{12} \times 9\right) = \left(5x - \dfrac{15}{4}\right)$.

$\therefore \dfrac{\left(7x - \dfrac{21}{4}\right)}{5x - \dfrac{15}{4} + 9} = \dfrac{7}{9}$ or $\dfrac{28x - 21}{20x + 21} = \dfrac{7}{9}$

or $252x - 189 = 140x + 147$ or $112x = 336$ or $x = 3$.

$\therefore$ Can contained 21 litres of A.

21. Simple Interest

General Concepts :

Principal or Sum : The money borrowed or lent out for a certain period is called the principal or the sum.

Interest : Extra money paid for using other's money is called interest.

Simple Interest : If the interest on a sum borrowed for a certain period is reckoned uniformly, then it is called simple interest.

FORMULAE : Let Principal $= P$, Rate $= R\%$ per annum and Time $= T$ years. Then,

(i) $\text{S.I.} = \left(\dfrac{P \times R \times T}{100} \right)$.

(ii) $P = \left(\dfrac{100 \times \text{S.I.}}{R \times T} \right)$, $R = \left(\dfrac{100 \times \text{S.I.}}{P \times T} \right)$ and $T = \left(\dfrac{100 \times \text{S.I.}}{P \times R} \right)$

Solved Problems

Ex.1 *Find :*

(i) *S.I. on Rs 68000 at $16\frac{2}{3}$ % per annum for 9 months.*

(ii) *S.I. on Rs 6250 at 14% per annum for 146 days.*

(ii) *S.I. on Rs 3000 at 18% per annum for the period from 4th Feb 1995 to 18th April 1995.*

Sol. (i) $P = 68000$, $R = \dfrac{50}{3}$ % p.a. & $T = \dfrac{9}{12}$ year $= \dfrac{3}{4}$ years.

$\therefore$ $\text{S.I.} = \left(\dfrac{P \times R \times T}{100} \right)$

$= \text{Rs} \left(68000 \times \dfrac{50}{3} \times \dfrac{3}{4} \times \dfrac{1}{100} \right) = \text{Rs } 8500$.

(ii) $P = \text{Rs } 6250$, $R = 14$ % p.a. & $T = \left(\dfrac{146}{365} \right)$ year $= \dfrac{2}{5}$ year.

$\therefore$ $\text{S.I.} = \text{Rs} \left(6250 \times 14 \times \dfrac{2}{5} \times \dfrac{1}{100} \right) = \text{Rs } 350$.

(iii) Time $= (24 + 31 + 18)$ days $= 73$ days $= \dfrac{1}{5}$ year.

$P = \text{Rs } 3000$ and $R = 18$ % p.a.

$\therefore$ $\text{S.I.} = \text{Rs} \left(3000 \times 18 \times \dfrac{1}{5} \times \dfrac{1}{100} \right) = \text{Rs } 108$.

Remark : The day on which money is deposited is not counted while the day on which money is withdrawn is counted.

Ex. 2. *A sum at simple interest at* $13\frac{1}{2}$ *% per annum amounts to Rs 2502.50 after 4 years. Find the sum.*

Sol. Let sum be x. Then,

$$\text{S.I.} = \left(x \times \frac{27}{2} \times 4 \times \frac{1}{100}\right) = \frac{27x}{50}.$$

$$\therefore \quad \text{Amount} = \left(x + \frac{27x}{50}\right) = \frac{77x}{50}.$$

$$\therefore \quad \frac{77x}{50} = 2502.50 \quad \text{or} \quad x = \frac{2502.50 \times 50}{77} = 1625.$$

Hence, sum = Rs 1625.

Ex. 3. *A certain sum of money amounts to Rs 1008 in 2 years and to Rs 1164 in* $3\frac{1}{2}$ *years. Find the sum and the rate of interest.*

Sol. S.I. for $1\frac{1}{2}$ years = Rs $(1164 - 1008)$ = Rs 156.

S.I. for 2 years = Rs $\left(156 \times \frac{2}{3} \times 2\right)$ = Rs 208.

$\therefore$ Principal = Rs $(1008 - 208)$ = *Rs* 800.

Now, $P = 800$, $T = 2$ and S.I. $= 208$.

$$\therefore \quad \text{Rate} = \left(\frac{100 \times \text{S.I.}}{P \times T}\right) = \left(\frac{100 \times 208}{800 \times 2}\right) \% = 13\%.$$

Ex. 4. *At what rate percent per annum will a sum of money double in 8 years ?*

Sol. Let principal $= P$. Then, S.I. $= P$ and Time $= 8$ years.

$$\therefore \quad \text{Rate} = \left(\frac{100 \times P}{P \times 8}\right) \% = 12.5\% \text{ per annum.}$$

Ex. 5. *A sum was put at simple interest at a certain rate for 3 years. Had it been put at 2% higher rate, it would have fetched Rs 360 more. Find the sum.*

Sol. Let, sum $= P$ and original rate $= R$. Then,

$$\frac{P \times (R+2) \times 3}{100} - \frac{P \times R \times 3}{100} = 360$$

or $3PR + 6P - 3PR = 36000$ or $6P = 36000$ or $P = 6000$.

Hence, sum = Rs 6000.

Ex. 6. *Simple interest on a certain sum is* $\frac{16}{25}$ *of the sum. Find the rate percent and time, if both are numerically equal.*

Sol. Let sum $= x$. Then, S.I. $= \frac{16x}{25}$.

Let rate $= R\%$ and time $= R$ years.

$$\therefore \ \frac{x \times R \times R}{100} = \frac{16x}{25} \quad \text{or} \quad R^2 = \frac{1600}{25} \quad R = \frac{40}{5} = 8.$$

∴ Rate = 8% and Time = 8 years.

Ex. 7. *A man borrowed Rs 24000 from two money lenders. For one loan, he paid 15% per annum and for the other 18% per annum. At the end of one year, he paid Rs 4050. How much did he borrow at each rate ?*

Sol. Let the sum at 15% be Rs x and that at 18% be Rs $(24000 - x)$.

$$\therefore \ \frac{x \times 15 \times 1}{100} + \frac{(24000 - x) \times 18 \times 1}{100} = 4050 .$$

or $15x + 432000 - 18x = 405000$ or $x = 9000$.

∴ Money borrowed at 15% = Rs 9000.

Money borrowed at 18% = Rs 15000.

Ex. 8. *What annual instalment will discharge a debt of Rs 1092 due in 3 years at 12% simple interest ?*

Sol. Let each instalment be Rs. x. then,

$$\left(x + \frac{x \times 12 \times 1}{100}\right) + \left(x + \frac{x \times 12 \times 2}{100}\right) + x = 1092 .$$

or $\dfrac{28x}{25} + \dfrac{31x}{25} + x = 1092$ or $(28x + 31x + 25x) = (1092 \times 25)$

or $x = \left(\dfrac{1092 \times 25}{84}\right) = 325 .$

∴ Each instalment = Rs 325.

EXERCISE 21

1. At the rate of 6% p.a. simple interest, a sum of Rs. 2500 will earn how much interest by the end of 5 years ? **(Bank P.O. 1992)**
    (*a*) Rs. 150   (*b*) Rs. 700   (*c*) Rs. 750   (*d*) Rs. 3250

2. A person borrowed Rs. 500 at the rate of 5% per annum S.I. What amount will he pay to clear the debt after 4 years ?
    (*a*) Rs. 200   (*b*) Rs. 550   (*c*) Rs. 600   (*d*) Rs. 700
    (Assistant Grade 1994)

3. If *A* lends Rs. 3500 to *B* at 10% p.a. and *B* lends the same sum to *C* at 11.5% p.a., then the gain of *B* (in Rs.) in a period of 3 years is :
    (*a*) 107.50   (*b*) 115.50   (*c*) 157.50   (*d*) 177.50
    (Clerk's Grade 1993)

4. In what time will Rs. 500 give Rs. 50 as interest at the rate of 5% p.a. S.I. ? **(I. Tax 1992)**
    (*a*) 2 years   (*b*) $2\frac{1}{2}$ years   (*c*) 3 years   (*d*) 4 years

5. Avinash borrowed Rs. 5000 from Sanjay at simple interest. After 3 years, Sanjay got Rs. 300 more than what he had given to Avinash. What was the rate of interest per annum ?   **(Bank P.O. 1993)**

(a) 2%   (b) 5%   (c) 8%   (d) 10%

6. Ashok took a loan of Rs. 15000 for 3 years at simple interest. If the total interest paid is R. 2700, what is the rate of interest per annum ?

(a) 5.4%   (b) 6%   (c) 9%   (d) 18%

(Bank P.O. 1993)

7. Rakesh took a loan for 6 years at the rate of 5% p.a. S.I. If the total interest paid was Rs. 1230, the principal was :   **(S.B.I.P.O. 1987)**

(a) Rs. 4100   (b) Rs. 4920   (c) Rs. 5000   (d) Rs. 5300

8. How much should a person lend at simple rate of interest of 15% in order to have Rs. 784 at the end of $1\frac{1}{2}$ years ?

(a) Rs. 640   (b) Rs. 620   (c) Rs. 610   (d) Rs. 680

9. Satish took a loan at 10% p.a. S.I. After 4 years, he returned the principal along with the interest. If he returns in all Rs. 3500, what is the principal amount ?   **(Bank P.O. 1988)**

(a) Rs. 3250   (b) Rs. 2500   (c) Rs. 3150   (d) Rs. 2100

10. Rs. 800 amounts to Rs. 920 in 3 years at simple interest. If the interest rate is increased by 3%, it would amount to how much ?

(a) Rs. 992   (b) Rs. 1056   (c) Rs. 1112   (d) Rs. 1182

(Bank P.O. 1991)

11. The simple interest at x% for x years will be Rs. x on a sum of :

(a) Rs. x   (b) Rs. 100x   (c) Rs. $\left(\dfrac{100}{x}\right)$ (d) Rs. $\left(\dfrac{100}{x^2}\right)$

12. If Rs. 64 amount to Rs. 83.20 in 2 years, what will Rs. 86 amount to in 4 years at the same rate percent per annum ?

(a) Rs. 127.40 (b) Rs. 124.70 (c) Rs. 114.80 (d) Rs. 137.60

13. The simple interest on a sum of money at 5% is Rs. 48 for 4 years. The simple interest on the same sum for 5 years at 4% will be :

(a) Rs. 40   (b) Rs. 48   (c) Rs. 50   (d) Rs. 60

14. A certain sum of money lent out at S.I. amounts to Rs. 690 in 3 years and Rs. 750 in 5 years. The sum lent is :   **(U.D.C. 1993)**

(a) Rs. 400   (b) Rs. 450   (c) Rs. 500   (d) Rs. 600

15. A certain sum of money at simple interest amounts to Rs. 1012 in $2\frac{1}{2}$ years and to Rs. 1067.20 in 4 years. The rate of interest per annum is :

(a) 2.5%   (b) 3%   (c) 4%   (d) 5%

16. A sum of money at simple interest amounts to Rs. 2240 in 2 years and to Rs. 2600 in 5 years. What is the principal amount ?

(*a*) Rs. 1520   (*b*) Rs. 1880   (*c*) Rs. 2120   (*d*) None

(Bank P.O. 1989)

17. For how many years should Rs. 600 be invested at 10% p.a. in order to earn the same simple interest as is earned by investing Rs. 800 at 12% p.a. for 5 years ?
    (*a*) 6   (*b*) 8   (*c*) 12   (*d*) 16

18. The simple interest on a certain sum of money at the rate of 5% p.a. for 8 years is Rs. 840. At what rate of interest the same amount of interest can be received on the same sum after 5 years ?   (S.B.I.P.O. 1986)
    (*a*) 6%   (*b*) 8%   (*c*) 9%   (*d*) 10%

19. The simple interest on Rs. 10 for 4 months at the rate of 3 paise per rupee per month is
    (*a*) Rs. 1.20   (*b*) Rs. 12   (*c*) Rs. 120   (*d*) Rs. 1200

20. A person takes a loan of Rs. 200 at 5% simple interest. He returns Rs. 100 at the end of 1 year. In order to clear his dues at the end of 2 years, he would pay :
    (*a*) Rs. 115.50   (*b*) Rs. 110   (*c*) Rs. 115   (*d*) Rs. 100

21. The interest on a certain deposit at 4.5% p.a. is Rs. 202.50 in one year. How much will the additional interest in one year be on the same deposit at 5% p.a. ?   (Bank P.O., 1990)
    (*a*) Rs. 22.5   (*b*) Rs. 20.25   (*c*) Rs. 225   (*d*) Rs. 427.50

22. A sum of money was lent at simple interest at 11% p.a. for $3\frac{1}{2}$ years and $4\frac{1}{2}$ years respectively. If the difference in interests for two periods was Rs. 412.50, then the sum is :
    (*a*) Rs. 3250   (*b*) Rs. 3500   (*c*) Rs. 3750   (*d*) Rs. 4250

23. Gulshan Kumar borrows Rs. 300 at 5% and Rs. 450 at 6% at the same time and on the condition that the whole loan will be repaid when the total interest amounts to Rs. 126. The loan will have to be repaid after how many years ?
    (*a*) 2   (*b*) 3   (*c*) 4   (*d*) 5

24. Prabhat took a certain amount as a loan from a bank at the rate of 8% p.a. S.I. and gave the same amount to Ashish as a loan at the rate of 12% p.a. If at the end of 12 years, he made a profit of Rs. 320 in the deal, what was the original amount ?   (Bank P.O. 1993)
    (*a*) Rs. 2000   (*b*) Rs. 3000   (*c*) Rs. 4000   (*d*) None of these

25. Vishal lent Rs. 150 to Sandeep for 4 years and Rs. 600 to Deepak for 2 years. If he receives Rs. 90 as simple interest altogether, the rate of interest is :
    (*a*) 12%   (*b*) 10%   (*c*) 5%   (*d*) 4%

26. A lent Rs. 1200 to *B* for 3 years at a certain rate of simple interest and Rs. 1000 to *C* for the same time at the same rate. If he gets Rs. 50 more from *B* than from *C*, then the rate percent is :

    (a) $8\frac{1}{3}\%$ (b) $6\frac{2}{3}\%$ (c) $10\frac{1}{3}\%$ (d) $9\frac{2}{3}\%$

27. Rahul borrowed Rs. 830 from Mr. Lal at 12% p.a. S.I. for 3 years. He then added some more money to the borrowed sum and lent it to Shobha for the same period at 14% p.a. rate of interest. If Rahul gains Rs. 93.90 in the whole transaction, how much money did he add from his side ?

    (a) Rs. 35   (b) Rs. 55   (c) Rs. 80   (d) Rs. 105

28. The difference between the interests received from two different banks on Rs. 500 for 2 years, is Rs. 2.50. The difference between their rates is :

    (a) 1%   (b) 0.5%   (c) 0.25%   (d) 2.5%

29. The simple interest on Rs. 1820 from March 9, 1994 to May 21, 1994 at $7\frac{1}{2}\%$ rate will be

    (a) Rs. 29   (b) Rs. 28.80   (c) Rs. 27.30   (d) Rs. 22.50

30. A sum was put at simple interest at a certain rate for 2 years. Had it been put at 3% higher rate, it would have fetched Rs. 72 more. The sum is :

    (a) Rs. 1200   (b) Rs. 1500   (c) Rs. 1600   (d) Rs. 1800

31. A money lender finds that due to a fall in the rate of interest from 8% to $7\frac{3}{4}\%$, his yearly income diminishes by Rs. 61.50. His capital is :

    (a) Rs. 26000   (b) Rs. 24600   (c) Rs. 23800   (d) Rs. 22400

32. Mr. Roopchand finds that an increase in the rate of interest from $4\frac{7}{8}\%$ to $5\frac{1}{8}\%$ per annum increases his yearly income by Rs. 25. His investment is :

    (a) Rs. 10,000   (b) Rs. 12,000   (c) Rs. 15,000   (d) Rs. 20,000

33. In how many years will a sum of money double itself at 12% per annum ?

    (a) 6 years 9 months   (b) 7 years 6 months
    (c) 8 years 3 months   (d) 8 years 4 months

34. If a sum of money doubles itself in 8 years at simple interest, the rate percent per annum is : **(I.Tax 1992)**

    (a) 11.5   (b) 12   (c) 12.5   (d) 13

35. The rate at which a sum becomes four times of itself in 15 years at S.I., will be : **(Assistant Grade 1993)**

    (a) 15%   (b) $17\frac{1}{2}\%$ (c) 20%   (d) 25%

36. If a sum of money at simple interest doubles in 6 years, it will become 4 times in :

    (a) 12 years   (b) 14 years   (c) 16 years   (d) 18 years

37. At a certain rate of simple interest, a certain sum doubles itself in 10 years. It will treble itself in :

(*a*) 12 years   (*b*) 15 years   (*c*) 20 years   (*d*) 30 years

38. A sum of money becomes $\left(\dfrac{8}{5}\right)$ of itself in 5 years at a certain rate of interest. The rate of interest is :

(*a*) 5%   (*b*) 8%   (*c*) 10%   (*d*) 12%

39. The simple interest accrued on a sum of money at the end of four years is $\dfrac{1}{5}$ th of its principal. What is the rate of interest per annum ?

(*a*) 4%   (*b*) 5%   (*c*) 6%   (*d*) Data inadequate

(Bank P.O. 1993)

40. The simple interest on a sum of money at 8% per annum for 6 years is half the sum. The sum is   **(C.B.I. 1991)**

(*a*) Rs. 4800   (*b*) Rs. 6000   (*c*) Rs. 8000   (*d*) Data inadequate

41. A sum of money trebles itself in 15 years 6 months. In how many years would it double itself ?

(*a*) 6 years 3 months   (*b*) 7 years 9 months

(*c*) 8 years 3 months   (*d*) 9 years 6 months

42. Simple interest on a certain sum at a certain rate is $\dfrac{9}{16}$ of the sum. If the numbers representing rate percent and time in years be equal, then the rate is :

(*a*) $5\dfrac{1}{2}$%   (*b*) $6\dfrac{1}{2}$%   (*c*) $6\dfrac{1}{4}$%   (*d*) $7\dfrac{1}{2}$%

43. The simple interest on a sum of money is $\dfrac{1}{9}$ of the sum. The number of years is numerically equal to the rate percent per annum. The rate percent per annum is :   **(I. Tax & Central Excise 1993)**

(*a*) $3\dfrac{1}{3}$ (*b*) 5   (*c*) $6\dfrac{2}{3}$ (*d*) 10

44. Consider the following statements :

If a sum of money is lent at simple interest, then the

1. money gets doubled in 5 years if the rate of interest is $16\dfrac{2}{3}$%.

2. money gets doubled in 5 years if the rate of interest is 20%.

3. money becomes four times in 10 years if it gets doubled in 5 years.

Of these statements,

(*a*) 1 and 3 are correct   (*b*) 3 alone is correct

(*c*) 2 alone is correct   (*d*) 2 and 3 are correct

45. A sum of Rs. 10 is lent to be returned in 11 monthly instalments of Re. 1 each, interest being simple. The rate of interest is :

(*a*) $9\dfrac{1}{11}$%   (*b*) 10%   (*c*) 11%   (*d*) $21\dfrac{9}{11}$%

46. What annual payment will discharge a debt of Rs. 580 due in 5 years, the rate being 8% per annum ?

(*a*) Rs. 65.60   (*b*) Rs. 100   (*c*) Rs. 166.40   (*d*) Rs. 120

47. The simple interest on a sum of money will be Rs. 600 after 10 years. If the principal is trebled after 5 years, what will be the total interest at the end of the tenth year ? **(Bank P.O. 1987)**

(*a*) Rs. 600   (*b*) Rs. 900   (*c*) Rs. 1200   (*d*) Data inadequate

48. The rate of simple interest on a sum of money is 6% p.a. for the first 3 years, 8% p.a. for the next 5 years and 10% p.a. for the period beyond 8 years. If the simple interest accrued by the sum for a total period of 10 years is Rs. 1560, what is the sum ? **(Bank P.O. 1993)**

(*a*) Rs. 1500   (*b*) Rs. 2000   (*c*) Rs. 3000   (*d*) Date inadequate

49. The rate of interest on a sum of money is 4% p.a. for the first 2 years, 6% p.a. for the next 3 years and 8% p.a. for the period beyond 5 years. If the simple interest accrued by the sum for a total period of 8 years is Rs. 1280, what is the sum ?

(*a*) Rs. 1523   (*b*) Rs. 1680   (*c*) Rs. 2560   (*d*) Rs. 2840

50. How long will it take a sum of money invested at 5% p.a. S.I. to increase its value by 40% ? **(Assistant Grade 1992)**

(*a*) 5 years   (*b*) 6 years   (*c*) 7 years   (*d*) 8 years

51. A monthly instalment of Rs. 180 is required to be paid for repayment of an interest free loan in 40 months. If it is decided to pay it in 30 months, how much will be the monthly instalment in rupees ?

(*a*) 60   (*b*) 198   (*c*) 240   (*d*) 330

(Bank P.O. 1993)

52. If x, y, z are three sums of money such that y is the simple interest on x, z is the simple interest on y for the same time and at the same rate of interest, then we have :

(a) $x^2 = yz$ (b) $y^2 = xz$ (c) $z^2 = xy$ (d) $xyz = 1$

53. Vinod Kumar invested Rs. 1600 for 3 years and Rs. 1100 for 4 years at the same rate of simple interest. If the total interest from these investments is Rs. 506, the rate of interest was :

(a) $2\frac{3}{4}\%$ (b) $5\frac{1}{3}\%$ (c) $5\frac{1}{2}\%$ (d) 6%

54. A sum of Rs. 1550 is lent out into two parts, one at 8% and another one at 6%. If the total annual income is Rs. 106, the money lent at 8% is :

(*a*) Rs. 650   (*b*) Rs. 720   (*c*) Rs. 840   (*d*) Rs. 900

55. A sum of Rs. 2600 is lent out in two parts in such a way that the interest on one part at 10% for 5 years is equal to that on another part at 9% for 6 years. The sum lent out at 10% is :

(a) Rs. 1150   (b) Rs. 1250   (c) Rs. 1350   (d) Rs. 1450

56. A sum of Rs. 1550 was lent partly at 5% and partly at 8% p.a. simple interest. The total interest received after 3 years was Rs. 300. The ratio of the money lent at 5% to that lent at 8% is :
    (a) 8 : 5   (b) 5 : 8   (c) 31 : 6   (d) 16 : 15

57. A man invests a certain sum of money at 6% p.a. simple interest and another sum at 7% p.a. simple interest. His income from interest after 2 years was Rs. 354. One fourth of the first sum is equal to one fifth of the second sum. The total sum invested was :
    (a) Rs. 2600   (b) Rs. 2700   (c) Rs. 2880   (d) Rs. 2900

58. What should be the least number of years in which the simple interest on Rs. 2600 at $6\frac{2}{3}$ % will be an exact number of rupees ?

    (a) 2   (b) 3   (c) 4   (d) 5

59. A man invested $\frac{1}{3}$ of his capital at 7% ; $\frac{1}{4}$ at 8% and the remainder at 10%. If his annual income is Rs. 561, the capital is
    (a) Rs. 5400   (b) Rs. 6000   (c) Rs. 6600   (d) Rs. 7200

60. A man invests an amount of Rs. 15860 in the names of his three sons A, B and C in such a way that they get the same amount after 2, 3 and 4 years respectively. If the rate of simple interest is 5%, then the ratio of amounts invested among A, B and C will be :
    (a) 10 : 15 : 20   (b) 22 : 23 : 24
    (c) 6 : 4 : 3   (d) 2 : 3 : 4

61. A man lends Rs. 10000 in four parts. If he gets 8% on Rs. 2000 ; $7\frac{1}{2}$ % on Rs. 4000 and $8\frac{1}{2}$ % on Rs. 1400 ; what percent must he get for the remainder, if his average annual interest is 8.13% ?
    (a) $10\frac{1}{2}$ %   (b) $9\frac{1}{4}$ %   (c) 9%   (d) 7%

62. Rs. 2189 are divided into three parts such that their amounts after 1, 2 and 3 years respectively may be equal, the rate of simple interest being 4% p.a. in all cases. The smallest part is : **(Assistant Grade 1992)**
    (a) Rs. 702   (b) Rs. 597   (c) Rs. 756   (d) Rs. 1093

63. The rates of simple interest in two banks A and B are in the ratio 5 : 4. A person wants to deposit his total savings in two banks in such a way that he received equal half yearly interest from both. He should deposit the savings in banks A and B in the ratio :
    (a) 2 : 5   (b) 4 : 5   (c) 5 : 2   (d) 5 : 4

ANSWERS

1. (c)	**2.** (c)	**3.** (c)	**4.** (a)	**5.** (a)	**6.** (b)	**7.** (a)	**8.** (a)	**9.** (b)
10. (a)	**11.** (c)	**12.** (d)	**13.** (b)	**14.** (d)	**15.** (c)	**16.** (d)	**17.** (b)	**18.** (b)
19. (a)	**20.** (c)	**21.** (a)	**22.** (c)	**23.** (b)	**24.** (d)	**25.** (c)	**26.** (a)	**27.** (d)
28. (c)	**29.** (c)	**30.** (a)	**31.** (b)	**32.** (a)	**33.** (d)	**34.** (c)	**35.** (c)	**36.** (d)
37. (c)	**38.** (d)	**39.** (b)	**40.** (d)	**41.** (b)	**42.** (d)	**43.** (a)	**44.** (c)	**45.** (d)
46. (b)	**47.** (c)	**48.** (b)	**49.** (c)	**50.** (d)	**51.** (c)	**52.** (b)	**53.** (c)	**54.** (a)
55. (c)	**56.** (d)	**57.** (b)	**58.** (b)	**59.** (c)	**60.** (c)	**61.** (c)	**62.** (b)	**63.** (b)

SOLUTION

1. S.I. $= Rs. \left(2500 \times 6 \times \dfrac{5}{100}\right) = Rs.\ 750.$

2. Amount $= Rs. \left(500 + \dfrac{500 \times 5 \times 4}{100}\right) = Rs.\ 600.$

3. Gain $= Rs. \left(\dfrac{3500 \times 11.5 \times 3}{100} - \dfrac{3500 \times 10 \times 3}{100}\right)$

$= Rs.\ (1207.5 - 1050) = Rs.\ 157.50.$

4. Time $= \left(\dfrac{100 \times 50}{500 \times 5}\right)$ years $= 2$ years.

5. Rate $= \left(\dfrac{100 \times 300}{5000 \times 2}\right)\% = 2\%.$

6. Rate $= \left(\dfrac{100 \times 2700}{15000 \times 3}\right)\% = 6\%.$

7. Principal $= Rs. \left(\dfrac{1230 \times 100}{6 \times 5}\right) = Rs.\ 4100.$

8. Let the required money be x. Then,

$\left(x + \dfrac{x \times 15}{100} \times \dfrac{3}{2}\right) = 784 \Leftrightarrow \dfrac{49x}{40} = 784 \Leftrightarrow x = \dfrac{784 \times 40}{49} = 640.$

9. Let the principal be Rs. x. Then,

$x + \dfrac{x \times 10 \times 4}{100} = 3500 \Leftrightarrow \dfrac{140x}{100} = 3500 \Leftrightarrow x = \dfrac{3500 \times 100}{140} = 2500.$

10. Principal = Rs. 800, S.I. = Rs. 120, Time = 3 years.

$\therefore$ Rate $= \left(\dfrac{100 \times 120}{800 \times 3}\right)\% = 5\%.$

New rate = 8%, Principal = Rs. 800, Time = 3 years.

S.I. $= Rs. \left(\dfrac{800 \times 8 \times 3}{100}\right) = Rs.\ 192.$

$\therefore$ New amount = Rs. $(800 + 192)$ = Rs. 992.

11. $\text{Sum} = \dfrac{100 \times \text{S.I.}}{\text{Rate} \times \text{Time}} = \dfrac{100 \times x}{x \times x} = \text{Rs.}\left(\dfrac{100}{x}\right).$

12. P = Rs. 64, T = 2 years, S.I. = Rs. 19.20.

$\text{Rate} = \left(\dfrac{100 \times 19.20}{64 \times 2}\right)\% = 15\%.$

Now, P = Rs. 86, T = 4 years, R = 15%..

$\therefore$ S.I. = Rs. $\left(\dfrac{86 \times 4 \times 15}{100}\right)$ = Rs. 51.60.

$\therefore$ Amount = Rs. $(86 + 51.60)$ = Rs. 137.60.

13. $\text{Principal} = \text{Rs.}\left(\dfrac{100 \times 48}{5 \times 4}\right)$ = Rs. 240.

$\text{S.I.} = \text{Rs.}\left(\dfrac{240 \times 5 \times 4}{100}\right)$ = Rs. 48.

14. S.I. for 2 years = $(750 - 690)$ = Rs. 60

S.I. for 3 years = Rs. $\left(\dfrac{60}{2} \times 3\right)$ = Rs. 90.

$\therefore$ Principal = Rs. $(690 - 90)$ = Rs. 600.

15. S.I. for $1\dfrac{1}{2}$ years = Rs. $(1067.20 - 1012)$ = Rs. 55.20.

S.I. for $2\dfrac{1}{2}$ years = Rs. $\left(55.20 \times \dfrac{2}{3} \times \dfrac{5}{2}\right)$ = Rs. 92.

$\therefore$ Principal = Rs. $(1012 - 92)$ = Rs. 920.

$\therefore$ Rate $= \dfrac{100 \times 92 \times 2}{920 \times 5} = 4\%.$

16. S.I. for 3 years = Rs. $(2600 - 2240)$ = Rs. 360.

S.I. for 2 years = Rs. $\left(\dfrac{360}{3} \times 2\right)$ = Rs. 240.

$\therefore$ Principal = Rs. $(2240 - 240)$ = Rs. 2000.

17. S.I. required = Rs. $\left(\dfrac{800 \times 12 \times 5}{100}\right)$ = Rs. 480.

$\text{Time} = \left(\dfrac{100 \times 480}{600 \times 10}\right)$ years = 8 years.

18. $\text{Sum} = \left(\dfrac{100 \times 840}{5 \times 8}\right)$ = Rs. 2100.

Rate required $= \left(\dfrac{100 \times 840}{2100 \times 5}\right)\% = 8\%.$

19. S.I. = Rs. $\left(10 \times \dfrac{3}{100} \times 4\right)$ = Rs. 1.20.

20. Amount to be paid = Rs. $\left(100 + \dfrac{200 \times 5 \times 1}{100} + \dfrac{100 \times 5 \times 1}{100}\right)$ = Rs. 115.

21. Sum = $\left(\dfrac{100 \times 202.50}{4.5 \times 1}\right)$ = Rs. 4500.

Additional interest = Rs. $\left(\dfrac{4500 \times 5 \times 1}{100} - 202.50\right)$ = Rs. 22.50.

22. Let the sum be Rs. x. Then,

$$\left(x \times 11 \times \dfrac{9}{2} \times \dfrac{1}{100} - x \times 11 \times \dfrac{7}{2} \times \dfrac{1}{100}\right) = 412.50$$

or $\dfrac{22x}{200} = 412.50 \Leftrightarrow 11x = 41250 \Leftrightarrow x = 3750.$

23. Let it be paid after x years. Then,

$$\dfrac{300 \times 5 \times x}{100} + \dfrac{450 \times 6 \times x}{100} = 126 \Leftrightarrow 42x = 126 \Leftrightarrow x = 3.$$

24. Let the original amount be Rs. x. Then,

$$\dfrac{x \times 12 \times 12}{100} - \dfrac{x \times 8 \times 12}{100} = 320 \Leftrightarrow x = \dfrac{2000}{3} = \text{Rs. } 666.67$$

25. Let the rate be $R\%$ per annum. Then,

$$\dfrac{150 \times R \times 4}{100} + \dfrac{600 \times R \times 2}{100} = 90 \Leftrightarrow 18R = 90 \Leftrightarrow R = 5\%.$$

26. $\dfrac{1200 \times R \times 3}{100} - \dfrac{1000 \times R \times 3}{100} = 50 \Leftrightarrow 6R = 50 \Leftrightarrow R = 8\dfrac{1}{3}\%.$

27. $\dfrac{(830 + x) \times 14 \times 3}{100} - \dfrac{830 \times 12 \times 3}{100} = 93.90$

or $830 \times 42 + 42x - 830 \times 36 = 9390$

or $42x + 830 \times (42 - 36) = 9390$

or $42x = 9390 - 4980 \Leftrightarrow x = \dfrac{4410}{42} = 105.$

∴ Money added = Rs. 105.

28. $\dfrac{500 \times R_1 \times 2}{100} - \dfrac{500 \times R_2 \times 2}{100} = 2.50$

or $1000 (R_1 - R_2) = 250$ or $R_1 - R_2 = \dfrac{250}{1000} = \dfrac{1}{4} = 0.25\%.$

29. March April May

$$22 + 30 + 21 = 73 \text{ days} = \dfrac{73}{365} \text{ year} = \dfrac{1}{5} \text{ year.}$$

∴ Interest = Rs. $\left(1820 \times \dfrac{1}{5} \times \dfrac{15}{2 \times 100}\right)$ = Rs. 27.30.

30. Let the sum be Rs. x and original rate be $R\%$. Then,

$$\frac{x \times (R+3) \times 2}{100} - \frac{x \times R \times 2}{100} = 72$$

or $2Rx + 6x - 2Rx = 7200$ or $x = 1200$.

31. Let the capital be Rs. x. Then,

$$\frac{x \times 8 \times 1}{100} - x \times \frac{31}{4} \times \frac{1}{100} = 61.50 \quad \text{or} \quad 32x - 31x = 6150 \times 4$$

$\therefore x = 24600$.

32. Let the investment be Rs. x. Then,

$$x \times \frac{41}{8} \times \frac{1}{100} - x \times \frac{39}{8} \times \frac{1}{100} = 25 \Leftrightarrow 2x = 20000 \Leftrightarrow x = 10000.$$

33. Let sum $= x$. Then, S.I. $= x$.

$$\therefore \text{ Time} = \frac{100 \times \text{S.I.}}{\text{Sum} \times \text{Rate}} = \left(\frac{100 \times x}{x \times 12}\right) \text{years} = 8\frac{1}{3} \text{ years.}$$

$$= 8 \text{ years 4 months.}$$

34. Let sum $= x$. Then, S.I. $= x$.

$$\text{Rate} = \left(\frac{100 \times x}{x \times 8}\right)\% = 12\frac{1}{2}\%.$$

35. Let sum $= x$. Then, S.I. $= 3x$.

$$\text{Rate} = \left(\frac{100 \times 3x}{x \times 15}\right)\% = 20\%.$$

36. Let sum $= x$. Then, S.I. $= x$.

$$\therefore \text{ Rate} = \left(\frac{100 \times x}{x \times 6}\right)\% = \frac{50}{3}\%.$$

Now, sum $= x$ and S.I. $= 3x$, Rate $= \frac{50}{3}\%$.

$$\therefore \text{ Time} = \frac{100 \times 3x}{x \times \frac{50}{3}} = 18 \text{ years.}$$

37. Let sum $= x$. Then, S.I. $= x$. Time $= 10$ years.

$$\therefore \text{ Rate} = \left(\frac{100 \times x}{x \times 10}\right)\% = 10\%.$$

Now, sum $= x$, S.I. $= 2x$, Rate $= 10\%$.

$$\therefore \text{ Time} = \left(\frac{100 \times 2x}{x \times 10}\right) \text{years} = 20 \text{ years.}$$

38. Let sum $= x$, S.I. $= \left(\frac{8x}{5} - x\right) = \frac{3x}{5}$, Time $= 5$ years.

$$\therefore \text{ Rate} = \left(100 \times \frac{3x}{5} \times \frac{1}{x \times 5}\right)\% = 12\%.$$

39. Let sum $= x$. Then, S.I. $= \frac{x}{5}$, Time $= 4$ years.

$\therefore$ Rate $= \left(100 \times \dfrac{x}{5} \times \dfrac{1}{x \times 4}\right)\% = 5\%$.

40. Let sum $= x$. Then, S.I. $= \dfrac{x}{2}$.

$\therefore \dfrac{x}{2} = \dfrac{x \times 8 \times 6}{100}$. Clearly, data is inadequate.

41. Let sum $= x$. Then, S.I. $= 2x$ & Time $= \dfrac{31}{2}$ years.

Rate $= \left(\dfrac{100 \times 2x}{x} \times \dfrac{2}{31}\right)\% = \left(\dfrac{400}{31}\right)\%$

Now, sum $= x$, S.I. $= x$ & Rate $= \left(\dfrac{400}{31}\right)\%$.

$\therefore$ Time $= \left(\dfrac{100 \times x}{x} \times \dfrac{31}{400}\right)$years $= 7$ years 9 months.

42. Let sum $= x$. Then, S.I. $= \dfrac{9x}{16}$.

Let time $= n$ years & rate $= n\%$.

$\therefore n = 100 \times \dfrac{9x}{16} \times \dfrac{1}{x} \times \dfrac{1}{n}$ or $n^2 = \dfrac{900}{16}$ or $n = \dfrac{30}{4} = 7\dfrac{1}{2}\%$.

43. Let sum $= x$. Then, S.I. $= \dfrac{x}{9}$.

Let time $= n$ years and rate $= n\%$.

Then, $n = 100 \times \dfrac{x}{9} \times \dfrac{1}{x \times n}$ or $n^2 = \dfrac{100}{9}$ or $n = \dfrac{10}{3} = 3\dfrac{1}{3}\%$.

44. Let sum be x. Then, S.I. $= x$

1. Time $= \dfrac{100 \times x}{x \times \dfrac{50}{3}} = 6$ years (False)

2. Time $= \dfrac{100 \times x}{x \times 20} = 5$ years (True)

3. Suppose sum $= x$. Then, S.I. $= x$ & Time $= 5$ years.

Rate $= \left(\dfrac{100 \times x}{x \times 5}\right)\% = 20\%$.

Now sum $= x$, S.I. $= 3x$ & Rate $= 20\%$.

$\therefore$ Time $= \left(\dfrac{100 \times 3x}{x \times 20}\right)$years $= 15$ years (False)

So, 2 alone is correct.

45. Rs. $10 +$ S.I. on Rs. 10 for 11 months
$=$ Rs. $11 +$ S.I. on Re 1 for $(1 + 2 + 3 + 4 + \ldots + 10)$ months
Rs. $10 +$ S.I. on Re 1. for 110 months $=$ Rs. $11 +$ S.I. on Re 1 for 55 months
S.I. on Re 1 for 55 months $=$ Re. 1.

$$\therefore \text{ Rate} = \left(\frac{100 \times 12}{1 \times 55}\right)\% = 21\frac{9}{11}\%.$$

46. Let the annual instalment be Rs. x. Then,

$$\left[x + \left(\frac{x \times 4 \times 8}{100}\right)\right] + \left[x + \left(\frac{x \times 3 \times 8}{100}\right)\right] + \left[x + \left(\frac{x \times 2 \times 8}{100}\right)\right]$$

$$+ \left[x + \left(\frac{x \times 1 \times 8}{100}\right)\right] + x = 580$$

or $\dfrac{33x}{25} + \dfrac{31x}{25} + \dfrac{29x}{25} + \dfrac{27x}{25} + x = 580$ or $x = 100$.

47. Let sum $= x$, S.I. $=$ Rs. 600, Time $= 10$ years.

$$\text{Rate} = \left(\frac{100 \times 600}{x \times 10}\right) = \left(\frac{6000}{x}\right)\%.$$

$$\text{S.I. for first 5 years} = \text{Rs.} \left(\frac{x \times 5 \times 6000}{x \times 100}\right) = \text{Rs. } 300.$$

$$\text{S.I. for last 5 years} = \text{Rs.} \left(3x \times 5 \times \frac{6000}{x \times 100}\right) = \text{Rs. } 900.$$

$\therefore$ Total interest $=$ Rs. 1200.

48. Let the sum be Rs. x. Then,

$$\frac{x \times 6 \times 3}{100} + \frac{x \times 8 \times 5}{100} + \frac{x \times 10 \times 2}{100} = 1560 \text{ or } 78x = 156000 \text{ or } x = 2000.$$

49. Let the sum be Rs. x. Then,

$$\frac{x \times 4 \times 2}{100} + \frac{x \times 6 \times 3}{100} + \frac{x \times 8 \times 3}{100} = 1280 \text{ or } 50x = 1280 \times 100$$

$\therefore \; x = 2560.$

50. Let the sum be x. Then, amount $= \dfrac{140}{100}x = \dfrac{7x}{5}$.

$$\therefore \text{ S.I.} = \left(\frac{7x}{5} - x\right) = \frac{2x}{5}.$$

Thus, sum $= x$, S.I. $= \dfrac{2x}{5}$ & Rate $= 5\%$.

$$\therefore \text{ Time} = \left(100 \times \frac{2x}{5} \times \frac{1}{x \times 5}\right) = 8 \text{ years}.$$

51. $180 \times 40 = x \times 30$ or $x = 240$.

52. $y = \dfrac{x \times R \times T}{100}$ or $RT = \dfrac{100y}{x}$.

$z = \dfrac{y \times R \times T}{100}$ or $RT = \dfrac{100z}{y}$.

$\therefore \dfrac{100y}{x} = \dfrac{100z}{y}$ or $y^2 = xz$.

53. $\dfrac{1600 \times 3 \times R}{100} + \dfrac{1100 \times 4 \times R}{100} = 506$ or $92R = 506$ or $R = 5\dfrac{1}{2}$ %.

54. Let the money lent at 8% be Rs. x. Then,

$\dfrac{x \times 8 \times 1}{100} + \dfrac{(1550 - x) \times 6 \times 1}{100} = 106$

or $2x + 9300 = 10600$ or $x = 650$.

55. Let the sum at 10% be Rs. x. Then,

$\dfrac{x \times 10 \times 5}{100} = \dfrac{(2600 - x) \times 9 \times 6}{100}$ or $104x = 2600 \times 54$ or $x = 1350$.

56. Let the sum at 5% be Rs. x. Then,

$\dfrac{x \times 5 \times 3}{100} + \dfrac{(1550 - x) \times 8 \times 3}{100} = 300$ or $x = 800$.

$\therefore \dfrac{\text{Money at 5\%}}{\text{Money at 8\%}} = \dfrac{800}{(1550 - 800)} = \dfrac{800}{750} = \dfrac{16}{15}$.

57. Let the sums be x and y.

$\dfrac{x \times 6 \times 2}{100} + \dfrac{y \times 7 \times 2}{100} = 354$ or $6x + 7y = 17700$

Also, $\dfrac{x}{4} = \dfrac{y}{5}$ or $5x - 4y = 0$

Solving these equations we get : $x = 1200$ and $y = 1500$.

$\therefore$ Total sum = Rs. 2700.

58. S.I. $= $ Rs $\left(2600 \times \dfrac{20}{3} \times \dfrac{1}{100} \times T \right)$

$= $ Rs $\left(\dfrac{520}{3} \times T \right)$, which is an exact number of rupees when $T = 3$.

59. Let total capital be x. Then,

$\left(\dfrac{x}{3} \times \dfrac{7}{100} \times 1 \right) + \left(\dfrac{x}{4} \times \dfrac{8}{100} \times 1 \right) + \left(\dfrac{5x}{12} \times \dfrac{10}{100} \times 1 \right) = 561$.

or $\dfrac{7x}{300} + \dfrac{x}{50} + \dfrac{x}{24} = 561$ or $51x = (561 \times 600)$

or $x = \left(\dfrac{561 \times 600}{51} \right) = 6600$.

60. Let the amounts invested be x, y, z respectively.

Then, $\dfrac{x \times 2 \times 5}{100} = \dfrac{y \times 3 \times 5}{100} = \dfrac{z \times 4 \times 5}{100} = k$.

$\therefore x = 10k, \ y = \dfrac{20}{3} k \ \& \ z = 5k$.

So, $x : y : z = 10k : \dfrac{20}{3} k : 5k$

$= 30 : 20 : 15 = 6 : 4 : 3$.

61. $\left(\dfrac{2000 \times 8 \times 1}{100}\right) + \left(4000 \times \dfrac{15}{2} \times \dfrac{1}{100}\right) + \left(1400 \times \dfrac{17}{2} \times \dfrac{1}{100}\right)$

$$+ 2600 \times R \times \dfrac{1}{100} = \dfrac{813}{10000} \times 10000 .$$

or $160 + 300 + 119 + 26R = 813$ or $R = 9$.

62. Let these parts be x, y and $[2189 - (x + y)]$. Then,

$$\dfrac{x \times 1 \times 4}{100} = \dfrac{y \times 2 \times 4}{100} = \dfrac{[2189 - (x + y)] \times 3 \times 4}{100}$$

$\therefore \ \dfrac{x}{y} = 2$ or $x = 2y$.

$\therefore \ \dfrac{2y \times 1 \times 4}{100} = \dfrac{(2189 - 3y) \times 3 \times 4}{100}$ or $44y = 2189 \times 12$.

$\therefore \ y = \left(\dfrac{2189 \times 12}{44}\right) = 597$.

$\therefore$ Smallest part = Rs 597.

63. Let the savings be X and Y and the rates of simple interest be $5x$ and $4x$ respectively. Then,

$$X \times 5x \times \dfrac{1}{2} \times \dfrac{1}{100} = Y \times 4x \times \dfrac{1}{2} \times \dfrac{1}{100} \quad \text{or} \quad \dfrac{X}{Y} = \dfrac{4}{5} .$$

i.e. $X : Y = 4 : 5$.

---

22. Compound Interest

Compound Interest : Sometimes it so happens that the borrower and the lender agree to fix up a certain unit of time, say *yearly* or *half-yearly* or *quarterly* to settle the previous account.

In such cases, the amount after first unit of time becomes the principal for the second unit, the amount after second unit becomes the principal for the third unit and so on.

After a specified period, *the difference between the amount and the money borrowed is called the* **Compound Interest** *(abbreviated as C.I.) for that period*

FORMULAE :

Let, **Principal** = P, **Rate** = R% *per annum*, **Time** = n *years*.

I. When interest is compounded Annually :

$$\text{Amount} = P\left(1 + \frac{R}{100}\right)^n$$

II. When interest is compounded Half-yearly :

$$\text{Amount} = P\left[1 + \frac{(R/2)}{100}\right]^{2n}$$

III. When interest is compounded Quarterly :

$$\text{Amount} = P\left[1 + \frac{(R/4)}{100}\right]^{4n}$$

IV. When interest is compounded Annually but time is in fraction, say $3\frac{2}{5}$ years.

$$\text{Amount} = P\left(1 + \frac{R}{100}\right)^3 \times \left(1 + \frac{\frac{2}{5}R}{100}\right)$$

V. When Rates are different for different years, say $R_1\%, R_2\%, R_3\%$ for 1st, 2nd and 3rd year respectively.

Then, $\text{Amount} = P\left(1 + \frac{R_1}{100}\right)\left(1 + \frac{R_2}{100}\right)\left(1 + \frac{R_3}{100}\right)$.

VI. Present worth of Rs. x due n years hence is given by :

$$\text{Present Worth} = \frac{x}{\left(1 + \frac{R}{100}\right)^n}.$$

Solved Problems

Ex. 1. *Find compound interest on Rs. 6250 at 16% per annum for 2 years, compounded annually.*

Sol. Amount = Rs. $\left[6250 \times \left(1 + \dfrac{16}{100} \right)^2 \right]$

$= $ Rs. $\left(6250 \times \dfrac{29}{25} \times \dfrac{29}{25} \right) = $ Rs. 8410.

∴ C.I. = Rs. $(8410 - 6250) = $ Rs. 2160.

Ex. 2. *Find compound interest on Rs. 5000 at 12% per annum for 1 year, compounded half-yearly.*

Sol. Principal = Rs. 5000, Rate = 6% per half year

Time = 1 year = 2 half-years.

∴ Amount = Rs. $\left[5000 \times \left(1 + \dfrac{6}{100} \right)^2 \right] = $ Rs. $\left(5000 \times \dfrac{53}{50} \times \dfrac{53}{50} \right)$

$= $ Rs. 5618

∴ C.I. = Rs. $(5618 - 5000) = $ Rs. 618.

Ex. 3. *Find compound interest on Rs. 16000 at 20% per annum for 9 months, compounded quarterly.*

Sol. Principal = Rs. 16000, Time = 9 months = 3 quarters

Rate = 20% per annum = 5% per quarter.

∴ Amount = Rs. $\left[16000 \times \left(1 + \dfrac{5}{100} \right)^3 \right]$

$= $ Rs. $\left(16000 \times \dfrac{21}{20} \times \dfrac{21}{20} \times \dfrac{21}{20} \right) = $ Rs. 18522.

∴ C.I. = Rs. $(18522 - 16000) = $ Rs. 2522.

Ex. 4. *The difference between the compound interest and simple interest on a certain sum at 10% per annum for 2 years is Rs. 631. Find the sum.*

Sol. Let the sum be Rs. x. Then,

C.I. $= x \left(1 + \dfrac{10}{100} \right)^2 - x = \dfrac{21x}{100}$,

S.I. $= \left(\dfrac{x \times 10 \times 2}{100} \right) = \dfrac{x}{5}$.

∴ (C.I.) − (S.I.) $= \left(\dfrac{21x}{100} - \dfrac{x}{5} \right) = \dfrac{x}{100}$.

$$\therefore \frac{x}{100} = 631 \Leftrightarrow x = 63100.$$

Hence, the sum is Rs. 63100.

Ex. 5. *If the compound interest on a certain sum for 2 years at 12% per annum is Rs. 1590, what would be the simple interest ?*

Sol. Let the sum be Rs. x. Then,

$$x\left(1 + \frac{12}{100}\right)^2 - x = 1590 \quad \text{or} \quad \frac{784x}{625} - x = 1590$$

or $\dfrac{159x}{625} = 1590$ or $x = \left(\dfrac{1590 \times 625}{159}\right) = 6250.$

$\therefore$ Sum = Rs. 6250.

$\therefore$ S.I. = Rs. $\left(\dfrac{6250 \times 12 \times 2}{100}\right)$ = Rs. 1500.

Ex. 6. *A sum of money amounts to Rs. 6690 after 3 years and to Rs. 10035 after 6 years on compound interest. Find the sum.*

Sol. Let the sum be Rs. P. Then,

$$P\left(1 + \frac{R}{100}\right)^3 = 6690 \ \dots \ (i) \quad \text{and} \quad P\left(1 + \frac{R}{100}\right)^6 = 10035 \ \dots \ (ii)$$

On dividing, we get $\left(1 + \dfrac{R}{100}\right)^3 = \dfrac{10035}{6690} = \dfrac{3}{2}.$

Substituting this value in (i), we get :

$$P \times \frac{3}{2} = 6690 \quad \text{or} \quad P = \left(6690 \times \frac{2}{3}\right) = 4460.$$

Hence, the sum is Rs. 4460.

Ex. 7. *A sum of money doubles itself at compound interest in 15 years. In how many years will it become eight times ?* (C.D.S. 1993)

Sol. $P\left(1 + \dfrac{R}{100}\right)^{15} = 2P \Rightarrow \left(1 + \dfrac{R}{100}\right)^{15} = 2 \ \dots \ (i)$

Let $P\left(1 + \dfrac{R}{100}\right)^n = 8P \Rightarrow \left(1 + \dfrac{R}{100}\right)^n = 8 = 2^3 = \left\{\left(1 + \dfrac{R}{100}\right)^{15}\right\}^3$

[*Using (i)*]

$$\Rightarrow \left(1 + \frac{R}{100}\right)^n = \left(1 + \frac{R}{100}\right)^{45}$$

$$\Rightarrow n = 45.$$

Thus, the required time = 45 years.

Ex. 8. *A certain sum amounts to Rs. 7350 in 2 years and to Rs. 8575 in 3 years. Find the sum and rate per cent.*

Sol. S.I. on Rs. 7350 for 1 year = Rs. (8575 − 7350) = Rs. 1225.

$$\therefore \text{ Rate} = \left(\frac{100 \times 1225}{7350 \times 1}\right)\% = 16\frac{2}{3}\%.$$

Let the sum be Rs. x. Then

$$x\left(1 + \frac{50}{3 \times 100}\right)^2 = 7350 \Leftrightarrow x \times \frac{7}{6} \times \frac{7}{6} = 7350$$

$$\Leftrightarrow x = \left(7350 \times \frac{36}{49}\right) = 5400.$$

$\therefore$ Sum = Rs. 5400.

EXERCISE 22

Mark ($\sqrt{}$) against the correct answer :

1. The amount of Rs. 7500 at compound interest at 4% per annum for 2 years, is :   **(Bank P.O. 1991)**

    (a) Rs. 7800   (b) Rs. 8100   (c) Rs. 8112   (d) Rs. 8082

2. If the simple interest on a sum of money at 5% per annum for 3 years is Rs. 1200, the compound interest on the same sum for the same period at the same rate, is :   **(Assistant Grade 1994)**

    (a) Rs. 1260   (b) Rs. 1261   (c) Rs. 1264   (d) Rs. 1265

3. The difference between the compound interest and the simple interest on a sum of money for 2 years at $12\frac{1}{2}\%$ per annum is Rs. 150. The sum is :   **(Assistant Grade 1994)**

    (a) Rs. 9000   (b) Rs. 9200   (c) Rs. 9500   (d) Rs. 9600

4. If the difference between the compound interest, compounded half yearly and the simple interest on a sum at 10% per annum for one year is Rs. 25, the sum is :   **(Assistant Grade 1994)**

    (a) Rs. 9000   (b) Rs. 9500   (c) Rs. 10000   (d) Rs. 10500

5. The difference in compound interest and simple interest on a certain amount at 10% per annum at the end of the third year is Rs. 620. What is the principal amount ?   **(Bank P.O. 1992)**

    (a) Rs. 40000   (b) Rs. 120000 (c) Rs. 10000   (d) Rs. 20000

6. A man borrowed Rs. 800 at 10% per annum simple interest and immediately lent the whole sum at 10% per annum compound interest. What does he gain at the end of 2 years ?   **(C.B.I. 1993)**

    (a) Rs. 6   (b) Rs. 8   (c) Rs. 10   (d) Rs. 12

7. On what sum of money will the simple interest for 3 years at 8% per annum be half of the compound interest on Rs. 400 for 2 years at 10% per annum ?   **(Hotel Management 1992)**

    (a) Rs. 125   (b) Rs. 150   (c) Rs. 175   (d) Rs. 200

8. If the compound interest on a certain sum at $16\frac{2}{3}$ % for 3 years is Rs. 1270, the simple interest on the same sum at the same rate and for the same period is :

    (*a*) Rs. 1200   (*b*) Rs. 1165   (*c*) Rs. 1080   (*d*) Rs. 1220

9. The compound interest on a certain sum at 5% per annum for 2 years is Rs. 328. The simple interest for that sum at the same rate and for the same period will be : **(Central Excise & I. Tax 1993)**

    (*a*) Rs. 320   (*b*) Rs. 322   (*c*) Rs. 325   (*d*) Rs. 326

10. The compound interest on Rs. 5600 for $1\frac{1}{2}$ years at 10% per annum, compounded annually, is :

    (*a*) Rs. 882.70   (*b*) Rs. 873.50   (*c*) Rs. 868   (*d*) Rs. 840

11. The compound interest on Rs. 20480 at $6\frac{1}{4}$ % per annum for 2 years 73 days, is :

    (*a*) Rs. 3000   (*b*) Rs. 3131   (*c*) Rs. 2929   (*d*) Rs. 3636

12. What is the principal amount which earns Rs. 132 as compound interest for the second year at 10% per annum ? **(Bank P.O. 1989)**

    (*a*) Rs. 1000   (*b*) Rs. 1200   (*c*) Rs. 1320   (*d*) Rs. 1188

13. A sum of money at compound interest amounts to Rs. 578.40 in 2 years and to Rs. 614.55 in 3 years. The rate of interest per annum is :

    (*a*) 4%   (*b*) 5%   (*c*) $6\frac{1}{4}$ %   (*d*) $8\frac{1}{3}$ %

    (Central Excise & I. Tax 1993)

14. A sum of money at compound interest amounts to Rs. 5290 in 2 years and to Rs. 6083.50 in 3 years. The rate of interest per annum is :

    (*a*) 12%   (*b*) 14%   (*c*) 15%   (*d*) $16\frac{2}{3}$ %

15. If the amount is $2\frac{1}{4}$ times the sum after 2 years at compound interest, the rate of interest per annum is : **(Assistant Grade 1994)**

    (*a*) 25%   (*b*) 30%   (*c*) 40%   (*d*) 50%

16. A sum of money amounts to Rs. 4624 in 2 years and to Rs. 4913 in 3 yeas at compound interest. The sum is :

    (*a*) Rs. 4096   (*b*) Rs. 4260   (*c*) Rs. 4335   (*d*) Rs. 4360

17. A sum of money placed at compound interest doubles itself in 5 years. It will amount to eight times itself in :

    (*a*) 10 years   (*b*) 12 years   (*c*) 15 years   (*d*) 20 years

18. A sum of money at compound interest amounts to thrice itself in 3 years. In how many years will it be 9 times itself ? **(Hotel Management 1992)**

    (*a*) 12   (*b*) 9   (*c*) 6   (*d*) 8

19. In how many years will a sum of Rs. 800 at 10% per annum compounded semi-annually become Rs. 926.10 ? **(Assistant Grade 1993)**

(a) $2\frac{1}{2}$　　　(b) $1\frac{1}{2}$　　　(c) $2\frac{1}{3}$　　　(d) $1\frac{1}{3}$

20. The present worth of Rs. 169 due in 2 years at 4% per annum compound interest is : **(Assistant Grade 1993)**

(a) Rs. 150.50　　(b) Rs. 154.75　(c) Rs. 156.25　(d) Rs. 158

21. To find out the total compound interest accrued on a sum of money after 5 years, which of the following informations given in the statements A and B is/are sufficient ?

A : the rate of interest was 6% per annum.

B : The total simple interest on the same amount after 5 years at the same rate will be Rs. 600. **(Bank P.O. 1994)**

(a) only A is fufficient　　　　(b) Either A or B is sufficient

(c) Both A & B together are needed

(d) only B is sufficient　　　　(e) Both A and B are not sufficient

22. To find out the total compound interest accrued on a sum of money after 5 years, which of the following informations given in the statements P and Q will be sufficient ? **(Bank P.O. 1993)**

P : The sum was Rs. 20000.

Q : The total amount of simple interest on the sum after 5 years was Rs. 4000.

(a) only P is sufficient　　　　(b) only Q is sufficient

(c) Either P or Q is sufficient　(d) Both P & Q are needed

(e) Both P and Q are not sufficient.

23. The difference between compound interest and the simple interest earned on a sum of money at the end of 4 years is Rs. 256.40. To find out the sum, which of the following informations given in the statements P and Q is/are necessary ?

P : Amount of simple interest accrued after 4 years.

Q : Rate of interest per annum.

(a) only P is necessary　　　　(b) only Q is necessary

(c) Either P or Q is necessary　(d) Neither P nor Q is necessary

(e) Both P and Q are necessary　　　　**(Bank P.O. 1993)**

24. The difference between the compound interest and simple interest earned at the end of second year on a sum of money at 10% per annum is Rs. 20. The sum is : **(Bank P.O. 1992)**

(a) Rs. 4000　　(b) Rs. 2000　(c) Rs. 1500　(d) Data inadequate

25. A sum of Rs. 12000 deposited at compound interest becomes double after 5 years. After 20 years it will become :

(a) Rs. 120000　(b) Rs. 192000　(c) Rs. 124000　(d) Rs. 96000

26. The least number of complete years in which a sum of money put out at 20% compound interest will be more than doubled is :

(a) 3　　　　　(b) 4　　　　　(c) 5　　　　　(d) 6

27. A tree increases annually by $\frac{1}{8}$th of its height. By how much will it increase after 2 years, if it stands today 64 cm high ?

    (*a*) 72 cm   (*b*) 74 cm   (*c*) 75 cm   (*d*) 81 cm

28. The difference between the compound interest and the simple interest for 2 years on a sum of money is Rs. 60. If the simple interest for 2 years be Rs. 1440, the rate per cent is :

    (*a*) $4\frac{1}{6}$ %   (*b*) $6\frac{1}{4}$ %   (*c*) 8%   (*d*) $8\frac{1}{3}$ %

29. The compound interest on a sum for 2 years is Rs. 832 and the simple interest on the same sum for the same period is Rs. 800. The difference between the compound interest and the simple interest for 3 years will be :

    (*a*) Rs. 48   (*b*) Rs. 66.56   (*c*) Rs. 98.56   (*d*) none of these

30. The difference between compound interest and simple interest on a sum for 2 years at 10% per annum, when the interest is compounded annually is Rs. 16. If the interest were compounded half yearly, the difference in two interests would be :

    (*a*) Rs. 24.81   (*b*) Rs. 31.61   (*c*) Rs. 32.40   (*d*) Rs. 26.90

31. A sum of money becomes Rs. 13380 after 3 years and Rs. 20070 after 6 years on compound interest. The sum is :

    (*a*) Rs. 8800   (*b*) Rs. 8890   (*c*) Rs. 8920   (*d*) Rs. 9040

32. A loan was repaid in two annual instalments of Rs. 121 each. If the rate of interest be 10% per annum, compounded annually, the sum borrowed was :

    (*a*) Rs. 200   (*b*) Rs. 210   (*c*) Rs. 217.80   (*d*) Rs. 216

33. A sum of Rs. 1100 was taken as a loan. This is to be repaid in two equal instalments. If the rate of interest be 20% compounded annually, then the value of each instalment is :

    (*a*) Rs. 842   (*b*) Rs. 792   (*c*) Rs. 720   (*d*) Rs. 700

34. A man borrows Rs. 12500 from a bank at 20% compound interest. At the end of every year he pays Rs. 2000 as part repayment. How much does he still owe to the bank after three such instalments ?

    (*a*) Rs. 15600   (*b*) Rs. 12864   (*c*) Rs. 12000   (*d*) none of these

35. The difference between simple interest and compound interest on Rs. 1200 for one year at 10% per annum, reckoned half-yearly is :

    (*a*) Nil   (*b*) Rs. 13.20   (*c*) Rs. 8.80   (*d*) Rs. 3

36. The difference between the compound interests on Rs. 1600 for one year at 20% per annum, when compounded half yearly and quarterly is :

    (*a*) Rs. 8.81   (*b*) Rs. 9.41   (*c*) Rs. 10.36   (*d*) Rs. 8.50

37. The compound interest on Rs. 8000 at 15% per annum for 2 years 4 months, compounded annually is :

    (*a*) Rs. 2980   (*b*) Rs. 3091   (*c*) Rs. 3109   (*d*) Rs. 3100

38. The present worth of Rs. 4913 due 3 years hence at $6\frac{1}{4}$ % per annum compound interest, is :

(a) Rs. 4216   (b) Rs. 4096   (c) Rs. 4200   (d) Rs. 4168

39. What annual payment will discharge a debt of Rs. 7620 due in 3 years at $16\frac{2}{3}$ % per annum compound interest ?

(a) Rs. 2540   (b) Rs. 3430   (c) Rs. 3260   (d) Rs. 3380

40. The compound interest on Rs. 30000 at 7% per annum for a certain period is Rs. 4347. The period is :

(a) 2 years   (b) $2\frac{1}{2}$ years   (c) 3 years   (d) 4 years

41. At what rate of compound interest per annum will a sum of Rs. 1200 become Rs. 1348.32 in 2 years ?

(a) 7%   (b) 6%   (c) 7.5%   (d) 6.5%

42. A sum of money invested at compound interest amounts to Rs. 800 in 3 years and Rs. 840 in 4 years. What is the rate of interest per annum ?   **(Central Excise & I. Tax 1991)**

(a) 2%   (b) 4%   (c) 5%   (d) 10%

43. A sum of money becomes 8 times of itself in 3 years at compound interest. The rate of interest is :   **(Hotel Management 1991)**

(a) 100%   (b) 8%   (c) 1%   (d) Data inadequate

ANSWERS

1. (c)   2. (b)   3. (d)   4. (c)   5. (d)   6. (b)   7. (c)   8. (c)   9. (a)
10. (c)   11. (c)   12. (b)   13. (c)   14. (c)   15. (d)   16. (a)   17. (c)   18. (c)
19. (b)   20. (c)   21. (c)   22. (d)   23. (b)   24. (b)   25. (b)   26. (b)   27. (d)
28. (d)   29. (c)   30. (a)   31. (c)   32. (b)   33. (c)   34. (d)   35. (d)   36. (a)
37. (c)   38. (b)   39. (b)   40. (a)   41. (b)   42. (c)   43. (a)

SOLUTIONS

1. Amount = Rs. $\left[7500 \times \left(1 + \frac{4}{100} \right)^2 \right]$

= Rs. $\left(7500 \times \frac{26}{25} \times \frac{26}{25} \right)$ = Rs. 8112.

2. Sum = Rs. $\left(\frac{100 \times 1200}{3 \times 5} \right)$ = Rs. 8000.

Amount = Rs. $\left[8000 \times \left(1 + \frac{5}{100} \right)^3 \right]$ = Rs. $\left(8000 \times \frac{21}{20} \times \frac{21}{20} \times \frac{21}{20} \right)$

$$= \text{Rs. } 9261.$$

$$\therefore \text{ C.I.} = \text{Rs. } (9261 - 8000) = \text{Rs. } 1261.$$

3. Let the sum be Rs. x. Then,

$$\text{C.I.} = x\left(1 + \frac{25}{2 \times 100}\right)^2 - x = \left(\frac{9}{8} \times \frac{9}{8}\right)x - x = \frac{17x}{64}.$$

$$\text{S.I.} = \left(x \times \frac{25}{2} \times 2 \times \frac{1}{100}\right) = \frac{x}{4}.$$

$$(\text{C.I.}) - (\text{S.I.}) = \left(\frac{17x}{64} - \frac{x}{4}\right) = \frac{x}{64}.$$

$$\therefore \frac{x}{64} = 150 \text{ or } x = 9600.$$

4. Let the sum be Rs. x. Then,

$$\text{C.I.} = x\left(1 + \frac{5}{100}\right)^2 - x = \left(\frac{441x}{400} - x\right) = \frac{41x}{400}.$$

$$\text{S.I.} = \frac{x \times 10 \times 1}{100} = \frac{x}{10}.$$

$$(\text{C.I.}) - (\text{S.I.}) = \frac{41x}{400} - \frac{x}{10} = \frac{x}{400}.$$

$$\therefore \frac{x}{400} = 25 \text{ or } x = 10000.$$

Hence, the sum is Rs. 10000.

5. Let the sum be Rs. x. Then,

$$\text{C.I.} = x\left(1 + \frac{10}{100}\right)^3 - x = \left(\frac{1331x}{1000} - x\right) = \frac{331x}{1000}.$$

$$\text{S.I.} = \frac{x \times 10 \times 3}{100} = \frac{3x}{10}.$$

$$\therefore (\text{C.I.}) - (\text{S.I.}) = \left(\frac{331x}{1000} - \frac{3x}{100}\right) = \frac{31x}{1000}.$$

$$\therefore \frac{31x}{1000} = 620 \text{ or } x = 20000.$$

Hence, the principal amount is Rs. 20000.

6.
$$\text{C.I.} = \text{Rs. } \left[800 \times \left(1 + \frac{10}{100}\right)^2 - 800\right] = \text{Rs. } 168.$$

$$\text{S.I.} = \text{Rs. } \left(\frac{800 \times 10 \times 2}{100}\right) = \text{Rs. } 160.$$

Gain $= (\text{C.I.}) - (\text{S.I.}) = \text{Rs. } (168 - 160) = \text{Rs. } 8.$

7. C.I. on Rs. 400 for 2 years at 10% p.a.

$$= Rs. \left[400 \times \left(1 + \frac{10}{100} \right)^2 - 400 \right] = Rs. \ 84$$

Required S.I. $= \frac{1}{2} \times Rs. \ 84 = Rs. \ 42.$

Now, S.I. = Rs. 42, Time = 3 years & Rate = 8%

$\therefore$ Sum $= Rs. \left(\frac{100 \times 42}{3 \times 8} \right) = Rs. \ 175.$

8. Let the sum be Rs. x. Then,

$$C.I. = \left[x \times \left(1 + \frac{50}{3 \times 100} \right)^3 - x \right] = \left(\frac{343x}{216} - x \right) = \frac{127x}{216}.$$

$\therefore \frac{127x}{216} = 1270$ or $x = \frac{1270 \times 216}{127} = 2160.$

Thus, the sum is Rs. 2160.

$\therefore$ S.I. $= Rs. \left(2160 \times \frac{50}{3} \times 3 \times \frac{1}{100} \right) = Rs. \ 1080.$

9. Let the sum be Rs. x. Then,

$$C.I. = x \left(1 + \frac{5}{100} \right)^2 - x = \left(\frac{441x}{400} - x \right) = \frac{41x}{400}.$$

$\therefore \frac{41x}{400} = 328$ or $x = \frac{328 \times 400}{41} = 3200.$

$\therefore$ S.I. $= Rs. \left(\frac{3200 \times 5 \times 2}{100} \right) = Rs. \ 320.$

10. Amount $= Rs. \left[5600 \times \left(1 + \frac{10}{100} \right) \times \left(1 + \frac{\frac{1}{2} \times 10}{100} \right) \right]$

$$= Rs. \left(5600 \times \frac{11}{10} \times \frac{21}{20} \right) = Rs. \ 6468.$$

$\therefore$ C.I. = Rs. $(6468 - 5600)$ = Rs. 868.

11. Time $= 2 \frac{73}{365}$ years $= 2 \frac{1}{5}$ years.

$$\therefore \text{ Amount} = Rs. \left[20480 \times \left(1 + \frac{25}{4 \times 100} \right)^2 \left(1 + \frac{\frac{1}{5} \times \frac{25}{4}}{100} \right) \right]$$

$$= Rs. \left(20480 \times \frac{17}{16} \times \frac{17}{16} \times \frac{81}{80} \right) = Rs. \ 23409.$$

$\therefore$ C.I. = Rs. $(23409 - 20480)$ = Rs. 2929.

12. Let the principal at the end of first year be Rs. x.

Then, $\dfrac{x \times 10 \times 1}{100} = 132$ or $x = 1320$.

Now, let the original principal be Rs. P.

Then, amount after 1 year $= P + \dfrac{P \times 10 \times 1}{100} = \dfrac{11P}{10}$.

$\therefore \dfrac{11P}{10} = 1320$ or $P = \dfrac{1320 \times 10}{11} = $ Rs. 1200.

13. Interest on Rs. 578.40 for 1 year = Rs. $(614.55 - 578.40) = $ Rs. 36.15.

$\therefore$ Rate $= \left(\dfrac{100 \times 36.15}{578.40}\right)\% = 6\dfrac{1}{4}\%$.

14. Interest on Rs. 5290 for 1 year = Rs. $(6083.50 - 5290) = $ Rs. 793.50

$\therefore$ Rate $= \left(\dfrac{100 \times 793.50}{5290}\right)\% = 15\%$.

15. $P\left(1 + \dfrac{R}{100}\right)^2 = \dfrac{9}{4}P \Leftrightarrow \left(1 + \dfrac{R}{100}\right)^2 = \dfrac{9}{4} = \left(\dfrac{3}{2}\right)^2$.

$\therefore 1 + \dfrac{R}{100} = \dfrac{3}{2}$ or $\dfrac{R}{100} = \dfrac{1}{2}$ or $R = 50$.

16. Interest on Rs. 4624 for 1 year = Rs. $(6083.50 - 5290) = $ Rs. 793.50.

$\therefore$ Rate $= \left(\dfrac{100 \times 793.50}{4624 \times 1}\right)\% = 6\dfrac{1}{4}\%$.

Now, $x\left(1 + \dfrac{25}{4 \times 100}\right)^2 = 4624$ or $x \times \dfrac{17}{16} \times \dfrac{17}{16} = 4624$

$\therefore x = \left(4624 \times \dfrac{16}{17} \times \dfrac{16}{17}\right) = $ Rs. 4096.

17. $P\left(1 + \dfrac{R}{100}\right)^5 = 2P \Rightarrow \left(1 + \dfrac{R}{100}\right)^5 = 2$ ... (i)

Let $P\left(1 + \dfrac{R}{100}\right)^n = 8P$. Then,

$\left(1 + \dfrac{R}{100}\right)^n = 8 = 2^3 = \left\{\left(1 + \dfrac{R}{100}\right)^5\right\}^3 = \left(1 + \dfrac{R}{100}\right)^{15}$ [*Using* (i)]

$\therefore n = 15$ years.

18. $P\left(1 + \dfrac{R}{100}\right)^3 = 3P \Rightarrow \left(1 + \dfrac{R}{100}\right)^3 = 3$ ...(i)

Let $P\left(1 + \dfrac{R}{100}\right)^n = 9P \Rightarrow \left(1 + \dfrac{R}{100}\right)^n = 9$

$$\therefore \left(1 + \frac{R}{100}\right)^n = 3^2 = \left[\left(1 + \frac{R}{100}\right)^3\right]^2 = \left(1 + \frac{R}{100}\right)^6 \qquad [Using\ (i)]$$

Hence, $n = 6$ years.

19. Rate = 5% per half-year. Let time = $2n$ half years = n years.

Then, $800\left(1 + \dfrac{5}{100}\right)^{2n} = 926.10$

$\Leftrightarrow \left(\dfrac{21}{20}\right)^{2n} = \dfrac{926.10}{800} = \dfrac{9261}{8000} = \left(\dfrac{21}{20}\right)^3.$

$\therefore 2n = 3$ or $n = \dfrac{3}{2}$ years.

20. Present worth

$= \text{Rs.}\left[\dfrac{169}{\left(1 + \dfrac{4}{100}\right)^2}\right] = \text{Rs.}\left(169 \times \dfrac{25}{26} \times \dfrac{25}{26}\right) = \text{Rs. } 156.25.$

21. Using A and B both, we may calculate :

Sum $= \left(\dfrac{100 \times 600}{6 \times 5}\right) = \text{Rs. } 2000.$

So, the compound interest may be obtained.

Thus, both A and B together are needed.

22. Clearly, both P and Q are needed.

Using P and Q, rate can be calculated as

Rate $= \left(\dfrac{100 \times 4000}{5 \times 20000}\right) = 4\%.$

Now, C.I. can be calculated.

23. To find out the sum we need rate, time and the difference between C.I. and S.I.

So, Q is necessary.

24. Let the principal be Rs. x. Then,

C.I. $= \left[x\left(1 + \dfrac{10}{100}\right)^2 - x\right] = \dfrac{21x}{100}.$

S.I. $= \left(\dfrac{x \times 10 \times 2}{100}\right) = \dfrac{x}{5}.$

$\therefore$ (C.I.) $-$ (S.I.) $= \left(\dfrac{21x}{100} - \dfrac{x}{5}\right) = \dfrac{x}{100}.$

$\therefore \dfrac{x}{100} = 20$ or $x = 2000.$

25. $12000 \times \left(1 + \dfrac{R}{100}\right)^5 = 24000 \Rightarrow \left(1 + \dfrac{R}{100}\right)^5 = 2$

$\therefore \left[\left(1 + \dfrac{R}{100}\right)^5\right]^4 = 2^4 = 16$ or $\left(1 + \dfrac{R}{100}\right)^{20} = 16$

or $P\left(1 + \dfrac{R}{100}\right)^{20} = 16P$

or $12000\left(1 + \dfrac{R}{100}\right)^{20}$

$\qquad = 16 \times 12000 = 192000.$

26. $P\left(1 + \dfrac{20}{100}\right)^n > 2P$ or $\left(\dfrac{6}{5}\right)^n > 2$

Now $\left(\dfrac{6}{5} \times \dfrac{6}{5} \times \dfrac{6}{5} \times \dfrac{6}{5}\right) > 2$. So, $n = 4$ years.

27. Increase % $= \left(\dfrac{1}{8} \times 100\right)\% = 12\dfrac{1}{2}\%$.

Height after 2 years $= \left[64 \times \left(1 + \dfrac{25}{2 \times 100}\right)^2\right]$ cm

$\qquad = \left(64 \times \dfrac{9}{8} \times \dfrac{9}{8}\right)$ cm $= 81$ cm.

28. S.I. for 1 year = Rs. 720.

S.I. on Rs. 720 for 1 year = Rs. 60

$\therefore$ Rate $= \left(\dfrac{100 \times 60}{720 \times 1}\right) = 8\dfrac{1}{3}\%$.

29. Diff. in C.I. & S.I. for 2 years = Rs. 32.

S.I. for 1 year = Rs. 400.

$\therefore$ S.I. on Rs. 400 for 1 year = Rs. 32.

$\therefore$ Rate $= \left(\dfrac{100 \times 32}{400 \times 1}\right)\% = 8\%$.

Hence, diff. in C.I. and S.I. for 3rd year

$\qquad = $ S.I. on Rs. 832 = Rs. $\left(832 \times \dfrac{8}{100} \times 1\right) = $ Rs. 66.56.

Total difference = Rs. $(32 + 66.56) = $ Rs. 98.56.

30. For first year, S.I. = C.I.

Now, Rs. 16 is the S.I. on S.I. for 1 year.

$\therefore$ Rs. 10 is S.I. on Rs. 100

$\therefore$ Rs. 16 is S.I. on Rs. $\left(\dfrac{100}{10} \times 16\right) = $ Rs. 160

364

∴ S.I. on principal for 1 year at 10% is Rs. 160.

∴ Principal = Rs. $\left(\dfrac{100 \times 160}{10 \times 1}\right)$ = Rs. 1600.

Amount for 2 years compounded half yearly

$$= Rs.\left[1600 \times \left(1 + \frac{5}{100}\right)^{4}\right] = Rs.\ 1944.81.$$

∴ C.I. = Rs. (1944.81 − 1600) = Rs. 344.81

S.I. = Rs. $\left(\dfrac{1600 \times 10 \times 2}{100}\right)$ = Rs. 320.

∴ (C.I.) − (S.I.) = Rs. (344.81 − 320) = Rs. 24.81.

31. Let the sum be Rs. x. Then,

$$x\left(1 + \frac{R}{100}\right)^{3} = 13380\ \&\ x\left(1 + \frac{R}{100}\right)^{6} = 20070$$

On dividing, we get $\left(1 + \dfrac{R}{100}\right)^{3} = \dfrac{20070}{13380} = \dfrac{3}{2}$

∴ $x \times \dfrac{3}{2} = 13380 \Rightarrow x = \left(13380 \times \dfrac{2}{3}\right) = 8920.$

Hence, the sum is Rs. 8920.

32. Principal

= (P.W. of Rs. 121 due 1 year hence) + (P.W. of Rs. 121 due 2 years hence)

$$= \left[\frac{121}{\left(1 + \dfrac{10}{100}\right)} + \frac{121}{\left(1 + \dfrac{10}{100}\right)^{2}}\right] = Rs.\ 210.$$

33. Let the value of each instalment be Rs. x. Then,

(P.W. of Rs. x due 1 year hence)+ (P.W. of Rs. x due 2 years hence)

= Rs. 1100.

∴ $\dfrac{x}{\left(1 + \dfrac{20}{100}\right)} + \dfrac{x}{\left(1 + \dfrac{20}{100}\right)^{2}} = 1100$

or $\dfrac{5x}{6} + \dfrac{25x}{36} = 1100$ or $55x = 36 \times 1100$

∴ $x = \left(\dfrac{36 \times 1100}{55}\right) = Rs.\ 720.$

34. Balance = Rs. $\left[12500 \times \left(1 + \dfrac{20}{100}\right)^{3}\right]$

$$- Rs. \left[2000 \times \left(1 + \frac{20}{100} \right)^2 + 2000 \times \left(1 + \frac{20}{100} \right) + 2000 \right]$$

$$= Rs. \left[\left(12500 \times \frac{6}{5} \times \frac{6}{5} \times \frac{6}{5} \right) \right] - \left[\left(2000 \times \frac{6}{5} \times \frac{6}{5} + 2000 \times \frac{6}{5} + 2000 \right) \right]$$

$$= Rs. [21600 - (2880 + 2400 + 2000)] = Rs. 14320.$$

35. $S.I. = Rs. \left(\dfrac{1200 \times 10 \times 1}{100} \right) = Rs. 120.$

$C.I. = Rs. \left[1200 \times \left(1 + \dfrac{5}{100} \right)^2 - 1200 \right] = Rs. 123.$

$\therefore (C.I.) - (S.I.) = Rs. (123 - 120) = Rs. 3.$

36. C.I. when interest is compounded half yearly

$$= Rs. \left[1600 \times \left(1 + \frac{10}{100} \right)^2 - 1600 \right] = Rs. 336.$$

C.I. when interest is compounded quarterly

$$= Rs. \left[1600 \times \left(1 + \frac{5}{100} \right)^4 - 1600 \right] = Rs. 344.81$$

$\therefore$ Difference $= Rs. (344.81 - 336) = Rs. 8.81.$

37. Time $= 2$ years 4 months $= 2\dfrac{4}{12}$ years $= 2\dfrac{1}{3}$ years.

$$\therefore C.I. = Rs. \left[8000 \times \left(1 + \frac{15}{100} \right)^2 \times \left(1 + \frac{\frac{1}{3} \times 15}{100} \right) - 8000 \right]$$

$$= Rs. \left(8000 \times \frac{23}{20} \times \frac{23}{20} \times \frac{21}{20} - 8000 \right) = Rs. 3109.$$

38. $P.W. = \dfrac{4813}{\left(1 + \dfrac{25}{4 \times 100} \right)^3} = \left(4813 \times \dfrac{16}{17} \times \dfrac{16}{17} \times \dfrac{16}{17} \right) = Rs. 4096.$

39. Let each instalment be Rs. x. Then,

$$\frac{x}{\left(1 + \dfrac{50}{3 \times 100} \right)} + \frac{x}{\left(1 + \dfrac{50}{3 \times 100} \right)^2} + \frac{x}{\left(1 + \dfrac{50}{3 \times 100} \right)^3} = 7620.$$

or $\dfrac{6x}{7} + \dfrac{36x}{49} + \dfrac{216x}{343} = 7620$

$294x + 252x + 216x = 7620 \times 343$ or $x = \dfrac{7620 \times 343}{762} = 3430$.

$\therefore$ Amount of each instalment = Rs 3430.

40. Amount = Rs. $(30000 + 4347)$ = Rs. 34347.

Let $30000\left(1 + \dfrac{7}{100}\right)^n = 34347$ or $\left(\dfrac{107}{100}\right)^n = \dfrac{34347}{30000} = \dfrac{11449}{10000} = \left(\dfrac{107}{100}\right)^2$

$\therefore$ $n = 2$ years.

41. $1200 \times \left(1 + \dfrac{R}{100}\right)^2 + 1348.32$ or $\left(1 + \dfrac{R}{100}\right)^2 = \dfrac{134832}{120000} = \dfrac{11236}{10000}$

$\therefore$ $\left(1 + \dfrac{R}{100}\right)^2 = \left(\dfrac{106}{100}\right)^2$ or $1 + \dfrac{R}{100} = \dfrac{106}{100}$ or $R = 6\%$.

42. Interest on Rs. 800 for 1 year = Rs. $(840 - 800)$ = Rs. 40.

$\therefore$ Rate = $\left(\dfrac{100 \times 40}{800 \times 1}\right)\% = 5\%$.

43. $P\left(1 + \dfrac{R}{100}\right)^3 = 8P$ or $\left(1 + \dfrac{R}{100}\right)^3 = 8 = 2^3$.

$\therefore$ $1 + \dfrac{R}{100} = 2$ or $\dfrac{R}{100} = 1$ or $R = 100$.

ARITHMETIC

(Subjective and Objective)

By : R. S. Aggarwal

¤ *For various competitive examinations – Bank P.O., LIC, GIC, Excise, Income Tax, Civil Services, Railways, I.F.S, Hotel Management, Defence Services, C.B.I etc.*

¤ *Containing more than 1500 subjective and 3000 objective questions with brief and concise solutions*

23. Logarithms

Logarithm : If a is a positive real number, other than 1 and $a^m = x$, then we write $m = \log_a x$ and say that the value of $\log x$ to the base a is m.

Ex. (i) $10^3 = 1000 \Leftrightarrow \log_{10} 1000 = 3$ (ii) $3^4 = 81 \Leftrightarrow \log_3 81 = 4$

(iii) $2^{-3} = \dfrac{1}{8} \Leftrightarrow \log_2 \dfrac{1}{8} = -3$ (iv) $(.1)^2 = .01 \Leftrightarrow \log_{(.1)} .01 = 2$

Properties of Logarithms :

(i) $\log_a (xy) = \log_a x + \log_a y$ (ii) $\log_a \left(\dfrac{x}{y}\right) = \log_a x - \log_a y$

(iii) $\log_x x = 1$ (iv) $\log_a 1 = 0$

(v) $\log_a (x^p) = p (\log_a x)$ (vi) $\log_a x = \dfrac{1}{\log_x a}$

(vii) $\log_a x = \dfrac{\log_b x}{\log_b a} = \dfrac{\log x}{\log a}$.

Remarks : (i) When base is not mentioned, it is taken as 10.

(ii) Logarithms to the base 10 are known as common logarithms.

Note : The logarithm of a number contains two parts, namely characteristic and mantissa. The integral part is known as characteristic and the decimal part is known as mantissa.

Characteristic :

Case I : When the number is greater than 1.

In this case, the characteristic is one less than the number of digits in the left of decimal point in the given number.

Case II : When the number is less than 1.

In this case, the characteristic is one more than the number of zeros between the decimal point and the first significant digit of the number and it is negative.

Instead of $-1, -2$ etc. we write, $\bar{1}$ (one bar), $\bar{2}$ (two bar) etc.

Ex. 1.

Number	Characteristic	Number	Characteristic
256.37	2	0.6173	$\bar{1}$
37.481	1	0.03125	$\bar{2}$
9.2193	0	0.00125	$\bar{3}$

For mantissa, we look through log table.

Antilog : If $\log x = y$, then antilog $y = x$.

How to Insert Decimal Point ?

Case I : When characteristic is positive.

In this case, if n is the characteristic, insert the decimal point after the $(n + 1)$ th digit.

Case II : When characteristic is negative.

If $\bar{n}$ is the characteristic, then insert the decimal point so that the first significant figure is at n th place.

Ex. 2. Find (*i*) *antilog (2.4567)* (*ii*) *antilog ($\bar{2}$.4567)*

Sol. From the table of antilog, we have antilog (.4567) = 2863.

(*i*) When characteristic is 2, we insert decimal point after (2 + 1),
    i.e. 3 places

∴ antilog (2.4567) = 286.3.

(*ii*) When characteristic is $\bar{2}$, we insert decimal point so that the
    first significant digit is at 2nd place.

∴ antilog ($\bar{2}$.4567) = .02863.

Solved Problems

Ex. 1. Evaluate :

(*i*) $\log_3 27$ (*ii*) $\log_7\left(\dfrac{1}{343}\right)$ (*iii*) $\log_{100}(0.01)$

Sol. (*i*) Let $\log_3 27 = n$.

Then, $3^n = 27 = 3^3$ or $n = 3$.   ∴ $\log_3 27 = 3$.

(*ii*) Let $\log_7\left(\dfrac{1}{343}\right) = n$.

Then, $7^n = \dfrac{1}{343} = \dfrac{1}{7^3} = 7^{-3}$ or $n = -3$. ∴ $\log_7\left(\dfrac{1}{343}\right) = -3$

(*iii*) Let $\log_{100}(0.01) = n$.

Then, $(100)^n = 0.01 = \dfrac{1}{100} = (100)^{-1}$

So, $n = -1$.   ∴ $\log_{100}(0.01) = -1$.

Ex. 2. Evaluate :   (*i*) $\log_7 1$ (*ii*) $\log_{34} 34$ (*iii*) $36^{\log_6 4}$.

Sol. (*i*) We know that $\log_a 1 = 0$, so $\log_7 1 = 0$.

(*ii*) We know that $\log_a a = 1$, so $\log_{34} 34 = 1$.

(*iii*) We know that $a^{\log_a x} = x$.

Now, $36^{\log_6 4} = (6^2)^{\log_6 4} = 6^{2(\log_6 4)} = 6^{\log_6 (4^2)} = 6^{\log_6 16} = 16$.

Ex. 3. Evaluate :

(*i*) $\log_5 3 \times \log_{27} 25$ (*ii*) $\log_9 27 - \log_{27} 9$.

Sol. (*i*) $\log_5 3 \times \log_{27} 25 = \dfrac{\log 3}{\log 5} \times \dfrac{\log 25}{\log 27} = \dfrac{\log 3}{\log 5} \times \dfrac{\log (5^2)}{\log (3^3)}$

$$= \dfrac{\log 3}{\log 5} \times \dfrac{2 \log 5}{3 \log 3} = \dfrac{2}{3}.$$

(*ii*) Let $\log_9 27 = n$.

Then, $9^n = 27 \Leftrightarrow 3^{2n} = 3^3 \Leftrightarrow 2n = 3 \Leftrightarrow n = \dfrac{3}{2}$.

Again, let $\log_{27} 9 = m$. Then, $27^m = 9 \Leftrightarrow 3^{3m} = 3^2 \Leftrightarrow 3m = 2 \Leftrightarrow m = \dfrac{2}{3}$.

$\therefore \log_9 27 - \log_{27} 9 = (n - m) = \left(\dfrac{3}{2} - \dfrac{2}{3}\right) = \dfrac{5}{6}$.

Ex. 4. *If* $\log_{\sqrt{8}} x = 3\dfrac{1}{3}$*, find the value of x.*

Sol. $\log_{\sqrt{8}} x = \dfrac{10}{3} \Leftrightarrow x = (\sqrt{8})^{10/3} = (2^{3/2})^{10/3} = 2^{\left(\frac{3}{2} \times \frac{10}{3}\right)} = 2^5 = 32.$

Ex. 5. *If* $\log 2 = 0.3010$ *and* $\log 3 = 0.4717$*, find the values of*
    (i) $\log 25$ *(ii)* $\log 4.5$*.*

Sol. *(i)* $\log 25 = \log\left(\dfrac{100}{4}\right) = \log 100 - \log 4 = 2 - 2\log 2$

$$= (2 - 2 \times 0.3010) = 1.398.$$

(ii) $\log 4.5 = \log\left(\dfrac{9}{2}\right) = \log 9 - \log 2 = \log 3^2 - \log 2$

$$= (2\log 3 - \log 2) = (2 \times 0.4714 - 0.3010) = 0.6532.$$

Ex. 6. *If* $\log 2 = 0.30103$*, find the number of digits in* 2^{56}*.*

Sol. $\log(2^{56}) = 56 \times \log 2 = (56 \times 0.30103) = 16.85768.$

Its characteristic is 16. Hence, the number of digits in 2^{56} is 17.

EXERCISE 23

Mark ($\sqrt{}$) against the correct statement :

1. The value of $\log_{343} 7$ is :

   (a) $\dfrac{1}{3}$ (b) -3 (c) $-\dfrac{1}{3}$ (d) 3

2. The value of $\log_5\left(\dfrac{1}{125}\right)$ is :

   (a) 3   (b) -3 (c) $\dfrac{1}{3}$ (d) $-\dfrac{1}{3}$

3. The value of $\log_{\sqrt{2}} 32$ is :

   (a) $\dfrac{5}{2}$ (b) 5   (c) 10   (d) $\dfrac{1}{10}$

4. The value of $\log_{10}(.0001)$ is :

   (a) $\dfrac{1}{4}$ (b) $-\dfrac{1}{4}$ (c) -4 (d) 4

5. The value of $\log_{(.01)}(1000)$ is :

   (a) $\dfrac{1}{3}$ (b) $-\dfrac{1}{3}$ (c) $\dfrac{3}{2}$ (d) $-\dfrac{3}{2}$

6. If $\log_3 x = -2$, then x is equal to :   **(C.D.S. 1994)**

    (a) -9 (b) -6 (c) -8 (d) $\dfrac{1}{9}$

7. If $\log_8 x = \dfrac{2}{3}$, then the value of x is :

    (a) $\dfrac{3}{4}$ (b) $\dfrac{4}{3}$ (c) 4 (d) 3

8. If $\log_x \left(\dfrac{9}{16}\right) = -\dfrac{1}{2}$, then x is equal to :

    (a) $\dfrac{3}{4}$ (b) $-\dfrac{3}{4}$ (c) $\dfrac{81}{256}$ (d) $\dfrac{256}{81}$

9. If $\log_{10000} x = -\dfrac{1}{4}$, then x is equal to :

    (a) $\dfrac{1}{10}$ (b) $\dfrac{1}{100}$ (c) $\dfrac{1}{1000}$ (d) $\dfrac{1}{10000}$

10. If $\log_x 4 = \dfrac{1}{4}$, then x is equal to :

    (a) 16 (b) 64 (c) 128 (d) 256

11. If $\log_x (0.1) = -\dfrac{1}{3}$, then the value of x is :

    (a) 10 (b) 100 (c) 1000 (d) $\dfrac{1}{1000}$

12. If $\log_{32} x = 0.8$, then x is equal to :

    (a) 25.6 (b) 16 (c) 10 (d) 12.8

13. If $\log_4 x + \log_2 x = 6$, then x is equal to :

    (a) 2 (b) 4 (c) 8 (d) 16

14. If $\log_8 x + \log_8 \dfrac{1}{6} = \dfrac{1}{3}$, then the value of x is :

    (a) 12 (b) 16 (c) 18 (d) 24

15. If $\log 2 = 0.30103$, then the number of digits in 4^{50} is :   **(C.D.S. 1994)**

    (a) 30 (b) 31 (c) 100 (d) 200

16. If $\log 2 = 0.30103$, then the number of digits in 5^{20} is :

    (a) 14 (b) 16 (c) 18 (d) 25

17. The value of $\log_{(-1/3)} 81$ is equal to :

    (a) -27 (b) -4 (c) 4 (d) 27

18. The value of $\log_{2\sqrt{3}} (1728)$ is equal to :

    (a) 3 (b) 5 (c) 6 (d) 9

19. The value of $\log_2 (\log_5 625)$ is :

    (a) 2 (b) 5 (c) 10 (d) 15

20. The value of $\left(\dfrac{1}{3} \log_{10} 125 - 2 \log_{10} 4 + \log_{10} 32\right)$ is :

    (a) 0 (b) $\dfrac{4}{5}$ (c) 2 (d) 1

21. $\left[\log\left(\dfrac{a^2}{bc}\right) + \log\left(\dfrac{b^2}{ac}\right) + \log\left(\dfrac{c^2}{ab}\right)\right]$ is equal to :

    (a) 0   (b) 1   (c) 2   (d) abc

22. $(\log_b a \times \log_c b \times \log_a c)$ is equal to :

    (a) 0   (b) 1   (c) abc   (d) $a+b+c$

23. $\left[\dfrac{1}{\log_{xy}(xyz)} + \dfrac{1}{\log_{yz}(xyz)} + \dfrac{1}{\log_{zx}(xyz)}\right]$ is equal to :

    (a) 1   (b) 2   (c) 3   (d) 4

24. $\left[\dfrac{1}{(\log_a bc)+1} + \dfrac{1}{(\log_b ca)+1} + \dfrac{1}{(\log_c ab)+1}\right]$ is equal to :

    (a) 1   (b) 2   (c) 3   (d) $\dfrac{3}{2}$

25. If $\log_2[\log_3(\log_2 x)] = 1$, then x is equal to :

    (a) 512   (b) 128   (c) 12   (d) 0

26. $(\log_5 3) \times (\log_3 625)$ equals :   **(C.D.S. 1994)**

    (a) 1   (b) 2   (c) 3   (d) 4

27. $(\log_5 5)(\log_4 9)(\log_3 2)$ is equal to :

    (a) 2   (b) 1   (c) 5   (d) $\dfrac{3}{2}$

28. If $\log_{10} 2 = 0.3010$ and $\log_{10} 3 = 0.4771$, then the value of $\log_{10} 1.5$ is :   **(C.D.S. 1993)**

    (a) 0.7161   (b) 0.1761   (c) 0.7116   (d) 0.7611

29. If $\log_{10} 2 = 0.3010$, then $\log_2 10$ is :

    (a) .3322   (b) 3.2320   (c) 3.3222   (d) 5

30. The value of $\left(\dfrac{1}{\log_3 60} + \dfrac{1}{\log_4 60} + \dfrac{1}{\log_5 60}\right)$ is :

    (a) 0   (b) 1   (c) 5   (d) 60

31. The value of $(\log_3 4)(\log_4 5)(\log_5 6)(\log_6 7)(\log_7 8)(\log_8 9)$

    (a) 2   (b) 7   (c) 8   (d) 33

32. If $\log_{10} 2 = 0.3010$, the value of $\log_{10} 5$ is :

    (a) 0.3241   (b) 0.6911   (c) 0.6990   (d) 0.7525

33. If $\log_{10} 2 = 0.30103$, the value of $\log_{10} 50$ is :

    (a) .69897   (b) 1.30103   (c) 1.69897   (d) 2.30103

34. If $\log_{10} 2 = 0.3010$, the value of $\log_{10} 80$ is :

    (a) 1.9030   (b) 1.6020   (c) 3.9030   (d) None of these

35. If $\log_{10} 2 = 0.3010$, the value of $\log_{10} 25$ is :

    (a) 1.5050   (b) 1.3980   (c) 1.2040   (d) 0.6020

36. The value of $(\log_9 27 + \log_8 32)$ is :

    (a) 4   (b) 7   (c) $\dfrac{7}{2}$ (d) $\dfrac{19}{6}$

37. If $\log_4 x + \log_2 x = 6$, then the value of x is :

    (a) 2   (b) 4   (c) 8   (d) 16

38. If $\log_{10}(0.1) = -1$, then $\log_{10}(.001)$ is :

    (a) -1.3 (b) -2 (c) -2.3 (d) -3

39. The value of $16^{\log_4 5}$ is :

    (a) 5   (b) 16   (c) 25   (d) $\dfrac{5}{64}$

40. If $\log_5(x^2 + x) - \log_5(x+1) = 2$, then the value of x is :

    (a) 5   (b) 32   (c) 25   (d) 10

41. If $\log \dfrac{a}{b} + \log \dfrac{b}{a} = \log(a+b)$, then :

    (a) $a + b = 1$ (b) $a - b = 1$ (c) $a^2 - b^2 = 1$ (d) $a = b$

42. If $\log x + \log y = \log(x + y)$, then :

    (a) $x = y$ (b) $xy = 1$ (c) $y = \dfrac{x-1}{x}$ (d) $y = \dfrac{x}{x-1}$

43. If $\log_{10} 125 + \log_{10} 8 = x$, then x is equal to :

    (a) 3   (b) -3 (c) $\dfrac{1}{3}$ (d) .064

44. The value of $\left[\dfrac{1}{\log_{(p/q)} x} + \dfrac{1}{\log_{(q/r)} x} + \dfrac{1}{\log_{(r/p)} x} \right]$ is :

    (a) 3   (b) 2   (c) 1   (d) 0

45. If $\log 2 = 0.3010$ and $\log 3 = 0.4771$ then the value of $\log 4.5$ is :

    (a) 0.6532   (b) 0.7727   (c) 0.3266   (d) None of these

ANSWERS

1. (a)	**2.** (b)	**3.** (c)	**4.** (c)	**5.** (d)	**6.** (d)	**7.** (c)	**8.** (d)	**9.** (a)
10. (d)	**11.** (c)	**12.** (b)	**13.** (d)	**14.** (a)	**15.** (b)	**16.** (a)	**17.** (b)	**18.** (c)
19. (a)	**20.** (d)	**21.** (a)	**22.** (b)	**23.** (b)	**24.** (a)	**25.** (a)	**26.** (d)	**27.** (b)
28. (b)	**29.** (c)	**30.** (b)	**31.** (a)	**32.** (c)	**33.** (c)	**34.** (a)	**35.** (b)	**36.** (d)
37. (d)	**38.** (d)	**39.** (c)	**40.** (c)	**41.** (a)	**42.** (d)	**43.** (a)	**44.** (d)	**45.** (a)

SOLUTIONS

1.   Let $\log_{343} 7 = m$.

     Then, $(343)^m = 7 \Leftrightarrow (7^3)^m = 7 \Leftrightarrow 7^{3m} = 7^1 \Leftrightarrow 3m = 1 \Leftrightarrow m = \dfrac{1}{3}$.

     $\therefore \ \log_{343} 7 = \dfrac{1}{3}$.

2.   Let $\log_5 \left(\dfrac{1}{125} \right) = m$. Then

$$5^m = \frac{1}{125} \Leftrightarrow 5^m = \frac{1}{5^3} \Leftrightarrow 5^m = 5^{-3} \quad \therefore \ m = -3 \text{ and so } \log_5\left(\frac{1}{125}\right) = -3.$$

3. Let $\log_{\sqrt{2}} 32 = m$. Then

$$(\sqrt{2})^m = 32 \Leftrightarrow 2^{m/2} = 2^5 \Leftrightarrow \frac{m}{2} = 5 \Leftrightarrow m = 10.$$

$$\therefore \ \log_{\sqrt{2}} 32 = 10.$$

4. Let $\log_{10} (.0001) = m$. Then,

$$10^m = .0001 \Leftrightarrow 10^m = \frac{1}{10000} \Leftrightarrow 10^m = \frac{1}{10^4} \Leftrightarrow 10^m = 10^{-4} \Leftrightarrow m = -4.$$

$$\therefore \ \log_{10} (.0001) = -4.$$

5. Let $\log_{(.01)} (1000) = m$. Then,

$$(.01)^m = 1000 \Leftrightarrow \left(\frac{1}{100}\right)^m = 1000$$

$$\Leftrightarrow \left(\frac{1}{10^2}\right)^m = 10^3 \Leftrightarrow (10^{-2})^m = 10^3 \Leftrightarrow 10^{-2m} = 10^3.$$

$$\therefore \ -2m = 3 \ \text{ or } \ m = -\frac{3}{2}.$$

6. $\log_3 x = -2 \Leftrightarrow x = 3^{-2} = \frac{1}{3^2} = \frac{1}{9}.$

7. $\log_8 x = \frac{2}{3} \Leftrightarrow x = 8^{2/3} = (2^3)^{2/3} = 2^{\left(3 \times \frac{2}{3}\right)} = 2^2 = 4.$

8. $\log_x \left(\frac{9}{16}\right) = -\frac{1}{2} \Leftrightarrow x^{-1/2} = \frac{9}{16} \Leftrightarrow \frac{1}{\sqrt{x}} = \frac{9}{16} \Leftrightarrow \sqrt{x} = \frac{16}{9}.$

$$\therefore \ x = \left(\frac{16}{9} \times \frac{16}{9}\right) = \frac{256}{81}.$$

9. $\log_{10000} x = -\frac{1}{4} \Leftrightarrow x = (10000)^{-1/4} = (10^4)^{-1/4} = 10^{-1} = \frac{1}{10}.$

10. $\log_x 4 = \frac{1}{4} \Leftrightarrow x^{1/4} = 4 \Leftrightarrow x = 4^4 = 256.$

11. $\log_x (0.1) = -\frac{1}{3} \Leftrightarrow x^{-1/3} = 0.1 \Leftrightarrow \frac{1}{x^{1/3}} = 0.1$

$$\therefore \ x^{1/3} = \frac{1}{0.1} = 10 \ \text{ or } \ x = (10)^3 = 1000.$$

12. $\log_{32} x = 0.8 \Leftrightarrow x = (32)^{0.8} = (2^5)^{4/5} = 2^4 = 16.$

13. $\log_4 x + \log_2 x = 6 \Leftrightarrow \frac{\log x}{\log 4} + \frac{\log x}{\log 2} = 6$

$$\therefore \ \frac{\log x}{2 \log 2} + \frac{\log x}{\log 2} = 6 \Leftrightarrow 3 \log x = 12 \log 2$$

or $\log x = 4 \log 2 \Leftrightarrow \log x = \log 2^4$ or $x = 2^4 = 16$.

14. $\log_8 x + \log_8 \frac{1}{6} = \frac{1}{3} \Leftrightarrow \dfrac{\log x}{\log 8} + \dfrac{\log \frac{1}{6}}{\log 8} = \frac{1}{3}$

$\therefore \log x + \log \frac{1}{6} = \frac{1}{3} \log 8$ or $\log x + \log \frac{1}{6} = \log (8^{1/3}) = \log (2^3)^{1/3}$.

$\therefore \log x + \log \frac{1}{6} = \log 2$ or $\log x = \log 2 - \log \frac{1}{6} = \log \left(2 \times \frac{6}{1} \right) = \log 12$.

$\therefore x = 12$.

15. $\log 4^{50} = 50 \log 4 = 50 \log 2^2 = (50 \times 2) \log 2 = 100 \times \log 2$
$$= (100 \times 0.30103) = 30.103.$$

$\therefore$ Characteristic $= 30$.

Hence, the number of digits in 4^{50} is 31.

16. $\log 5^{20} = 20 \log 5 = 20 \times \left[\log \left(\frac{10}{2} \right) \right] = 20 \times [\log 10 - \log 2]$
$$= 20 \times [1 - 0.3010] = 20 \times .6990 = 13.9800$$

$\therefore$ Characteristic $= 13$.

$\therefore$ Number of digits in 5^{20} is 14.

17. Let $\log_{(-1/3)} 81 = x$. Then, $\left(-\frac{1}{3} \right)^x = 81 = 3^4 = (-3)^4 = \left(-\frac{1}{3} \right)^4$.

$\therefore x = -4$.

18. Let $\log_{2\sqrt{3}} (1728) = x$. Then,

$(2\sqrt{3})^x = 1728 = (12)^3 = [(2\sqrt{3})^2]^3 = (2\sqrt{3})^6$.

$\therefore x = 6$.

19. Let $\log_5 625 = x$. Then, $5^x = 625 = 5^4$ or $x = 4$.

Let $\log_2 (\log_5 625) = y$. Then, $\log_2 (4) = y$ or $2^y = 4 = 2^2$. So, $y = 2$.

$\therefore \log_2 (\log_5 625) = 2$.

20. $\frac{1}{3} \log_{10} 125 - 2 \log_{10} 4 + \log_{10} 32$

$= \log_{10} (125)^{1/3} - \log_{10} (4^2) + \log_{10} 32 = \log_{10} 5 - \log_{10} 16 + \log_{10} 32$

$= \log_{10} \left(\frac{5 \times 32}{16} \right) = \log_{10} 10 = 1$.

21. Given Expression $= \log \left[\dfrac{a^2}{bc} \times \dfrac{b^2}{ac} \times \dfrac{c^2}{ab} \right] = \log 1 = 0$.

22. Given Expression $= \left(\dfrac{\log a}{\log b} \times \dfrac{\log b}{\log c} \times \dfrac{\log c}{\log a} \right) = 1$.

23. Given Expression $= \log_{xyz} (xy) + \log_{xyz} (yz) + \log_{xyz} (zx)$

$= \log_{xyz} (xy \times yz \times zx) = \log_{xyz} (xyz)^2$

$$= 2 \log_{xyz} (xyz) = 2 \times 1 = 2.$$

24. Given Exp. $= \dfrac{1}{\log_a bc + \log_a a} + \dfrac{1}{\log_b ca + \log_b b} + \dfrac{1}{\log_c ab + \log_c c}$

$$= \dfrac{1}{\log_a (abc)} + \dfrac{1}{\log_b (abc)} + \dfrac{1}{\log_c (abc)}$$

$$= \log_{abc} a + \log_{abc} b + \log_{abc} c$$

$$= \log_{abc} (abc) = 1.$$

25. $\log_2 [\log_3 (\log_2 x)] = 1 = \log_2 2$

$$\Leftrightarrow \log_3 (\log_2 x) = 2 \Leftrightarrow \log_2 x = 3^2 = 9 \Leftrightarrow x = 2^9 = 512.$$

26. Given Expression $= \left(\dfrac{\log 3}{\log 5} \times \dfrac{\log 625}{\log 3} \right) = \dfrac{\log 3}{\log 5} \times \dfrac{\log 5^4}{\log 3}$

$$= \dfrac{4 \log 5}{\log 5} = 4.$$

27. Given Exp. $= \dfrac{\log 9}{\log 4} \times \dfrac{\log 2}{\log 3}$ $[\because \log_5 5 = 1]$

$$= \dfrac{\log 3^2}{\log 2^2} \times \dfrac{\log 2}{\log 3} = \dfrac{2 \log 3}{2 \log 2} \times \dfrac{\log 2}{\log 3} = 1.$$

28. $\log_{10} (1.5) = \log_{10} \left(\dfrac{3}{2} \right) = \log_{10} 3 - \log_{10} 2 = (0.4771 - 0.3010) = 0.1761.$

29. $\log_2 10 = \dfrac{1}{\log_{10} 2} = \dfrac{1}{.3010} = \dfrac{10000}{3010} = 3.3222.$

30. Given Expression $= \log_{60} 3 + \log_{60} 4 + \log_{60} 5$

$$= \log_{60} (3 \times 4 \times 5) = \log_{60} 60 = 1.$$

31. Given Expression $= \left(\dfrac{\log 4}{\log 3} \times \dfrac{\log 5}{\log 4} \times \dfrac{\log 6}{\log 5} \times \dfrac{\log 7}{\log 6} \times \dfrac{\log 8}{\log 7} \times \dfrac{\log 9}{\log 8} \right)$

$$= \dfrac{\log 9}{\log 3} = \dfrac{\log 3^2}{\log 3} = \dfrac{2 \log 3}{\log 3} = 2.$$

32. $\log_{10} 5 = \log_{10} \left(\dfrac{10}{2} \right) = \log_{10} 10 - \log_{10} 2$

$$= 1 - \log_{10} 2 = (1 - 0.3010) = 0.6990.$$

33. $\log_{10} 50 = \log_{10} \left(\dfrac{100}{2} \right) = \log_{10} 100 - \log_{10} 2 = 2 - 0.30103 = 1.69897.$

34. $\log_{10} 80 = \log_{10} (8 \times 10) = \log_{10} 8 + \log_{10} 10 = \log_{10} 2^3 + 1$

$$= (3 \log_{10} 2) + 1 = (3 \times 0.3010) + 1 = 1.9030.$$

35. $\log_{10} 25 = \log_{10} \left(\dfrac{100}{4} \right) = \log_{10} 100 - \log_{10} 4 = 2 - 2 \log_{10} 2$

$$= (2 - 2 \times 0.3010) = (2 - 0.6020) = 1.3980.$$

36. Let $\log_9 27 = x$. Then, $9^x = 27 \Leftrightarrow (3^2)^x = 3^3$

$\therefore 3^{2x} = 3^3$. So, $2x = 3$ or $x = \dfrac{3}{2}$.

Let $\log_8 32 = y$. Then, $8^y = 32$ or $(2^3)^y = 2^5$.

$\therefore 2^{3y} = 2^5$. So, $3y = 5$ or $y = \dfrac{5}{3}$.

$\therefore \log_9 27 + \log_8 32 = \left(\dfrac{3}{2} + \dfrac{5}{3}\right) = \dfrac{19}{6}$.

37. Given equation is $\dfrac{\log x}{\log 4} + \dfrac{\log x}{\log 2} = 6$

or $\dfrac{\log x}{2 \log 2} + \dfrac{\log x}{\log 2} = 6$ or $3 \log x = 12 \log 2$.

$\therefore \log x = 4 \log 2 = \log 2^4$. So, $x = 16$.

38. $\log_{10}(.001) = \log_{10}\left(\dfrac{.1}{100}\right) = \log_{10}(.1) - \log_{10}(100) = (-1 - 2) = -3$.

39. Remember that $a^{\log_a x} = x$.

$\therefore 16^{\log_4 5} = (4^2)^{\log_4 5} = 4^{2 \log_4 5} = 4^{\log_4 (5^2)} = 4^{\log_4 (25)} = 25$.

40. $\log_5 (x^2 + x) - \log_5 (x + 1) = 2 \Rightarrow \log_5 \left(\dfrac{x^2 + x}{x + 1}\right) = 2$

$\therefore \log_5 \left[\dfrac{x(x+1)}{x+1}\right] = 2$ or $\log_5 x = 2$ or $x = 5^2 = 25$.

41. $\log \dfrac{a}{b} + \log \dfrac{b}{a} = \log(a + b)$

$\therefore \log(a + b) = \log\left(\dfrac{a}{b} \times \dfrac{b}{a}\right) = \log 1$. So, $a + b = 1$.

42. $\log x + \log y = \log(x + y) \Rightarrow \log(x + y) = \log(xy)$

$\therefore x + y = xy$ or $y(x - 1) = x$ or $y = \dfrac{x}{x - 1}$.

43. $\log_{10} 125 + \log_{10} 8 = x \Rightarrow \log_{10}(125 \times 8) = x$.

$\therefore x = \log_{10}(1000) = \log_{10}(10^3) = 3 \log_{10} 10 = (3 \times 1) = 3$.

44. Given Expression $= \log_x\left(\dfrac{p}{q}\right) + \log_x\left(\dfrac{q}{r}\right) + \log_x\left(\dfrac{r}{p}\right)$

$= \log_x\left(\dfrac{p}{q} \times \dfrac{q}{r} \times \dfrac{r}{p}\right) = \log 1 = 0$.

45. $\log 4.5 = \log\left(\dfrac{9}{2}\right) = \log 9 - \log 2 = \log(3^2) - \log 2 = 2 \log 3 - \log 2$

$= (2 \times 0.4771 = 0.3010) = 0.6532$.

24. Area

FORMULAE :

I. (*i*) Area of a rectangle = (length × breadth)

$$\therefore \text{ Length} = \left(\frac{\text{Area}}{\text{Breadth}}\right) \text{ and Breadth} = \left(\frac{\text{Area}}{\text{Length}}\right)$$

(*ii*) Perimeter of a rectangle = 2 (length + breadth)

II. Area of a square = $(\text{side})^2 = \frac{1}{2}(\text{diagonal})^2$.

III. Area of 4 walls of a room = 2 (length + breadth) × height.

IV. (*i*) Area of a triangle = $\frac{1}{2} \times$ Base × Height.

(*ii*) Area of a triangle = $\sqrt{s(s-a)(s-b)(s-c)}$, where

$s = \frac{1}{2}(a+b+c)$, and a, b, c are the sides of the triangle.

(*iii*) Area of an equilateral triangle = $\frac{\sqrt{3}}{4} \times (\text{side})^2$.

(*iv*) Radius of incircle of an equilateral triangle of side $a = \frac{a}{2\sqrt{3}}$.

(*v*) Radius of circumcircle of an equilateral triangle of side $a = \frac{a}{\sqrt{3}}$.

V. (*i*) Area of a parallelogram = Base × Height.

(*ii*) Area of a rhombus = $\frac{1}{2} \times$ (Product of diagonals).

(*iii*) The halves of diagonals and a side of a rhombus form a right angled triangle with side as the hypotenuse.

(*iv*) Area of a trapezium

$$= \frac{1}{2} \times (\text{sum of parallel sides}) \times (\text{distance between them}).$$

VI. (*i*) Area of a circle = πR^2.

(*ii*) Circumference of a circle = $2\pi R$.

(*iii*) Length of an arc = $\frac{2\pi R\theta}{360}$.

(*vi*) Area of a sector = $\frac{1}{2}(\text{arc} \times R) = \frac{\pi R^2 \theta}{360}$.

Solved Problems

Ex. 1. *One side of a rectangular field is 15 m and one of its diagonals is 17 m. Find the area of the field.*

Sol. Other side $= \sqrt{(17)^2 - (15)^2} = \sqrt{289 - 225} = \sqrt{64} = 8$ m.

$\therefore$ Area $= (15 \times 8)$ sq. m $= 120$ sq. m.

Ex. 2. *Find the area of a square, one of whose diagonals is 3.8 m long.*

Sol. Area of the square $= \frac{1}{2} \times (\text{diagonal})^2$.

$$= \left(\frac{1}{2} \times 3.8 \times 3.8 \right) m^2 = 7.22 \ m^2.$$

Ex. 3. *Find the area of a triangle whose sides measure 13 cm, 14 cm and 15 cm.*

Sol. Let $a = 13$, $b = 14$ and $c = 15$.

Then, $s = \frac{1}{2}(a + b + c) = 21.$

$\therefore (s - a) = 8$, $(s - b) = 7$ and $(s - c) = 6$.

$\therefore$ Area $= \sqrt{s(s - a)(s - b)(s - c)}$

$$= \sqrt{21 \times 8 \times 7 \times 6} = 84 \ cm^2.$$

Ex. 4. *Find the area of an equilateral triangle each of whose sides is 8 cm long.*

Sol. Area of the triangle $= \left(\frac{\sqrt{3}}{4} \times 8 \times 8 \right) cm^2 = 16\sqrt{3} \ cm^2.$

Ex. 5. *Find the area of a right angled triangle whose base is 12 cm and hypotenuse 13 cm.*

Sol. Height of the triangle $= \sqrt{(13)^2 - (12)^2} = \sqrt{25} = 5$ cm.

$\therefore$ Its area $= \frac{1}{2} \times \text{Base} \times \text{Height} = \left(\frac{1}{2} \times 12 \times 5 \right) cm^2 = 30 \ cm^2.$

Ex. 6. *The base of a triangular field is three times its altitude. If the cost of cultivating the field at Rs. 24.68 per hectare be Rs. 333.18, find its base and height.*

Sol. Area of the field $= \dfrac{\text{Total cost}}{\text{Rate}} = \left(\dfrac{333.18}{24.68} \right)$ hectares $= 13.5$ hectares

$$= (13.5 \times 10000) \ m^2 = 135000 \ m^2.$$

Let, altitude $= x$ metres and base $= 3x$ metres.

Then, $\frac{1}{2} \times 3x \times x = 135000$ or $x^2 = 90000$ or $x = 300.$

$\therefore$ Base $= 900$ m & Altitude $= 300$ m.

Ex. 7. *Find the area of a rhombus one side of which measures 20 cm and one diagonal 24 cm.*

Sol. Let, other diagonal = $2x$ cm.

Since halves of diagonals and one side of a rhombus form a right angled triangle with side as hypotenuse, we have :

$$(20)^2 = (12)^2 + x^2 \text{ or } x = \sqrt{(20)^2 - (12)^2} = \sqrt{256} = 16 \text{ cm.}$$

∴ Other diagonal = 32 cm.

∴ Area of the rhombus $= \dfrac{1}{2} \times$ (Product of diagonals)

$$= \left(\dfrac{1}{2} \times 24 \times 32 \right) \text{cm}^2 = 384 \text{ cm}^2.$$

Ex. 8. *A lawn is in the form of a rectangle having its sides in the ratio 2 : 3. The area of the lawn is $\dfrac{1}{6}$ hectares. Find the length and breadth of the lawn.*

Sol. Let, length = $2x$ metres and breadth = $3x$ metres.

$$\text{Now, area} = \left(\dfrac{1}{6} \times 10000 \right) \text{m}^2 = \left(\dfrac{5000}{3} \right) \text{m}^2.$$

$$\therefore 2x \times 3x = \dfrac{5000}{3} \text{ or } x^2 = \dfrac{2500}{9} \text{ or } x = \left(\dfrac{50}{3} \right) \text{m.}$$

$$\therefore \text{ Length} = 2x = \dfrac{100}{3} \text{ m} = 33\dfrac{1}{3} \text{ m \& Breadth} = 3x = \left(3 \times \dfrac{50}{3} \right) \text{m} = 50 \text{ m.}$$

Ex. 9. *Find the cost of carpeting a room 13 m long and 9 m broad with a carpet 75 cm wide at the rate of Rs. 12.40 per square metre.*

Sol. Area of the carpet = Area of the room = $(13 \times 9) \text{ m}^2 = 117 \text{ m}^2.$

Length of the carpet $= \left(\dfrac{\text{Its area}}{\text{Its breadth}} \right) = \left(117 \times \dfrac{4}{3} \right) \text{m} = 156 \text{ m.}$

∴ Cost = Rs. (156×12.40) = Rs. 1934.40.

Ex. 10. *A room is half as long again as its is broad. The cost of carpeting the room at Rs. 5 per sq. m. is Rs. 270 and the cost of papering the four walls at Rs. 10 per m^2 is Rs. 1720. If a door and 2 windows occupy 8 sq. metres, find the dimensions of the room.*

Sol. Let, breadth = x metres & length = $\dfrac{3x}{2}$ metres.

Area of the floor $= \left(\dfrac{\text{Total cost of carpeting}}{\text{Rate/m}^2} \right) \text{m}^2$

$$= \left(\dfrac{270}{5} \right) \text{m}^2 = 54 \text{ m}^2.$$

$$\therefore \quad x \times \frac{3x}{2} = 54 \quad \text{or} \quad x^2 = 54 \times \frac{2}{3} = 36 \quad \text{or} \quad x = 6.$$

$$\therefore \quad \text{Breadth} = 6 \text{ m \& length} = \left(\frac{3}{2} \times 6\right) \text{m} = 9 \text{ m}.$$

Now, papered area $= \left(\frac{1720}{10}\right) \text{m}^2 = 172 \text{ m}^2$.

Area of 1 door and 2 windows $= 8 \text{m}^2$.

Total area of 4 walls $= (172 + 8) \text{ m}^2 = 180 \text{ m}^2$.

$\therefore$ 2 (length + breadth) × height = 180

or $2 (9 + 6) \times H = 180$ or $H = \left(\frac{180}{30}\right) = 6$ m.

Ex. 11. *A rectangular grassy plot 110 m by 65 m has a gravel path 2.5 m wide all round it on the inside. Find the cost of gravelling the path at 80 paise per sq. metre.*

Sol. Area of the plot $= (110 \times 65) \text{ m}^2 = 7150 \text{ m}^2$.
Area of the plot excluding the path

$$= [(110 - 5) \times (65 - 5)] \text{ m}^2 = 6300 \text{ m}^2.$$

$\therefore$ Area of the path $= (7150 - 6300) \text{ m}^2 = 850 \text{ m}^2$.

$\therefore$ Cost of gravelling the path $= \text{Rs.} \left(850 \times \frac{80}{100}\right) = \text{Rs.} 680.$

Ex. 12. *The circumference of a circle is 88 m. Find its area.*

Sol. $2 \pi R = 88 \Rightarrow 2 \times \frac{22}{7} \times R = 88.$

$$\therefore \quad R = \left(88 \times \frac{7}{44}\right) = 14 \text{ m}.$$

$$\therefore \quad \text{Area} = \pi R^2 = \left(\frac{22}{7} \times 14 \times 14\right) \text{m}^2 = 616 \text{ m}^2.$$

Ex. 13. *The area of a circle is 154 cm^2. Find its circumference.*

Sol. $\pi R^2 = 154 \Rightarrow \frac{22}{7} \times R^2 = 154$ or $R^2 = \left(154 \times \frac{7}{22}\right) = 7^2$.

So, $R = 7$ cm.

$$\therefore \quad \text{Circumference} = 2 \pi R = \left(2 \times \frac{22}{7} \times 7\right) \text{cm} = 44 \text{ cm}.$$

Ex. 14. *Two concentric circles form a ring. The inner and outer circumferences of the ring are $50 \frac{2}{7}$ m and $75 \frac{3}{7}$ m respectively. Find the width of the ring.*

Sol. Let the inner and outer radii be r and R metres.

Then, $2 \pi r = \dfrac{352}{7} \Rightarrow r = \left(\dfrac{352}{7} \times \dfrac{7}{44} \right) = 8$ m.

$2 \pi R = \dfrac{528}{7} \Rightarrow R = \left(\dfrac{528}{7} \times \dfrac{7}{44} \right) = 12$ m.

$\therefore$ Width of the ring $= (R - r) = (12 - 8)$ m $= 4$ m.

Ex. 15. *The inner circumference of a circular race track, 14 m wide, is 440 m. Find the radius of the outer circle.*

Sol. Let inner radius be r metres.

Then, $2 \pi r = 440 \Rightarrow r = \left(440 \times \dfrac{7}{44} \right) = 70$ m.

$\therefore$ Radius of outer circle $= (70 + 14)$ m $= 84$ m.

Ex. 16. *The diameter of the driving wheel of a bus is 140 cm. How many revolutions per minute must the wheel make in order to keep a speed of 66 kmph ?*

Sol. Distance to be covered in 1 min. $= \left(\dfrac{66 \times 1000}{60} \right)$ m $= 1100$ m.

Circumference of the wheel $= \left(2 \times \dfrac{22}{7} \times 0.70 \right)$ m $= 4.4$ m.

$\therefore$ Number of revolutions per min. $= \left(\dfrac{1100}{4.4} \right) = 250$.

EXERCISE 24

Mark ($\sqrt{}$) against the correct answer :

1. The perimeter of a rectangular field is 480 metres and the ratio between the length and breadth is 5 : 3. The area of the field is :

    (a) 7200 m^2 (b) 15000 m^2 (c) 13500 m^2 (d) 54000 m^2
    (Central Excise & I. Tax 1993)

2. If the length and breadth of a rectangular plot are increased by 50% and 20% respectively, then the new area is how many times the original area ?   **(Bank P.O. 1993)**

    (a) $\dfrac{5}{9}$ (b) 10   (c) $\dfrac{9}{5}$ (d) None of these

3. The length of a rectangle is increased by 60%. By what percent would the width have to be decreased to maintain the same area ? **(Bank P.O. 1988)**

    (a) 37.5%   (b) 60%   (c) 75%   (d) 120%

4. If each side of a square is increased by 50%, the ratio of the area of the resulting square to the area of the given square is :

    (a) 5 : 4   (b) 9 : 4   (c) 4 : 5   (d) 4 : 9
    (Central Excise & I. Tax 1993)

5.   The length of a blackboard is 8 cm more than its breadth. If the length is increased by 7 cm and breadth is decreased by 4 cm, the area remains the same. The length and breadth of the black board (in cms) will be : **(Central Excise & I. Tax 1991)**
     (a) 28, 20   (b) 34, 26   (c) 40, 32   (d) 56, 48

6.   If the diagonal of a square is doubled to make the diagonal of another square, the area of the new square will :   **(Assistant Grade 1993)**
     (a) become two-fold   (b) become three-fold
     (c) become four-fold   (d) remain the same

7.   The area of a rectangle is equal to the area of a circle. What is the length of that rectangle ?   **(Bank P.O. 1993)**
     To find out the answer, which of the following informations given in statements P and Q is/are sufficient.
     P : The diameter of the circle is 28 cm.
     Q : The breadth of the rectangle is 22 cm.
     (a) Only P is sufficient   (b) Only Q is sufficient
     (c) Both P and Q are needed
     (d) Even both P & Q are not sufficient

8.   A hall 20 m long and 15 m broad is surrounded by a verandah of uniform width of 2.5 m. The cost of flooring the verandah at Rs. 3.50 per square metre is :   **(Railways 1991)**
     (a) Rs. 500   (b) Rs. 600   (c) Rs. 700   (d) Rs. 800

9.   The number of marble slabs of size 20 cm × 30 cm required to pave the floor of a square room of side 3 metres, is :   **(C.D.S. 1993)**
     (a) 100   (b) 150   (c) 225   (d) 25

10. If each side of a square is increased by 25%, its area is increased by :
     (a) 25%   (b) 50%   (c) 40.5%   (d) 56.25%
                                                (Central Excise & I. Tax 1992)

11. A man walking at the speed of 4 kmph crosses a square field diagonally in 3 minutes. The area of the field is :   **(Assistant Grade 1993)**
     (a) 18000 m^2 (b) 20000 m^2 (c) 19000 m^2 (d) 25000 m^2

12. A square and a rectangle have equal areas. If their perimeters are p_1 and p_2 respectively, then :   **(I. Tax 1992)**
     (a) $p_1 < p_2$ (b) $p_1 = p_2$ (c) $p_1 > p_2$ (d) None

13. If the perimeters of a square and a rectangle are the same, then the areas A and B enclosed by them would satisfy the condition : **(C.D.S. 1989)**
     (a) $A < B$ (b) $A \leq B$ (c) $A > B$ (d) $A \geq B$

14. The ratio of the area of a square to that of the square drawn on its diagonal is :
     (a) 1 : 1   (b) 1 : 2   (c) 1 : 3   (d) 1 : 4

15. If the ratio of the areas of two squares is 9 : 1, the ratio of their perimeters is :   **(Assistant Grade 1990)**

    (*a*) 9 : 1   (*b*) 3 : 1   (*c*) 1 : 3   (*d*)·3 : 4

16. If the diagonal of a rectangle is 17 cm long and the perimeter of the rectangle is 46 cm, then the area of the rectangle is :

    (*a*) 112 cm^2 (*b*) 120 cm^2 (*c*) 132 cm^2 (*d*) 289 cm^2

17. If the perimeter of a rectangle and a square, each is equal to 80 cm and the difference of their areas is 100 sq. cm, the sides of the rectangle are :   **(C.D.S. 1991)**

    (*a*) 35 cm, 15 cm   (*b*) 30 cm, 10 cm

    (*c*) 28 cm, 12 cm   (*d*) 25 cm, 15 cm

18. Of the two square fields, the area of one is 1 hectare, while the other one is broader by 1%. The difference in their areas is :

    (*a*) 100 m^2 (*b*) 101 m^2 (*c*) 200 m^2 (*d*) 201 m^2

19. The length of a rectangle is twice its breadth. If its length is decreased by 5 cm and breadth is increased by 5 cm, the area of the rectangle is increased by 75 sq. cm. The length of the rectangle is :

    (*a*) 20 cm   (*b*) 30 cm   (*c*) 40 cm   (*d*) 50 cm

20. The cost of cultivating a square field at the rate of Rs. 135 per hectare is Rs. 1215. The cost of putting a fence around it at the rate of 75 paise per metre would be :

    (*a*) Rs. 360   (*b*) Rs. 810   (*c*) Rs. 900   (*d*) Rs. 1800

21. Within a rectangular garden 10 m wide and 20 m long, we wish to pave a walk around the borders of uniform width so as to leave an area of 96 m^2 for flowers. How wide should the walk be ?   **(C.D.S. 1994)**

    (*a*) 1 m   (*b*) 2 m   (*c*) 2.1 m   (*d*) 2.5 m

22. The cost of carpeting a room 18 m long with a carpet 75 cm wide at 45 paise per metre is Rs. 81. The breadth of the room is :

    (*a*) 7 m   (*b*) 7.5 m   (*c*) 8 m   (*d*) 8.5 m

23. A rectangular lawn 55 m by 35 m has two roads each 4 m wide running in the middle of it, one parallel to length and the other parallel to breadth. The cost of gravelling the roads at 75 paise per sq. metre is :

    (*a*) Rs. 270   (*b*) Rs. 262.50   (*c*) Rs. 258   (*d*) Rs. 254.50

24. A rectangular field has dimensions 25 m by 15 m. Two mutually perpendicular passages, 2 m wide have been left in the central part. In rest of the field, grass has bee grown. The area under the grass is :

    (*a*) 295 m^2 (*b*) 299 m^2 (*c*) 300 m^2 (*d*) 375 m^2

                                (Central Excise & I. Tax 1991)

25. The ratio between the length and breadth of a rectangular field is 5 : 4. If the breadth is 20 m less than the length, the perimeter of the field is :   **(Bank P.O. 1990)**

(a) 260 m   (b) 280 m   (c) 360 m   (d) None

26. The length and breadth of a rectangular piece of land are in the ratio of 5 : 3. The owner spent Rs. 3000 for surrounding it from all the sides at Rs. 7.50 per metre. The difference between its length and breadth is :   **(Bank P.O. 1991)**

    (a) 50 m   (b) 100 m   (c) 150 m   (d) 200 m

27. The length of a plot is four times its breadth. A play ground measuring 1200 sq. m. occupies one-third of the total area of the plot. What is the length of the plot ?   **(Bank P.O. 1990)**

    (a) 20 m   (b) 30 m   (c) 60 m   (d) None

28. The length of a rectangle is twice its breadth and one of its diagonals measures $10\sqrt{5}$ cm. The perimeter of the rectangle is :

    (a) 60 cm   (b) 50 cm   (c) 250 cm   (d) None

29. If the side of a square is increased by 5 cm, the area increases by 165 sq. cm. The side of the square is :

    (a) 13 cm   (b) 14 cm   (c) 15 cm   (d) 12 cm

30. The length of a rectangle is doubled while its breadth is halved. What is change in area ?

    (a) 50% increase   (b) 75% increase
    (c) 37.5% decrease   (d) No change

31. A hall 36 m long and 15 m broad is to be paved with stones, each measuring 6 dm by 5 dm. The number of stones required is :

    (a) 180   (b) 1800   (c) 18   (d) 18000

32. A rectangular plot is half as long again as it is broad and its area is $\frac{2}{3}$ hectares. Then, its length is :

    (a) 100 m   (b) 33.33 m   (c) 66.66 m   (d) $\frac{100\sqrt{3}}{3}$ m

33. The area of a rectangle is thrice that of a square. If the length of the rectangle is 40 cm and its breadth is $\frac{3}{2}$ times that of the side of the square, then the side of the square is :   **(Bank P.O. 1989)**

    (a) 15 cm   (b) 20 cm   (c) 30 cm   (d) 60 cm

34. A rectangle has 15 cm as its length and 150 sq. cm as its area. If the area is increased to $1\frac{1}{3}$ times the original area by increasing its length only, then the new perimeter is :   **(Bank P.O. 1989)**

    (a) 50 cm   (b) 60 cm   (c) 70 cm   (d) 80 cm

35. A rectangular carpet has an area of 120 sq. metres and a perimeter of 46 metres. The length of its diagonal is :   **(Railways 1991)**

    (a) 15 m   (b) 16 m   (c) 17 m   (d) 20 m

36. A room 5.44 m long and 3.74 m broad is to be paved with square tiles. The least number of square tiles required to cover the floor is :

(a) 176   (b) 192   (c) 184   (d) 162

37. A man cycles round the boundary of a rectangular park at the rate of |12|kmph and completes one full round in 8 minutes. If the ratio between the length and breadth of the park be 3 : 2, then its area is :

(a) 1536 m^2 (b) 15360 m^2 (c) 153600 m^2 (d) None

38. One side of a rectangle is 8 metres long and its diagonal measures 17 metres. The area of the rectangle is :

(a) 126 m^2 (b) 63 m^2 (c) 144.5 m^2 (d) 120 m^2

39. The area of a rectangle 108 m long is the same as that of a square having each side 72 m long. The width of the rectangle is :

(a) 36 m   (b) 48 m   (c) 42 m   (d) 37.5 m

40. The area of a square is 0.5 hectare. Its diagonal is :

(a) 50 m   (b) 100 m   (c) 250 m   (d) $50\sqrt{2}$ m

41. If the base of a rectangle is increased by 10% and the area is unchanged, then the corresponding altitude must be decreased by :   (C.B.I. 1990)

(a) 10%   (b) $9\frac{1}{11}$ %   (c) 11%   (d) $11\frac{1}{9}$ %

42. A rectangular carpet has an area of 60 sq. m. If its diagonal and longer side together equal 5 times the shorter side, the length of the carpet is :   (I. Tax 1991)

(a) 5 m   (b) 12 m   (c) 13 m   (d) 14.5 m

43. The number of square shaped tin sheets of side 20 cm that can be cut off from a square tin sheet of side 1 metre, is :

(a) 5   (b) 10   (c) 25   (d) 20

44. The length and breadth of a square are increased by 40% and 30% respectively. The area of the resulting rectangle exceeds the area of the square by :

(a) 35%   (b) 42%   (c) 62%   (d) 82%

45. The cost of papering the four walls of a room is Rs. 475. Each one of the length, breadth and height of another room is double that of this room. The cost of papering the walls of this new room is :

(a) Rs. 950   (b) Rs. 1425   (c) Rs. 1900   (d) Rs. 712.50

46. The height of a room to its semi-perimeter is 2 : 5. It costs Rs. 260 to paper the walls of the room with paper 50 cm wide at Rs. 2 per metre allowing an area of 15 sq. m. for doors and windows. The height of the room is :   (Central Excise & I. Tax 1993)

(a) 2.6 m   (b) 3.9 m   (c) 4 m   (d) 4.2 m

47. If the area of a rhombus is 15 sq. cm and the length of one of its diagonals is 5 cm, then the length of the other diagonal is :   (U.D.C. 1993)

(a) 3 cm   (b) 5 cm   (c) 6 cm   (d) 7 cm

48. If one side and one diagonal of a rhombus are 5 cm and 8 cm respectively, then its area is :   (Excise & I. Tax 1993)

(a) 20 cm^2 (b) 24 cm^2 (c) 40 cm^2 (d) 26 cm^2

49. In a rhombus whose area is 144 sq. cm, one of its diagonals is twice as long as the other. The lengths of its diagonals are :   **(C.D.S. 1989)**

(a) 12 cm, 24 cm   (b) 6 cm, 12 cm
(c) 24 cm, 48 cm   (d) 18 cm, 32 cm

50. The perimeter of a rhombus is 52 metres and its shorter diagonal is 10 metres long. The length of longer diagonal is :

(a) 12 m   (b) 18 m   (c) 10.4 m   (d) 24 m

51. The length of one diagonal of a rhombus is 80% of the other diagonal. The area of the rhombus is how many times the square of the length of the longer diagonal ?

(a) $\frac{4}{5}$ (b) $\frac{2}{5}$ (c) $\frac{3}{4}$ (d) $\frac{1}{4}$

52. If a square and a rhombus stand on the same base, then the ratio of the areas of the square and the rhombus is :

(a) greater than 1 (b) equal to 1   (c) equal to $\frac{1}{2}$ (d) equal to $\frac{1}{4}$

53. One side of a parallelogram is 18 cm and its distance from the opposite side is 8 cm. The area of the parallelogram is :

(a) 144 cm^2 (b) 72 cm^2 (c) 48 cm^2 (d) 100 cm^2

54. A parallelogram has sides 30 m and 14 m and one of its diagonals is 40 m long. Then, its area is :

(a) 336 m^2 (b) 168 m^2 (c) 480 m^2 (d) 372 m^2

55. The two parallel sides of a trapezium are 1.5 m and 2.5 m respectively. If the perpendicular distance between them is 6.5 metres, the area of the trapezium is :

(a) 26 m^2 (b) 13 m^2 (c) 20 m^2 (d) 10 m^2

56. The parallel sides of a trapezium are in the ratio of 3 : 5 and the perpendicular distance between them is 12 cm. If the area of the trapezium is 384 sq. cm, then the smaller of the parallel sides is :

(a) 16 cm   (b) 24 cm   (c) 32 cm   (d) 40 cm

57. The cross section of a canal is trapezium in shape. The canal is 12 m wide at the top and 8 m wide at the bottom. If the area of the cross section is 840 sq. m, the depth of the canal is :

(a) 42 m   (b) 84 m   (c) 63 m   (d) 8.75 m

58. The three sides of a triangle are 3 cm, 4 cm and 5 cm respectively. Then, its area (in sq. cm) is :   **(I. Tax 1993)**

(a) 4 $\sqrt{2}$ (b) 2 $\sqrt{3}$ (c) $\sqrt{23}$ (d) 6

59. The perimeter of an isosceles triangle is 14 cm and the lateral side is to the base in the ratio 5 : 4. The area of the triangle (in sq. cm.) is :

(a) $\dfrac{\sqrt{21}}{2}$ (b) $\dfrac{3\sqrt{21}}{2}$ (c) $2\sqrt{21}$ (d) $\sqrt{21}$

60. If the area of an equilateral triangle is $24\sqrt{3}$ sq. cm, then its perimeter is :

   (a) 96 cm   (b) $12\sqrt{6}$ cm   (c) $4\sqrt{6}$ cm   (d) $2\sqrt{6}$ cm

61. The ratio between the area of a square of side a and an equilateral triangle of side a, is :   **(Railways 1992)**

   (a) $2 : 1$ (b) $4 : 3$ (c) $2 : \sqrt{3}$ (d) $4 : \sqrt{3}$

62. If x is the length of a median of an equilateral triangle, then its area is :

   (a) x^2 (b) $\dfrac{1}{2}x^2$ (c) $\dfrac{x^2\sqrt{3}}{2}$ (d) $\dfrac{x^2\sqrt{3}}{3}$

63. The altitude of an equilateral triangle of side $3\sqrt{3}$ cm is :

   (a) 3 cm   (b) $2\sqrt{3}$ cm   (c) 4.5 cm   (d) $\dfrac{\sqrt{3}}{4}$ cm

64. A triangle of area $(9 \times y)$ cm^2 has been drawn such that its area is equal to the area of an equilateral triangle of side 6 cm. Then, the value of y is :   **(C.D.S. 1992)**

   (a) $\sqrt{2}$ (b) $\sqrt{3}$ (c) 2   (d) 3

65. If the area of a square with side a is equal to the area of a triangle with base a, then the altitude of the triangle is :

   (a) $\dfrac{a}{2}$ (b) a (c) $2a$ (d) $4a$

66. The area of a right angled triangle is 30 sq. cm and the length of its hypotenuse is 13 cm. The length of the shorter leg is :

   (a) 4 cm   (b) 5 cm   (c) 6 cm   (d) 7 cm

67. In a $\triangle ABC$ we have : $BC = 5$ cm, $AC = 12$ cm and $AB = 13$ cm. The length of the altitude drawn from B on AC is :

   (a) 4 cm   (b) 5 cm   (c) 6 cm   (d) 7 cm

68. If the altitude of an equilateral triangle is $\sqrt{6}$, then its area is :

   (a) $3\sqrt{3}$ (b) $2\sqrt{3}$ (c) $2\sqrt{2}$ (d) $6\sqrt{2}$

69. A square and an equilateral triangle have equal perimeters. If the diagonal of the square is $12\sqrt{2}$ cm, then the area of the triangle is :

   (a) $24\sqrt{2}$ cm^2 (b) $24\sqrt{3}$ cm^2 (c) $48\sqrt{3}$ cm^2 (d) $64\sqrt{3}$ cm^2

    (C.D.S. 1994)

70. If the circumference of a circle is 352 metres, then its area (in sq. m) is :

   (a) 5986   (b) 6589   (c) 8956   (d) 9856

71. The area of a circle is 38.5 sq. cm. Its circumference is :

   (a) 6.2 cm   (b) 11 cm   (c) 22 cm   (d) 121 cm

72. The difference between the circumference and the radius of a circle is 37 cm. The area of the circle is :

   (a) 111 cm^2 (b) 148 cm^2 (c) 154 cm^2 (d) 259 cm^2

73. The areas of two concentric circles forming a ring are 154 sq. cm and 616 sq. cm. The breadth of the ring is : **(Assistant Grade 1993)**
    (a) 7 cm　　(b) 14 cm　　(c) 21 cm　　(d) 28 cm

74. The circumferences of two concentric circles forming a ring are 88 cm and 66 cm respectively. The width of the ring is :
    (a) 3.5 cm　　(b) 10.5 cm　　(c) 7 cm　　(d) 14 cm
    (Hotel Management 1992)

75. A circular road runs round a circular ground. If the difference between the circumferences of the outer circle and inner circle is 66 metres, the width of the road is :
    (a) 5.25 m　　(b) 7 m　　(c) 10.5 m　　(d) 21 m

76. The diameter of a wheel is 1.26 m. How far will it travel in 500 revolutions ? **(Hotel Management 1992)**
    (a) 2530 m　　(b) 1980 m　　(c) 1492 m　　(d) 2880 m

77. The radius of a wheel is 7 cm. How many revolutions will it make in moving 44 km ? **(Central Excise & I. Tax 1993)**
    (a) 2000　　(b) 10000　　(c) 70000　　(d) 100000

78. If the wheel of an engine of train $4\frac{2}{7}$ m in circumference makes seven revolutions in 4 seconds, then the speed of the train is :
    (a) 25 km/hr　　(b) 27 km/hr　　(c) 30 km/hr　　(d) 35 km/hr
    (Assistant Grade 1994)

79. A toothed wheel of diameter 50 cm is attached to a smaller wheel of diameter 30 cm. How many revolutions will the smaller wheel make when the larger one makes 15 revolutions ? **(Income Tax 1991)**
    (a) 18　　(b) 20　　(c) 25　　(d) 30

80. A wheel makes 1000 revolutions in covering a distance of 88 km. The radius of the wheel is :
    (a) 7 m　　(b) 12 m　　(c) 14 m　　(d) 20 m

81. The diameter of the wheel of a vehicle is 1.4 m. The wheel makes 10 revolutions in 5 seconds. The speed of the vehicle (in kmph) is :
    (a) 29.46　　(b) 31.68　　(c) 32.72　　(d) 36.25

82. The number of rounds that a wheel of diameter $\frac{7}{11}$ m will make in going 4 km, is : **(C.D.S. 1991)**
    (a) 1000　　(b) 1500　　(c) 1700　　(d) 2000

83. If the radius of a circle is decreased by 50%, its area will decrease by :
    (a) 25%　　(b) 50%　　(c) 75%　　(d) None

84. If the diameter of a circle is increased by 100%, its area is increased by : **(Railways 1991)**
    (a) 100%　　(b) 200%　　(c) 300%　　(d) 400%

85. If the circumference of a circle is increased by 50%, then its area will be increased by :

(a) 50%   (b) 100%   (c) 125%   (d) 225%

86. The area of a circular field is 13.86 hectares. The cost of fencing it at the rate of 40 paise per metre is :
    (a) Rs. 554.40   (b) Rs. 528   (c) Rs. 396   (d) Rs. 648

87. The area of the largest circle that can be drawn inside a square of side 14 cm in length, is :
    (a) 154 cm^2 (b) 84 cm^2 (c) 204 cm^2 (d) None of these

88. The area of the largest circle that can be drawn inside a rectangle with sides 7 metres by 3.5 metres, is :
    (a) $38 \frac{1}{2} \text{ m}^2$ (b) $9 \frac{5}{8} \text{ m}^2$ (c) 77 m^2 (d) None of these

89. The area of largest possible square inscribed in a circle of unit radius (in sq. units) is :
    (a) 2   (b) π (c) $2\sqrt{2}\,\pi$ (d) $4\sqrt{2}\,\pi$

90. The ratio of the areas of the incircle and circumcircle of a square is :
    (a) $1 : \sqrt{2}$ (b) $1 : \sqrt{3}$ (c) $1 : 4$ (d) $1 : 2$

91. The ratio of the areas of the incircle and circumcircle of an equilateral triangle is :
    (a) $1 : 2$ (b) $1 : 3$ (c) $1 : 4$ (d) $1 : 9$

92. The area of a circle inscribed in an equilateral triangle of side 24 cm, is :
    (a) $18\,\pi\,\text{cm}^2$ (b) $24\,\pi\,\text{cm}^2$ (c) $36\,\pi\,\text{cm}^2$ (d) $48\,\pi\,\text{cm}^2$

93. The area of a circle inscribed in an equilateral triangle is 462 cm^2. The perimeter of the triangle is :
    (a) $42\sqrt{3}$ cm   (b) 126 cm   (c) 72.6 cm   (d) 168 cm

94. A circular wire of radius 42 cm is cut and bent into the form of a rectangle whose sides are in the ratio of 6 : 5. The smaller side of the rectangle is :
    (a) 30 cm   (b) 60 cm   (c) 72 cm   (d) 132 cm

95. Four circular cardboard pieces, each of radius 7 cm are placed in such a way that each piece touches two other pieces. The area of the space enclosed by the four pieces is :
    (a) 21 cm^2 (b) 42 cm^2 (c) 84 cm^2 (d) 168 cm^2

96. Four horses are tethered at four corners of a square plot of side 63 metres so that they just can not reach one another. The area left ungrazed is :
    (a) 675.5 m^2 (b) 780.6 m^2 (c) 785.8 m^2 (d) 850.5 m^2

ANSWERS

1. (c)	**2.** (c)	**3.** (a)	**4.** (b)	**5.** (a)	**6.** (c)	**7.** (c)	**8.** (c)	**9.** (b)
10. (d)	**11.** (b)	**12.** (a)	**13.** (c)	**14.** (b)	**15.** (b)	**16.** (b)	**17.** (b)	**18.** (d)
19. (c)	**20.** (c)	**21.** (b)	**22.** (b)	**23.** (c)	**24.** (b)	**25.** (c)	**26.** (a)	**27.** (d)
28. (a)	**29.** (b)	**30.** (d)	**31.** (b)	**32.** (a)	**33.** (b)	**34.** (b)	**35.** (c)	**36.** (a)
37. (c)	**38.** (d)	**39.** (b)	**40.** (b)	**41.** (b)	**42.** (b)	**43.** (c)	**44.** (d)	**45.** (c)
46. (c)	**47.** (c)	**48.** (b)	**49.** (a)	**50.** (d)	**51.** (b)	**52.** (b)	**53.** (a)	**54.** (a)
55. (b)	**56.** (b)	**57.** (b)	**58.** (d)	**59.** (c)	**60.** (b)	**61.** (d)	**62.** (d)	**63.** (c)
64. (b)	**65.** (c)	**66.** (b)	**67.** (b)	**68.** (b)	**69.** (d)	**70.** (d)	**71.** (c)	**72.** (c)
73. (a)	**74.** (a)	**75.** (c)	**76.** (b)	**77.** (d)	**78.** (b)	**79.** (c)	**80.** (c)	**81.** (b)
82. (d)	**83.** (c)	**84.** (c)	**85.** (c)	**86.** (b)	**87.** (a)	**88.** (b)	**89.** (a)	**90.** (d)
91. (c)	**92.** (d)	**93.** (b)	**94.** (b)	**95.** (b)	**96.** (d)			

SOLUTIONS

1. Let length $= 5x$ and breadth $= 3x$. Then,

$2(5x + 3x) = 480$ or $x = 30$.

$\therefore$ Length $= 150$ m & breadth $= 90$ m.

Area $= (150 \times 90) \text{ m}^2 = 13500 \text{ m}^2$.

2. Let, length $= a$ and breadth $= b$. Then, area $= ab$

New length $= 150\%$ of $a = \dfrac{150}{100} a = \dfrac{3a}{2}$,

New breadth $= 120\%$ of $b = \dfrac{120b}{100} = \dfrac{6b}{5}$.

New area $= \left(\dfrac{3a}{2} \times \dfrac{6b}{5} \right) = \dfrac{9}{5} ab = \dfrac{9}{5}$ (original area).

3. Let, length $= a$ & breadth $= b$. Then, area $= ab$.

New length $= \dfrac{160a}{100} = \dfrac{8a}{5}$. Let new breadth $= c$

Then $\dfrac{8a}{5} \times c = ab$ or $c = \dfrac{5b}{8}$.

Decrease in breadth $= \left(\dfrac{3b}{8} \times \dfrac{1}{b} \times 100 \right) \% = 37.5\%$.

4. Let, each side $= a$. Then, original area $= a^2$.

New side $= \dfrac{150a}{100} = \dfrac{3a}{2}$. New area $= \dfrac{9a^2}{4}$.

Required ratio $= \dfrac{9a^2}{4} : a^2 = 9 : 4$.

5. Let breadth $= x$. Then, length $= (x + 8)$ cm.

$\therefore$ $(x+8)\,x = (x+15)\,(x-4)$

or $x^2 + 8x = x^2 + 11x - 60$ or $x = 20$.

$\therefore$ Length = 28 cm & breadth = 20 cm.

6. Let the diagonal be a. Then, area $= \dfrac{1}{2}\,a^2$.

New diagonal = $2a$.

$\therefore$ New area $= \dfrac{1}{2}(2a)^2 = 2a^2 = 4\left(\dfrac{1}{2}a^2\right) = 4$ (original area).

7. Area of rectangle = Area of circle $= \left(\dfrac{22}{7} \times 14 \times 14\right) \text{cm}^2 = 616\,\text{cm}^2$.

Breadth = 22 cm. So, length $= \left(\dfrac{616}{22}\right) \text{cm} = 28$ cm.

Thus, both P and Q are needed.

8. Area of the verandah $= (25 \times 20 - 20 \times 15)\,\text{m}^2 = 200\,m^2$.

$\therefore$ Cost of flooring = Rs. $\left(200 \times \dfrac{7}{2}\right)$ = Rs. 700.

9. Area of floor $= (300 \times 300)$ sq. cm.

Area of 1 slab $= (20 \times 30)$ sq. cm.

$\therefore$ Number of slabs $= \left(\dfrac{300 \times 300}{20 \times 30}\right) = 150$.

10. Let, each side $= a$. Then, area $= a^2$.

New side $= \dfrac{125a}{100} = \dfrac{5a}{4}$. New area $= \dfrac{25a^2}{16}$.

Increase percent in area $= \left(\dfrac{9a^2}{16} \times \dfrac{1}{a^2} \times 100\right)\% = 56.25\%$.

11. Length of diagonal = Distance covered in 3 min. at 4 km/hr

$= \left(\dfrac{4000}{60} \times 3\right) \text{m} = 200$ m.

$\therefore$ Area of the field $= \dfrac{1}{2}\,(\text{diagonal})^2$

$= \left(\dfrac{1}{2} \times 200 \times 200\right) \text{m}^2 = 20000\,\text{m}^2$.

12. Let the side of the square be a and length and breadth of the rectangle be x and y. Then, $a^2 = xy$.

Also, $p_1 = 4a$ & $2(x+y) = p_2$ or $\dfrac{x+y}{2} = \dfrac{p_2}{4}$ & $xy = a^2 = \left(\dfrac{p_1}{4}\right)^2 = \dfrac{p_1^2}{16}$.

Now, $\dfrac{x+y}{2} > x^{1/2}\,y^{1/2}$ [Since A.M. > G.M.]

$\Rightarrow \left(\dfrac{x+y}{2}\right)^2 > xy$ or $\left(\dfrac{p_2}{4}\right)^2 > \dfrac{p_1^2}{16}$ or $p_2^2 > p_1^2$ or $p_2 > p_1$

Hence, $p_1 < p_2$

Remember : If a square & a rectangle have same area, then (Perimeter of Square) < (Perimeter of Rectangle).

13. Let, side of square = a, length of rect. = x & breadth of rect. = y.

$4a = 2\,(x+y) \Rightarrow \dfrac{x+y}{2} = a.$

Area of square = $a^2 = \left(\dfrac{x+y}{2}\right)^2$. So, $A = \left(\dfrac{x+y}{2}\right)^2$

Area of rect. = xy. So, $B = xy$.

$\dfrac{x+y}{2} > x^{1/2}\,y^{1/2}$ $[\because$ A.M. > G.M.]

$\Rightarrow \left(\dfrac{x+y}{2}\right)^2 > xy$ i.e. $A > B$.

Remember : If a square & a rectangle have same perimeter, then : (Area of square) > (Area of rectangle).

14. Let, side of a square = a. Then, its diagonal = $\sqrt{2}\,a$.
Ratio of areas of squares with sides a & $\sqrt{2}\,a$

$= \dfrac{a^2}{\left(\sqrt{2}\,a\right)^2} = \dfrac{1}{2}$ or 1 : 2.

15. Let the sides of two squares be a and b respectively.

Then, $\dfrac{a^2}{b^2} = \dfrac{9}{1}$ or $\left(\dfrac{a}{b}\right)^2 = \left(\dfrac{3}{1}\right)^2$ or $\dfrac{a}{b} = \dfrac{3}{1}$

$\therefore$ Ratio of their perimeters $= \dfrac{4a}{4b} = \dfrac{a}{b} = \dfrac{3}{1}$ or 3 : 1.

16. Let, length = x and breadth = y.

Then, $2\,(x+y) = 46$ or $x+y = 23$ and $x^2 + y^2 = (17)^2 = 289$.

Now, $(x+y)^2 = (23)^2 \Rightarrow (x^2 + y^2) + 2xy = 529$

$\Rightarrow 289 + 2xy = 529$ or $xy = 120$.

$\therefore$ Area = $xy = 120$ cm^2

17. Perimeter of square = 80 cm. So, side of square = 20 cm.

Area of the square = (20×20) cm^2 = 400 cm^2.
With same perimeter, area of the square is larger.

$\therefore$ Area of rectangle = $(400 - 100)$ cm^2 = 300 cm^2.

Let, length of rect. $= x$ & its breadth $= y$. Then,

$xy = 300$ and $x + y = 40$

$\therefore (x - y) = \sqrt{(x + y)^2 - 4xy} = \sqrt{1600 - 1200} = 20.$

Solving $x + y = 40$ & $x - y = 20$, we get $x = 30, y = 10.$

$\therefore$ Sides are 30 cm, 10 cm.

18. Area of first square = 10000 sq. metres.

Side of this square $= \sqrt{10000}$ m = 100 m

Side of the new square = 101 m

Difference in areas $= (101)^2 - (100)^2 = 201$ m^2.

19. Let, breadth $= x$. Then, length $= 2x$.

$(2x - 5)(x + 5) - 2x \times x = 75$ or $x = 20.$

$\therefore$ Length = 40 cm.

20. Area $= \dfrac{\text{Total Cost}}{\text{Rate}} = \left(\dfrac{1215}{135}\right)$ hectares $= (9 \times 10000)$ sq. m.

$\therefore$ Side of the square $= \sqrt{90000} = 300$ m.

Perimeter of the field $= (300 \times 4)$ m = 1200 m.

Cost of fencing = Rs. $\left(1200 \times \dfrac{3}{4}\right)$ = Rs. 900.

21. Let the width of walk be x metres. Then,

$(20 - 2x)(10 - 2x) = 96$

or $4x^2 + 60x - 104 = 0$ or $x^2 + 15x - 26 = 0$

or $(x - 13)(x - 2) = 0.$

So, $x = 2$ $[\because x \neq 13]$

22. Length of the carpet $= \dfrac{\text{Total Cost}}{\text{Rate/m}} = \left(\dfrac{8100}{45}\right)$ m = 180 m.

Area of the carpet $= \left(180 \times \dfrac{75}{100}\right)$ m^2 = 135 m^2.

$\therefore$ Area of the room = Area of the carpet = 135 m^2.

$\therefore$ Breadth of the room $= \left(\dfrac{\text{Area}}{\text{Length}}\right) = \left(\dfrac{135}{18}\right)$ m = 7.5 m.

23. Area of cross roads $= (55 \times 4 + 35 \times 4 - 4 \times 4)$ m^2 = 344 m^2.

$\therefore$ Cost of gravelling = Rs. $\left(344 \times \dfrac{75}{100}\right)$ = Rs. 258.

24. Area of cross roads $= (25 \times 2 + 15 \times 2 - 2 \times 2)$ m^2 = 76 m^2.

Area of the field $= (25 \times 15)$ m^2 = 375 m^2

Area under grass $= (375 - 76)$ m^2 = 299 m^2.

25. Let, length $= 5x$ and breadth $= 4x$ in metres. Then,

$5x - 4x = 20 \Rightarrow x = 20.$

$\therefore$ Length = 100 m & Breadth = 80 m.

$\therefore$ Perimeter $= 2\,(100 + 80)$ m $= 360$ m.

26. Let, length $= 5x$ and breadth $= 3x$ in metres.

Then, perimeter $= 2\,(5x + 3x)$ metres $= 16x$ metres.

But, perimeter $= \dfrac{\text{Total cost}}{\text{Rate/m}} = \left(3000 \times \dfrac{2}{15}\right)$ m $= 400$ m.

$\therefore$ $16x = 400$ or $x = 25$.

$\therefore$ Diff. in length & breadth $= (5x - 3x) = 2x = 50$ m.

27. Area of the plot $= (1200 \times 3)$ sq. m $= 3600$ m^2.

Let, breadth $= x$ and length $= 4x$ metres. Then,

$4x \times x = 3600$ or $x = 30$.

$\therefore$ Length $= 4x = 120$ m.

28. Let breadth $= x$ cm and length $= 2x$ cm. Then,

$x^2 + (2x)^2 = (10\sqrt{5})^2$ or $5x^2 = 500$ or $x^2 = 100$ or $x = 10$.

$\therefore$ Perimeter $= 2\,(2x + x)$ cm $= 6x$ cm $= 60$ cm.

29. Let, original side $= x$ cm. Then,

$(x + 5)^2 - x^2 = 165 \Rightarrow 10x = 140$ or $x = 14$.

$\therefore$ Side of the square $= 14$ cm.

30. Let, length $= a$ & breadth $= b$. Then, area $= ab$.

New length $= 2a$ & New breadth $= \dfrac{b}{2}$.

$\therefore$ New Area $= \left(2a \times \dfrac{b}{2}\right) = ab = $ original area.

Thus, there is no change in area.

31. Area of the hall $= (3600 \times 1500)$ sq. cm.

Area of each stone $= (60 \times 50)$ sq. cm.

$\therefore$ Number of stones $= \left(\dfrac{3600 \times 1500}{60 \times 50}\right) = 1800$.

32. Let breadth $= x$. Then, length $= \dfrac{3}{2}\,x$ metres.

Area $= \left(\dfrac{2}{3} \times 10000\right)$ sq. m.

$\therefore$ $\dfrac{3}{2}\,x \times x = \dfrac{2}{3} \times 10000$ or $x^2 = \dfrac{4}{9} \times 10000$ or $x = \dfrac{2}{3} \times 100$.

$\therefore$ Length $= \dfrac{3}{2}\,x = \left(\dfrac{3}{2} \times \dfrac{2}{3} \times 100\right)$ m $= 100$ m.

33. Let the side of the square be x.

Then, breadth of rectangle $= \dfrac{3}{2}\,x$.

$\therefore$ $40 \times \dfrac{3}{2}\,x = 3x^2$ or $x = 20$.

Hence, the side of the square is 20 cm.

34. Breadth $= \left(\dfrac{150}{15}\right)$ cm $= 10$ cm.

New area $= \left(\dfrac{4}{3} \times 150\right)$ sq. cm $= 200$ sq. cm.

$\therefore$ New length $= \left(\dfrac{200}{10}\right)$ cm $= 20$ cm.

New perimeter $= 2\,(20 + 10)$ cm $= 60$ cm.

35. Let length $= a$ metres and breadth $= b$ metres.

Then, $2\,(a + b) = 46$ or $a + b = 23$. Also, $ab = 120$.

$\therefore$ Diagonal $= \sqrt{(a^2 + b^2)} = \sqrt{(a + b)^2 - 2ab}$

$\qquad\qquad = \sqrt{(23)^2 - 240} = \sqrt{289} = 17$ m.

36. Area of the room $= (544 \times 374)$ sq. cm.

Size of largest square tile $=$ H.C.F. of 544 cm & 374 cm

$\qquad\qquad\qquad\qquad\qquad = 34$ cm.

Area of 1 tile $= (34 \times 34)$ sq. cm.

$\therefore$ Number of tiles $= \left(\dfrac{544 \times 374}{34 \times 34}\right) = 176$.

37. Perimeter $=$ Distance covered in 8 min.

$\qquad\quad = \left(\dfrac{12000}{60} \times 8\right)$ m $= 1600$ m.

Let, length $= 3x$ metres and breadth $= 2x$ metres.

Then, $2\,(3x + 2x) = 1600$ or $x = 160$.

$\therefore$ Length $= 480$ m and breadth $= 320$ m

$\therefore$ Area $= (480 \times 320)\ \text{m}^2 = 153600\ \text{m}^2$

38. Other side $= \sqrt{(17)^2 - 8^2} = \sqrt{289 - 64} = \sqrt{225} = 15$ m.

$\therefore$ Area $= (15 \times 8)\ \text{m}^2 = 120\ \text{m}^2$.

39. Let, breadth $= x$ metres. Then,

$108 \times x = 72 \times 72$ or $x = \left(\dfrac{72 \times 72}{108}\right) = 48$ m.

40. Area $= \left(\dfrac{1}{2} \times 10000\right)\text{m}^2 = 5000\ \text{m}^2$.

$\therefore$ $\dfrac{1}{2}\,(\text{diagonal})^2 = 5000$ or $(\text{diagonal})^2 = 10000$.

$\therefore$ Diagonal $= \sqrt{10000} = 100$ m.

41. Let, length $= a$ & breadth $= b$. Then, area $= ab$.

New length $= \dfrac{110}{100}\,a = \dfrac{11a}{10}$. Let new breadth $= c$.

Then, $\dfrac{11a}{10} \times c = ab$ or $c = \dfrac{10b}{11}$.

$\therefore$ Decrease in breadth $= \left(\dfrac{b}{11} \times \dfrac{1}{b} \times 100 \right) \% = 9\dfrac{1}{11}\%.$

42. Let, length $= x$ metres and breadth $= y$ metres.

Then $xy = 60$ and $\sqrt{x^2 + y^2} + x = 5y$

$\therefore\ xy = 60$ and $(x^2 + y^2) = (5y - x)^2$

or $xy = 60$ and $24y^2 - 10xy = 0$

$\therefore\ 24y^2 - 10 \times 60 = 0$ or $y^2 = 25$ or $y = 5.$

$\therefore\ x = \left(\dfrac{60}{5} \right) m = 12$ m. So, length of the carpet $= 12$ m.

43. Number of sheets $= \left(\dfrac{100 \times 100}{20 \times 20} \right) = 25.$

44. Let, side of the square be a. Then, area $= a^2.$

New length $= \left(\dfrac{140}{100}\, a \right) = \dfrac{7a}{5},$ New breadth $= \left(\dfrac{130}{100}a \right) = \dfrac{13a}{10}.$

New area $= \dfrac{7a}{5} \times \dfrac{13a}{10} = \dfrac{91a^2}{50}.$

Increase in area $= \left(\dfrac{41}{50}a^2 \times \dfrac{1}{a^2} \times 100 \right) \% = 82\%.$

45. Let the dimensions of former room be x, y and z.

Then, the area of its 4 walls $= 2\,(x + y) \times z$ sq. units.

Dimensions of another room are $2x, 2y$ and $2z$ units.

$\therefore$ Area of 4 walls of this room

$$= 2\,(2x + 2y) \times 2z = 4 \times [2\,(x + y) \times z]$$
$$= 4 \times (\text{Area of 4 walls of 1st room})$$

$\therefore$ Required cost $=$ Rs. $(475 \times 4) =$ Rs. 1900.

46. Let, height $= 2x$ metres & (length + breadth) $= 5x$ metres.

Length of paper $= \left(\dfrac{260}{2} \right) m = 130$ m.

$\therefore$ Area of paper $= \left(130 \times \dfrac{50}{100} \right) m^2 = 65\ m^2.$

Area of 4 walls $= (65 + 15)\ m^2 = 80\ m^2.$

2 (length + breadth) $\times$ height $= 80$

$\therefore\ 2 \times 5x \times 2x = 80$ or $x^2 = 4$ or $x = 2.$

$\therefore$ Height of the room $= 4$ m.

47. Area $= \dfrac{1}{2} \times$ (Product of diagonals)

$\therefore\ \dfrac{1}{2} \times 5 \times x = 15 \Rightarrow x = \left(15 \times \dfrac{2}{5} \right) = 6$ cm.

48. Halves of diagonals & a side of a rhombus form a right angled triangle with side as hypotenuse.

Let another diagonal = $2x$.

Then, $x^2 + \left(\dfrac{8}{2}\right)^2 = 5^2$ or $x^2 = (5^2 - 4^2) = 9$ or $x = 3$.

∴ Another diagonal = 6 cm.

∴ Area = $\left(\dfrac{1}{2} \times 8 \times 6\right)$ sq. cm = 24 sq. cm.

49. Let the diagonals be x and $2x$ cm.

Then, $\dfrac{1}{2}(x \times 2x) = 144$ or $x = 12$.

∴ Diagonals are 12 cm and 24 cm.

50. Side = $\left(\dfrac{52}{4}\right)$ m = 13 m, Half of one diagonal = 5 m.

Let another diagonal = $2x$ metres. Then,

$x^2 + 5^2 = (13)^2$ or $x^2 = 144$ or $x = 12$ m.

∴ Longer diagonal = 24 m.

51. Let one diagonal = x cm. Another diagonal = $\dfrac{80}{100}x = \dfrac{4x}{5}$ cm.

Area of rhombus = $\dfrac{1}{2}\left(x \times \dfrac{4x}{5}\right) = \dfrac{2}{5}x^2$

$= \dfrac{2}{5}$ (square of longer diagonal).

52. A square and a rhombus on the same base are equal in area.

53. Area = (Base × Height) = (18×8) cm^2 = 144 cm^2.

54. Let $ABCD$ be a ‖ gm in which $AB = 30$ m, $BC = 14$ m & $AC = 40$ m.

Clearly, area of ‖ gm $ABCD$ = 2 (area of $\triangle ABC$).

Let $a = 30$, $b = 14$ & $c = 40$.

Then, $s = \dfrac{1}{2}(a + b + c) = 42$

∴ Area of $\triangle ABC = \sqrt{s(s-a)(s-b)(s-c)}$

$= \sqrt{42 \times 12 \times 28 \times 2} = 168$ m^2.

∴ Area of ‖ gm = (2×168) m^2 = 336 m^2.

55. Area of trap. = $\dfrac{1}{2}$ (Sum of parallel sides × distance between them)

$= \left[\dfrac{1}{2}(1.5 + 2.5) \times 6.5\right]$ m^2 = 13 m^2.

56. Let the parallel sides be $3x$ cm and $5x$ cm.

Then, $\frac{1}{2}(3x+5x) \times 12 = 384$ or $x=8$.

∴ Smaller of parallel sides $= 24$ cm.

57. $\frac{1}{2}(12+8) \times d = 840$ or $d = 84$ m.

58. $a=3, b=4$ and $c=5$.

∴ $s = \frac{1}{2}(3+4+5) = 6$

∴ Area $= \sqrt{6 \times 3 \times 2 \times 1} = \sqrt{36} = 6$ sq. cm.

59. Let the sides be $5x, 5x$ & $4x$. Then, $5x+5x+4x=14$ or $x=1$.

∴ Sides are 5 cm, 5 cm and 4 cm.

∴ $s = \frac{1}{2}(5+5+4) = 7$.

∴ Area $= \sqrt{7 \times 2 \times 2 \times 3} = 2\sqrt{21}$ cm^2.

60. $\frac{\sqrt{3}\, a^2}{4} = 24\sqrt{3} \Rightarrow a^2 = 96$ or $a = 4\sqrt{6}$.

∴ Perimeter $= (3 \times 4\sqrt{6})$ cm $= 12\sqrt{6}$ cm.

61. $\dfrac{\text{Area of square}}{\text{Area of triangle}} = \dfrac{a^2}{\frac{\sqrt{3}}{4}a^2} = \dfrac{4}{\sqrt{3}}$, i.e. $4 : \sqrt{3}$.

62. Let the side of the triangle be a.

$a^2 = \left(\frac{a}{2}\right)^2 + x^2$ or $\frac{3a^2}{4} = x^2$ or $a^2 = \frac{4x^2}{3}$.

∴ Area $= \frac{\sqrt{3}}{4}a^2 = \frac{\sqrt{3}}{4} \times \frac{4}{3}x^2 = \frac{x^2}{\sqrt{3}} = \frac{x^2\sqrt{3}}{3}$.

63. Area $= \frac{\sqrt{3}}{4} \times (3\sqrt{3})^2 = \frac{27\sqrt{3}}{4}$.

Now $\frac{1}{2} \times 3\sqrt{3} \times \text{height} = \frac{27\sqrt{3}}{4}$

∴ Height $= \frac{27\sqrt{3}}{4} \times \frac{2}{3\sqrt{3}} = \frac{9}{2} = 4.5$ cm.

64. $\frac{\sqrt{3}}{4} \times (6 \times 6) = 9 \times y \Rightarrow y = \sqrt{3}$.

65. $\frac{1}{2} \times a \times \text{altitude} = a^2 \Rightarrow \text{altitude} = 2a$.

66. Let the other sides be x and y. Then,

$x^2 + y^2 = (13)^2 = 169$. Also, $\frac{1}{2}xy = 30 \Rightarrow xy = 60$.

∴ $(x+y) = \sqrt{(x^2+y^2) + 2xy} = \sqrt{169 + 120} = \sqrt{289} = 17$.

$(x - y) = \sqrt{(x^2 + y^2) - 2xy} = \sqrt{169 - 120} = \sqrt{49} = 7.$

Solving $x + y = 17$, $x - y = 7$, we get $x = 12$ and $y = 5$.

∴ Shorter side = 5 cm.

67. $a = 5$, $b = 12$ and $c = 13$.

∴ $s = \dfrac{1}{2}(5 + 12 + 13)$ cm = 15 cm.

∴ Area $= \sqrt{15 \times 10 \times 3 \times 2} = 30$ cm^2.

$\dfrac{1}{2} \times 12 \times$ Height $= 30 \Rightarrow$ Height = 5 cm.

68. $\dfrac{1}{2} \times$ Base $\times$ Height = Area.

∴ $\dfrac{1}{2} \times a \times \sqrt{6} = \dfrac{\sqrt{3}}{4} a^2$ or $a = \dfrac{2\sqrt{6}}{\sqrt{3}} = 2\sqrt{2}$.

∴ Area $= \dfrac{\sqrt{3}}{4} \times (2\sqrt{2})^2 = 2\sqrt{3}$.

69. Let the side of the square be a. Then, $\sqrt{2}\,a = 12\sqrt{2} \Rightarrow a = 12$.

∴ Perimeter of the triangle = Perimeter of the square = 48 cm.

∴ Side of the triangle = 16 cm.

∴ Area of the triangle $= \left(\dfrac{\sqrt{3}}{4} \times 16 \times 16\right)$ cm$^2 = 64\sqrt{3}$ cm^2.

70. $2\pi r = 352 \Rightarrow 2 \times \dfrac{22}{7} \times r = 352$.

∴ $r = \left(352 \times \dfrac{7}{44}\right) = 56$ cm.

∴ Area $= \left(\dfrac{22}{7} \times 56 \times 56\right)$ cm$^2 = 9856$ cm^2.

71. $\pi r^2 = 38.5 \Rightarrow r^2 = \left(38.5 \times \dfrac{7}{22}\right) = \left(\dfrac{7}{2}\right)^2$ or $r = \dfrac{7}{2}$.

∴ Circumference $= 2\pi r = \left(2 \times \dfrac{22}{7} \times \dfrac{7}{2}\right)$ cm = 22 cm.

72. $2\pi r - r = 37$ or $(2\pi - 1)r = 37$

or $\left(2 \times \dfrac{22}{7} - 1\right)r = 37$ or $\dfrac{37r}{7} = 37$ or $r = 7$.

∴ Area $= \pi r^2 = \left(\dfrac{22}{7} \times 7 \times 7\right)$ cm$^2 = 154$ cm^2.

73. Let, inner radius $= r$ & outer radius $= R$.

Then, $\dfrac{22}{7} \times r^2 = 154$ or $r^2 = \left(154 \times \dfrac{7}{22}\right)$. So, $r = 7$.

Also, $\dfrac{22}{7} \times R^2 = 616$ or $R^2 = \left(616 \times \dfrac{7}{22}\right)$ or $R = 14$.

∴ Breadth of the ring $= (R - r) = (14 - 7) = 7$ cm.

74. Let, inner radius $= r$ & outer radius $= R$ cm.

Then, $2 \times \dfrac{22}{7} \times R = 88 \Rightarrow R = \left(88 \times \dfrac{7}{44}\right) = 14$ cm.

$2 \times \dfrac{22}{7} \times r = 66 \Rightarrow r = \left(66 \times \dfrac{7}{44}\right) = \dfrac{21}{2}$ cm $= 10.5$ cm.

∴ Width of the ring $= (14 - 10.5)$ cm $= 3.5$ cm.

75. $2\pi(R - r) = 60 \Rightarrow 2 \times \dfrac{22}{7} \times (R - r) = 60$.

∴ $(R - r) = \left(66 \times \dfrac{7}{44}\right) = 10.5$ m.

76. Radius of the wheel $= 0.63$ m.

Distance moved in 1 revolution = circumference

$$= \left(2 \times \dfrac{22}{7} \times 0.63\right) m = 3.96 \text{ m}.$$

Distance moved in 500 revolutions $= (500 \times 3.96)$ m $= 1980$ m.

77. Distance covered in 1 revolution = circumference

$$= \left(2 \times \dfrac{22}{7} \times 7\right) cm = 44 \text{ cm}.$$

∴ Number of revolutions made in moving 44 km

$$= \left(\dfrac{44 \times 1000 \times 100}{44}\right) = 100000.$$

78. Distance moved in 4 sec. $= \left(\dfrac{30}{7} \times 7\right) m = 30$ m.

∴ Speed $= \left(\dfrac{30}{4} \times 60 \times 60 \times \dfrac{1}{1000}\right)$ km/hr $= 27$ km/hr.

79. Distance moved by toothed wheel in 15 revolutions

$$= \left(15 \times 2 \times \dfrac{22}{7} \times 25\right) cm.$$

Distance moved by smaller wheel in 1 revolution $= \left(2 \times \dfrac{22}{7} \times 15\right)$ cm.

∴ Required number of revolutions $= \left(15 \times \dfrac{44}{7} \times 25 \times \dfrac{7}{44 \times 15}\right) = 25$.

80. Distance covered in 1 revolution $= \left(\dfrac{88 \times 1000}{1000}\right) m = 88$ m.

∴ $2\pi R = 88$ or $2 \times \dfrac{22}{7} \times R = 88$ or $R = \left(88 \times \dfrac{7}{44}\right) = 14$ m.

81. Distance covered in 10 revolutions $= \left(10 \times 2 \times \dfrac{22}{7} \times 0.7\right) m = 44$ m.

∴ Distance covered in 5 sec. = 44 m.

∴ Speed $= \left(\dfrac{44}{5} \times 60 \times 60 \times \dfrac{1}{1000}\right)$ kmph $= 31.68$ kmph.

82. Distance moved in 1 revolution $= \left(2 \times \dfrac{22}{7} \times \dfrac{7}{22}\right)$ m $= 2$ m.

Number of revolutions in going 4 km $= \left(\dfrac{4 \times 1000}{2}\right) = 2000$.

83. Let original radius $= R$. New radius $= \dfrac{50}{100} R = \dfrac{R}{2}$.

Original area $= \pi R^2$ & New area $= \pi \left(\dfrac{R}{2}\right)^2 = \dfrac{\pi R^2}{4}$.

Decrease in area $= \left(\dfrac{3 \pi R^2}{4} \times \dfrac{1}{\pi R^2} \times 100\right) \% = 75\%$.

84. Let original radius $= R$, New Radius $= \dfrac{200}{100} R = 2R$.

∴ Original area $= \pi R^2$, New area $= \pi (2R)^2 = 4 \pi R^2$

∴ Increase % $= \left(\dfrac{3 \pi R^2}{\pi R^2} \times 100\right) \% = 300 \%$.

85. Let original radius $= r$.

Then, circumference $= 2 \pi r$ and area $= \pi r^2$.

New circumference $= \left(\dfrac{150}{100} \times 2 \pi r\right) = 3 \pi r$

Let radius now be R. $\quad 2 \pi R = 3 \pi r \Rightarrow R = \dfrac{3r}{2}$.

New area $= \pi R^2 = \pi \left(\dfrac{9r^2}{4}\right) = \dfrac{9 \pi r^2}{4}$

Increase in area $= \left(\dfrac{9 \pi r^2}{4} - \pi r^2\right) = \dfrac{5 \pi r^2}{4}$.

∴ Increase % $= \left(\dfrac{5 \pi r^2}{4} \times \dfrac{1}{\pi R^2} \times 100\right) \% = 125\%$.

86. Area $= (13.86 \times 10000)$ sq. m $= 138600$ m^2.

$\pi R^2 = 138600$ or $R^2 = \left(138600 \times \dfrac{7}{22}\right) \Rightarrow R = 210$ m

Circumference $= 2 \pi R = \left(2 \times \dfrac{22}{7} \times 210\right)$ m $= 1320$ m.

Cost of fencing = Rs. $\left(1320 \times \dfrac{40}{100}\right)$ = Rs. 528.

87. Radius of the required circle = 7 cm.

$\therefore$ Its area $= \left(\dfrac{22}{7} \times 7 \times 7\right)$ cm^2 = 154 cm^2.

88. Radius of required circle $= \dfrac{7}{4}$ cm.

$\therefore$ Its area $= \left(\dfrac{22}{7} \times \dfrac{7}{4} \times \dfrac{7}{4}\right)$ cm^2 $= 9\dfrac{5}{8}$ cm^2.

89. Diagonal of square = Diameter of circle = 2 units.

$\therefore$ Area of the square $= \dfrac{1}{2} \times (\text{diagonal})^2 = \left(\dfrac{1}{2} \times 2 \times 2\right) = 2$ sq. units.

90. Let the side of the square be x. Then, its diagonal $= \sqrt{2}\, x$.

$\therefore$ Radius of incircle $= \dfrac{x}{2}$ & radius of circumcircle $= \dfrac{\sqrt{2}x}{2} = \dfrac{x}{\sqrt{2}}$.

$\therefore$ Required ratio $= \left(\dfrac{\pi x^2}{4} : \dfrac{\pi x^2}{2}\right) = \dfrac{1}{4} : \dfrac{1}{2} = 1 : 2$.

91. Let radius of incircle be r. Then, radius of circumcircle = $2r$.

$\therefore$ Required ratio $= \dfrac{\pi r^2}{\pi (2r)^2} = \dfrac{1}{4}$.

92. $\dfrac{1}{2} \times 24 \times h = \dfrac{\sqrt{3}}{4} \times 24 \times 24$ or $h = 12\sqrt{3}$.

$\therefore 3r = 12\sqrt{3}$ or $r = 4\sqrt{3}$.

$\therefore$ Area of the circle $= \pi \times (4\sqrt{3})^2 = (48\,\pi)$ cm^2.

93. $\pi r^2 = 462 \Rightarrow r^2 = \left(462 \times \dfrac{7}{22}\right) = 147 \Rightarrow r = 7\sqrt{3}$.

$\therefore$ Height of the triangle $= 3r = 21\sqrt{3}$.

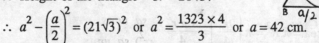

$\therefore a^2 - \left(\dfrac{a}{2}\right)^2 = (21\sqrt{3})^2$ or $a^2 = \dfrac{1323 \times 4}{3}$ or $a = 42$ cm.

$\therefore$ Perimeter $= 3a = 126$ cm.

94. Length of wire = circumference of circle of radius 42 cm

$$= \left(2 \times \dfrac{22}{7} \times 42\right) \text{cm} = 264 \text{ cm}.$$

$\therefore$ Perimeter of rectangle = 264 cm.

Let, length = 6x cm & breadth = 5x cm.

$\therefore 2(6x + 5x) = 264$ or $x = 12$. $\therefore$ Smaller side = 60 cm.

95. Required area $= \left(14 \times 14 - 4 \times \dfrac{1}{4} \times \dfrac{22}{7} \times 7 \times 7\right)$ cm^2

$$= (196 - 154) \text{ cm}^2 = 42 \text{ cm}^2.$$

96. Required area $= \left(63 \times 63 - 4 \times \dfrac{1}{4} \times \dfrac{22}{7} \times \dfrac{63}{2} \times \dfrac{63}{2}\right)$ m^2 = 850.5 m^2.

25. Volume & Surface Area

FORMULAE

1. **CUBOID**

   Let length = l, breadth = b & height = h units. Then,

   (i) **Volume** = $(l \times b \times h)$ *cubic units.*

   (ii) **Surface Area** = $2\,(lb + bh + lh)$ *sq. units.*

   (iii) **Diagonal** = $\sqrt{l^2 + b^2 + h^2}$ units.

2. **CUBE**

   Let each edge of a cube be of length a. Then,

   (i) **Volume** = a^3 *cubic units.*

   (ii) **Surface Area** = $6a^2$ *sq. units.*

   (iii) **Diagonal** = $\sqrt{3}\ a$ *units.*

3. **CYLINDER**

   Let radius of base = r & Height (or length) = h. Then,

   (i) **Volume** = $(\pi r^2 h)$ *cu. units*

   (ii) **Curved Surface Area** = $(2\pi rh)$ *sq. units*

   (iii) **Total surface Area** = $(2\pi rh + 2\pi r^2)$ *sq. units.*

4. **CONE**

   Let radius of base = r & Height = h. Then,

   (i) **Slant height,** $l = \sqrt{h^2 + r^2}$ *units.*

   (ii) **Volume** = $\left(\dfrac{1}{3}\,\pi r^2 h\right)$ *cubic units.*

   (iii) **Curved Surface Area** = (πrl) *sq. units.*

   (iv) **Total Surface Area** = $(\pi rl + \pi r^2)$ *sq. units.*

5. **SPHERE**

   Let the radius of the sphere be r. Then,

   (i) **Volume** = $\left(\dfrac{4}{3}\,\pi r^3\right)$ *cubic units.*

   (ii) **Surface Area** = $(4\pi r^2)$ *sq. units.*

6. **HEMI–SPHERE**

   Let the radius of a hemi–sphere be r. Then,

   (i) **Volume** = $\left(\dfrac{2}{3}\,\pi r^3\right)$ *cubic units.*

   (ii) **Curved Surface Area** = $(2\pi r^2)$ *sq. units.*

   (iii) **Total Surface Area** = $(3\pi r^2)$ *sq. units.*

Solved Problems

Ex. 1. *Find the volume and surface area of a cuboid 16 m long, 14 m broad and 7 m high.*

Sol. Volume = $(16 \times 14 \times 17)$ cu.m = 1568 cu.m

Surface Area = $2(16 \times 14 + 14 \times 7 + 16 \times 7)$ sq.cm = 868 sq.cm.

Ex. 2. *Find the length of longest pole that can be placed in a room 12 m long, 8 m broad and 9 m high.*

Sol. Length of longest pole

$$= \text{Length of the diagonal of the room}$$
$$= \sqrt{(12)^2 + 8^2 + 9^2} = \sqrt{289} = 17 \text{ m}.$$

Ex. 3. *The diagonal of a cube is $6\sqrt{3}$ cm. Find its volume and surface area.*

Sol. Let the edge of the cube be a.

$\therefore \quad \sqrt{3}a = 6\sqrt{3} \Rightarrow a = 6$.

$\therefore \quad$ Volume = $a^3 = (6 \times 6 \times 6)$ cm^3 = 216 cm^3

Surface Area = $6a^2 = (6 \times 6 \times 6)$ sq.cm = 216 cm^2.

Ex. 4. *The surface area of a cube is 486 sq.cm. Find its volume.*

Sol. $6a^2 = 468 \Rightarrow a^2 = 81 \Rightarrow a = 9$ cm.

$\therefore \quad$ Volume = $(9 \times 9 \times 9)$ cm^3 = 729 cm^3

Ex. 5. *Find the number of bricks, each measuring 25 cm by 12.5 cm by 7.5 cm, required to build a wall 6 m long, 5 m high and 50 cm thick, while the mortar occupies 5% of the volume of the wall.*

Sol. Volume of the wall = $(600 \times 500 \times 50)$ cu.cm.

Volume of bricks = 95 % of the volume of the wall

$$= \left(\frac{95}{100} \times 600 \times 500 \times 50 \right) \text{cu.cm.}$$

Volume of 1 brick = $\left(25 \times \frac{25}{2} \times \frac{75}{10} \right)$ cu.cm.

$$\therefore \quad \text{Number of bricks} = \left(\frac{95}{100} \times \frac{600 \times 500 \times 50 \times 2 \times 10}{25 \times 25 \times 75} \right) = 6080.$$

Ex. 6. *Three solid cubes of sides 1 cm, 6 cm and 8 cm are melted to form a new cube. Find the surface area of the cube so formed.*

Sol. Volume of new cube = $(1^3 + 6^3 + 8^3)$ cu.cm = 729 cm^3.

Edge of new cube = $(9 \times 9 \times 9)^{1/3}$ cm = 9 cm.

$\therefore$ Surface area of the new cube = $(6 \times 9 \times 9)$ cm^2 = 486 cm^2.

Ex. 7. *Find the volume, curved surface area and the total surface area of a cylinder with diameter of base 7 cm and height 40 cm.*

Sol. Volume = $\pi r^2 h$

$$= \left(\frac{22}{7} \times \frac{7}{2} \times \frac{7}{2} \times 40\right) \text{cu.cm} = 1540 \text{ cu.cm.}$$

Curved surface Area = $2\pi rh$

$$= \left(2 \times \frac{22}{7} \times \frac{7}{2} \times 40\right) \text{sq.cm} = 880 \text{ sq.cm.}$$

Total Surface Area $= 2\pi rh + 2\pi r^2 = 2\pi r\,(h+r)$

$$= \left[2 \times \frac{22}{7} \times \frac{7}{2} \times (40+3.5)\right] \text{cm}^2 = 957 \text{ cm}^2.$$

Ex. 8. *Find the volume and surface area of a sphere of radius 10.5 cm.*

Sol. Volume $= \frac{4}{3}\pi r^3 = \left(\frac{4}{3} \times \frac{22}{7} \times \frac{21}{2} \times \frac{21}{2} \times \frac{21}{2}\right) \text{cm}^3 = 4851 \text{ cm}^3.$

Surface Area $= 4\pi r^2 = \left(4 \times \frac{22}{7} \times \frac{21}{2} \times \frac{21}{2}\right) \text{cm}^2 = 1386 \text{ cm}^2.$

Ex. 9. *Find the volume, curved surface area and the total surface area of a hemisphere of radius 10.5 cm.*

Sol. Volume $= \frac{2}{3}\pi r^3 = \left(\frac{2}{3} \times \frac{22}{7} \times \frac{21}{2} \times \frac{21}{2} \times \frac{21}{2}\right) = 2425.5 \text{ cm}^3.$

Curved Surface Area $= 2\pi r^2 = \left(2 \times \frac{22}{7} \times \frac{21}{2} \times \frac{21}{2}\right) = 693 \text{ cm}^2.$

Total Surface Area $= 3\pi r^2 = \left(3 \times \frac{22}{7} \times \frac{21}{2} \times \frac{21}{2}\right) = 1039.5 \text{ cm}^2.$

Ex. 10. *How many bullets can be made out of a lead cylinder 15 cm high and with base radius 6 cm, each bullet being 1.5 cm in diameter ?*

Sol. Volume of cylinder $= (\pi \times 6 \times 6 \times 15) \text{ cm}^3 = (540\pi) \text{ cm}^3.$

Volume of each bullet $= \left(\frac{4}{3}\pi \times \frac{3}{4} \times \frac{3}{4} \times \frac{3}{4}\right) \text{cm}^3 = \frac{9\pi}{16} \text{ cm}^3.$

Number of bullets $= \dfrac{\text{Volume of cylinder}}{\text{Volume of each bullet}}$

$$= \left(540\pi \times \frac{16}{9\pi}\right) = 960.$$

Ex. 11. *Find the number of lead balls, each 1 cm in diameter that can be made from a sphere of diameter 12 cm.*

Sol. Volume of larger sphere $= \left(\frac{4}{3}\pi \times 6 \times 6 \times 6\right) \text{cm}^3 = 288\pi \text{ cm}^3.$

Volume of 1 small lead ball $= \left(\frac{4}{3}\pi \times \frac{1}{2} \times \frac{1}{2} \times \frac{1}{2}\right) \text{cm}^3 = \frac{\pi}{6} \text{ cm}^3.$

∴   Number of lead balls $= \left(288\pi \times \dfrac{6}{\pi}\right) = 1728.$

Ex. 12. *A copper sphere of diameter 18 cm is drawn into a wire of diameter 4 mm. Find the length of the wire.*

Sol. Volume of sphere $= \left(\dfrac{4}{3}\pi \times 9 \times 9 \times 9\right) cm^3 = 972\pi \ cm^3.$

Volume of wire $= (\pi \times 0.2 \times 0.2 \times h) \ cm^3$

∴ $972\pi = \pi \times \dfrac{2}{10} \times \dfrac{2}{10} \times h$

∴ $h = (972 \times 5 \times 5) \ cm = \left(\dfrac{972 \times 5 \times 5}{100}\right) m = 243 \ m.$

Ex. 13. *How many iron rods, each of length 7 m and diameter 2 cm can be made out of 0.88 cubic metre of iron ?*

Sol. Volume of 1 rod $= \left(\dfrac{22}{7} \times \dfrac{1}{100} \times \dfrac{1}{100} \times 7\right) cu.m = \dfrac{11}{5000} \ cu.m.$

Volume of iron $= 0.88 \ cu.m.$

Number of rods $= \left(0.88 \times \dfrac{5000}{11}\right) = 400.$

Ex. 14. *Find the slant height, volume, curved surface area and the whole surface area of a cone of radius 21 cm and height 28 cm.*

Sol. Here $r = 21$ cm and $h = 28$ cm.

∴   Slant height, $l = \sqrt{r^2 + h^2} = \sqrt{(21)^2 + (28)^2} = \sqrt{1225} = 35 \ cm.$

Volume $= \dfrac{1}{3}\pi r^2 h = \left(\dfrac{1}{3} \times \dfrac{22}{7} \times 21 \times 21 \times 28\right) cm^3 = 12936 \ cm^3.$

Curved Surface Area $= \pi r l = \left(\dfrac{22}{7} \times 21 \times 35\right) cm^3 = 2310 \ cm^2.$

Total Surface Area $= (\pi r l + \pi r^2)$

$$= \left(2310 + \dfrac{22}{7} \times 21 \times 21\right) cm^2 = 3696 \ cm^2.$$

Ex. 15. *A solid metallic cone of base radius 2.1 cm, and height 8.4 cm is melted and recast into a sphere. Find the radius of the sphere.*

Sol. Let the radius of the sphere be R cm. Then,

Volume of cone = Volume of sphere

∴ $\dfrac{1}{3}\pi \times 2.1 \times 2.1 \times 8.4 = \dfrac{4}{3}\pi R^3 \Rightarrow R^3 = (2.1)^3$ or $R = 2.1$ cm.

Hence, the radius of the sphere $= 2.1$ cm.

Ex. 16. *Find the length of canvas 1.25 m wide required to form a conical tent of base radius 7 metres and height 24 metres.*

Sol. Here $r = 7$ m and $h = 24$ m.

$$\therefore \ l = \sqrt{r^2 + h^2} = \sqrt{7^2 + (24)^2} = \sqrt{625} = 25 \text{ m.}$$

Area of canvas $= \pi r l = \left(\dfrac{22}{7} \times 7 \times 25\right)$ sq.m $= 550$ sq.m.

$$\therefore \ \text{Length of canvas} = \left(\dfrac{\text{Area}}{\text{Breadth}}\right) = \left(\dfrac{550}{1.25}\right) \text{m} = 440 \text{ metres.}$$

Ex. 17. *If each edge of a cube is increased by 50%, find the percentage increase in its surface area.*

Sol. Let original length of each edge $= a$.

Then, original surface area $= 6a^2$.

New edge $= (150 \%$ of $a) = \left(\dfrac{150}{100} a\right) = \dfrac{3a}{2}$.

New surface area $= 6 \times \left(\dfrac{3a}{2}\right)^2 = \dfrac{27}{2} a^2$.

Increase percent in surface area $= \left(\dfrac{15}{2} a^2 \times \dfrac{1}{6a^2} \times 100\right) \% = 125 \%$.

Ex. 18. *If the radius of a sphere is increased by 50%, find the increase percent in volume and the increase percent in the surface area.*

Sol. Let original radius $= R$. Then, new radius $= \dfrac{150}{100} R = \dfrac{3R}{2}$.

Original volume $= \dfrac{4}{3} \pi R^3$, New volume $= \dfrac{4}{3} \pi \left(3 \dfrac{R}{2}\right)^3 = \dfrac{9\pi R^3}{2}$.

Increase $\%$ in volume $= \left(\dfrac{19}{6} \pi R^3 \times \dfrac{3}{4\pi R^3} \times 100\right) \% = 237.5 \%$.

Original surface area $= 4\pi R^2$. New Surface area $= 4\pi \left(\dfrac{3R}{2}\right)^2 = 9\pi R^2$.

Increase $\%$ in surface area $= \left(\dfrac{5\pi R^2}{4\pi R^2} \times 100\right) \% = 125. \%$.

Ex. 19. *Two cubes have their volumes in the ratio 1 : 27. Find the ratio of their surface areas.*

Sol. Let their edges be a and b. Then,

$$\dfrac{a^3}{b^3} = \dfrac{1}{27} \quad \text{or} \quad \left(\dfrac{a}{b}\right)^3 = \left(\dfrac{1}{3}\right)^3 \quad \text{or} \quad \dfrac{a}{b} = \dfrac{1}{3}.$$

$$\therefore \ \text{Ratio of their surface areas} = \dfrac{6a^2}{6b^2} = \dfrac{a^2}{b^2} = \left(\dfrac{a}{b}\right)^2 = \dfrac{1}{9}, \ i.e. \ 1 : 9.$$

Ex. 20. *The radii of two cylinders are in the ratio 3 : 5 and their heights are in the ratio of 2 : 3. Find the ratio of their curved surface areas.*

Sol. Let the radii of the cylinders be $3x$, $5x$ and their heights be $2y$, $3y$ respectively. Then,

Ratio of their curved surface area $= \dfrac{2\pi \times 3x \times 2y}{2\pi \times 5x \times 3y} = \dfrac{2}{5} = 2 : 5.$

Ex. 21. *If the heights of two cones are in the ratio of 1 : 3 and their diameters are in the ratio of 3 : 5, find the ratio of their volumes.*

Sol. Let the heights of the cones be h, $3h$ and their radii $3r$, $5r$ respectively. Then,

Ratio of their volume $= \dfrac{\frac{1}{3} \pi (3r)^2 \times h}{\frac{1}{3} \pi (5r)^2 \times 3h} = \dfrac{3}{25} = 3 : 25.$

EXERCISE 25

Mark ($\sqrt{}$) against the correct answer :

1. The capacity of a tank of dimensions (8 m × 6 m × 2.5 m), is :
    (a) 120 litres   (b) 1200 litres   (c) 12000 litres (d) 120000 litres

2. A rectangular box is 2 m long and 3.5 m wide. How many cubic metres of sand are needed to fill the box upto a depth of 12 cm ?
    (a) 84   (b) 8.4   (c) 0.84   (d) 0.084

3. A beam 9 m long, 40 cm wide and 20 cm high is made up of iron which weighs 50 kg per cubic metre. The weight of the beam is :
    (a) 56 kg   (b) 48 kg   (c) 36 kg   (d) 27 kg
    (N.D.A. 1992)

4. The length of the longest rod that can be placed in a room 30 m long, 24 m broad and 18 m high, is :   **(C.D.S. 1991)**
    (a) 30 m   (b) $15\sqrt{2}$ m   (c) $30\sqrt{2}$ m   (d) 60 m

5. The maximum length of a pencil that can be kept is a rectangular box of dimensions 8 cm × 6 cm × 2 cm, is :   **(N.D.A. 1990)**
    (a) $2\sqrt{13}$ cm   (b) $2\sqrt{14}$ cm   (c) $2\sqrt{26}$ m   (d) $10\sqrt{2}$ cm

6. A wooden box of dimensions 8 m × 7 m × 6 m is to carry rectangular boxes of dimensions 8 cm × 7 cm × 6 cm. The maximum number of boxes that can be carried in the wooden box, is :   **(C.D.S. 1992)**
    (a) 9800000   (b) 7500000   (c) 1000000   (d) 1200000

7. A wall 8 m long, 6 m high and 22.5 cm thick is made up of bricks, each measuring (25 cm × 11.25 cm × 6 cm). The number of bricks required is :
    (a) 6000   (b) 5600   (c) 6400   (d) 7200

8. The dimensions of a brick are 24 cm × 12 cm × 8 cm. How many bricks will be required to build a wall 24 m long, 8 m high and 60 cm thick, if 10% of the wall is filled with mortar ?   **(Hotel Management 1992)**

(a) 40000   (b) 20000   (c) 50000   (d) 45000

9. A rectangular block 6 cm by 12 cm by 15 cm is cut up into exact number of equal cubes. The least possible number of cubes will be :

(a) 6   (b) 11   (c) 33   (d) 40

(U.D.C. 1993)

10. The breadth of a room is twice its height and half its length. The volume of the room is 512 cu.m. The length of the room is :

(a) 12 m   (b) 16 m   (c) 32 m   (d) 20 m

(Hotel Management 1992)

11. Three cubes of iron whose edges are 6 cm, 8 cm and 10 cm respectively are melted and formed into a single cube. The edge of the new cube formed is : **(Excise & I. Tax 1993)**

(a) 12 cm   (b) 14 cm   (c) 16 cm   (d) 18 cm

12. The surface area of a cube is 1734 sq.cms. Its volume is :

(a) 2197 cu.cm   (b) 4913 cu.cm   (c) 2744 cu.cm   (d) 4096 cu.cm

13. The surface area of a cube is 600 cm^2. The length of its diagonal is :

(a) $\dfrac{10}{\sqrt{3}}$ cm   (b) $\dfrac{10}{\sqrt{2}}$ cm   (c) $10\sqrt{3}$ cm   (d) $10\sqrt{2}$ cm

(Assistant Grade 1993)

14. The volume of a cube is 2744 cu.cm. Its surface area is :

(a) 196 cm^2 (b) 1176 cm^2 (c) 784 cm^2 (d) 588 cm^2

15. The sum of the length, breadth and depth of a cuboid is 19 cm and its diagonal is $5\sqrt{5}$ cm. Its surface area is :

(a) 361 cm^2 (b) 125 cm^2 (c) 236 cm^2 (d) 486 cm^2

16. The area of the base of a rectangular tank is 6500 cm^2 and the volume of water contained in it is 2.6 cubic metres. The depth of water in the tank is :

(a) 3.5 m   (b) 4 m   (c) 5 m   (d) 6 m

17. Given that 1 cu.cm of marble weighs 25 gms, the weight of a marble block 28 cm in width and 5 cm thick is 112 kg. The length of the block is :

(a) 36 cm   (b) 37.5 cm   (c) 32 cm   (d) 26.5 cm

18. The volume of a wall, 5 times as high as it is broad and 8 times as long as it is high, is 12.8 cu. metres. The breadth of the wall is :

(a) 30 m   (b) 40 m   (c) 22.5 m   (d) 25 m

19. Half cubic metre of goldsheet is extended by hammering so as to cover an area of 1 hectare. The thickness of the sheet is :

(a) 0.5 cm   (b) 0.05 cm   (c) 0.005 cm   (d) .0005 cm

20. In a shower, 5 cm of rain falls. The volume of water that falls on 1.5 hectares of ground is :

(a) 75 cu.m   (b) 750 cu.m   (c) 7500 cu.m   (d) 75000 cu.m

21. A river 1.5 m deep and 36 m wide is flowing at the rate of 3.5 km per hour. The amount of water that runs into the sea per minute (in cubic metres) is :

    (a) 3150   (b) 31500   (c) 6300   (d) 63000

22. The area of the card board needed to make a box of size 24 cm × 12 cm × 5 cm will be :

    (a) 1440 cm^2 (b) 468 cm^2 (c) 936 cm^2 (d) 720 cm^2

23. A hall is 15 m long and 12 m broad. The sum of the areas of the floor and the ceiling is equal to the sum of areas of the four walls. The volume of the hall is :

    (a) 1200 m^3 (b) 1800 m^3 (c) 900 m^3 (d) 720 m^3

24. An open box is made of wood 3 cm thick. Its external dimensions are 1.46 m, 1.16 m and 8.3 dm. The cost of painting the inner surface of the box at 50 paise per 100 sq.cm is :

    (a) Rs. 277   (b) Rs. 138.50   (c) Rs. 415.50   (d) Rs. 554

25. The dimensions of an open box are 50 cm, 40 cm and 23 cm. Its thickness is 3 cm. If 1 cubic cm of metal used in the box weighs 0.5 gms, the weight of the box is :

    (a) 8.56 kg   (b) 8.04 kg   (c) 7.576 kg   (d) 6.832 kg

26. How many bags of grain can be stored in a cuboid granary 12 m × 6 m × 5 m, if each bag occupies a space of 0.48 cu. metre ?

    (a) 75   (b) 750   (c) 480   (d) 288

27. If the length of diagonal of a cube is $4\sqrt{3}$ cm, then its surface area is :

    (a) 24 cm^2 (b) 54 cm^2 (c) 96 cm^2 (d) 216 cm^2

28. If the length of diagonal of a cube is $8\sqrt{3}$ cm, then its volume is :

    (a) 512 cm^3 (b) 384 cm^3 (c) 64 cm^3 (d) 192 cm^3

29. The number of small cubes with edge 10 cm that can be accomodated in a cubical box of 1 metre edge, is :

    (a) 10   (b) 100   (c) 1000   (d) 10000

30. The total surface area of a cuboid is 63200 sq.cm and its length, breadth and height are in the ratio of 8 : 5 : 3. The length, breadth and height of the cuboid are respectively :

    (a) 120 cm, 75 cm, 45 cm   (b) 128 cm, 80 cm, 48 cm
    (c) 160 cm, 100 cm, 60 cm   (d) 144 cm, 90 cm, 54 cm

31. A metal sheet 27 cm long, 8 cm broad and 1 cm thick is melted into a cube. The difference between surface areas of two solids, is :

    (a) 284 cm^2 (b) 286 cm^2 (c) 296 cm^2 (d) 300 cm^2

                                                                            (C.D.S. 1991)

32. A tank 4 m long, 2.5 m wide and 1.5 m wide is dug in a field 31 m long and 10 m wide. If the earth dug out is evenly spread out over the field, the rise in level of the field is :

(a) 3.1 cm   (b) 6.2 cm   (c) 5 cm   (d) 4.8 cm

33. If each edge of a cube is doubled, then its volume :
    (a) is doubled   (b) becomes 4 times
    (c) becomes 6 times   (d) becomes 8 times

34. If each edge of a cube is increased by 25%, then the percentage increase in its surface area is :
    (a) 25%   (b) 50%   (c) 48.75%   (d) 56.25%

35. Two cubes have their volumes in the ratio 8 : 27. The ratio of their surface areas is :
    (a) 2 : 3   (b) 3 : 2   (c) 4 : 9   (d) 64 : 729

36. A sphere and a cube have equal surface areas. The ratio of the volume of the sphere to that of the cube is :
    (a) $\sqrt{\pi} : \sqrt{6}$ (b) $\sqrt{2} : \sqrt{\pi}$ (c) $\sqrt{\pi} : \sqrt{3}$ (d) $\sqrt{6} : \sqrt{\pi}$

37. The ratio of the volume of a cube to that of a sphere which will fit inside the cube is :   **(Assistant Grade 1994)**
    (a) $4 : \pi$ (b) $4 : 3\pi$ (c) $6 : \pi$ (d) $2 : \pi$

38. Two cubes each with 6 cm edge are joined end to end. The surface area of the resulting cuboid is :
    (a) 864 cm^2 (b) 360 cm^2 (c) 576 cm^2 (d) 432 cm^2

39. If the areas of three adjacent faces of a cuboid are x, y, z respectively, then the volume of the cuboid is :   **(C.D.S. 1994)**
    (a) xyz (b) $2xyz$ (c) $\sqrt{xyz}$ (d) $3\sqrt{xyz}$

40. If V be the volume and S be the surface area of a cuboid of dimensions a, b, c, then $\dfrac{1}{V}$ is equal to :

    (a) $\dfrac{S}{2}(a+b+c)$ (b) $\dfrac{2}{S}\left(\dfrac{1}{a}+\dfrac{1}{b}+\dfrac{1}{c}\right)$

    (c) $\dfrac{2S}{a+b+c}$ (d) $2S(a+b+c)$

41. A cube of side 6 cm is cut into a number of cubes, each of side 2 cm. The number of cubes will be :   **(C.D.S. 1994)**
    (a) 6   (b) 9   (c) 12   (d) 27

42. A 4 cm cube is cut into 1 cm cubes. The total surface area of all the small cubes is :
    (a) 96 cm^2 (b) 24 cm^2 (c) 384 cm^2 (d) None

43. If the areas of three adjacent faces of a rectangular block are in the ratio of 2 : 3 : 4 and its volume is 9000 cu.cm; then the length of the shortest side is :   **(N.D.A. 1994)**
    (a) 10 cm   (b) 15 cm   (c) 20 cm   (d) 30 cm

44. The percentage increase in the surface area of a cube when each side is doubled, is :
    (a) 25%   (b) 50%   (c) 150%   (d) 300%

45. If the diameter of a cylinder is 28 cm and its height is 20 cm, then total surface area is : **(C.D.S 1994)**

(a) 2993 cm^2 (b) 2992 cm^2 (c) 2292 cm^2 (d) 2229 cm^2

46. The volume of the cylinder whose height is 84 cm and the diameter of base 5 cm is :

(a) 1320 cm^3 (b) 1650 cm^3 (c) 3300 cm^3 (d) 1339.64 cm^3

47. If the curved surface area of a cylinder is 1760 sq.cm and its base radius is 14 cm, then its volume is :

(a) 12320 cm^3 (b) 6160 cm^3 (c) 77440 cm^3 (d) None

48. The height of a cylinder is 14 cm and its curved surface area is 704 sq.cm, then its volume is :

(a) 2816 cm^3 (b) 5632 cm^3 (c) 1408 cm^3 (d) 9856 cm^3

49. The curved surface area of a cylinder is 2640 sq.cm and the circumference of its base is 66 cm. The volume of the cylinder is :

(a) 174240 cm^3 (b) 6930 cm^3 (c) 13860 cm^3 (d) 27620 cm^3

50. The curved surface area of a right circular cylinder of base radius r is obtained by multiplying its volume by : **(Central Excise & I.Tax 1992)**

(a) $2r$ (b) $\dfrac{2}{r}$ (c) $2r^2$ (d) $\dfrac{2}{r^2}$

51. A copper sphere of radius 3 cm is beaten and drawn into a wire of diameter 0.2 cm. The length of the wire is : **(Assistant Grade 1993)**

(a) 9 m   (b) 12 m   (c) 18 m   (d) 36 m

52. The ratio of total surface area to lateral surface area of a cylinder whose radius is 20 cm and height 60 cm, is :

(a) 2 : 1   (b) 3 : 2   (c) 4 : 3   (d) 5 : 3

53. The radii of two cylinders are in the ratio of 2 : 3 and their heights are in the ratio of 5 : 3. The ratio of their volumes is :

(a) 4 : 9   (b) 9 : 4   (c) 20 : 27   (d) 27 : 20

(Hotel Management 1991)

54. The ratio between the radius of the base and the height of a cylinder is 2 : 3. If its volume is 12936 cu.cm, the total surface area of the cylinder is :

(a) 3080 cm^2 (b) 38808 cm^2 (c) 25872 cm^2 (d) 2587.2 cm^2

55. A solid cylinder has a total surface area of 231 sq.cm. If its curved surface area is two-third of the total surface area, the volume of the cylinder is :

(a) 269.5 cm^3 (b) 385 cm^3 (c) 308 cm^3 (d) 363.4 cm^3

56. The sum of the radius of the base and the height of a solid cylinder is 37 metres. If the total surface area of the cylinder be 1628 sq. metres, its volume is :

(a) 5240 m^3 (b) 4620 m^3 (c) 3180 m^3 (d) None of these

57. The ratio between the curved surface area and the total sruface area of a right circular cylinder is 1 : 2. If the total surface area is 616 sq.cm, the volume of the cylinder is :

    (a) 1848 cm^3 (b) 1232 cm^3 (c) 1078 cm^3 (d) None of these

58. The number of coins 1.5 cm in diameter and 0.2 cm thick to be melted to form a right circular cylinder of height 10 cm and diameter 4.5 cm, is :

    (a) 380   (b) 450   (c) 472   (d) 540

59. A cylindrical vessel 60 cm in diameter is partially filled with water. A sphere 30 cm is diameter is dropped into it. The increase in the level of water in the vessel is :   **(U.D.C. 1993)**

    (a) 2 cm   (b) 3 cm   (c) 4 cm   (d) 5 cm

60. A cylindrical vessel of radius 8 cm contains water. A solid sphere of radius 6 cm is lowered into the water until it is completely immersed. The water level in the vessel will rise by :

    (a) 3.5 cm   (b) 4.5 cm.   (c) 4 cm   (d) 7 cm

61. The curved surface area of a cylindrical pillar is 528 sq. m and its volume is 2772 cu.m. The height of the pillar is :

    (a) 10.5 m   (b) 7.5 m   (c) 8 m   (d) 5.25 m

62. The number of solid spheres, each of diameter 3 cm that could be moulded to form a solid cylinder of height 54 cm and diameter 4 cm, is :

    (a) 16   (b) 24   (c) 36   (d) 48

63. The radius of a wire is decreased to one-third and its volume remains the same. The new length is how many times the original length ?

    (a) 1 time   (b) 3 times   (c) 6 times   (d) 9 times

                                                   (Railways 1990)

64. Two cylindrical vessels with radii 15 cm and 10 cm and heights 35 cm and 15 cm respectively are filled with water. If this water is poured into a cylindrical vessel 15 cm in height, then the radius of the vessel is :

    (a) 17.5 cm   (b) 18 cm   (c) 20 cm   (d) 25 cm

65. A hollow garden roller 63 cm wide with a girth of 440 cm is made of iron 4 cm thick. The volume of the iron used is :

    (a) 57636 cm^3 (b) 54982 cm^3 (c) 56372 cm^3 (d) 58752 cm^3

66. If 1 cubic cm of cast iron weighs 21 gms, then the weight of a cast iron pipe of length 1 metre with a bore of 3 cm and in which the thickness of the metal is 1 cm, is :

    (a) 18.6 kg   (b) 21 kg   (c) 24.2 kg   (d) 26.4 kg

67. Two circular cylinders of equal volumes have their heights in the ratio 2 : 1. The ratio of their radii is :

    (a) 2 : 1   (b) 1 : 2   (c) $\sqrt{2}$: 1   (d) 1 : $\sqrt{2}$

68. If the radius of the base of a right circular cylinder is halved, keeping the height same, what is the ratio of the volume of the reduced cylinder to that of the original one ?

(a) 1 : 4   (b) 1 : 8   (c) 1 : 2   (d) 8 : 1

69. In what ratio are the volumes of a cylinder, a cone and a sphere, if each has the same diameter and the same height ?   **(Assistant Grade 1994)**

(a) 1 : 3 : 2   (b) 2 : 3 : 1   (c) 3 : 1 : 2   (d) 3 : 2 : 1

70. The radius of a sphere is R and the radius of the base as well as the height of a cylinder is R. The ratio of the volume of the sphere to that of the cylinder is :   **(Assistant Grade 1994)**

(a) 4 : 3   (b) 3 : 4   (c) 2 : 3   (d) 3 : 2

71. Two cylindrical jars have their diameters in the ratio of 3 : 1 and their heights in the ratio of 1 : 3. The volumes are in the ratio of :

(a) 1 : 2   (b) 3 : 1   (c) 3 : 4   (d) 2 : 3

(Assistant Grade 1994)

72. The volume of a sphere is 4851 cu.cm. Its curved surface area is :

(a) 1716 cm^2 (b) 1386 cm^2 (c) 1625 cm^2 (d) 3087 cm^2

73. The curved surface area of a sphere is 5544 sq.cm. Its volume is :

(a) 38808 cm^3 (b) 42304 cm^3 (c) 22176 cm^3 (d) 33951 cm^3

74. Three spherical metal balls of radii 6 cm, 8 cm and R cm are melted into a solid sphere of radius 12 cm. The value of R is :

(a) 8 cm   (b) 10 cm   (c) 14 cm   (d) 18 cm

(Assistant Grade 1994)

75. If the volume of a sphere is divided by its surface area, the result is 27 cm. The radius of the sphere is :   **(Assistant Grade 1993)**

(a) 81 cm   (b) 9 cm   (c) 54 cm   (d) 36 cm

76. A cone and a sphere have equal radii and equal volumes. The ratio of the diameter of the sphere to the height of the cone is :

(a) 3 : 1   (b) 1 : 3   (c) 6 : 1   (d) 1 : 2

(Assistant Grade 1994)

77. The radius of a sphere is increased by 50%. The increase in the surface area of the sphere is :   **(Assistant Grade 1993)**

(a) 100%   (b) 125%   (c) 150%   (d) None

78. How many bullets can be made out of a cube of lead whose edge measures 22 cm, each bullet being 2 cm in diameter ?

(a) 5324   (b) 2662   (c) 1347   (d) 2541

79. A spherical ball of lead, 3 cm in diameter is melted and recast into three spherical balls. The diameter of two of these are 1.5 cm and 2 cm respectively. The diameter of the third ball is :

(a) 2.66 cm   (b) 2.5 cm   (c) 3 cm   (d) 3.5 cm

80. If the radius of a sphere is doubled, then its surface area is increased by :

(a) 50%   (b) 100%   (c) 200%   (d) 300%

81. If a solid sphere of radius 10 cm is moulded into 8 spherical solid balls of equal radius, then the raidus of each such ball is :

(a) 1.25 cm   (b) 2.5 cm   (c) 3.75 cm   (d) 5 cm

82. How many lead shots each 0.3 cm in diameter can be made from a cuboid of dimensions 9 cm × 11 cm × 12 cm ?

(a) 7200   (b) 8400   (c) 84000   (d) 72000

83. A metallic sphere of radius 10.5 cm is melted and recast into small cones, each of radius 3.5 cm and height 3 cm. The number of such cones will be :

(a) 21   (b) 63   (c) 126   (d) 130

84. Two metallic right circular cones having their heights 4.1 cm and 4.3 cm and the radii of their bases 2.1 cm each, have been melted together and recast into a sphere. The diameter of the sphere is :

(a) 4.2 cm   (b) 1.4 cm   (c) 3.5 cm   (d) 6.3 cm

85. A sphere of radius 6.3 cm is melted and cast into a right circular cone of height 25.2 cm. The radius of the base of the cone is :

(a) 6.3 cm   (b) 2.1 cm   (c) 2 cm   (d) 3 cm

86. If the height and diameter of a right circular cylinder are 32 cm and 6 cm respectively, then the radius of the sphere whose volume is equal to the volume of the cylinder is :

(a) 3 cm   (b) 4 cm   (c) 6 cm   (d) None

87. A hemisphere of lead of radius 6 cm is cast into a right circular cone of height 75 cm. The radius of the base of the cone is :

(a) 1.4 cm   (b) 2 cm   (c) 2.4 cm   (d) 4.2 cm

(Assistant Grade 1994)

88. The diameter and the slant height of a conical tomb are 28 m and 50 m respectively. The cost of whitewashing its curved surface at the rate of 80 paise per square metre is :   **(Assistant Grade 1993)**

(a) Rs. 2640   (b) Rs. 1760   (c) Rs. 264   (d) Rs. 176

89. The height and the radius of the base of a cone are each increased by 100%. The volume of the new cone becomes how many times of the volume of the original cone ?   **(Assistant Grade 1993)**

(a) 8 times   (b) 6 times   (c) 4 times   (d) 3 times

90. The capacities of two hemispherical vessels are 6.4 litres and 21.6 litres. The areas of inner curved surfaces of the vessels will be in the ratio of :

(a) 4 : 9   (b) 2 : 3   (c) $\sqrt{2} : \sqrt{3}$ (d) 16 : 81

91. If a solid sphere of radius r is melted and cast into the shape of a solid cone of height r, then the radius of the base of the cone is :

(a) 2r   (b) r   (c) 4r   (d) 3r

(C.D.S. 1993)

92. A right cylinder and a right circular cone have the same radius and the same volume. The ratio of the height of the cylinder to that of the cone is :   (C.D.S. 1991)

   (a) 3 : 5   (b) 2 : 5   (c) 3 : 1   (d) 1 : 3

93. A right cylindrical vessel is full of water. How many right cones having the same radius and height as those of the right cylinder will be needed to store that water ?

   (a) 2   (b) 3   (c) 4   (d) 8

94. A cylindrical piece of metal of radius 2 cm and height 6 cm is shaped into a cone of same radius. The height of the cone is :   (Railways 1991)

   (a) 8 cm   (b) 12 cm   (c) 14 cm   (d) 18 cm

95. If a right circular cone of height 24 cm has volume of 1232 cu. cm, then the area of its curved surface is :

   (a) 154 cm^2 (b) 550 cm^2 (c) 704 cm^2 (d) 1254 cm^2

96. The length of canvas 1.1 m wide required to build a conical tent of height 14 m and the floor area 346.5 sq. m is :

   (a) 525 m   (b) 490 m   (c) 665 m   (d) 860 m

97. How many metres of cloth 2.5 m wide will be required to make a conical tent whose base radius is 7 m and height is 24 m ?

   (a) 120 m   (b) 180 m   (c) 220 m   (d) 550 m

98. It the volumes of two cones are in the ratio of 1 : 4 and their diameters are in the ratio of 4 : 5, then the ratio of their heights is :

   (a) 1 : 5   (b) 5 : 4   (c) 5 : 16   (d) 25 : 64

99. Volume of a hemisphere is 19404 cu. cm. Its radius is :

   (a) 10.5 cm   (b) 21 cm   (c) 17.5 cm   (d) 42 cm

100. A well with 14 m inside diameter is dug 10 m deep. Earth taken out of it has been evenly spread all around it to a width of 21 m to form an embankment. The height of the embankment is :

   (a) $\frac{1}{2}$ m   (b) $\frac{2}{3}$ m   (c) $\frac{3}{4}$ m   (d) $\frac{3}{5}$ m

101. The radii of the bases of a cylinder and a cone are in the ratio of 3 : 4 and their heights are in the ratio 2 : 3. Their volumes are in the ratio of :

   (a) 9 : 8·   (b) 3 : 4   (c) 8 : 9   (d) 4 : 3

102. A cylindrical vessel 32 cm high and 18 cm as the radius of the base is filled with sand. This is emptied on the ground and a conical heap of sand is formed. If the height of the conical heap is 24 cm, the radius of its base is :

   (a) 12 cm   (b) 24 cm   (c) 36 cm   (d) 48 cm

103. A solid metallic cylinder of base radius 3 cm and height 5 cm is melted to form cones, each of height 1 cm and base radius 1 mm. The number of cones is :

(a) 450　　　　(b) 1350　　　　(c) 4500　　　　(d) 13500

104. If the ratio of volumes of two spheres is 1 : 8, then the ratio of their surface areas is :

(a) 1 : 2　　　　(b) 1 : 4　　　　(c) 1 : 8　　　　(d) 1 : 16

105. If the surface areas of two spheres are in the ratio of 4 : 25, then the ratio of their volumes is : **(U.D.C. 1993)**

(a) 4 : 25　　　　(b) 25 : 4　　　　(c) 125 : 8　　　　(d) 8 : 125

106. The total surface area of a solid hemisphere of diameter 14 cm, is :

(a) 462 cm^2　　　(b) 308 cm^2　　　(c) 1232 cm^2　　　(d) 1848 cm^2

107. Water flows at the rate of 10 metres per minute from a cylindrical pipe 5 mm in diameter. How long will it take to fill up a conical vessel whose diameter at the base is 40 cm and depth 24 cm ?

(a) 55 min.　　　　　　　　　　(b) 52 min. 1 sec.

(c) 51 min. 12 sec.　　　　　　　(d) 48 min. 15 sec.

108. A cone, a hemisphere and a cylinder stand on equal bases and have the same height. The ratio of their volumes is :

(a) 1 : 2 : 3　　　(b) 2 : 1 : 3　　　(c) 2 : 3 : 1　　　(d) 3 : 2 : 1

109. A cylindrical tub of radius 12 cm contains water upto a depth of 20 cm. A spherical iron ball is dropped into the tub and thus the level of water is raised by 6.75 cm. The radius of the ball is :

(a) 4.5 cm　　　(b) 6 cm　　　(c) 7.25 cm　　　(d) 9 cm

110. A hemispherical bowl of internal radius 9 cm contains a liquid. This liquid is to be filled into cylindrical shaped small bottles of diameter 3 cm and height 4 cm. How many bottles will be needed to empty the bowl ?

(a) 27　　　(b) 35　　　(c) 54　　　(d) 63

111. A cone of height 7 cm and base radius 3 cm is carved from a rectangular block of wood 10 cm × 5 cm × 2 cm. The percentage of wood wasted is :

(a) 34%　　　(b) 46%　　　(c) 54%　　　(d) 66%

112. If the height of a cone is doubled, then its volume is increased by :

(a) 100%　　　(b) 200%　　　(c) 300%　　　(d) 400%

113. Two circular cylinders of equal volumes have their heights in the ratio 1 : 2. The ratio of their radii is :

(a) $1 : \sqrt{2}$　　　(b) $\sqrt{2} : 1$　　　(c) 1 : 2　　　(d) 1 : 4

114. The radius of a cylinder is the same as that of a sphere. Their volumes are equal. The height of the cylinder is how many times its radius ?

(a) $\dfrac{4}{3}$　　　(b) $\dfrac{2}{3}$　　　(c) 1　　　(d) 2

115. The material of a cone is converted into the shape of a cylinder of equal radius. If the height of the cylinder is 6 cm, the height of the cone is :

(a) 2 cm　　　(b) 6 cm　　　(c) 18 cm　　　(d) 36 cm

116. A powder tin has a square base with side 8 cm and height 14 cm. Another tin has a circular base with diameter 8 cm and height 14 cm. The difference in their capacities is :

(a) 0   (b) 132 cm^3 (c) 192 cm^3 (d) 137.1 cm^3

ANSWERS

1. (d)	**2.** (c)	**3.** (c)	**4.** (c)	**5.** (c)	**6.** (c)	**7.** (c)	**8.** (d)	**9.** (d)
10. (b)	**11.** (a)	**12.** (b)	**13.** (c)	**14.** (b)	**15.** (c)	**16.** (b)	**17.** (c)	**18.** (b)
19. (c)	**20.** (b)	**21.** (a)	**22.** (c)	**23.** (a)	**24.** (a)	**25.** (b)	**26.** (b)	**27.** (c)
28. (a)	**29.** (c)	**30.** (c)	**31.** (b)	**32.** (c)	**33.** (d)	**34.** (d)	**35.** (c)	**36.** (d)
37. (c)	**38.** (b)	**39.** (c)	**40.** (b)	**41.** (d)	**42.** (c)	**43.** (b)	**44.** (d)	**45.** (b)
46. (b)	**47.** (a)	**48.** (a)	**49.** (c)	**50.** (b)	**51.** (d)	**52.** (c)	**53.** (c)	**54.** (a)
55. (a)	**56.** (b)	**57.** (c)	**58.** (b)	**59.** (d)	**60.** (b)	**61.** (c)	**62.** (d)	**63.** (d)
64. (d)	**65.** (d)	**66.** (d)	**67.** (d)	**68.** (a)	**69.** (c)	**70.** (a)	**71.** (b)	**72.** (b)
73. (a)	**74.** (b)	**75.** (a)	**76.** (d)	**77.** (d)	**78.** (d)	**79.** (b)	**80.** (d)	**81.** (d)
82. (c)	**83.** (c)	**84.** (a)	**85.** (a)	**86.** (c)	**87.** (c)	**88.** (b)	**89.** (a)	**90.** (a)
91. (a)	**92.** (d)	**93.** (b)	**94.** (d)	**95.** (b)	**96.** (a)	**97.** (c)	**98.** (d)	**99.** (b)
100. (b)	**101.** (a)	**102.** (c)	**103.** (d)	**104.** (b)	**105.** (d)	**106.** (a)	**107.** (c)	**108.** (a)
109. (d)	**110.** (c)	**111.** (a)	**112.** (a)	**113.** (b)	**114.** (a)	**115.** (c)	**116.** (c)	

SOLUTIONS

1. Capacity of the tank = Volume of the tank

$$= \left(\frac{8 \times 100 \times 6 \times 100 \times 2.5 \times 100}{1000} \right) \text{litres} = 120000 \text{ litres.}$$

2. Volume $= \left(2 \times \dfrac{7}{2} \times \dfrac{12}{100} \right) = 0.84$ cu.m.

3. Volume $= \left(9 \times \dfrac{40}{100} \times \dfrac{20}{100} \right)$ cu.m $= \dfrac{18}{25}$ cu.m.

∴ Weight $= \left(\dfrac{18}{25} \times 50 \right)$ kg $= 36$ kg.

4. Length of longest rod = length of diagonal $= \sqrt{l^2 + b^2 + h^2}$

$$= \sqrt{(30)^2 + (24)^2 + (18)^2} = \sqrt{1800} = 30\sqrt{2}\,\text{m}.$$

5. Required length $= \left(\sqrt{8^2 + 6^2 + 2^2} \right)$ cm $= \sqrt{104}$ cm $= 2\sqrt{26}$ cm.

6. Number of boxes $= \left(\dfrac{800 \times 700 \times 600}{8 \times 7 \times 6} \right) = 1000000.$

7. Number of bricks $= \left(\dfrac{800 \times 600 \times 22.5}{25 \times 11.25 \times 6} \right) = 6400$.

8. Volume of wall $= (2400 \times 800 \times 60)$ cu.cm.
   Volume of wall (apart from mortar)
   $$= \left(\dfrac{90}{100} \times 2400 \times 800 \times 60 \right) \text{ cu.cm.}$$
   Volume of 1 brick $= (24 \times 12 \times 8)$ cu.cm.
   ∴ Number of bricks required
   $$= \left(\dfrac{90}{10} \times 2400 \times 800 \times 60 \times \dfrac{1}{24 \times 12 \times 8} \right) = 45000.$$

9. Volume of block $= (6 \times 12 \times 15)$ cu.cm $= 1080$ cu.cm.
   The side of largest cube $=$ H.C.F. of 6 cm, 12 cm, 15 cm $= 3$ cm.
   Volume of this cube $= (3 \times 3 \times 3)$ cm$^3 = 27$ cm^3.
   Number of cubes $= \left(\dfrac{1080}{27} \right) = 40$.

10. Suppose height $= x$ metres. Then,
    breadth $= 2x$ metres and length $= 4x$ metres.
    ∴ $x \times 2x \times 4x = 512$ or $x^3 = 64$ or $x = 4$.
    ∴ Length $= 4x = 16$ m.

11. Volume of the new cube $= [6^3 + 8^3 + (10)^3]$ cu.cm $= 1728$ cu.cm.
    Let the edge of new cube be a cm.
    Then, $a^3 = 1728 = (4 \times 4 \times 4 \times 3 \times 3 \times 3)$ or $a = 12$ cm.

12. $6a^2 = 1734 \Rightarrow a^2 = 289$ or $a = 17$ cm.
    ∴ Volume $= (17 \times 17 \times 17)$ cu.cm $= 4913$ cu.cm.

13. $6a^2 = 600 \Rightarrow a^2 = 100$ or $a = 10$ cm.
    ∴ Diagonal $= \sqrt{3}\, a = 10\sqrt{3}$ cm.

14. $a^3 = 2744 = (2 \times 2 \times 2 \times 7 \times 7 \times 7) \Rightarrow a = 14$ cm.
    ∴ Surface Area $= 6a^2 = (6 \times 14 \times 14)$ cm$^2 = 1176$ cm^2.

15. $(l + b + h) = 19$ & $\sqrt{l^2 + b^2 + h^2} = 5\sqrt{5}$ and so $(l^2 + b^2 + h^2) = 125$
    Now $(l + b + h)^2 = 19^2$
    $\Rightarrow (l^2 + b^2 + h^2) + 2(lb + bh + lh) = 361$
    $\Rightarrow 2(lb + bh + lh) = (361 - 125) = 236$.
    ∴ Surface area $= 236$ cm^2.

16. Volume $= (2.6 \times 100 \times 100 \times 100)$ cubic cm.
    Depth $= \dfrac{\text{Volume}}{\text{Area of the base}} = \left(\dfrac{2.6 \times 100 \times 100 \times 100}{6500} \right)$ cm $= 4$m.

17. Let length $= x$ cm.

Then $x \times 28 \times 5 \times \dfrac{25}{1000} = 112.$

$\therefore \ x = \left(112 \times \dfrac{1000}{25} \times \dfrac{1}{28} \times \dfrac{1}{5}\right)$ cm $= 32$ cm.

$\therefore$ Length of block $= 32$ cm.

18. Let, breadth $= x$ metres. Then,

Height $= 5x$ metres and length $= 40\,x$ metres.

$\therefore \ x \times 5x \times 40x = 12.8$ or $x^3 = \dfrac{12.8}{200} = \dfrac{128}{2000} = \dfrac{64}{1000}.$

$\therefore \ x = \dfrac{4}{10}$ m $= \left(\dfrac{4}{10} \times 100\right)$ cm $= 40$ cm.

19. Volume of gold $= \left(\dfrac{1}{2} \times 100 \times 100 \times 100\right)$ cu. cm.

Area of sheet $= 10000$ sq. m $= (10000 \times 100 \times 100)$ sq. cm.

$\therefore$ Thickness of the sheet $= \left(\dfrac{1 \times 100 \times 100 \times 100}{2 \times 10000 \times 100 \times 100}\right)$ cm $= 0.005$ cm.

20. Area $= (1.5 \times 10000)$ sq. metres $= 15000$ sq. metres.

Depth $= \dfrac{5}{100}$ m $= \dfrac{1}{20}$ m.

$\therefore$ Volume $= (\text{Area} \times \text{Depth}) = \left(15000 \times \dfrac{1}{20}\right)$ cu. m $= 750$ cu. metres.

21. Length of water column flown in 1 min. $= \left(\dfrac{3.5 \times 1000}{60}\right)$ m $= \dfrac{175}{3}$ m.

$\therefore$ Volume flown per minute $= \left(\dfrac{175}{3} \times 36 \times \dfrac{3}{2}\right)$ cu. m $= 3150$ cu. m.

22. Area of the cardboard $= 2\,(24 \times 12 + 12 \times 5 + 24 \times 5)$ cm^2 $= 936$ cm^2.

23. $2\,(15 + 12) \times h = 2\,(15 \times 12)$ or $h = \dfrac{180}{27}$ m $= \dfrac{20}{3}$ m.

$\therefore$ Volume $= \left(15 \times 12 \times \dfrac{20}{3}\right)$ m^3 $= 1200$ m^3.

24. Internal length $= (146 - 6)$ cm $= 140$ cm,

Internal breadth $= (116 - 6)$ cm $= 110$ cm.

Internal depth $= (83 - 3)$ cm $= 80$ cm.

$\therefore$ Area of inner surface $= [2\,(l + b) \times h] + lb$

$\qquad\qquad\qquad\qquad = [2\,(140 + 110) \times 80 + 140 \times 110]$ sq. cm

$\qquad\qquad\qquad\qquad = 55400$ sq. cm.

Cost of painting $= $ Rs. $\left(\dfrac{1}{2} \times \dfrac{1}{100} \times 55400\right) = $ Rs. 277.

25. Volume of the metal

$\qquad = [(50 \times 40 \times 23) - (44 \times 34 \times 20)]$ cu. cm. $= 16080$ cu. cm.

Weight of the metal $= \left(\dfrac{16080 \times 0.5}{1000}\right)$ kg $= 8.04$ kg.

26. Number of bags $= \dfrac{\text{Volume of granary}}{\text{Volume of one bag}} = \left(\dfrac{12 \times 6 \times 5}{0.48}\right) = 750.$

27. $\sqrt{3}\, a = 4\sqrt{3} \Rightarrow a = 4$ cm.

   $\therefore$ Surface area $= 6a^2 = (6 \times 4 \times 4)$ cm$^2 = 96$ cm^2.

28. $\sqrt{3}\, a = 8\sqrt{3} \Rightarrow a = 8$ cm.

   $\therefore$ Volume $= (8 \times 8 \times 8)$ cm$^3 = 512$ cm^3.

29. Number of cubes $= \left(\dfrac{100 \times 100 \times 100}{10 \times 10 \times 10}\right) = 1000.$

30. Let length $= 8x$, breadth $= 5x$ and height $= 3x$ in cms.

   Then, $2\,(8x \times 5x + 5x \times 3x + 8x \times 3x) = 63200$

   or $158x^2 = 63200$ or $x = 20.$

   $\therefore$ Length $= 160$ cm, breadth $= 100$ cm & height $= 60$ cm.

31. Surface area of given cuboid $= 2\,(27 \times 8 + 8 \times 1 + 27 \times 1)$ cm^2

   $\qquad\qquad\qquad\qquad\qquad = 502$ cm^2.

   Volume of cube $= (27 \times 8 \times 1)$ cm$^3 = 216$ cm^3.

   $\therefore$ Edge of the cube $= (6 \times 6 \times 6)^{1/3}$ cm $= 6$ cm.

   Surface area of this cube $= 6 \times (6 \times 6)$ cm$^2 = 216$ cm^2.

   Required difference $= (502 - 216)$ cm$^2 = 286$ cm^2.

32. Volume of earth dug out $= \left(4 \times \dfrac{5}{2} \times \dfrac{3}{2}\right)$ m$^3 = 15$ m^3.

   Area over which earth is spread $= \left(31 \times 10 - 4 \times \dfrac{5}{2}\right)$ m$^2 = 300$ m^2.

   Rise in Level $= \left(\dfrac{\text{Volume}}{\text{Area}}\right) = \left(\dfrac{15}{300} \times 100\right)$ cm $= 5$ cm.

33. Let original edge $= a$. Then, volume $= a^3$.

   New edge $= 2a$. So, new volume $= (2a)^3 = 8a^3$.

   $\therefore$ Volume becomes 8 times.

34. Let original edge $= a$. Then, surface area $= 6a^2$.

   New edge $= \dfrac{125}{100}\, a = \dfrac{5a}{4}$.

   New surface area $= 6 \times \left(\dfrac{5a}{4}\right)^2 = \dfrac{75a^2}{8}$.

   Increase in surface area $= \left(\dfrac{75a^2}{8} - 6a^2\right) = \dfrac{27a^2}{8}$.

Increase % $= \left(\dfrac{27a^2}{8} \times \dfrac{1}{6a^2} \times 100 \right) \% = 56.25\%.$

35. Let their edges be a and b. Then,

$$\dfrac{a^3}{b^3} = \dfrac{8}{27} \Leftrightarrow \left(\dfrac{a}{b} \right)^3 = \left(\dfrac{2}{3} \right)^3 \Leftrightarrow \dfrac{a}{b} = \dfrac{2}{3}$$

$$\Leftrightarrow \dfrac{a^2}{b^2} = \dfrac{4}{9} \Leftrightarrow \dfrac{6a^2}{6b^2} = \dfrac{4}{9}.$$

36. $4\pi R^2 = 6a^2 \Rightarrow \dfrac{R^2}{a^2} = \dfrac{3}{2\pi} \Rightarrow \dfrac{R}{a} = \dfrac{\sqrt{3}}{\sqrt{2\pi}}.$

$$\dfrac{\text{Volume of sphere}}{\text{Volume of cube}} = \dfrac{\frac{4}{3}\pi R^3}{a^3} = \dfrac{4}{3}\pi \cdot \left(\dfrac{R}{a} \right)^3 = \dfrac{4}{3}\pi \cdot \dfrac{3\sqrt{3}}{2\pi\sqrt{2\pi}}$$

$$= \dfrac{2\sqrt{3}}{\sqrt{2\pi}} = \dfrac{\sqrt{12}}{\sqrt{2\pi}} = \dfrac{\sqrt{6}}{\sqrt{\pi}}.$$

37. Let the edge of the cube be a.

Then, volume of the cube $= a^3$.

Radius of the sphere $= (a/2)$.

Volume of the sphere $= \dfrac{4}{3}\pi \left(\dfrac{a}{2} \right)^3 = \dfrac{\pi a^3}{6}.$

$\therefore$ Required Ratio $= a^3 : \dfrac{\pi a^3}{6} = 6 : \pi.$

38. New cuboid has length $= 12$ cm, breadth $= 6$ cm & height $= 6$ cm.

$\therefore$ Its surface area $= 2 (12 \times 6 + 6 \times 6 + 12 \times 6)$ cm$^2 = 360$ cm^2.

39. Let length $= l$, breadth $= b$ & height $= h$. Then,

$lb = x$, $bh = y$ and $lh = z$.

On multiplying, we get $(lbh)^2 = xyz$ or $lbh = \sqrt{xyz}$.

$\therefore$ Volume $= \sqrt{xyz}.$

40. $\dfrac{1}{V} = \dfrac{1}{S} \times \dfrac{S}{V} = \dfrac{2(ab+bc+ca)}{S \times abc} = \dfrac{2}{S}\left(\dfrac{1}{a} + \dfrac{1}{b} + \dfrac{1}{c} \right)$

41. Number of cubes $= \dfrac{\text{Volume of bigger cube}}{\text{Volume of smaller cube}} = \left(\dfrac{6 \times 6 \times 6}{2 \times 2 \times 2} \right) = 27.$

42. Number of cubes $= \left(\dfrac{4 \times 4 \times 4}{1 \times 1 \times 1} \right) = 64.$

Surface area of all small cubes $= 64 \times [6 \times (1)^2] = 384$ cm^2.

43. Let $lb = 2x$, $bh = 3x$ and $lh = 4x$.

Then, $24x^3 = (lbh)^2 = 9000 \times 9000$

$\therefore x^3 = 375 \times 9000$ or $x = 150.$

$\therefore lb = 300, bh = 450 \ \& \ lh = 600 \ \& \ lbh = 9000.$

$\therefore h = \dfrac{9000}{300} = 30, l = \dfrac{9000}{450} = 20 \ \& \ b = \dfrac{9000}{600} = 15.$

$\therefore$ Shortest side $= 15$ cm.

44. Let the edge of the cube be a. Then, new edge $= 2a$.

Original surface area $= 6a^2$, New surface area $= 6 \times (2a)^2 = 24a^2$.

$\therefore$ Increase in surface area $= \left(\dfrac{18a^2}{6a^2} \times 100 \right) \% = 300\%.$

45. Total surface area $= (2\pi rh + 2\pi r^2) \ cm^2$

$= \left(2 \times \dfrac{22}{7} \times 14 \times 20 + 2 \times \dfrac{22}{7} \times 14 \times 14 \right) cm^2 = 2992 \ cm^2.$

46. Volume $= \pi r^2 h = \left(\dfrac{22}{7} \times \dfrac{5}{2} \times \dfrac{5}{2} \times 84 \right) cm^3 = 1650 \ cm^3.$

47. $\dfrac{2\pi rh}{r} = \dfrac{1760}{14} \Rightarrow h = \dfrac{1760}{14} \times \dfrac{1}{2\pi} = \left(\dfrac{1760}{14} \times \dfrac{1}{2} \times \dfrac{7}{22} \right) = 20$ cm.

$\therefore$ Volume $= \pi r^2 h = \left(\dfrac{22}{7} \times 14 \times 14 \times 20 \right) cm^3 = 12320 \ cm^3.$

48. $\dfrac{2\pi rh}{h} = \dfrac{704}{14} \Rightarrow 2\pi r = \dfrac{704}{14}.$

$\therefore r = \left(\dfrac{704}{14} \times \dfrac{1}{2} \times \dfrac{7}{22} \right) = 8$ cm.

$\therefore$ Volume $= \left(\dfrac{22}{7} \times 8 \times 8 \times 14 \right) cm^3 = 2816 \ cm^3.$

49. $2\pi r = 66 \Rightarrow r = \left(66 \times \dfrac{1}{2} \times \dfrac{7}{22} \right) = \dfrac{21}{2}$ cm.

$\dfrac{2\pi rh}{2\pi r} = \left(\dfrac{2640}{66} \right) \Rightarrow h = 40$ cm.

$\therefore$ Volume $= \left(\dfrac{22}{7} \times \dfrac{21}{2} \times \dfrac{21}{2} \times 40 \right) cm^3 = 13860 \ cm^3.$

50. Curved surface Area $= 2\pi rh$

$= (\pi r^2 h) \cdot \dfrac{2}{r} = \left(\text{Volume} \times \dfrac{2}{r} \right).$

51. Volume of sphere $=$ Volume of wire

$\therefore \dfrac{4}{3} \pi \times (3)^3 = \pi \times (0.1)^2 \times h \Rightarrow h = \dfrac{36}{.01}$ cm $= 3600$ cm $= 36$ m.

52. $\dfrac{\text{Total surface Area}}{\text{Lateral surface Area}} = \dfrac{2\pi rh + 2\pi r^2}{2\pi rh} = \dfrac{(h+r)}{h} = \dfrac{80}{60} = \dfrac{4}{3}$

53. Let their radii be $2x$, $3x$ and heights be $5y$, $3y$.

Ratio of their volumes $= \dfrac{\pi (2x)^2 \times 5y}{\pi (3x)^2 \times 3y} = \dfrac{20}{27}$.

54. Let radius $= 2x$ & height $= 3x$. Then,

$\dfrac{22}{7} \times (2x)^2 \times 3x = 12936$ or $x^3 = \left(12936 \times \dfrac{7}{22} \times \dfrac{1}{12}\right) = 343 = 7^3$

$\therefore x = 7$. So, radius $= 14$ cm & height $= 21$ cm.

$\therefore$ Total surface area $= \left(2 \times \dfrac{22}{7} \times 14 \times 21 + 2 \times \dfrac{22}{7} \times 14 \times 14\right)$ sq. cm.

$= 3080$ cm^2.

55. Curved Surface Area $= \left(\dfrac{2}{3} \times 231\right)$ cm^2 $= 154$ cm^2.

$\therefore 2\pi rh + 2\pi r^2 = 231 \Rightarrow 154 + 2\pi r^2 = 231$.

$\therefore r^2 = \left(77 \times \dfrac{1}{2} \times \dfrac{7}{22}\right) = \dfrac{49}{4}$ or $r = \dfrac{7}{2}$.

Now, $2\pi rh = 154 \Rightarrow 2 \times \dfrac{22}{7} \times \dfrac{7}{2} \times h = 154$ or $h = 7$.

$\therefore$ Volume $= \pi r^2 h = \left(\dfrac{22}{7} \times \dfrac{7}{2} \times \dfrac{7}{2} \times 7\right)$ cm^2 $= 269.5$ cm^3.

56. $(h + r) = 37$ and $2\pi r (h + r) = 1628$.

$\therefore 2\pi r \times 37 = 1628$ or $r = \left(\dfrac{1628}{2 \times 37} \times \dfrac{7}{22}\right) = 7$.

$\therefore r = 7$ m and $h = 30$ m.

$\therefore$ Volume $= \pi r^2 h = \left(\dfrac{22}{7} \times 7 \times 7 \times 30\right)$ m^3 $= 4620$ m^3.

57. $\dfrac{2\pi rh}{2\pi rh + 2\pi r^2} = \dfrac{1}{2} \Rightarrow \dfrac{2\pi rh}{2\pi r (h + r)} = \dfrac{1}{2}$ or $\dfrac{h}{h + r} = \dfrac{1}{2}$ or $h = r$.

Now, Total surface area $= 2\pi rh + 2\pi r^2 = 4\pi r^2$ $[\because h = r]$

$\therefore 4\pi r^2 = 616$ or $r^2 = \left(616 \times \dfrac{1}{4} \times \dfrac{7}{22}\right) = 49$ or $r = 7$.

Thus, $h = 7$ cm and $r = 7$ cm.

$\therefore$ Volume $= \left(\dfrac{22}{7} \times 7 \times 7 \times 7\right)$ cm^3 $= 1078$ cm^3.

58. Volume of 1 coin $= \left(\dfrac{22}{7} \times \dfrac{1.5}{2} \times \dfrac{1.5}{2} \times 0.2\right)$ cm^3 $= \dfrac{99}{280}$ cm^3.

Volume of larger cylinder

$= \left(\dfrac{22}{7} \times \dfrac{4.5}{2} \times \dfrac{4.5}{2} \times 10\right)$ cm^3 $= \left(\dfrac{99 \times 45}{28}\right)$ cm^3.

$$\therefore \text{ Number of coins} = \left(\frac{99 \times 45}{28} \times \frac{280}{99}\right) = 450.$$

59. Let h and H be the heights of water level before and after dropping the sphere. Then,

$$[\pi \times (30)^2 \times H] - [\pi \times (30)^2 \times h] = \frac{4}{3}\pi \times (15)^3$$

$$900\,\pi\,(H-h) = 4500\,\pi \text{ or } (H-h) = 5 \text{ cm}.$$

60. $\pi \times (8)^2 \times h = \frac{4}{3}\pi \times (6)^3$ or $h = \frac{4 \times 72}{64} = 4.5$ cm.

61. $2\,\pi\,rh = 528$ and $\pi\,r^2 h = 2772.$

$$\therefore \frac{\pi\,r^2 h}{2\,\pi\,rh} = \frac{2772}{528} \Rightarrow r = \frac{2 \times 2772}{528} = \frac{21}{2}.$$

$$\therefore 2 \times \frac{22}{7} \times \frac{21}{2} \times h = 528 \Rightarrow h = \left(\frac{528}{66}\right) = 8 \text{ m}.$$

62. Volume of cylinder $= \pi \times 2^2 \times 54 = (216\,\pi) \text{ cm}^3$

Volume of 1 sphere $= \frac{4}{3}\pi \times \left(\frac{3}{2}\right)^3 = \left(\frac{9\,\pi}{2}\right) \text{ cm}^2.$

Number of spheres $= \left(216\,\pi \times \frac{2}{9\,\pi}\right) = 48.$

63. Let, original radius $= r$ and original length $= h$.
New radius $= (r/3)$ and let new length $= H$.

Then, $\pi\,r^2 h = \pi\left(\frac{r}{3}\right)^2 \times H$ or $H = 9h.$

64. Volume of new vessel $= [\pi \times (15)^2 \times 35 + \pi \times (10)^2 \times 15] = 9375\,\pi$

$$\therefore \pi R^2 \times 15 = 9375\,\pi \text{ or } R^2 = 625. \text{ So, } R = 25 \text{ cm}.$$

65. Circumference of the girth $= 440$ cm.

$$\therefore 2\,\pi R = 440 \Rightarrow R = \left(440 \times \frac{1}{2} \times \frac{7}{22}\right) = 70 \text{ cm}.$$

$\therefore$ Outer radius $= 70$ cm. Inner radius $= (70-4)$ cm $= 66$ cm.

Volume of iron $= \pi\,[(70)^2 - (66)^2] \times 63$

$$= \left(\frac{22}{7} \times 136 \times 4 \times 63\right) \text{cm}^3 = 58752 \text{ cm}^3.$$

66. Inner radius $= 1.5$ cm, outer radius $= 2.5$ cm.

$\therefore$ Volume of iron $= [\pi \times (2.5)^2 \times 100 - \pi \times (1.5)^2 \times 100] \text{ cm}^3$

$$= \frac{22}{7} \times 100 \times [(2.5)^2 - (1.5)^2] \text{ cm}^3 = \left(\frac{8800}{7}\right) \text{cm}^3$$

$\therefore$ Weight of iron $= \left(\frac{8800}{7} \times \frac{21}{1000}\right) \text{kg} = 26.4 \text{ kg}.$

67. Let their heights be $2h$ and h & radii R and r. Then,

$$\pi R^2 (2h) = \pi r^2 h \Rightarrow \frac{R^2}{r^2} = \frac{1}{2} \Rightarrow \frac{R}{r} = \frac{1}{\sqrt{2}}, \text{ i.e. } 1 : \sqrt{2}$$

68. Let original radius $= R$. Then, new radius $= (R/2)$.

$$\frac{\text{Volume of reduced cylinder}}{\text{Volume of original cylinder}} = \frac{\pi \times \left(\dfrac{R}{2}\right)^2 \times h}{\pi \times R^2 \times h} = \frac{1}{4}.$$

69. Let radius $= R$ and height $= H$. Then,

Ratio of their volumes $= \pi R^2 H : \dfrac{1}{3}\pi R^2 H : \dfrac{4}{3}\pi R^3$

$= H : \dfrac{1}{3} H : \dfrac{4}{3} R$ $\left[\text{In sphere } H = 2R \text{ or } R = \dfrac{H}{2}\right]$

$= H : \dfrac{1}{3} H : \dfrac{4}{3} \times \dfrac{H}{2} = 3 : 1 : 2.$

70. $\dfrac{\text{Volume of sphere}}{\text{Volume of cylinder}} = \dfrac{\dfrac{4}{3}\pi R^3}{\pi R^2 \times R} = \dfrac{4}{3}.$

71. Let their radii be $3x$ and x & heights be y & $3y$.

Ratio of their volumes $= \dfrac{\pi \times (3x)^2 \times y}{\pi \times x^2 \times 3y} = \dfrac{3}{1}$, i.e. $3 : 1$.

72. $\dfrac{4}{3} \times \dfrac{22}{7} \times R^3 = 4851 \Rightarrow R^3 = \left(4851 \times \dfrac{3}{4} \times \dfrac{7}{22}\right) = \left(\dfrac{21}{2}\right)^3.$

So, $R = \dfrac{21}{2}.$

$\therefore$ Curved Surface Area $= \left(4 \times \dfrac{22}{7} \times \dfrac{21}{2} \times \dfrac{21}{2}\right) \text{cm}^2 = 1386 \text{ cm}^2.$

73. $4\pi R^2 = 5544 \Rightarrow R^2 = \left(5544 \times \dfrac{1}{4} \times \dfrac{7}{22}\right) = 441.$

$\therefore R = 21.$ So, volume $= \left(\dfrac{4}{3} \times \dfrac{22}{7} \times 21 \times 21 \times 21\right) \text{cm}^3 = 38808 \text{ cm}^3.$

74. $\dfrac{4}{3}\pi \times (6)^3 + \dfrac{4}{3}\pi \times (8)^3 + \dfrac{4}{3}\pi \times R^3 = \dfrac{4}{3}\pi \times (12)^3.$

$\therefore \dfrac{4}{3}\pi \times [216 + 512 + R^3] = \dfrac{4}{3}\pi \times 1728$

or $728 + R^3 = 1728$ or $R^3 = 1000.$ So, $R = 10$ cm.

75. $\dfrac{\dfrac{4}{3}\pi R^3}{4\pi R^2} = 27 \Rightarrow R = 81$ cm.

76. Let radius of each be R and height of the cone be H.

Then, $\dfrac{4}{3}\pi R^3 = \dfrac{1}{3}\pi R^2 H$ or $\dfrac{R}{H} = \dfrac{1}{4}$ or $\dfrac{2R}{H} = \dfrac{2}{4} = \dfrac{1}{2}$.

77. Let original radius $= R$.

Then, original volume $= \dfrac{4}{3}\pi R^3 = V$ (say)

New radius $= \dfrac{150}{100}R = \dfrac{3}{2}R$.

New volume $= \dfrac{4}{3}\pi\left(\dfrac{3}{2}R\right)^3 = \left(\dfrac{4}{3}\pi R^3\right)\cdot\dfrac{27}{8} = \dfrac{27}{8}V$.

Increase $\% = \left(\dfrac{19}{8}V \times \dfrac{1}{V} \times 100\right)\% = 237.5\%$.

78. Number of bullets $= \dfrac{\text{Volume of the cube}}{\text{Volume of 1 bullet}}$

$= \left(\dfrac{22 \times 22 \times 22}{\dfrac{4}{3}\times\dfrac{22}{7}\times 1\times 1\times 1}\right) = 2541.$

79. $\dfrac{4}{3}\pi\times\left(\dfrac{3}{4}\right)^3 + \dfrac{4}{3}\pi\times(1)^3 + \dfrac{4}{3}\pi\times x^3 = \dfrac{4}{3}\pi\times\left(\dfrac{3}{2}\right)^3$

or $\dfrac{27}{64} + 1 + x^3 = \dfrac{27}{8}$ or $x^3 = \dfrac{125}{64} = \left(\dfrac{5}{4}\right)^3$ or $x = \dfrac{5}{4}$.

$\therefore$ Radius of the third ball is $\dfrac{5}{4}$ cm.

Hence, the diameter of this ball is $\dfrac{5}{2}$ cm $= 2.5$ cm.

80. Let original radius be R. Then, original area $= 4\pi R^2$.

New radius $= 2R$, New area $= 4\pi(2R)^2 = 16\pi R^2$.

Increase $\% = \left(\dfrac{12\pi R^2}{4\pi R^2} \times 100\right)\% = 300\%$.

81. Volume of each ball $= \dfrac{1}{8}\times\left(\dfrac{4}{3}\pi\times 10\times 10\times 10\right)$ cm^3.

$\therefore \dfrac{4}{3}\pi R^3 = \dfrac{1}{8}\times\dfrac{4}{3}\pi\times 10\times 10\times 10$ or $R^3 = \left(\dfrac{10}{2}\right)^3 = 5^3$. So, $R = 5$.

82. Volume of each lead shot $= \dfrac{4}{3}\pi\times\left(\dfrac{0.3}{2}\right)^3$

$$= \frac{4}{3} \times \frac{22}{7} \times \frac{27}{8000} = \frac{99}{7000} \text{ cu. cm.}$$

$$\therefore \text{ Number of lead shots} = \left(9 \times 11 \times 12 \times \frac{7000}{99}\right) = 84000.$$

83. Volume of the sphere $= \left(\frac{4}{3}\pi \times \frac{21}{2} \times \frac{21}{2} \times \frac{21}{2}\right) \text{cm}^3 = \frac{3087\,\pi}{2} \text{ cm}^3.$

Volume of each cone $= \left(\frac{1}{3}\pi \times \frac{7}{2} \times \frac{7}{2} \times 3\right) \text{cm}^3 = \frac{49\,\pi}{4} = \text{cm}^3.$

$\therefore$ Number of cones $= \left(\frac{3087\,\pi}{2} \times \frac{4}{49\,\pi}\right) = 126.$

84. Volume of 2 cones $= \left[\frac{1}{3}\pi \times (2.1)^2 \times 4.1 + \frac{1}{3}\pi \times (2.1)^2 \times 4.3\right] \text{cm}^3.$

$$= \frac{1}{3}\pi \times (2.1)^2 (8.4) \text{ cm}^3.$$

Volume of sphere $= \frac{1}{3}\pi \times (2.1)^2 (8.4) \text{ cm}^3.$

$\therefore \frac{4}{3}\pi R^3 = \frac{1}{3}\pi (2.1)^3.4$ or $R = 2.1$ cm.

$\therefore$ Diameter of the sphere $= 4.2$ cm.

85. $\frac{4}{3}\pi \times (6.3)^3 = \frac{1}{3}\pi R^2 \times 25.2 \Rightarrow R^2 = \frac{4 \times 6.3 \times 6.3 \times 6.3}{25.2} = (6.3)^2.$

$\therefore R = 6.3$ cm.

86. $\frac{4}{3}\pi R^3 = \pi \times 3 \times 3 \times 32 \Rightarrow R = 6$ cm.

87. $\frac{2}{3}\pi \times 6 \times 6 \times 6 = \frac{1}{3}\pi \times R^2 \times 75$

or $R^2 = \frac{2 \times 6 \times 6 \times 6}{75}$ or $R = \frac{12}{5} = 2.4$ cm.

88. $r = 14$ m and $l = 50$ m.

$\therefore$ Area of curved surface $= \pi\, rl = \left(\frac{22}{7} \times 14 \times 50\right) \text{m}^2 = 2200 \text{ m}^2.$

$\therefore$ Cost of white washing $= \text{Rs.} \left(2200 \times \frac{80}{100}\right) = \text{Rs. } 1760.$

89. Let radius $= r$ & height $= h$. Then, volume $= \frac{1}{3}\pi\, r^2 h.$

New radius $= \frac{200}{100} r = 2r$ and new height $= \frac{200}{100} h = 2h.$

$\therefore$ New volume

$$= \frac{1}{3}\pi \times (2r)^2 \times 2h = 8 \times \frac{1}{3}\pi\, r^2 h = 8 \times \text{(original volume)}.$$

90. $\dfrac{\dfrac{2}{3}\pi R^3}{\dfrac{2}{3}\pi r^3} = \dfrac{6.4}{21.6}$ or $\left(\dfrac{R}{r}\right)^3 = \dfrac{8}{27} = \left(\dfrac{2}{3}\right)^3$. So, $\dfrac{R}{r} = \dfrac{2}{3}$.

$\therefore$ Ratio of curved surface areas $= \dfrac{2\pi R^2}{2\pi r^2} = \left(\dfrac{R}{r}\right)^2 = \dfrac{4}{9}$.

91. $\dfrac{4}{3}\pi r^3 = \dfrac{1}{3}\pi R^2 \times r \Rightarrow R^2 = 4r^2 \Rightarrow R = 2r$.

92. Let radius of each be r, the height of cylinder be H & the height of the cone be h. Then,

$\pi r^2 H = \dfrac{1}{3}\pi r^2 h$ or $\dfrac{H}{h} = \dfrac{1}{3}$, i.e. 1 : 3.

93. Let radius of each be r & height of each be h.

Then, volume of cylinder $= \pi r^2 h$.

Volume of 1 cone $= \dfrac{1}{3}\pi r^2 h$.

Number of cones needed $= \dfrac{\pi r^2 h}{\dfrac{1}{3}\pi r^2 h} = 3$.

94. $\pi \times 2^2 \times 6 = \dfrac{1}{3}\pi \times 2^2 \times h \Rightarrow h = 18$ cm.

95. $\dfrac{1}{3}\pi r^2 \times 24 = 1232 \Rightarrow r^2 = \left(154 \times \dfrac{7}{22}\right) = 49$ or $r = 7$ cm.

$\therefore$ Slant height, $l = \sqrt{(24)^2 + 7^2} = \sqrt{625} = 25$ cm.

$\therefore$ Area of Curved Surface $= \pi r l = \left(\dfrac{22}{7} \times 7 \times 25\right)$ cm^2 = 550 cm^2.

96. $\pi r^2 = 346.5 \Rightarrow r^2 = 346.5 \times \dfrac{7}{22} = \dfrac{441}{4} \Rightarrow r = \dfrac{21}{2}$.

$\therefore l = \sqrt{r^2 + h^2} = \sqrt{\dfrac{441}{4} + (14)^2} = \sqrt{\dfrac{1225}{4}} = \dfrac{35}{2}$.

$\therefore$ Area of canvas needed $= \pi r l = \left(\dfrac{22}{7} \times \dfrac{21}{2} \times \dfrac{35}{2}\right)$ m^2 = $\left(\dfrac{33 \times 35}{2}\right)$ m^2.

$\therefore$ Length of canvas $= \left(\dfrac{33 \times 35}{2 \times 1.1}\right)$ m = 525 m.

97. $l = \sqrt{(7)^2 + (24)^2} = \sqrt{625} = 25$ m.

$\therefore$ Area of cloth needed $= \pi r l = \left(\dfrac{22}{7} \times 7 \times 25\right)$ m^2 = 550 m^2.

$\therefore$ Length of cloth $= \left(\dfrac{550}{2.5}\right)$ m = 220 m.

98. Let their radii be $4x$ & $5x$ & heights be h & H.

Then, $\dfrac{\frac{1}{3}\pi(4x)^2 \times h}{\frac{1}{3}\pi(5x)^2 \times H} = \dfrac{1}{4}$ or $\dfrac{h}{H} = \dfrac{1}{4} \times \dfrac{25}{16} = \dfrac{25}{64}$.

99. $\dfrac{2}{3} \times \dfrac{22}{7} \times R^3 = 19404 \Rightarrow R^3 = \left(19404 \times \dfrac{21}{44}\right) = (21)^3$ or $R = 21$ cm.

100. Volume of earth dug out $= \left(\dfrac{22}{7} \times 7 \times 7 \times 10\right) m^2 = 1540\ m^2$.

Area of embankment

$$= \dfrac{22}{7} \times [(28)^2 - (7)^2] = \left(\dfrac{22}{7} \times 35 \times 21\right) m^2 = 2310\ m^2.$$

Height of embankment $= \left(\dfrac{\text{Volume}}{\text{Area}}\right) = \left(\dfrac{1540}{2310}\right) m = \dfrac{2}{3}\ m$.

101. Let their radii be $3x$, $4x$ & heights be $2x$ and $3x$.

Ratio of their volumes $= \dfrac{\pi \times (3x)^2 \times 2x}{\frac{1}{3}\pi \times (4x)^2 \times 3x} = \dfrac{18}{16} = \dfrac{9}{8}$.

102. $\pi \times 18 \times 18 \times 32 = \dfrac{1}{3}\pi \times R^2 \times 24 \Rightarrow R^2 = \left(\dfrac{18 \times 18 \times 32}{8}\right)$

$\therefore\ R = 36$ cm.

103. Volume of cylinder $= (\pi \times 3 \times 3 \times 5)\ cm^3 = (45\,\pi)\ cm^3$.

Volume of 1 cone $= \left(\dfrac{1}{3}\pi \times \dfrac{1}{10} \times \dfrac{1}{10} \times 1\right) = \dfrac{\pi}{300}\ cm^3$.

Number of cones $= \left(45\,\pi \times \dfrac{300}{\pi}\right) = 13500$.

104. Let their radii be R and r. Then,

$$\dfrac{\frac{4}{3}\pi R^3}{\frac{4}{3}\pi r^3} = \dfrac{1}{8} \Rightarrow \left(\dfrac{R}{r}\right)^3 = \dfrac{1}{8} = \left(\dfrac{1}{2}\right)^3.\ \text{So,}\ \dfrac{R}{r} = \dfrac{1}{2}.$$

Ratio of surface areas $= \dfrac{4\,\pi R^2}{4\,\pi r^2} = \left(\dfrac{R}{r}\right)^2 = \dfrac{1}{4}$.

105. Let their radii be R and r. Then,

$$\dfrac{4\,\pi R^2}{4\,\pi r^2} = \dfrac{4}{25} \Rightarrow \left(\dfrac{R}{r}\right)^2 = \left(\dfrac{2}{5}\right)^2\ \text{or}\ \dfrac{R}{r} = \dfrac{2}{5}.$$

$\therefore$ Ratio of their volumes $= \dfrac{\dfrac{4}{3}\pi R^3}{\dfrac{4}{3}\pi r^3} = \left(\dfrac{R}{r}\right)^3 = \left(\dfrac{2}{5}\right)^3 = \dfrac{8}{125}.$

106. Total surface area $= 3\pi R^2$

$$= \left(3 \times \dfrac{22}{7} \times 7 \times 7\right) cm^2 = 462\ cm^2.$$

107. Volume flown in conical vessel $= \dfrac{1}{3}\pi \times (20)^2 \times 24 = 3200\ \pi.$

Volume flown in 1 min. $= \left(\pi \times \dfrac{2.5}{10} \times \dfrac{2.5}{10} \times 1000\right) = 62.5\ \pi.$

$\therefore$ Time taken $= \dfrac{3200\ \pi}{62.5\ \pi} = 51$ min. 12 sec.

108. Let R be the radius of each.
Height of hemi-sphere = its radius = R.
$\therefore$ Height of each $= R$.
Ratio of their volumes $= \dfrac{1}{3}\pi R^2 \times R : \dfrac{2}{3}\pi R^3 : \pi R^2 \times R = 1 : 2 : 3.$

109. Volume of ball = Volume of water displaced by it

$\therefore \dfrac{4}{3}\pi R^3 = \pi \times 12 \times 12 \times 6.75 \Rightarrow R^3 = 9 \times 9 \times 9$ or $R = 9$ cm.

110. Volume of bowl $= \left(\dfrac{2}{3}\pi \times 9 \times 9 \times 9\right) cm^3 = 486\ \pi\ cm^3.$

Volume of 1 bottle $= \left(\pi \times \dfrac{3}{2} \times \dfrac{3}{2} \times 4\right) cm^3 = 9\ \pi\ cm^3.$

Number of bottles $= \left(\dfrac{486\ \pi}{9\ \pi}\right) = 54.$

111. Volume of the block $= (10 \times 5 \times 2)\ cm^3 = 100\ cm^3.$

Volume of the cone carved out $= \left(\dfrac{1}{3} \times \dfrac{22}{7} \times 3 \times 3 \times 7\right) cm^3 = 66\ cm^3.$

Wood wasted $= (100 - 66)\ \% = 34\%.$

112. Let, original height $= h$. Then, volume $= \dfrac{1}{3}\pi r^2 h.$

New height $= 2h$. So, volume $= \dfrac{1}{3}\pi r^2 \times (2h) = 2\left(\dfrac{1}{3}\pi r^2 h\right).$

$\therefore$ Increase $= \left(\dfrac{\dfrac{1}{3}\pi r^2 h}{\dfrac{1}{3}\pi r^2 h} \times 100\right)\% = 100\%.$

113. Let their heights be h and $2h$ & let their radii be R and r. Then,

$$\pi R^2 h = \pi r^2 (2h) \Rightarrow \frac{R^2}{r^2} = \frac{2}{1} \Rightarrow \frac{R}{r} = \frac{\sqrt{2}}{1}.$$

114. $\frac{4}{3} \pi R^3 = \pi R^2 h \Rightarrow h = \frac{4}{3} R.$

115. $\frac{1}{3} \pi R^2 h = \pi R^2 \times 6$ or $h = 18$ cm.

116. Difference in capacities

$$= \left(8 \times 8 \times 14 - \frac{22}{7} \times 4 \times 4 \times 14 \right) \text{cm}^3 = 192 \text{ cm}^3.$$

---

26 Races & Games of Skill

Races : *A contest of speed in running, riding, driving, sailing or rowing is called a race.*

Race Course : *The ground or path on which contests are made is called a race course.*

Starting Point : *The point from which a race begins is known as a starting point.*

Winning Point or Goal : *The point set to bound a race is called a winning point or a goal.*

Winner : *The person who first reaches the winning point is called a winner.*

Dead Heat Race : *If all the persons contesting a race reach the goal exactly at the same time, then the race is said to be a dead heat race.*

Start : Suppose *A* and *B* are two contestants in a race. If before the start of the race, *A* is at the starting point and *B* is ahead of *A* by 12 metres, then we say that '*A gives B, a start of 12 metres*'.

To cover a race of 100 metres in this case, *A* will will have to cover 100 metres while *B* will have to cover only $(100 - 12) = 88$ metres.

In a 100 m race, '*A can given B 12 m*' or '*A can give B a start of 12 m*' or '*A beats B by 12 m*' means that while *A* runs 100 m, *B* runs $(100 - 12) = 88$ m.

Games : '*A game of 100, means that the person among the contestants who scores 100 points first is the winner.*

If *A* scores 100 points while *B* scores only 80 points, then we say that *A* can give *B* 20 points.

Solved Problems

Ex. 1. In a km race, A beats B by 28 metres or 7 seconds. Find A's time over the course.

Sol. Clearly, *B* covers 28 m in 7 seconds.

$\therefore$ *B*'s time over the course $= \left(\dfrac{7}{28} \times 1000 \right)$ sec $= 250$ seconds.

$\therefore$ *A*'s time over the course $= (250 - 7)$ sec $= 243$ sec.
$$= 4 \text{ min. } 3 \text{ sec.}$$

Ex. 2. A runs $1\dfrac{3}{4}$ times as fast as B. If A gives B a start of 84 m, how far must the winning post be so that A and B might reach it at the same time ?

Sol. The ratio of the rates of A and $B = \dfrac{7}{4} : 1 = 7 : 4$.

So, in a race of 7 m, A gains 3 m over B.

∴ 3m are gained by A in a race of 7m.

∴ 84 m are gained by A in a race of $\left(\dfrac{7}{3} \times 84\right)$ m = 196 m.

∴ Winning post must be 196 m away from the starting point.

Ex. 3. *A can run 1 km in 3 min. 10 sec. and B can cover the same distance in 3 min. 20 sec. By what distance can A beat B ?*

Sol. Clearly, A beats B by 10 sec.

Distance covered by B in 10 sec. $= \left(\dfrac{1000}{200} \times 10\right)$ m = 50 m.

∴ A beats B by 50 metres.

Ex. 4. *In a 100 m race, A runs at 8 km per hour. If A gives B a start of 4 m and still beats him by 15 seconds, what is the speed of B ?*

Sol. Time taken by A to cover 100 m $= \left(\dfrac{60 \times 60}{8000} \times 100\right)$ sec = 45 sec.

∴ B covers $(100 - 4)$ m = 96 m in $(45 + 15)$ sec = 60 sec.

∴ B's speed $= \left(\dfrac{96 \times 60 \times 60}{60 \times 1000}\right)$ km/hr = 5.76 km/hr.

Ex. 5. *A, B and C are three contestants in a km race. If A can give B a start of 40 m and A can give C a start of 64 m, how many metre's start can B give C ?*

Sol. While A covers 1000 m, B covers $(1000 - 40)$ m = 960 m and C covers $(1000 - 64)$ m or 936 m.

When B covers 960 m, C covers 936 m

When B covers 1000 m, C covers $\left(\dfrac{936}{960} \times 1000\right)$ m = 975 m.

∴ B can give C a start of $(1000 - 975)$ or 25 m.

Ex. 6. *In a game of 80 points, A can give B 5 points and C 15 points. Then how many points B can give C in a game of 60 ?*

Sol. $A : B = 80 : 75, A : C = 80 : 65$

$$\dfrac{B}{C} = \left(\dfrac{B}{A} \times \dfrac{A}{C}\right) = \left(\dfrac{75}{80} \times \dfrac{80}{65}\right) = \dfrac{15}{13} = \dfrac{60}{52} = 60 : 52.$$

∴ In a game of 60, B can give C 8 points.

EXERCISE 26

Mark (√) **against the correct answer :**

1. In a 100 m race, A covers the distance in 36 seconds and B in 45 seconds. In this race A beats B by :

(a) 20 m   (b) 25 m   (c) 22.5 m   (d) 9 m

2. In a 200 metres race A beats B by 35 m or 7 seconds. A's time over the course is :

(a) 40 sec   (b) 47 sec   (c) 33 sec   (d) None of these

3. In a 300 m race A beats B by 22.5 m or 6 seconds. B's time over the course is :

(a) 86 sec   (b) 80 sec   (c) 76 sec   (d) None of these

4. A can run 22.5 m while B runs 25 m. In a kilometre race B beats A by :

(a) 100 m   (b) $111\frac{1}{9}$ m   (c) 25 m   (d) 50 m

5. In a 500 m race, the ratio of the speeds of two contestants A and B is 3 : 4. A has a start of 140 m. Then, A wins by :

(a) 60 m   (b) 40 m   (c) 20 m   (d) 10 m

6. A runs $1\frac{2}{3}$ times as fast as B. If A gives B a start of 80 m, how far must the winning post be so that A and B might reach it the same time ?

(a) 200 m   (b) 300 m   (c) 270 m   (d) 160 m

7. In a 100 m race, A can beat B by 25 m and B can beat C by 4 m. In the same race, A can beat C by :

(a) 21 m   (b) 26 m   (c) 28 m   (d) 29 m

8. In a 100 m race, A can give B 10 m and C 28 m. In the same race B can give C :

(a) 18 m   (b) 20 m   (c) 27 m   (d) 9 m

9. In a 100 m race, A beats B by 10 m and C by 13 m. In a race of 180 m, B will beat C by :

(a) 5.4 m   (b) 4.5 m   (c) 5 m   (d) 6 m

10. In a race of 200 m, A can beat B by 31 m and C by 18 m. In a race of 350 m, C will beat B by :

(a) 22.75 m   (b) 25 m   (c) 19.5 m   (d) $7\frac{4}{7}$ m

11. A and B take part in a 100 m race. A runs at 5 km per hour. A gives B a start of 8 m and still beats him by 8 seconds. The speed of B is :

(a) 5.15 kmph   (b) 4.14 kmph   (c) 4.25 kmph   (d) 4.4 kmph

12. In a game of 100 points, A can give B 20 points and C 28 points. Then, B can give C :

(a) 8 points   (b) 10 points   (c) 14 points   (d) 40 points

13. At a game of billiards, A can give B 15 points in 60 and A can give C 20 in 60. How many can B give C in a game of 90 ?

(a) 30 points   (b) 20 points   (c) 10 points   (d) 12 points

ANSWERS

1 . (a)   **2.** (c)   **3.** (b)   **4.** (a)   **5.** (c)   **6.** (a)   **7.** (c)   **8.** (b)   **9.** (d)
10. (b)   **11.** (b)   **12.** (b)   **13.** (c)

SOLUTIONS

1.   Distance covered by B in 9 sec. $= \left(\dfrac{100}{45} \times 9 \right) m = 20$ m.

∴ A beats B by 20 metres.

2. B runs 35 m in 7 sec.

∴ B covers 200 m in $\left(\dfrac{7}{35} \times 200 \right) = 40$ sec.

∴ B's time over the course $= 40$ sec.

∴ A's time over the course $= (40 - 7)$ sec $= 33$ sec.

3. B runs $\dfrac{45}{2}$ m in 6 sec.

∴ B covers 300 m in $\left(6 \times \dfrac{2}{45} \times 300 \right)$ sec $= 80$ sec.

4.   When B runs 25 m, A runs $\dfrac{45}{2}$ m

When B runs 1000 m, A runs $\left(\dfrac{45}{2} \times \dfrac{1}{25} \times 1000 \right) m = 900$ m.

∴ B beats A by 100 m.

5.   To reach the winning post A will have to cover a distance of $(500 - 140)$ m, i.e. 360 m.

While A covers 3m, B covers 4 m

While A covers 360 m, B covers $\left(\dfrac{4}{3} \times 360 \right) m = 480$ m.

Thus, when A reaches the winning post, B covers 480 m and therefore remains 20 m behind.

∴ A wins by 20 m.

6.   Ratio of the speeds of A and $B = \dfrac{5}{3} : 1 = 5 : 3$.

Thus, in a race of 5m, A gains 2 m over B.

2m are gained by A in a race of 5m.

80 m will be gained by A in a race of $\left(\dfrac{5}{2} \times 80 \right) m = 200$ m.

∴ Winning post is 200 m away from the starting point.

7. $A : B = 100 : 75$ and $B : C = 100 : 96$.

$$\therefore \; A:C = \left(\frac{A}{B} \times \frac{B}{C}\right) = \left(\frac{100}{75} \times \frac{100}{96}\right) = \frac{100}{72} = 100:72.$$

$\therefore \; A$ beats C by $(100 - 72)$ m $= 28$ m.

8. $A:B = 100:90$ and $A:C = 100:72$

$$B:C = \frac{B}{A} \times \frac{A}{C} = \frac{90}{100} \times \frac{100}{72} = \frac{90}{72}.$$

When B runs 90 m, C runs 72 m

When B runs 100 m, C runs $\left(\frac{72}{90} \times 100\right)$ m $= 80$ m.

$\therefore \; B$ can give C 20 m.

9. $A:B = 100:90, A:C = 100:87$

$$\frac{B}{C} = \frac{B}{A} \times \frac{A}{C} = \frac{90}{100} \times \frac{100}{87} = \frac{30}{29}.$$

When B runs 30 m, C runs 29 m

When B runs 180 m, C runs $\left(\frac{29}{30} \times 180\right)$ m $= 174$ m.

$\therefore \; B$ beats C by $(180 - 174)$ m $= 6$ m.

10. $A:B = 200:169$ and $A:C = 200:182$.

$$\frac{C}{B} = \left(\frac{C}{A} \times \frac{A}{B}\right) = \left(\frac{182}{200} \times \frac{200}{169}\right) = 182:169.$$

When C covers 182 m, B covers 169 m

When C covers 350 m, B covers $\left(\frac{169}{182} \times 350\right)$ m $= 325$ m.

11. A's speed $= \left(5 \times \frac{5}{18}\right)$ m/sec $= \frac{25}{18}$ m/sec.

Time taken by A to cover 100 m $= \left(100 \times \frac{18}{25}\right)$ sec $= 72$ sec.

$\therefore$ Time taken by B to cover 92 m in $(72 + 8)$ sec or 80 sec.

$\therefore \; B$'s speed $= \left(\frac{92}{80} \times \frac{18}{5}\right)$ kmph $= 4.14$ kmph.

12. $A:B = 100:80$ and $A:C = 100:72$.

$$\therefore \; \frac{B}{C} = \left(\frac{B}{A} \times \frac{A}{C}\right) = \left(\frac{80}{100} \times \frac{100}{72}\right) = \frac{10}{9} = \frac{100}{90} = 100:90.$$

$\therefore \; B$ can give C 10 points.

13. $A:B = 60:45$ and $A:C = 60:40$.

$$\therefore \; \frac{B}{C} = \left(\frac{B}{A} \times \frac{A}{C}\right) = \left(\frac{45}{60} \times \frac{60}{40}\right) = \frac{45}{40} = \frac{90}{80} = 90:80$$

$\therefore \; B$ can give C 10 points in a game of 90.

27. Calendar

General Concepts : Under this heading we mainly deal with finding the day of the week on a particular given date. The process of finding it lies on obtaining the number of odd days.

I.   **Odd Days :** Number of days more than the complete number of weeks in a given period is the number of odd days during that period.

II.   **Leap Year :** Every year which is divisible by 4 is called a leap year. Thus, each one of the years 1992, 96, 2004, 2008, 2012, etc. is a leap year.

Every 4th century is a leap year but no other century is a leap year. Thus, each one of 400, 800, 1200, 1600, 2000 etc. is a leap year. None of 1900, 2010, 2020, 2100 etc. is a leap year.

An year which is not a leap year is called an ordinary year.

III.   *(i) An ordinary year has 365 days.*

    (ii) A leap year has 366 days.

IV.   Counting of odd days :

    (i) 1 ordinary year = 365 days = (52 weeks + 1 day)

    ∴ *An ordinary year has 1 odd day.*

    (ii) 1 leap year = 366 days = (52 weeks + 2 days).

    ∴ *A leap year has 2 odd days.*

    (iii) 100 years = 76 ordinary years + 24 leap years

$$= [(76 \times 52) \text{ weeks} + 76 \text{ days}] + [(24 \times 52) \text{ weeks} + 48 \text{ days}]$$
$$= 5200 \text{ weeks} + 124 \text{ days}$$
$$= (5217 \text{ weeks} + 5 \text{ days}).$$

    ∴ *100 years contain 5 odd days.*

    200 years contain 10 and therefore 3 odd days.

    300 years contain 15 and therefore 1 odd days.

    400 years contain (20 + 1) *and therefore 0 odd day.*

    Similarly, each one of 800, 1200, 1600, 2000 etc. contains 0 odd days.

    Remark : $(7n + m)$ odd days, where $m < 7$ is equivalent to m odd days. Thus, 8 odd days ≡ 1 odd day etc.

V.   **Counting of Days :**

We have : **Sunday** *for 0 odd day;* **Monday** *for 1 odd day;* **Tuesday** *of 2 odd days and so on.*

Solved Problems

Ex.1. *Find the day of the week on 16th July, 1776.*

Sol. *(i)* 16th July, 1776 means

        = (1775 years + period from 1st January to 16th July)

Now, 1600 years have 0 odd day.

100 years have 5 odd days.

75 years = (18 leap years + 57 ordinary years)

$$= (36 + 57) \text{ odd days} = 93 \text{ odd days}$$
$$= (13 \text{ weeks} + 2 \text{ days}) \text{ of odd days}$$
$$= 2 \text{ odd days}.$$

∴ 1775 years have $(0 + 5 + 2)$ odd days i.e. 0 odd days.

Now, days from 1st Jan, 16 th July; 1776

Jan	Feb	March	April	May	June	July	
31 +	29 +	31 +	30 +	31 +	30 +	16	= 198 days

$$= (28 \text{ weeks} + 2 \text{ days}) = 2 \text{ odd days}.$$

∴ Total number of odd days = $(0 + 2) = 2$.

∴ The day of the week was 'Tuesday'.

Ex. 2. *What was the day of the week on 12th January, 1979 ?*

Sol. Number of odd days in $(1600 + 300)$ years $= (0 + 1) = 1$.

78 years = (19 leap years + 59 ordinary years)

$$= (38 + 59) \text{ odd days} = 97 \text{ odd days} = 6 \text{ odd days}.$$

12 days of January have 5 odd days.

∴ Total number of odd days $= (1 + 6 + 5) \equiv 5$ odd days.

∴ The desired day was 'Friday.'

Ex. 3. *Find the day of the week on 25th December, 1995.*

Sol. 1600 years have 0 odd day.

300 years have 1 odd day.

94 years = (23 leap years + 71 ordinary years)

$$= (46 + 71) \text{ odd days} = 117 \text{ odd days} \equiv 5 \text{ odd days}.$$

Number of days from 1st Jan, 1995 to 25 th Dec, 1995 = 359 days.

$$= (51 \text{ weeks} + 2 \text{ days}) = 2 \text{ odd days}.$$

∴ Total number of odd days $= (0 + 1 + 5 + 2)$ odd days $\equiv 1$ odd day.

∴ Required day is 'Monday'.

Ex.4. *On what dates of October, 1994 did Monday fall ?*

Sol. Find the day on 1st October, 1994.

1600 years contain 0 odd day.

300 years contain 1 odd day.

93 years = (23 leap years + 70 ordinary years)

$$= (46 + 70) \text{ odd days} = 116 \text{ odd days} \equiv 4 \text{ odd days}.$$

Days from 1st Jan, 1994 to 1st Oct, 1994

Jan	Feb	March	April	May	June	July	Aug	Sept	Oct
31 +	28 +	31 +	30 +	31 +	30 +	31 +	31 +	30 +	1

$$= 274 \text{ days} = 39 \text{ weeks} + 1 \text{ day} = 1 \text{ odd day}.$$

∴ Total number of odd days $= (0 + 1 + 4 + 1) = 6$.

∴ 1st Oct, 1994 was 'Saturday'.

∴ Monday fell on 3rd October, 1994.

During October 1994, Monday fell on 3rd, 10th, 17th and 24 th.

Ex. 5. *Prove that the calendar for 1995 will serve for 2006.*

Sol. In order that the calendar for 1995 and 2006 be the same, 1st
January of both the years must be on the same day of the week.
For this, the total number of odd days between 31st Dec, 1994
and 31 st Dec, 2005 must be zero.

We know that an ordinary year has 1 odd day and a leap year
has 2 odd days. During this period there are 3 leap years, namely
1996, 2000 and 2004 and 8 ordinary years.

∴ Total number of odd days during this period $(6 + 8) + 14 \equiv 0$.
i.e. 0 odd day.

Hence, the calendar for 1995 will serve for 2006.

Ex. 6. *Prove that any date in March is the same day of the week as the
corresponding date in November of that year.*

Sol. In order to prove the required result, we have to show that the
number of odd days between last day of February and last day of
October is zero.

Number of days between these dates are :

March April May June July Aug Sep   Oct
 31 + 30 + 31 + 30 + 31 + 31 + 30 + 31

$= 241$ days $= 35$ weeks

∴ Number of odd days during this period $= 0$.

Hence, the result follows.

Ex. 7. *Prove that the last day of a century cannot be any of Tuesday,
Thursday or Saturday.*

Sol. 100 years contain 5 odd days.

∴ Last day of 1st century is 'Friday'.

200 years contain $(5 \times 2) = 10$ odd days $\equiv 3$ odd days.

∴ Last day of 2nd century is 'Wednesday'.

300 years contain $(5 \times 3) = 15$ odd days $\equiv 1$ odd day.

∴ Last day of 3rd century is 'Monday'.

400 years contain 0 odd day.

∴ Last day of 4th century is 'Sunday'.

Since the order is continually kept in successive cycles, we see that
the last day of a century can not be Tuesday, Thursday or Saturday.

EXERCISE 27

Mark (√) against the correct answer :

1. January 1, 1995 was a Sunday. What day of the week lies on January
    1, 1996 ?

    (*a*) Sunday   (*b*) Monday   (*c*) Saturday   (*d*) None of these

2. On 8th Feb, 1995 it was Wednesday. The day of the week on 8th Feb,
    1994 was :

(a) Wednesday   (b) Thursday   (c) Tuesday   (d) None of these

3. January 1, 1992 was Wednesday. What day of the week was on January 1, 1993 ?

   (a) Tuesday   (b) Thursday   (c) Friday   (d) Monday

4. May 6, 1993 was Thursday. What day of the week was on May 6, 1992 ?

   (a) Saturday   (b) Tuesday   (c) Wednesday (d) Friday

5. Monday falls on 20th March, 1995. What was the day on 3rd November, 1994 ?

   (a) Thursday   (b) Sunday   (c) Tuesday   (d) Saturday

6. Today is Tuesday. After 62 days it will be :

   (a) Wednesday   (b) Monday   (c) Thursday   (d) Sunday

7. Today is 1st April. The day of the week is Wednesday. This is a leap year. The day of the week on this day after 3 years will be :

   (a) Saturday   (b) Sunday   (c) Friday   (d) Tuesday

8. The year next to 1996 having the same calender as that of 1996 is :

   (a) 2003   (b) 2002   (c) 2001   (d) 2004

9. How many days are there from 2nd January 1995 to 15th March, 1995 ?

   (a) 71   (b) 72   (c) 73   (d) 74

10. The first republic day of India was celebrated on 26th January, 1950. It was :

    (a) Monday   (b) Tuesday   (c) Thursday   (d) Friday

11. What was the day of the week on 28th Feb, 1995 ?

    (a) Tuesday   (b) Wednesday (c) Monday   (d) Thursday

12. What will be the day of the week on 1st Jan 2001 ?

    (a) Friday   (b) Tuesday   (c) Sunday   (d) Wednesday

13. If the first day of the year 1991 was Tuesday, what day of the week must have been on 1st January, 1998 ?

    (a) Monday   (b) Tuesday   (c) Wednesday (d) Thursday

14. On what dates of April, 1994 did Sunday fall ?

    (a) 2, 9, 16, 23, 30   (b) 3, 10, 17, 24
    (c) 4, 11, 18, 25   (d) 1, 8, 15, 22, 29

15. The calendar for 1990 is the same as for :

    (a) 1997   (b) 1994   (c) 2000   (d) 1996

16. The day on 5th March of a year is the same day on what date of the same year ?

    (a) 5th Aug.   (b) 5th Oct.   (c) 5th Nov.   (d) 5th Dec.

ANSWERS

1. (b)   2. (c)   3. (c)   4. (b)   5. (a)   6. (b)   7. (a)   8. (c)   9. (c)
10. (c)   11. (a)   12. (c)   13. (d)   14. (b)   15. (d)   16. (c)

SOLUTIONS

1. 1995 being on ordinary year, it has 1 odd day. So, the first day of 1996 will be one day beyond Sunday, i.e. it will be Monday.

2. 1994 being an ordinary year, it has 1 odd day.
   So, the day on 8th Feb, 1995 is one day beyond the day on 8th Feb, 1994.
   But, 8th Feb, 1995 was Wednesday.
   ∴ 8th Feb, 1994 was Tuesday.

3. 1992 being a leap year, it has 2 odd days. So, the first day of the year 1993 must be two days beyond Wednesday.
   So, it was Friday.

4. 1992 being a leap year, it has 2 odd days.
   So, the day on May, 1993 is 2 days beyond the day on May 6, 1992.
   But, on May 6, 1993 it was Thursday.
   So, on May 6, 1992 it was Tuesday.

5. Counting the number of days after 3rd November, 1994 we have :
   Nov. Dec. Jan. Feb. March
   27 + 31 + 31 + 28 + 20 = 137 days = 19 weeks + 4 days
   ∴ Number of odd days = 4.
   ∴ The day on 3rd November, 1994 is (7 – 4) days beyond the day on 20th March, 1995.
   So, the required day is Thursday.

6. Each day of the week is repeated after 7 days.
   ∴ After 63 days, it will be Tuesday.
   ∴ After 62 days, it will be Monday.

7. This being a leap year, none of the next 3 years is a leap year.
   So, the day of the week will be 3 days beyond Wednesday.
   ∴ The day after 3 years will be Saturday.

8. Starting with 1996, we go on counting the number of odd days till the sum is divisible by 7.

Year	1996	1997	1998	1999	2000	
Odd days	2	1	1	1	2	= 7 odd days

   i.e. 0 odd day.
   ∴ Calendar for 2001 will be the same as that of 1995.

9. Jan Feb March
   30 + 28 + 15 = 73 days.

10. Do yourself. It was Thursday.

11. Do yourself. It was Tuesday.

12. 1600 years contain 0 odd day.
    300 years contain 1 odd day.
    100 years contain 5 odd days.

∴ 2000 years contain $(0 + 1 + 5)$ odd days = 6 odd days.

1st Jan, 2001 has one odd day.

∴ Total number of odd days upto 1st Jan, 2001 = 7 odd days
$$= 0 \text{ odd days.}$$

∴ The day will be Sunday.

13. Total number of odd days from 1st Jan, 1991 to 1st Jan, 1998

Year   1991   1992   1993   1994   1995   1996   1997

Odd days   1 +   2 +   1 +   1 +   1   + 2 + 1 = 9 odd days

i.e. 2 odd days

∴ The day is 2 days beyond the day on 1st Jan, 1991.

i.e. The required day must be Thursday.

14. Find the day on 1st April, 1994.

1600 years contain 0 odd day

300 years contain 1 odd day

93 years = (23 leap years + 70 ordinary years)
$$= (46 + 70) \text{ odd days} = 4 \text{ odd days.}$$

Number of days upto 1st April, 1994

Jan   Feb   March   April

31 +   28 +   31   +   1   = 91 days = 0 odd day.

∴ Total number of odd days = $(0 + 1 + 4 + 0) = 5$ odd day.

∴ Day on 1st April 1994 is 'Friday'.

∴ Sunday was on 3rd April, 1994.

Thus, Sunday fell on 3rd, 10th, 17th & 24th.

15. Count the number of days for 1990 onwards to get 0 odd day.

Year   1990 1991 1992 1993 1994 1995

Odd days   1   1   2   1   1   1   = 7 or 0 odd day.

∴ Calendar for 1990 is the same as for the year 1996.

16. Since any date in March is the same day of the week as the corresponding date in November of that year, so the same day falls on 5th November.

28. Clocks

GENERAL CONCEPTS

The face or dial of a watch is a circle whose circumference is divided into 60 equal parts, callled minute spaces.

A clock has two hands, the smaller one is called the *hour hand* or *short hand* while the larger one is called the *minute hand* or *long hand.*

(*i*) In 60 minutes, the minute hand gains 55 minutes on the hour hand.

(*ii*) In every hour, both the hands coincide once.

(*iii*) The hands are in the same straight line when they are coincident or opposite to each other.

(*iv*) When the two hands are at right angles, they are 15 minute spaces apart.

(*v*) When the hands are in opposite directions, they are 30 minute spaces apart.

Too Fast and Too slow : *If a watch or a clock indicates 8.15, when the correct time is 8, it is said to be 15 minutes too fast.*

On the other hand, *if it indicates 7.45, when the correct time is 8, it is said to be 15 minutes too slow.*

Solved Problems

Ex. 1. *Find the angle between the minute hand and hour hand of a clock when the time is 7.20.*

Sol. Angle traced by the hour hand in 12 hours = 360°

Angle traced by it in 7 hrs 20 min i.e. $\dfrac{22}{3}$ hrs

$$= \left(\frac{360}{12} \times \frac{22}{3} \right)^{\circ} = 220°.$$

Angle traced by minute hand in 60 min = 360°

Angle traced by it in 20 min = $\left(\dfrac{360}{60} \times 20 \right)^{\circ} = 120°.$

∴ Required angle = (220° − 120°) = 100°.

Ex. 2. *At what time between 2 and 3 o'clock will the hands of a clock together ?*

Sol. At 2 o'clock, the hour hand is at 2 and the minute hand is at 12, i.e. they are 10 min spaces apart.

To be together, the minute hand must gain 10 minutes over the hour hand.

Now, 55 minutes are gained by it in 60 min.

$\therefore$ 10 miniutes will be gained in $\left(\dfrac{60}{55} \times 10\right)$ min. $= 10\dfrac{10}{11}$ min.

$\therefore$ The hands will coincide at $10\dfrac{10}{11}$ min. past 2.

Ex. 3. *At what time between 4 and 5 o'clock will the hands of a clock be at right angle ?*

Sol. At 4 o'clock, the minute hand will be 20 min. spaces behind the hour hand.

Now, when the two hands are at right angles, they are 15 min. spaces apart.

So, they are at right angles in following two cases.

Case I. *When minute hand is 15 min spaces behind the hour hand :*

In this case min. hand will have to gain $(20 - 15) = 5$ minute spaces.

55 min. spaces are gained by it in 60 min.

5 min. spaces will be gained by it in $\left(\dfrac{60}{55} \times 5\right)$ min. $= 5\dfrac{5}{11}$ min.

$\therefore$ They are at right angles at $5\dfrac{5}{11}$ min. past 4.

Case II : *When the minute hand is 15 min. spaces ahead of the hour hand :*

To be in this position, the minute hand will have to gain

$$(20 + 15) = 35 \text{ minute spaces.}$$

55 min. spaces are gained in 60 min.

35 min. spaces are gained in $\left(\dfrac{60}{55} \times 35\right)$ min. $= 38\dfrac{2}{11}$ min.

$\therefore$ They are at right angles at $38\dfrac{2}{11}$ min. past 4.

Ex. 4. *Find at what time between 8 and 9 o'clock will the hands of a clock be in the same straight line but not together.*

Sol. At 8 o'clock, the hour hand is at 8 and the minute hand is at 12, i.e. the two hands are 20 min. spaces apart.

To be in the same straight line but not together they will be 30 minute spaces apart.

So, the minute hand will have to gain $(30 - 20) = 10$ minute spaces over the hour hand.

55 minute spaces are gained in 60 min.

10 minute spaces will be gained in $\left(\dfrac{60}{55} \times 10\right)$ min $= 10\dfrac{10}{11}$ min.

$\therefore$ The hands will be in the same straight line but not together at

$$10\dfrac{10}{11} \text{ min. part 8.}$$

Ex. 5. *At what time between 5 and 6 o'clock are the hands of a clock 3 minutes apart ?*

Sol. At 5 o'clock, the minute hand is 25 min. spaces behind the hour hand.

Case I : *Minute hand is 3 min. spaces behind the hour hand.*

In this case, the minute hand has to gain $(25 - 3) = 22$ minute spaces.

55 min. are gained in 60 min.

22 min. are gained in $\left(\dfrac{60}{55} \times 22\right)$ min. $= 24$ min.

∴ The hands will be 3 min. apart at 24 min. past 5.

Case II : *Minute hand is 3 min. spaces ahead of the hour hand.*

In this case, the minute hand has to gain $(25 + 3) = 28$ minute spaces.

55 min. are gained in 60 min.

28 min. are gained in $\left(\dfrac{60}{55} \times 28\right) = 31\dfrac{5}{11}$ min.

∴ The hands will be 3 min. apart at $31\dfrac{5}{11}$ min. past 5.

Ex. 6. *The minute hand of a clock overtakes the hour hand at intervals of 65 minutes of the correct time. How much a day does the clock gain or lose ?*

Sol. In a correct clock, the minute hand gains 55 min. spaces over the hour hand in 60 minutes.

To be together again, the minute hand must gain 60 minutes over the hour hand.

55 min. are gained in 60 min.

60 min. are gained in $\left(\dfrac{60}{55} \times 60\right)$ min $= 65\dfrac{5}{11}$ min.

But, they are together after 65 min.

∴ Gain in 65 min. $= \left(65\dfrac{5}{11} - 65\right) = \dfrac{5}{11}$ min.

Gain in 24 hours $= \left(\dfrac{5}{11} \times \dfrac{60 \times 24}{65}\right)$ min $= 10\dfrac{10}{43}$ min.

∴ The clock gains $10\dfrac{10}{43}$ minutes in 24 hours.

Ex. 7. *A watch which gains uniformly, is 5 min. slow at 8 o'clock in the morning on Sunday and it is 5 min. 48 sec. fast at 8 p.m. on following Sunday. When was it correct ?*

Sol. Time from 8 a.m. on Sunday to 8 p.m. on following Sunday

$= 7$ days 12 hours $= 180$ hours.

∴ The watch gains $\left(5 + 5\dfrac{4}{5}\right)$ min or $\dfrac{54}{5}$ min. in 180 hrs.

Now $\dfrac{54}{5}$ min. are gained in 180 hrs.

$\therefore$ 5 min. are gained in $\left(180 \times \dfrac{5}{54} \times 5\right)$ hrs.

$\qquad$ = 83 hrs 20 min. = 3 days 11 hrs 20 min.

$\therefore$ Watch is correct 3 days 11 hrs 20 min. after 8 a.m. of Sunday.

$\therefore$ It will be correct at 20 min. past 7 p.m. on Wednesday.

Ex. 8. *A clock is set right at 5 a.m. The clock loses 16 minutes in 24 hours. What will be the true time when the clock indicates 10 p.m. on 4 th day ?*

Sol. Time from 5 a.m. on a day to 10 p.m. on 4th day = 89 hours.

Now 23 hrs 44 min. of this clock = 24 hours of correct clock.

$\therefore \dfrac{356}{15}$ hrs of this clock = 24 hours of correct clock

89 hrs of this clock = $\left(24 \times \dfrac{15}{356} \times 89\right)$ hrs of correct clock.

$\qquad$ = 90 hrs of correct clock.

So, the correct time is 11 p.m.

Ex. 9. *A clock is set right at 8 a.m. The clock gains 10 minutes in 24 hours. What will be the true time when the clock indicates 1 p.m. on the following day ?*

Sol. Time from 8 a.m. on a day to 1 p.m. on the following day = 29 hours.

24 hours 10 min. of this clock = 24 hours of the correct clock.

$\dfrac{145}{6}$ hrs of this clock = 24 hrs of the correct clock

29 hrs of this clock = $\left(24 \times \dfrac{6}{145} \times 29\right)$ hrs of the correct clock

$\qquad$ = 28 hrs 48 min of correct clock

$\therefore$ The correct time is 28 hrs 48 min. after 8 a.m.

This is 48 min. past 12.

EXERCISE 28

Mark ($\sqrt{}$) agaainst the correct answer :

1. At 3.40, the hour hand and the minute hand of a clock form an angle of :

    (a) 120° $\qquad$ (b) 125° $\qquad$ (c) 130° $\qquad$ (d) 135°

2. The angle between the minute hand and the hour hand of a clock when the time is 8.30, is :

    (a) 80° $\qquad$ (b) 75° $\qquad$ (c) 60° $\qquad$ (d) 105°

3. The angle between the minute hand and the hour hand of a clock when the time is 4.20, is :

    (a) 0° $\qquad$ (b) 10° $\qquad$ (c) 5° $\qquad$ (d) 20°

4. At what angle the hands of a clock are inclined at 15 minutes past 5 ?

(a) $72\frac{1}{2}^{\circ}$ (b) $67\frac{1}{2}^{\circ}$ (c) 64° (d) $58\frac{1}{2}^{\circ}$

5.   How many times do the hands of a clock coincide in a day ?
     (a) 24   (b) 20   (c) 21   (d) 22
6.   How many times in a day, the hands of a clock are straight ?
     (a) 22   (b) 24   (c) 44   (d) 48
7.   How many times are the hands of a clock at right angles in a day ?
     (a) 22   (b) 24   (c) 44   (d) 48
8.   How many times do the hands of a clock point towards each other in
     a day ?
     (a) 12   (b) 20   (c) 22   (d) 24
9.   How much does a watch lose per day, if its hands coincide every 64
     minutes ?

     (a) 96 min.   (b) 90 min.   (c) $36\frac{5}{11}$ min. (d) $32\frac{8}{11}$ min.

10. At what time between 5 and 6 o'clock are the hands of a clock
     coincident ?
     (a) 22 min. past 5   (b) 30 min. psrt 5

     (c) $22\frac{8}{11}$ min. past 9   (d) $27\frac{3}{11}$ min. past 5

11. At what time between 9 and 10 o'clock will the hands of a watch be
     together ?
     (a) 45 min. past 9   (b) 50 min.past 9

     (c) $49\frac{1}{11}$ min. past 9   (d) $48\frac{2}{11}$ min. past 9

12. At what time between 7 and 8 o'clock will the hands of a clock be in
     the same straight line but, not together ?

     (a) 5 min.past 7   (b) $5\frac{2}{11}$ min. past 7

     (c) $5\frac{3}{11}$ min. past 7   (d) $5\frac{5}{11}$ min. past 7

13. At what time between 4 and 5 o'clock will the hands of a watch point
     in opposite directions ?
     (a) 45 min. past 4   (b) 40 min. past 4

     (c) $50\frac{4}{11}$ min. past 4   (d) $54\frac{6}{11}$ min . past 4

14. At what time between 5.30 and 6 will the hands of a clock be at right
     angles ?

     (a) $43\frac{5}{11}$ min. past 5   (b) $43\frac{7}{11}$ min. past 5

     (c) 40 min. past 5   (d) 45 min. past 5

15. A watch which gains uniformly is 2 minute slow at noon on Monday and is 4 min. 48 sec fast at 2 p.m. on the following Monday. When was it correct ?
    (a) 2 p.m. on Tuesday
    (b) 2 p.m. on Wednesday
    (c) 3 p.m. on Thursday
    (d) 1 p.m. on Friday

16. A watch which gains 5 seconds in 3 minutes was set right at 7 a.m. In the afternoon of the same day, when the watch indicated quarter past 4 o'clock, the true time is :

    (a) $59\dfrac{7}{12}$ min. past 3

    (b) 4 p.m.

    (c) $58\dfrac{7}{11}$ min. past 3

    (d) $2\dfrac{3}{11}$ min. past 4

ANSWERS

1. (c)   2. (b)   3. (b)   4. (b)   5. (d)   6. (c)   7. (c)   8. (c)   9. (d)
10. (d)   11. (c)   12. (d)   13. (d)   14. (b)   15. (b)   16. (b)

SOLUTIONS

1. Angle traced by hour hand in 12 hrs = 360°.

   Angle traced by it in $\dfrac{11}{3}$ hrs $=\left(\dfrac{360}{12}\times\dfrac{11}{3}\right)^\circ=110°$.

   Angle traced by minute hand in 60 min. = 360°.

   Angle traced by it in 40 min $=\left(\dfrac{360}{60}\times40\right)^\circ=240°$.

   ∴ Required angle = $(240-110)° = 130°$.

2. Angle traced by hour hand in $\dfrac{17}{2}$ hrs $=\left(\dfrac{360}{12}\times\dfrac{17}{2}\right)^\circ=255°$.

   Angle traced by min. hand in 30 min. $=\left(\dfrac{360}{60}\times30\right)^\circ=180°$.

   ∴ Required angle = $(255-180)° = 75°$.

3. Angle traced by hour hand in $\dfrac{13}{3}$ hrs $=\left(\dfrac{360}{12}\times\dfrac{13}{3}\right)^\circ=130°$.

   Angle traced by min. hand in 20 min. $=\left(\dfrac{360}{60}\times20\right)^\circ=120°$.

   ∴ Required angle = $(130-120)° = 10°$.

4. Angle traced by hour hand in $\dfrac{21}{4}$ hrs $=\left(\dfrac{360}{12}\times\dfrac{21}{4}\right)^\circ=157\dfrac{1}{2}°$.

Angle traced by min. hand in 15 min. $= \left(\dfrac{360}{12} \times 15\right)^{\circ} = 90^{\circ}$

$\therefore$ Required angle $= \left(157\dfrac{1}{2}\right)^{\circ} - 90^{\circ} = 67\dfrac{1}{2}^{\circ}$.

5. The hands of a clock coincide 11 times in every 12 hours (Since between 11 and 1, they coincide only once, i.e. at 12 o'clock).
   $\therefore$ The hands coincide 22 times in a day.

6. In 12 hours, the hands coincide or are in opposite direction 22 times.
   $\therefore$ In 24 hours, the hands coincide or are in opposite direction 44 times a day.

7. In 12 hours, they are at right angles 22 times.
   $\therefore$ In 24 hours, they are at right angles 44 times.

8. The hands of a clock point towards each other 11 times in every 12 hours (Because between 5 and 7 they point towards each other at 6 o'clock only).
   So, in a day, the hands point towards each other 22 times.

9. 55 min. spaces are covered in 60 min.
   60 min. spaces are covered in $\left(\dfrac{60}{55} \times 60\right)$ min. $= 65\dfrac{5}{11}$ min.

   Loss in 64 min. $= \left(65\dfrac{5}{11} - 64\right) = \dfrac{16}{11}$ min.

   Loss in 24 hrs $= \left(\dfrac{16}{11} \times \dfrac{1}{64} \times 24 \times 60\right)$ min. $= 32\dfrac{8}{11}$ min.

10. At 5 o'clock, the minute hand is 25 min. spaces apart.
    To be coincident, it must gain 25 min. spaces.
    55 min. are gained in 60 min.
    25 min are gained in $\left(\dfrac{60}{55} \times 25\right)$ min. $= 27\dfrac{3}{11}$ min.

    $\therefore$ The hands are coincident at $27\dfrac{3}{11}$ min. past 5.

11. To be together between 9 and 10 o'clock, the minute hand has to gain 45 min. spaces.
    55 min. spaces gained in 60 min.
    45 min. spaces are gained in $\left(\dfrac{60}{55} \times 45\right)$ min or $49\dfrac{1}{11}$ min.

    $\therefore$ The hands are together at $49\dfrac{1}{11}$ min. past 9.

12. When the hands of the clock are in the same straight line but not together, they are 30 minute spaces apart.
    At 7 o'clock, they are 25 min. spaces apart.
    $\therefore$ Minute hand will have to gain only 5 min. spaces.

55 min. spaces are gained in 60 min.

5 min. spaces are gained in $\left(\dfrac{60}{55} \times 5\right)$ min. $= 5\dfrac{5}{11}$ min.

$\therefore$ Required time $= 5\dfrac{5}{11}$ min. past 7.

13. At 4 o'clock, the hands of the watch are 20 min. spaces apart.

To be in opposite directions, they must be 30 min. spaces apart.

$\therefore$ Minute hand will have to gain 50 min. spaces.

55 min. spaces are gained in 60 min.

50 min. spaces are gained in $\left(\dfrac{60}{55} \times 50\right)$ min. or $54\dfrac{6}{11}$ min.

$\therefore$ Requied time $= 54\dfrac{6}{11}$ min. past 4.

14. At 5 o'clock, the hands are 25 min. spaces apart.

To be at right angles and that too between 5.30 and 6, the minute hand has to gain $(25 + 15) = 40$ min. spaces.

55 min. spaces are gained in 60 min.

40 min. spaces are gained in $\left(\dfrac{60}{55} \times 40\right)$ min. $= 43\dfrac{7}{11}$ min.

$\therefore$ Required time $= 43\dfrac{7}{11}$ min. past 5.

29. Stock & Shares

Stock : In order to meet the expenses of a certain plan, the Government of India sometimes raises a loan from the public at a certain fixed rate of interest. Bonds, each of a fixed value are issued for sale to the public.

If a man purchases a bond of Rs. 100 at which 8% interest has been fixed by the Government, then the holder of such a bond is said to have, *a Rs. 100 stock at 8%*. Clearly, Rs. 100 is the *face value* of the stock.

These bonds or stocks are sold and bought in the open market through brokers at *stock exchanges*.

The broker's charge is called *'brokerage'*.

Remark (*i*) When stock is purchased, brokerage is added to the cost price.

      (*ii*) When stock is sold, brokerage is subtracted from the selling price.

The selling price of a Rs. 100 stock is said to be :

  (*i*) **at par,** if S.P. is Rs. 100 exactly ;

 (*ii*) **above par** (or **at premium**), if S.P. is more than Rs. 100 ;

(*iii*) **below par** (or **at discount**), if S.P. is less than Rs. 100.

Remarks : By *'a Rs. 800, 9% stock at 95'*, we mean a stock whose face value is Rs. 800, annual interest is 9% of the face value and the market price of a Rs. 100 stock is Rs. 95.

Solved Problems

Ex. 1. *Find the cost of :*

 (*i*) *Rs. 7200, 8% stock at 90 ;*

 (*ii*) *Rs. 4500, 8.5% stock at 4 premium ;*

(*iii*) *Rs. 6400, 10% stock at 15 discount.*

Sol. (*i*) Cost of Rs. 100 stock = Rs. 90

$$\text{Cost of Rs. 7200 stock} = \text{Rs.} \left(\frac{90}{100} \times 7200 \right) = \text{Rs. 6480.}$$

(*ii*) Cost of Rs. 100 stock = Rs. (100 + 4)

$$\text{Cost of Rs. 4500 stock} = \text{Rs.} \left(\frac{104}{100} \times 4500 \right) = \text{Rs. 4680.}$$

(*iii*) Cost of Rs. 100 stock = Rs. (100 − 15)

$$\therefore \ \text{Cost of Rs. 6400 stock} = \text{Rs.} \left(\frac{85}{100} \times 6400 \right) = \text{Rs. 5440.}$$

Ex. 2. *Find the cash required to purchase Rs. 3200, $7\frac{1}{2}$ % stock at 107* $\left(brokerage\ \frac{1}{2}\ \%\right).$

Sol. Cash required to purchase Rs. 100 stock= Rs. $\left(107 + \frac{1}{2}\right) = $ Rs. $\frac{215}{2}.$

Cash required to purchase Rs. 3200 stock = Rs. $\left(\frac{215}{2} \times \frac{1}{100} \times 3200\right)$
$$= \text{Rs. } 3440.$$

Ex. 3. *Find the cash realised by selling Rs. 2400, 9.5% stock at 4 discount* $\left(brokerage\ \frac{1}{4}\ \%\right).$

Sol. By selling Rs. 100 stock, cash realised
$$= \text{Rs. } \left[(100 - 4) - \frac{1}{4}\right] = \text{Rs. } \frac{383}{4}$$
By selling Rs. 2400 stock, cash realised = Rs. $\left(\frac{383}{4} \times \frac{1}{100} \times 2400\right)$
$$= \text{Rs. } 2298.$$

Ex. 4. *Find the annual income derived from Rs. 2500, 8% stock at 106.*
Sol. Income from Rs. 100 stock = Rs. 8
Income from Rs. 2500 stock = Rs. $\left(\frac{8}{100} \times 2500\right) = $ Rs. 200.

Ex. 5. *Find the annual income by investing Rs. 6800 in 10% stock at 136.*
Sol. By investing Rs. 136, income obtained = Rs. 10
By investing Rs. 6800, income obtained = Rs. $\left(\frac{10}{136} \times 6800\right) = $ Rs. 500.

Ex. 6. *Which is better investment ?*
$7\frac{1}{2}$ % *stock at 105 or* $6\frac{1}{2}$ % *stock at 94.*

Sol. Let the investment in each case be Rs. (105×94).

Case I : $7\frac{1}{2}$ % stock at 105 :

On investing Rs. 105, income = Rs. $\frac{15}{2}$

On investing Rs. (105×94), income = Rs. $\left(\frac{15}{2} \times \frac{1}{105} \times 105 \times 94\right)$
$$= \text{Rs. } 705.$$

Case II : $6\frac{1}{2}$ % stock at 94 :

On investing Rs. 94, income = Rs. $\frac{13}{2}$

On investing Rs. (105×94), income $= $ Rs. $\left(\dfrac{13}{2} \times \dfrac{1}{94} \times 105 \times 94 \right)$

$$= \text{Rs.} \ \dfrac{1365}{2} = \text{Rs. } 682.50.$$

Clearly, the income from $7\dfrac{1}{2}\%$ stock at 105 is more.

Hence, the investment in $7\dfrac{1}{2}\%$ stock at 105 is better.

Ex. 7. *Find the cost of 96 shares of Rs. 10 each at $\dfrac{3}{4}$ discount, brokerage being $\dfrac{1}{4}$ per share.*

Sol. Cost of 1 share $= $ Rs. $\left[\left(10 - \dfrac{3}{4} \right) + \dfrac{1}{4} \right] = $ Rs. $\dfrac{19}{2}$.

Cost of 96 shares $= $ Rs. $\left(\dfrac{19}{2} \times 96 \right) = $ Rs. 912.

Ex. 8. *Find the income derived from 88 shares of Rs. 25 each at 5 premium, brokerage being $\dfrac{1}{4}$ per share and the rate of dividend being $7\dfrac{1}{2}\%$ per annum. Also, find the rate of interest on the investment.*

Sol. Cost of 1 share $= $ Rs. $\left(25 + 5 + \dfrac{1}{4} \right) = $ Rs. $\dfrac{121}{4}$.

Cost of 88 shares $= $ Rs. $\left(\dfrac{121}{4} \times 88 \right) = $ Rs. 2662.

$\therefore$ Investment made $= $ Rs. 2662.

Face value of 88 shares $= $ Rs. $(88 \times 25) = $ Rs. 2200.

Dividend on Rs. $100 = \dfrac{15}{2}$.

Dividend on Rs. $2200 = $ Rs. $\left(\dfrac{15}{2} \times \dfrac{1}{100} \times 2200 \right) = $ Rs. 165.

$\therefore$ Income derived $= $ Rs. 165

Rate of interest on investment $= \left(\dfrac{165}{2662} \times 100 \right) = 6.2\%$.

Ex. 9. *A man buys Rs. 25 shares in a company which pays 9% dividend. The money invested is such that it gives 10% on investment. At what price did he buy the shares ?*

Sol. Suppose he buys each share for Rs. x.

Then, $\left(25 \times \dfrac{9}{100} \right) = \left(x \times \dfrac{10}{100} \right)$ or $x = 22.50$.

$\therefore$ Cost of each share $= $ Rs. 22.50.

Ex. 10. *A man sells Rs. 5000, 12% stock at 156 and invests the proceeds partly in 8% stock at 90 and 9% stock at 108. He thereby increases his income by Rs. 70. How much of the proceeds were invested in each stock ?*

Sol. S.P. of Rs. 5000 stock = Rs. $\left(\dfrac{156}{100} \times 5000\right)$ = Rs. 7800.

Income from this stock = Rs. $\left(\dfrac{12}{100} \times 5000\right)$ = Rs. 600.

Let investment in 8% stock be x & that in 9% stock = $(7800 - x)$.

$\therefore \left(x \times \dfrac{8}{90}\right) + (7800 - x) \times \dfrac{9}{108} = (600 + 70)$

or $\dfrac{4x}{45} + \dfrac{7800 - x}{12} = 670$

or $16x + 117000 - 15x = (670 \times 180)$ or $x = 3600$.

$\therefore$ Money invested in 8% stock at 90 = Rs. 3600.

Money invested in 9% stock at 108 = Rs. $(7800 - 3600)$ = Rs. 4200.

EXERCISE 29

Mark ($\sqrt{}$) against the correct answer :

1. To produce an annual income of Rs. 1200 from a 12% stock at 90, the amount of stock needed is :
   (*a*) Rs. 10800   (*b*) Rs. 14400   (*c*) Rs. 10000   (*d*) Rs. 16000

2. Rajinder invests a part of Rs. 12000 in 12% stock at Rs. 120 and the remainder in 15% stock at Rs. 125. If his total dividend per annum is Rs. 1360, how much does he invest in 12% stock at Rs. 120 ?
   (*a*) Rs. 4500   (*b*) Rs. 5500   (*c*) Rs. 6000   (*d*) Rs. 4000
   (Hotel Management 1992)

3. Rs. 9800 are invested partly in 9% stock at 75 and 10% stock at 80 to have equal amount of incomes. The investment in 9% stock is :
   (*a*) Rs. 4800   (*b*) Rs. 5000   (*c*) Rs. 5400   (*d*) Rs. 5600

4. A man invests some money partly in 9% stock at 96 and partly in 12%stock at 120. To obtain equal dividends from both, he must invest the money in the ratio :
   (*a*) 4 : 5   (*b*) 16 : 15   (*c*) 3 : 4   (*d*) 3 : 5

5. Which is better investment –11% stock at 143 or $9\frac{3}{4}$ % stock at 117?

   (*a*) 11% at 143   (*b*) $9\frac{3}{4}$ % at 117

   (*c*) both are equally good

6. A man invests in a 16% stock at 128. The interest obtained by him is :
   (*a*) 16%   (*b*) 8%   (*c*) 12.5%   (*d*) 12%

7. In order to obtain an income of Rs. 650 from 10% stock at Rs. 96, one must make an investment of :
    (a) Rs. 6500   (b) Rs. 9600   (c) Rs. 3100   (d) Rs. 6240

8. A 6% stock yields 8%. The market value of the stock is :
    (a) Rs. 48   (b) Rs. 96   (c) Rs. 75   (d) Rs. 133.33

9. A 9% stock yields 8%. The market value of the stock is :
    (a) Rs. 72   (b) Rs. 90   (c) Rs. 116.50   (d) Rs. 112.50

10. By investing Rs. 1620 in 8% stock, Sandeep earns Rs. 135. The stock is then quoted at :   **(Bank P.O. 1990)**
    (a) Rs. 106   (b) Rs. 96   (c) Rs. 80   (d) Rs. 108

11. A 12% stock yielding 10% is quoted at :
    (a) Rs. 120   (b) Rs. 112   (c) Rs. 83.33   (d) Rs. 110

12. The income derived from a Rs. 100, 13% stock at Rs. 105, is
    (a) Rs. 5   (b) Rs. 13   (c) Rs. 8   (d) Rs. 18

13. The cost price of a Rs. 100 stock at 4 discount, when brokerage is $\frac{1}{4}$ % is :
    (a) Rs. 96   (b) Rs. 96.25   (c) Rs. 95.75   (d) Rs. 104.25

14. The cash realised on selling a 14% stock at Rs. 106.25, brokerage being $\frac{1}{4}$ %, is :
    (a) Rs. 105.50   (b) Rs. 106.50   (c) Rs. 106   (d) Rs. 113.75

15. A man invested Rs. 1552 in a stock at 97 to obtain an income of Rs. 128. The dividend from the stock is :
    (a) 8%   (b) 7.5%   (c) 9.7%   (d) None of these

16. By investing in $16\frac{2}{3}$ % stock at 64, one earns Rs. 1500. The investment made is :
    (a) Rs. 9600   (b) Rs. 5760   (c) Rs. 5640   (d) Rs. 7500

17. Which is better investment, 12% stock at par with an income tax at the rate of 5 paise per rupee or $14\frac{2}{7}$ % stock at 120 free from income tax ?

    (a) 12% stock   (b) $14\frac{2}{7}$ % stock   (c) both are equally good

18. A invested some money in 10% stock at Rs. 96. If B wants to invest in an equally good 12% stock, he must purchase a stock worth of :
    (a) Rs. 120   (b) Rs. 115.20   (c) Rs. 80   (d) Rs. 125.40

19. A man bought 20 shares of Rs. 50 at 5 discount, the rate of dividend being $13\frac{1}{2}$ %. The rate of interest obtained is :

    (a) $13\frac{1}{2}$ %   (b) $12\frac{1}{2}$ %   (c) 15%   (d) $16\frac{2}{3}$ %

20. A man buys Rs. 20 shares paying 9% dividend. The man wants to have an interest of 12% on his money. The market value of each share is :
(*a*) Rs. 12   (*b*) Rs. 15   (*c*) Rs. 18   (*d*) Rs. 21

21. A man invested Rs. 4455 in Rs. 10 shares quoted at Rs. 8.25. If the rate of dividend be 12%, his annual income is :
(*a*) Rs. 534.60   (*b*) Rs. 655.60   (*c*) Rs. 648   (*d*) Rs. 207.40

22. A man buys Rs. 50 shares in a company which pays 10% dividend. If the man gets 12.5% on his investment, at what price did he buy the shares ?
(*a*) Rs. 40   (*b*) Rs. 48   (*c*) Rs. 52   (*d*) Rs. 37.50

23. A man buys Rs. 20 shares paying 9% dividend. If the man gets 6% interest on his money, the market value of each share is :
(*a*) Rs. 54   (*b*) Rs. 30   (*c*) Rs. 13.33   (*d*) Rs. 10.80

24. The market value of a 10.5% stock, in which an income of Rs. 756 is derived by investing Rs. 9000, brokerage being $\frac{1}{4}$ %, is :

(*a*) Rs. 124.75   (*b*) Rs. 125.25   (*c*) Rs. 108.25 (*d*) Rs. 112.20

ANSWERS

1. (*c*)   **2.** (*d*)   **3.** (*b*)   **4.** (*b*)   **5.** (*b*)   **6.** (*c*)   **7.** (*d*)   **8.** (*c*)   **9.** (*d*)
10. (*b*)   **11.** (*a*)   **12.** (*b*)   **13.** (*b*)   **14.** (*c*)   **15.** (*a*)   **16.** (*b*)   **17.** (*b*)   **18.** (*b*)
19. (*c*)   **20.** (*b*)   **21.** (*c*)   **22.** (*a*)   **23.** (*b*)   **24.** (*a*)

SOLUTIONS

1. For an income of Rs. 12, stock needed = Rs. 100
For an income of Rs. 1200, stock needed = Rs. $\left(\frac{100}{12} \times 1200 \right)$ = Rs. 10000.

2. Let investment in 12% stock be Rs. *x*.
Then, investment in 15% stock = Rs. (12000 – *x*).

$$\frac{12}{120} \times x + \frac{15}{125} \times (12000 - x) = 1360$$

or $\frac{x}{10} + \frac{3}{25} (12000 - x) = 1360$

or 5*x* + 72000 – 6*x* = 1360 × 50 or *x* = 4000.

3. Let the investment in 9% stock be Rs. *x*.
Then, investment in 10% stock = Rs. (9800 – *x*)
$\frac{9}{75} \times x = \frac{10}{80} \times (9800 - x)$ or $\frac{3x}{25} = \frac{9800 - x}{8}$
or 24*x* = 9800 × 25 – 25*x* or 49*x* = 9800 × 25 or *x* = 5000.

4. For an income of Re 1 in 9% stock at 96, investment

$$= \text{Rs.} \left(\frac{96}{9}\right) = \text{Rs.} \frac{32}{3}.$$

For an income of Re 1 in 12% stock at 120, investment

$$= \text{Rs} \left(\frac{120}{12}\right) = \text{Rs. }10.$$

∴ Ratio of investments $= \frac{32}{3} : 10 = 32 : 30 = 16 : 15.$

5. Let investment in each case be Rs. (143×117) .

Income in Ist case $= \text{Rs.} \left[\frac{11}{143} \times 143 \times 117\right] = \text{Rs. }1287.$

Income in 2nd case $= \text{Rs.} \left[\frac{39}{4 \times 117} \times 143 \times 117\right] = \text{Rs. }1394.25.$

Clearly, $9\frac{3}{4}$ % stock at 117 is better.

6. By investing Rs. 128, income derived $= \text{Rs. }16.$

By investing Rs. 100, income derived $= \text{Rs.} \left(\frac{16}{128} \times 100\right) = 12\frac{1}{2}$ %.

7. To obtain Rs. 10, investment $= \text{Rs. }96$

To obtain Rs. 650, investment $= \text{Rs.} \left(\frac{96}{10} \times 650\right) = \text{Rs. }6240.$

8. For an income of Rs. 8, investment $= \text{Rs. }100$

For an income of Rs. 6, investment $= \text{Rs.} \left(\frac{100}{8} \times 6\right) = \text{Rs. }75.$

∴ Market value of Rs. 100 stock $= \text{Rs. }75.$

9. To obtain Rs. 8, investment $= \text{Rs. }100$

To obtain Rs. 9, investment $= \text{Rs.} \left(\frac{100}{8} \times 9\right) = \text{Rs. }112.50.$

∴ Market value of Rs. 100 stock $= \text{Rs. }112.50.$

10. To earn Rs. 135, investment $= \text{Rs. }1620.$

To earn Rs. 8, investment $= \text{Rs.} \left(\frac{1620}{135} \times 8\right) = \text{Rs. }96.$

∴ Market value of Rs. 100 stock $= \text{Rs. }96.$

11. To earn Rs. 10, money invested $= \text{Rs. }100$

To earn Rs. 12, money invested $= \text{Rs.} \left(\frac{100}{10} \times 12\right) = \text{Rs. }120.$

∴ Market value of Rs. 100 stock $= \text{Rs. }120.$

12. Income on Rs. 100 stock $= \text{Rs. }13.$

13. C.P. $= \text{Rs.} \left(100 - 4 + \frac{1}{4}\right) = \text{Rs. }96.25.$

14. Cash realised = Rs. $(106.25 - 0.25)$ = Rs. 106.

15. By investing Rs. 1552, income = Rs. 128.

By investing Rs. 97, income = Rs. $\left(\dfrac{128}{1552} \times 97\right)$ = Rs. 8.

∴ Dividend = 8%.

16. To earn Rs. $\dfrac{50}{3}$, investment = Rs. 64

To earn Rs. 1500, investment = Rs. $\left(64 \times \dfrac{3}{50} \times 1500\right)$ = Rs. 5760.

17. Let investment in each case = Rs. (100×120).

Income from 12% stock = Rs. $\left(\dfrac{12}{100} \times 100 \times 120\right)$ = Rs. 1440.

Net income = Rs. $\left(1440 - \dfrac{5}{100} \times 1440\right)$ = Rs. 1368.

Income from $14\dfrac{2}{7}$% stock = Rs. $\left(\dfrac{100}{7 \times 120} \times 100 \times 120\right)$ = Rs. 1428.57.

Clearly, $14\dfrac{2}{7}$% stock in better.

18. For an income of Rs. 10, investment = Rs. 96.

For an income of Rs. 12, investment = Rs. $\left(\dfrac{96}{10} \times 12\right)$ = Rs. 115.20.

19. Investment = Rs. $[20 \times (50 - 5)]$ = Rs. 900.

Face value = Rs. (50×20) = Rs. 1000.

Dividend = Rs. $\left(\dfrac{27}{2} \times \dfrac{1000}{100}\right)$ = Rs. 135.

Interest obtained = $\left(\dfrac{135}{900} \times 100\right)$% = 15%.

20. Dividend on Rs. 20 = Rs. $\left(\dfrac{9}{100} \times 20\right)$ = Rs. $\dfrac{9}{5}$.

Rs. 12 is an income on Rs. 100.

∴ Rs. $\dfrac{9}{5}$ is an income on Rs. $\left(\dfrac{100}{12} \times \dfrac{9}{5}\right)$ = Rs. 15.

21. Number of shares = $\left(\dfrac{4455}{8.25}\right)$ = 540.

Face value = Rs. (540×10) = Rs. 5400.

Annual income = Rs. $\left(\dfrac{12}{100} \times 5400\right)$ = Rs. 648.

22. Dividend on 1 share = Rs. $\left(\dfrac{10}{100} \times 50\right)$ = Rs. 5.

Rs. 12.5 is an income on an investment of Rs. 100

Rs. 5 is an income on an investment of Rs. $\left(100 \times \dfrac{2}{25} \times 5 \right)$ = Rs. 40.

∴ Cost of 1 share = Rs. 40.

23. Dividend on each share = Rs. $\left(20 \times \dfrac{9}{100} \right)$ = Rs. 1.80.

To have an income of Rs. 6, investment = Rs. 100

To have an income of Rs. 1.80, investment = Rs. $\left(\dfrac{100}{6} \times 1.80 \right)$

$$= \text{Rs. } 30.$$

∴ Market value of each share = Rs. 30.

24. For an income of Rs. 756, investment = Rs. 9000

For an income of Rs. $\dfrac{21}{2}$, investment = Rs. $\left(\dfrac{9000}{756} \times \dfrac{21}{2} \right)$ = Rs. 125.

∴ For a Rs. 100 stock, investment = Rs. 125.

Market value of Rs. 100 stock = Rs. $\left(125 - \dfrac{1}{4} \right)$ = Rs. 124.75.

---

30. True Discount

General Concepts : Suppose a man has to pay Rs. 156 after 4 years and the rate of interest is 14% per annum. Clearly, Rs. 100 at 14% will amount to Rs. 156 in 4 years. So, the payment of Rs. 100 now will clear off the debt of Rs. 156 due 4 years hence. We say that :

Sum due = *Rs. 156 due 4 years hence* ;

Present Worth (P.W.)= Rs. 100 ;

True Dicount (T.D.) = Rs. (156 − 100) = Rs. 56
= (Sum due) − (P.W.).

We define :

(*i*) T.D. = *Interest on P.W.*

(*ii*) Amount = (*P.W.*) + (*T.D.*)

Remark : Interest is reckoned on P.W. and true discount is reckoned on the amount.

FORMULAE : Let rate = $R\%$ per annum & Time = T years. Then,

(*i*) P.W. = $\dfrac{100 \times (\text{Amount})}{100 + (R \times T)} = \dfrac{100 \times \text{T.D.}}{R \times T}$

(*ii*) T.D. = $\dfrac{(\text{P.W.}) \times R \times T}{100} = \dfrac{(\text{Amount}) \times R \times T}{100 + (R \times T)}$.

(*iii*) Sum = $\dfrac{(\text{S.I.}) \times (\text{T.D.})}{(\text{S.I.}) - (\text{T.D.})}$.

(*iv*) (S.I.) − (T.D.) = S.I. on T.D.

(*v*) When the sum is put at compound interest, then

$$\text{P.W.} = \dfrac{\text{Amount}}{\left(1 + \dfrac{R}{100}\right)^{T}}.$$

Solved Problems

Ex. 1. *Find the present worth of Rs. 930 due 3 years hence at 8% per annum. Also find the discount* .

Sol. P.W. = $\dfrac{100 \times \text{Amount}}{100 + (R \times T)}$ = Rs. $\left[\dfrac{100 \times 930}{100 + (8 \times 3)}\right]$

$$= \text{Rs.} \left(\dfrac{100 \times 930}{124}\right) = \text{Rs. } 750.$$

T.D. = (Amount) − (P.W.) = Rs. (930 − 750) = Rs. 180.

Ex. 2. *The true discount on a bill due 9 months hence at 12% per annum is Rs. 540. Find the amount of the bill and its present worth.*

Sol. Let amount be Rs. x. Then,

$$\frac{x \times R \times T}{100 + (R \times T)} = \text{T.D.} \Rightarrow \frac{x \times 12 \times \frac{3}{4}}{100 + \left(12 \times \frac{3}{4}\right)} = 540$$

or $x = \left(\dfrac{540 \times 109}{9}\right) = \text{Rs. } 6540.$

$\therefore$ Amount = Rs. 6540.

P.W. = Rs. (6540 – 540) = Rs. 6000.

Ex. 3. *The true discount on a certain sum of money due 3 years hence is Rs. 250 and the simple interest on the same sum for the same time and at the same rate is Rs. 375. Find the sum and the rate percent.*

Sol. T.D. = Rs. 250 and S.I. = Rs. 375.

$\therefore$ Sum due $= \dfrac{\text{S.I.} \times \text{T.D.}}{(\text{S.I.}) - (\text{T.D.})} = \text{Rs. } \left(\dfrac{375 \times 250}{375 - 250}\right) = \text{Rs. } 750.$

Rate. $= \left(\dfrac{100 \times 375}{750 \times 3}\right)\% = 16\dfrac{2}{3}\%.$

Ex. 4. *The difference between the simple interest and true discount on a certain sum of money for 6 months at $12\frac{1}{2}$ % per annum is Rs. 25. Find the sum.*

Sol. Let the sum be Rs. x. Then,

$$\text{T.D.} = \frac{x \times \frac{25}{2} \times \frac{1}{2}}{100 + \left(\frac{25}{2} \times \frac{1}{2}\right)} = \left(x \times \frac{25}{4} \times \frac{4}{425}\right) = \frac{x}{17}.$$

$$\text{S.I.} = \left(x \times \frac{25}{2} \times \frac{1}{2} \times \frac{1}{100}\right) = \frac{x}{16}.$$

$\therefore \dfrac{x}{16} - \dfrac{x}{17} = 25 \Rightarrow 17x - 16x = 25 \times 16 \times 17$ or $x = 6800.$

Hence, sum due = Rs. 6800.

Ex. 5. *A bill falls due in 1 year. The creditor agrees to accept immediate payment of the half and to defer the payment of the other half for 2 years. By this arrangement he gains Rs. 40. What is the amount of the bill, if the money be worth $12\frac{1}{2}$ % ?*

Sol. Let the sum be Rs. x. Then,

$$\left[\frac{x}{2} + \frac{\frac{x}{2} \times 100}{100 + \left(\frac{25}{2} \times 2\right)}\right] - \frac{x \times 100}{100 + \left(\frac{25}{2} \times 1\right)} = 40$$

$$\Rightarrow \frac{x}{2} + \frac{2x}{5} - \frac{8x}{9} = 40 \text{ or } x = 3600.$$

∴ Amount of the bill = Rs. 3600.

EXERCISE 30

Mark (√) against the correct answer :

1. The present worth of Rs. 2310 due $2\frac{1}{2}$ years hence, the rate of interest being 15% per annum, is :
   (a) Rs. 1750   (b) Rs. 1680   (c) Rs. 1840   (d) Rs. 1443.75

2. If the true discount on a sum due 2 years hence at 14% per annum be Rs. 168, the sum due is :
   (a) Rs. 768   (b) Rs. 968   (c) Rs. 1960   (d) Rs. 2400

3. The true discount on Rs. 2562 due 4 months hence is Rs. 122. The rate per cent is :
   (a) 12%   (b) $13\frac{1}{3}$%   (c) 15%   (d) 14%

4. The true discount on Rs. 1760 due after a certain time at 12% per annum is Rs. 160. The time after which it is due is :
   (a) 6 months   (b) 8 months   (c) 9 months   (d) 10 months

5. The true discount on a bill due 9 months hence at 16% per annum is Rs. 189. The amount of the bill is :
   (a) Rs. 1386   (b) Rs. 1764   (c) Rs. 1575   (d) Rs. 2268

6. The interest on Rs. 750 for 2 years is the same as the true discount on Rs. 960 due 2 years hence. If the rate of interest is the same in both cases, it is :
   (a) 12%   (b) 14%   (c) 15%   (d) $16\frac{2}{3}$%

7. The simple interest and the true discount on a certain sum for a given time and at a given rate are Rs. 85 and Rs. 80 respectively. The sum is :
   (a) Rs. 1800   (b) Rs. 1450   (c) Rs. 1360   (d) Rs. 6800

8. If Rs. 10 be allowed as true discount on a bill of Rs. 110 due at the end of a certain time, then the discount allowed on the same sum due at the end of double the time is :
   (a) Rs. 20   (b) Rs. 21.81   (c) Rs. 22   (d) Rs. 18.33

9. A man wants to sell his scooter. There are two offers, one at Rs. 12000 cash and the other at a credit of Rs. 12880 to be paid after 8 months, money being at 18% per annum. Which is the better offer ?
   (a) Rs. 12000 in cash   (b) Rs. 12880 at credit
   (c) Both are equally good

10. Goods were bought for Rs. 600 and sold the same day for Rs. 688.50 at a credit of 9 months and thus gaining 2%. The rate of interest per annum is :
    (a) $16\frac{2}{3}$%   (b) $14\frac{1}{2}$%   (c) $13\frac{1}{3}$%   (d) 15%

11. The present worth of Rs. 1404 due in two equal half yearly instalments at 8% per annum simple interest is :

(*a*) Rs. 1325   (*b*) Rs. 1300   (*c*) Rs. 1350   (*d*) Rs. 1500

12. A trader owes a merchant Rs. 10028 due 1 year hence. The trader wants to settle the account after 3 months. If the rate of interest is 12% per annum, how much cash should he pay ?

(*a*) Rs. 9025.20   (*b*) Rs. 9200   (*c*) Rs. 9600   (*d*) Rs. 9560

13. A man buys a watch for Rs. 1950 in cash and sells it for Rs. 2200 at a credit of 1 year. If the rate of interest is 10% per annum, the man :

(*a*) gains Rs. 55   (*b*) gains Rs. 50

(*c*) loses Rs. 30   (*d*) gains Rs. 30

14. A man purchased a cow for Rs. 3000 and sold it the same day for Rs. 3600, allowing the buyer a credit of 2 years. If the rate of interest be 10% per annum, then the man has a gain of :

(*a*) 0%   (*b*) 5%   (*c*) 7.5%   (*d*) 10%

15. A owes B, Rs. 1573 payable $1\frac{1}{2}$ years hence, Also B owes A, Rs. 1444.50 payable 6 months hence. If they want to settle the account forth with, keeping 14% as the rate of interest, then who should pay and how much ?

(*a*) A, Rs. 28.50   (*b*) B, Rs. 37.50 (*c*) A, Rs. 50   (*d*) B, Rs. 50

16. A has to pay Rs. 220 to B after 1 year. B asks A to pay Rs. 110 in cash and defer the payment of Rs. 110 for 2 years. A agrees to it. If the rate of interest be 10% per annum, in this mode of payment :

(*a*) There is no gain or loss to any one

(*b*) A gains Rs. 7.34   (*c*) A loses Rs. 7.34

(*d*) A gains Rs. 11

17. Rs. 20 is the true discount on Rs. 260 due after a certain time. What will be the true discount on the same sum due after half of the former time, the rate of interest being the same ?

(*a*) Rs. 10   (*b*) Rs. 10.40   (*c*) Rs. 15.20   (*d*) Rs. 13

ANSWERS

1. (*b*)   **2.** (*a*)   **3.** (*c*)   **4.** (*d*)   **5.** (*b*)   **6.** (*b*)   **7.** (*c*)   **8.** (*d*)   **9.** (*a*)

10. (*a*)   **11.** (*a*)   **12.** (*b*)   **13.** (*b*)   **14.** (*a*)   **15.** (*d*)   **16.** (*b*)   **17.** (*b*)

SOLUTIONS

1. P.W. = Rs. $\left(\dfrac{100 \times 2310}{100 + \left(15 \times \dfrac{5}{2}\right)} \right)$ = Rs. 1680.

2. P.W. = $\dfrac{100 \times \text{T.D.}}{R \times T} = \dfrac{100 \times 168}{14 \times 2} = 600.$

∴ Sum = (P.W. + T.D.) = Rs. (600 + 168) = Rs. 768.

3. P.W. = Rs. (2562 − 122) = Rs. 2440.

∴ S.I. on Rs. 2440 for 4 months is Rs. 122.

∴ Rate = $\left(\dfrac{100 \times 122}{2440 \times \dfrac{1}{3}}\right)\% = 15\%$.

4. P.W. = (1760 − 160) = Rs. 1600.

∴ S.I. on Rs. 1600 at 12% is Rs. 160.

∴ Time = $\left(\dfrac{100 \times 160}{1600 \times 12}\right) = \dfrac{5}{6}$ years = $\left(\dfrac{5}{6} \times 12\right)$ months = 10 months.

5. Let P.W. be Rs. x.

Then, S.I. on Rs. x at 16% for 9 months = Rs. 189.

∴ $x \times 16 \times \dfrac{9}{12} \times \dfrac{1}{100} = 189$ or $x = 1575$.

∴ P.W. = Rs. 1575.

∴ Sum due = P.W. + T.D. = Rs. (1575 + 189) = Rs. 1764.

6. S.I. on Rs. 750 = T.D. on Rs. 960.

This means P.W. of Rs. 960 due 2years hence is Rs. 750.

∴ T.D. = Rs. (960 − 750) = Rs. 210.

Thus, S.I. on Rs. 750 for 2 years is Rs. 210.

∴ Rate = $\left(\dfrac{100 \times 210}{750 \times 2}\right)\% = 14\%$.

7. Sum = $\dfrac{\text{S.I.} \times \text{T.D.}}{(\text{S.I.}) - (\text{T.D.})} = \dfrac{85 \times 80}{(85 - 80)} =$ Rs. 1360.

8. S.I. on Rs. (110 − 10) for a certain time = Rs. 10.

S.I. on Rs. 100 for double the time = Rs. 20.

T.D. on Rs. 120 = Rs. (120 − 100) = Rs. 20.

T.D. on Rs. 110 = Rs. $\left(\dfrac{20}{120} \times 110\right) =$ Rs. 18.33.

9. P.W. of Rs. 12880 due 8 months hence

= Rs. $\left[\dfrac{12880 \times 100}{100 + \left(18 \times \dfrac{8}{12}\right)}\right] =$ Rs. $\left(\dfrac{12880 \times 100}{112}\right) =$ Rs. 11500.

Clearly, Rs. 12000 in cash is a better offer.

10. S.P. = 102% of Rs. 600 = Rs. $\left(\dfrac{102}{100} \times 600\right) =$ Rs. 612.

Now, P.W. = Rs. 612 and sum = Rs. 688.50.

∴ T.D. = Rs. (688.50 − 612) = Rs. 76.50.

Thus, S.I. on Rs. 612 for 9 months is Rs. 76.50.

∴ Rate = $\left(\dfrac{100 \times 76.50}{612 \times \dfrac{3}{4}}\right)\% = 16\dfrac{2}{3}\%$.

11. Required sum = P.W. of Rs. 702 due 6 months hence + P.W. of Rs. 702 due 1 year hence

$$= Rs. \left[\left(\frac{100 \times 702}{100 + 8 \times \frac{1}{2}} \right) + \left(\frac{100 \times 702}{100 + (8 \times 1)} \right) \right] = Rs. (675 + 650)$$

= Rs. 1325.

12. Required money = P.W. of Rs. 10028 due 9 months hence

$$= Rs. \left[\frac{10028 \times 100}{100 + \left(12 \times \frac{9}{12} \right)} \right] = Rs. 9200.$$

13. S.P. = P.W. of Rs. 2200 due 1 year hence

$$= Rs. \left[\frac{2200 \times 100}{100 + (10 \times 1)} \right] = Rs. 2000.$$

∴ Gain = Rs. (2000 − 1950) = Rs. 50.

14. C.P. = Rs. 3000.

$$S.P. = Rs. \left[\frac{3600 \times 100}{100 + (10 \times 2)} \right] = Rs. 3000.$$

Gain = 0%.

15. A owes = P.W. of Rs. 1573 due $\frac{3}{2}$ years hence

$$= Rs. \left[\frac{1573 \times 100}{100 + \left(14 \times \frac{3}{2} \right)} \right] = Rs. \left(\frac{1573 \times 100}{121} \right) = Rs. 1300.$$

B owes = P.W. of Rs. 1444.50 due 6 months hence

$$= Rs. \left[\frac{1444.50 \times 100}{100 + \left(14 \times \frac{1}{2} \right)} \right] = Rs. \left(\frac{1444.50 \times 100}{107} \right) = Rs. 1350.$$

∴ B must pay Rs. 50 to A.

16. A has to pay = P.W. of Rs. 220 due 1 year hence

$$= Rs. \left[\frac{220 \times 100}{100 + (10 \times 1)} \right] = Rs. 200.$$

A actually pays = Rs. 110 + P.W. of Rs. 110 due 2 years hence

$$= \left[110 + \frac{110 \times 100}{100 + (10 \times 2)} \right] = Rs. 192.66.$$

∴ A gains = Rs. (200 − 192.66) = Rs. 7.34.

17. S.I. on Rs. (260 − 20) for a given time = Rs. 20.
    S.I. on Rs. 240 for half the time = Rs. 10.
    T.D. on Rs. 250 = Rs. 10.

∴ T.D. on Rs. 260 = Rs. $\left(\frac{10}{250} \times 260 \right)$ = Rs. 10.40.

31. Banker's Discount

General Concepts : Suppose a merchant A buys goods worth, say Rs. 10000 from another merchant B at a credit of say 5 months. Then, B prepares a bill, called the bill of exchange. A signs this bill and allows B to withdraw the amount from his bank account after exactly 5 months.

The date exactly after 5 months is called *nominally due date*. Three days (known as *grace days*) are added to it to get a date, known as *legally due date*.

The bill can be presented to the bank any day on or after the legally due date.

Suppose B wants to have the money before the legally due date. Then he can have the money from the banker or a broker, who deducts S.I. on the face value (i.e. Rs. 10000 in this case) for the period from the date on which the bill was discounted (i.e. paid by the banker) and the legally due date. This amount is known as *Banker's Discount (B.D.)*

Thus, **B.D.** *is the S.I. on the face value for the period from the date on which the bill was discounted and the legally due date.*

Banker's Gain *(B.G.) = (B.D.) − (T.D.) for the unexpired time.*

Note : When the date of the bill is not given, grace days are not to be added.

FORMULAE :

(*i*) B.D. = S.I. on bill for unexpired time.

(*ii*) B.G. = (B.D.) − (T.D.) = S.I. on T.D. = $\dfrac{(T.D)^2}{P.W.}$

(*iii*) T.D. = $\sqrt{P.W. \times B.G.}$

(*iv*) B.D. = $\left(\dfrac{\text{Amount} \times \text{Rate} \times \text{Time}}{100}\right)$.

(*v*) T.D. = $\left(\dfrac{\text{Amount} \times \text{Rate} \times \text{Time}}{100 + (\text{Rate} \times \text{Time})}\right)$.

(*vi*) Amount = $\left(\dfrac{B.D \times T.D}{B.D - T.D.}\right)$.

(*vii*) T.D. = $\left(\dfrac{B.G \times 100}{\text{Rate} \times \text{Time}}\right)$.

Solved Problems

Ex. 1. *A bill for Rs. 6000 is drawn on July 14 at 5 months. It is discounted on 5th October at 10%. Find the banker's discount, true discount, banker's gain and the money that the holder of the bill receives.*

Sol. Face value of the bill = Rs. 6000.

Date on which the bill was drawn = July 14 at 5 months.

Nominally due date = December, 14.

Legally due date = December, 17.

Date on which the bill was discounted = October, 5.

Unexpired time : Oct   Nov.   Dec

$$26 + \quad 30 + \quad 17 = 73 \text{ days} = \frac{1}{5} \text{ year.}$$

∴ B.D. = S.I. on Rs. 6000 for $\frac{1}{5}$ year.

$$= \text{Rs.} \left(6000 \times 10 \times \frac{1}{5} \times \frac{1}{100} \right) = \text{Rs. 120.}$$

$$\text{T.D.} = \text{Rs.} \left[\frac{6000 \times 10 \times \frac{1}{5}}{100 + (10 \times \frac{1}{5})} \right] = \text{Rs.} \left(\frac{12000}{102} \right) = \text{Rs. 117.64.}$$

∴ B.G. = (B.D.) − (T.D.) = Rs. (120 − 117.64) = Rs. 2.36.

Money received by the holder of the bill

$$= \text{Rs. (6000 − 120) = Rs. 5880.}$$

Ex. 2. *If the true discount on a certain sum due 6 months hence at 15% is Rs. 120, what is the banker's discount on the same for the same time and at the same rate ?*

Sol. B.G. = S.I. on T.D.

$$= \text{Rs.} \left(120 \times 15 \times \frac{1}{2} \times \frac{1}{100} \right) = \text{Rs. 9.}$$

∴ (B.D.) − (T.D.) = Rs. 9.

∴ B.D. = Rs. (120 − 9) = Rs. 129.

Ex. 3. *The banker's discount on Rs. 1800 at 12% per annum is equal to the true discount on Rs. 1872 for the same time at the same rate. Find the time.*

Sol. S.I. on Rs. 1800 = T.D. on Rs. 1872.

∴ P.W. of Rs. 1872 is Rs. 1800.

∴ Rs. 72 is S.I. on Rs. 1800 at 12%.

∴ Time $= \left(\dfrac{100 \times 72}{12 \times 1800} \right)$ year $= \dfrac{1}{3}$ year = 4 months.

Ex. 4. *The banker's discount and the true discount on a sum of money due 8 months hence are Rs. 120 and Rs. 110 respectively. Find the sum and the rate per cent.*

Sol. Sum $= \left(\dfrac{\text{B.D.} \times \text{T.D}}{\text{B.D.} - \text{T.D.}} \right) = \text{Rs.} \left(\dfrac{120 \times 110}{120 - 110} \right) = \text{Rs. 1320.}$

Since B.D. is S.I. on sum due, so S.I. on Rs. 1320 for 8 months is Rs. 120.

$$\therefore \; \text{Rate} = \left(\dfrac{100 \times 120}{1320 \times \dfrac{2}{3}} \right) \% = 13 \dfrac{7}{11} \%.$$

Ex. 5. *The present worth of a bill due sometime hence is Rs. 1100 and the true discount on the bill is Rs. 110. Find the banker's discount and the banker's gain.*

Sol. T.D. $= \sqrt{\text{P.W.} \times \text{B.G.}}$

$$\therefore \; \text{B.G.} = \dfrac{(\text{T.D})^2}{\text{P.W.}} = \text{Rs.} \left(\dfrac{110 \times 110}{1100} \right) = \text{Rs. 11.}$$

$\therefore$ B.D. = (T.D. + B.G.) = Rs. (110 + 11) = Rs. 121.

Ex. 6. *The banker's discount on Rs. 1650 due a certain time hence is Rs. 165. Find the true discount and the banker's gain.*

Sol. Sum $= \dfrac{\text{B.D.} \times \text{T.D}}{\text{B.D.} - \text{T.D.}} = \dfrac{\text{B.D.} \times \text{T.D.}}{\text{B.G.}}$

$$\therefore \; \dfrac{\text{T.D}}{\text{B.G.}} = \dfrac{\text{Sum}}{\text{B.D}} = \dfrac{1650}{165} = \dfrac{10}{1}$$

Thus, if B.G. is Re 1, T.D. = Rs. 10.

If B.D. is Rs. 11, T.D. = Rs. 10.

If B.D. is Rs. 165, T.D. = Rs. $\left(\dfrac{10}{11} \times 165 \right)$ = Rs. 150.

And, B.G. = Rs. (165 – 150) = Rs. 15.

Ex. 7. *What rate percent does a man get for his money when in discounting a bill due 10 months hence , he deducts 10% of the amount of the bill ?*

Sol. Let, amount of the bill = Rs. 100.

Money deducted = Rs. 10.

Money received by the holder of the bill = Rs. (100 – 10) = Rs. 90.

$\therefore$ S.I. on Rs. 90 for 10 months = Rs. 10

$$\therefore \; \text{Rate} = \left(\dfrac{100 \times 10}{90 \times \dfrac{10}{12}} \right) \% = 13 \dfrac{1}{3} \%$$

EXERCISE 31

Mark ($\surd$) against the correct answer :

1. The true discount on a bill of Rs. 540 is Rs. 90. The banker's discount is :
   (a) Rs. 60   (b) Rs. 108   (c) Rs. 110   (d) Rs. 112

2. The present worth of a certain bill due sometimes hence is Rs. 800 and the true discount is Rs. 36. The banker's disount is :
   (a) Rs. 37   (b) Rs. 37.62 (c) Rs. 34.38   (d) Rs. 38.98

3. The present worth of a certain sum due sometime hence is Rs. 1600 and the true discount is Rs. 160. The banker's gain is :

(a) Rs. 20   (b) Rs. 24   (c) Rs. 16   (d) Rs. 12

4. The banker's gain of a certain sum due 2 years hence at 10% per annum is Rs. 24. The present worth is :

(a) Rs. 480   (b) Rs. 520   (c) Rs. 600   (d) Rs. 960

5. The banker's gain on a bill due 1 year hence at 12% per annum is Rs. 6. The true discount is :

(a) Rs. 72   (b) Rs. 36   (c) Rs. 54   (d) Rs. 50

6. The banker's discount on a bill due 4 months hence at 15% is Rs. 420. The true discount is :

(a) Rs. 400   (b) Rs. 360   (c) Rs. 480   (d) Rs. 320

7. The banker's gain on a sum due 3 years hence at 12% per annum is Rs. 270. The banker's discount is :

(a) Rs. 960   (b) Rs. 840   (c) Rs. 1020   (d) Rs. 760

8. The present worth of a sum due sometime hence is Rs. 576 and the banker's gain is Rs. 16. The true discount is :

(a) Rs. 36   (b) Rs. 72   (c) Rs. 48   (d) Rs. 96

9. The banker's discount on Rs. 1600 at 15% per annum is the same as true discount on Rs. 1680 for the same time and at the same rate. The time is :

(a) 3 months   (b) 4 months   (c) 6 months   (d) 8 months

10. The banker's discount on a sum of money for $1\frac{1}{2}$ years is Rs. 558 and the true discount on the same sum for 2 years is Rs. 600. The rate percent is :

(a) 10%   (b) 13%   (c) 12%   (d) 15%

11. The banker's discount of a certain sum of money is Rs. 72 and the true discount on the same sum for the same time is Rs. 60. The sum due is :

(a) Rs. 360   (b) Rs. 432   (c) Rs. 540   (d) Rs. 1080

12. The banker's discount on a certain sum due 2 years hence is $\frac{11}{10}$ of the true discount. The rate percent is :

(a) 11%   (b) 10%   (c) 5%   (d) 5.5%

13. The banker's gain on a certain sum due $1\frac{1}{2}$ years hence is $\frac{3}{25}$ of the banker's discount. The rate percent is :

(a) $5\frac{1}{5}\%$ (b) $9\frac{1}{9}\%$ (c) $8\frac{1}{8}\%$ (d) $6\frac{1}{6}\%$

ANSWERS

1. (b)   **2.** (b)   **3.** (c)   **4.** (c)   **5.** (d)   **6.** (a)   **7.** (c)   **8.** (d)   **9.** (b)
10. (c)   **11.** (a)   **12.** (c)   **13.** (b)

SOLUTIONS

1. P.W. = Rs. $(540 - 90)$ = Rs. 450

∴ S.I. on Rs 450 = Rs. 90

S.I. on Rs. 540 = $\left(\dfrac{90}{450} \times 540\right)$ = Rs. 108.

∴ B.D. = Rs. 108.

2. B.G. = $\dfrac{(\text{T.D.})^2}{\text{P.W}}$ = Rs. $\left(\dfrac{36 \times 36}{800}\right)$ = Rs.1.62

∴ B.D = (T.D. + B.G.) = Rs. $(36 + 1.62)$ = Rs. 37.62.

3. B.G. = $\dfrac{(\text{T.D})^2}{\text{P.W.}}$ = Rs. $\left(\dfrac{160 \times 160}{1600}\right)$ = Rs. 16.

4. T.D. = $\left(\dfrac{\text{B.G.} \times 100}{\text{Rate} \times \text{Time}}\right)$ = Rs. $\left(\dfrac{24 \times 100}{10 \times 2}\right)$ = Rs. 120.

∴ P.W. = $\dfrac{100 \times \text{T.D.}}{\text{Rate} \times \text{Time}}$ = Rs $\left(\dfrac{100 \times 120}{10 \times 2}\right)$ = Rs. 600.

5. T.D. = $\dfrac{\text{B.G.} \times 100}{R \times T}$ = $\left(\dfrac{6 \times 100}{12 \times 1}\right)$ = Rs. 50.

6. T.D. = $\dfrac{\text{B.D.} \times 100.}{100 + (R \times T)}$ = Rs. $\left[\dfrac{420 \times 100}{100 + (15 \times \frac{1}{3})}\right]$ = Rs. $\left(\dfrac{420 \times 100}{105}\right)$ = Rs. 400.

7. T.D. = $\left(\dfrac{\text{B.G.} \times 100}{R \times T}\right)$ = Rs. $\left(\dfrac{270 \times 100}{12 \times 3}\right)$ = Rs. 750.

∴ B.D. = Rs. $(750 + 270)$ = Rs. 1020.

8. T.D. = $\sqrt{\text{P.W.} \times \text{B.G.}}$ = $\sqrt{576 \times 16}$ = 96.

9. S.I. on Rs. 1600 = T.D. on Rs. 1680.

∴ Rs. 1600 is the P.W. of Rs. 1680.

i.e. Rs. 80 is S.I. on Rs. 1600 at 15%

∴ Time = $\left(\dfrac{100 \times 80}{1600 \times 15}\right)$ years = $\dfrac{1}{3}$ year = 4 months.

10. B.D. for $\dfrac{3}{2}$ years = Rs. 558.

B.D. for 2 years = Rs. $\left(558 \times \dfrac{2}{3} \times 2\right)$ = Rs. 744.

T.D. for 2 years = Rs. 600.

∴ Sum = $\dfrac{\text{B.D} \times \text{T.D.}}{\text{B.D.} - \text{T.D.}}$ = Rs. $\left(\dfrac{744 \times 600}{144}\right)$ = Rs. 3100.

Thus, Rs. 744 is S.I. on Rs. 3100 for 2 years.

$$\therefore \ \text{Rate} = \left(\frac{100 \times 744}{3100 \times 2}\right)\% = 12\,\%.$$

11. $\text{Sum} = \dfrac{\text{B.D.} \times \text{T.D.}}{\text{B.D.} - \text{T.D.}} = \text{Rs.}\left(\dfrac{72 \times 60}{72 - 60}\right) = \text{Rs.}\left(\dfrac{72 \times 60}{12}\right) = \text{Rs. } 360.$

12. Let T.D. be Re 1. Then, B.D. = Rs. $\dfrac{11}{10}$ = Rs. 1.10.

$$\therefore \ \text{Sum} = \text{Rs.}\left(\frac{1.10 \times 1}{1.10 - 1}\right) = \text{Rs.}\left(\frac{110}{10}\right) = \text{Rs. } 11.$$

$\therefore$ S.I. on Rs. 11 for 2 years is Rs. 1.10.

$$\therefore \ \text{Rate} = \left(\frac{100 \times 1.10}{11 \times 2}\right)\% = 5\,\%.$$

13. Let, B.D. = Re 1. Then, B.G. = Re $\dfrac{3}{25}$.

$$\therefore \ \text{T.D.} = (\text{B.D.} - \text{B.G.}) = \text{Re}\left(1 - \frac{3}{25}\right) = \text{Re} = \frac{22}{25}.$$

$$\text{Sum} = \left(\frac{1 \times \dfrac{22}{25}}{1 - \dfrac{22}{25}}\right) = \text{Rs. } \frac{22}{3}.$$

S.I. on Rs. $\dfrac{22}{3}$ for $1\dfrac{1}{2}$ years is Re 1.

$$\therefore \ \text{Rate} = \left(\frac{100 \times 1}{\dfrac{22}{3} \times \dfrac{3}{2}}\right)\% = 9\frac{1}{9}\,\%.$$

32. Odd Man Out and Series

1. **Turn odd man out :** As the phrase speaks itself, in this type of problems, a set of numbers is given in such a way that each one, except one satisfies a particular definite property. The one which does not satisfy that characteristic is to be taken out.

   Some important properties of numbers are given below :

   (i) **Prime Numbers :** A counting number greater than 1, which is divisible by itself and 1 only, is called a prime number. e.g. 2, 3, 5, 7, 11, 13, 17, 19, 23, 29, 31, 37, 41, 43, 47, 53, 59, 61, 67, 71, 73, 79, 83, 89, 97 etc.

   (ii) **Even Numbers :** A number divisible by 2, is an even number e.g. 2, 4, 6, 8, 10 etc.

   (iii) **Odd Numbers :** A number not divisible by 2, is called an odd number.

   (iv) **Perfect squares :** A counting number whose square root is a counting number, is called a perfect square, e.g. 1, 4, 9, 16, 25, 36, 49, 64 etc.

   (v) **Perfect Cubes :** A counting number whose cube-root is a counting number is called a perfect cube, e.g. 1, 8, 27, 64, 125 etc.

   (vi) **Multiples of a number :** A number which is divisible by a given number a, is called the multiple of a e.g. 3, 6, 9, 12 etc. are all multiples of 3.

   (vii) **Numbers in A.P. :** Some given numbers are said to be in A.P. if the difference between two consecutive numbers is same e.g. 13, 11, 9, 7 etc.

   (viii) **Numbers in G.P. :** Some given numbers are in G.P. if the ratio between two consecutive numbers remains the same, e.g. 48, 12, 3 etc.

   ## EXERCISE 32

Turn odd man out :

1. 3, 5, 7, 12, 17, 19.
   (a) 19   (b) 17   (c) 13   (d) 12
2. 10, 14, 16, 18, 21, 24, 26.
   (a) 26   (b) 24   (c) 21   (d) 18
3. 3, 5, 9, 11, 14, 17, 21.
   (a) 21   (b) 17   (c) 14   (d) 9
4. 1, 4, 9, 16, 23, 25, 36.
   (a) 9   (b) 23   (c) 25   (d) 36
5. 6, 9, 15, 21, 24, 28, 30.
   (a) 28   (b) 21   (c) 24   (d) 30
6. 41, 43, 47, 53, 61, 71, 73, 81.
   (a) 61   (b) 71   (c) 73   (d) 81
7. 16, 25, 36, 72, 144, 196, 225.

     (*a*) 36   (*b*) 72   (*c*) 196   (*d*) 225

8. 10, 25, 45, 54, 60, 75, 80.
     (*a*) 10   (*b*) 45   (*c*) 54   (*d*) 75

9. 1, 4, 9, 16, 20, 36, 49.
     (*a*) 1   (*b*) 9   (*c*) 20   (*d*) 49

10. 8, 27, 64, 100, 125, 216, 343.
     (*a*) 27   (*b*) 100   (*c*) 125   (*d*) 343

11. 1, 5, 14, 30, 50, 55, 91.
     (*a*) 5   (*b*) 50   (*c*) 55   (*d*) 91

12. 385, 462, 572, 396, 427, 671, 264.
     (*a*) 385   (*b*) 427   (*c*) 671   (*d*) 264

13. 835, 734, 642, 751, 853, 981, 532
     (*a*) 751   (*b*) 853   (*c*) 981   (*d*) 532

14. 331, 482, 551, 263, 383, 242, 111.
     (*a*) 263   (*b*) 383   (*c*) 242   (*d*) 111

15. 2, 5, 10, 17, 26, 37, 50, 64
     (*a*) 50   (*b*) 26   (*c*) 37   (*d*) 64

16. 19, 28, 39, 52, 67, 84, 102
     (*a*) 52   (*b*) 102   (*c*) 84   (*d*) 67

17. 253, 136, 352, 460, 324, 631, 244
     (*a*) 136   (*b*) 324   (*c*) 352   (*d*) 631

18. 2, 5, 10, 50, 500, 5000
     (*a*) 0   (*b*) 5   (*c*) 10   (*d*) 5000

19. 4, 5, 7, 10, 14, 18, 25, 32
     (*a*) 7   (*b*) 14   (*c*) 18   (*d*) 33

Find out the wrong number in each squence :

20. 22, 33, 66, 99, 121, 279, 594
     (*a*) 33   (*b*) 121   (*c*) 279   (*d*) 594

21. 36, 54, 18, 27, 9, 18.5, 4.5
     (*a*) 4.5   (*b*) 18.5   (*c*) 54   (*d*) 18

22. 582, 605, 588, 611, 634, 617, 600
     (*a*) 634   (*b*) 611   (*c*) 605   (*d*) 600

23. 46080, 3840, 384, 48, 24, 2, 1
     (*a*) 1   (*b*) 2   (*c*) 24   (*d*) 384

24. 1, 8, 27, 64, 124, 216, 343
     (*a*) 8   (*b*) 27   (*c*) 64   (*d*) 124

25. 5, 16, 6, 16, 7, 16, 9
     (*a*) 9   (*b*) 7   (*c*) 6   (*d*) None of these

26. 6, 13, 18, 25, 30, 37, 40
     (*a*) 25   (*b*) 30   (*c*) 37   (*d*) 40

27. 56, 72, 90, 110, 132, 150
     (*a*) 72   (*b*) 110   (*c*) 132   (*d*) 150

28. 8, 13, 21, 32, 47, 63, 83

    (*a*) 47   (*b*) 63   (*c*) 32   (*d*) 83

29. 25, 36, 49, 81, 121, 169, 225
    (*a*) 36   (*b*) 49   (*c*) 121   (*d*) 169

30. 1, 2, 6, 15, 31, 56, 91
    (*a*) 31   (*b*) 91   (*c*) 56   (*d*) 15

31. 52, 51, 48, 43, 34, 27, 16
    (*a*) 27   (*b*) 34   (*c*) 43   (*d*) 48

32. 105, 85, 60, 30, 0, − 45, − 90
    (*a*) 0   (*b*) 85   (*c*) − 45 (*d*) 60

33. 4, 6, 8, 9, 10, 11, 12
    (*a*) 10   (*b*) 11   (*c*) 12   (*d*) 9

34. 125, 127, 130, 135, 142, 153, 165
    (*a*) 130   (*b*) 142   (*c*) 153   (*d*) 165

35. 16, 36, 64, 81, 100, 144, 190
    (*a*) 81   (*b*) 100   (*c*) 190   (*d*) 36

36. 125, 123, 120, 115, 108, 100, 84
    (*a*) 123   (*b*) 115   (*c*) 100   (*d*) 84

37. 3, 10, 21, 36, 55, 70, 105
    (*a*) 105   (*b*) 70   (*c*) 36   (*d*) 55

38. 4, 9, 19, 39, 79, 160, 319
    (*a*) 319   (*b*) 160   (*c*) 79   (*d*) 39

39. 10, 14, 28, 32, 64, 68, 132
    (*a*) 32   (*b*) 68   (*c*) 132   (*d*) 28

40. 8, 27, 125, 343, 1331
    (*a*) 1331   (*b*) 343   (*c*) 125   (*d*) None

Insert the missing number :

41. 4, − 8, 16, − 32, 64, (......)
    (*a*) 128   (*b*) − 128 (*c*) 192   (*d*) − 192

42. 5, 10, 13, 26, 29, 58, 61, (......)
    (*a*) 122   (*b*) 64   (*c*) 125   (*d*) 128

43. 1, 4, 9, 16, 25, 36, 49, (......)
    (*a*) 54   (*b*) 56   (*c*) 64   (*d*) 81

44. 1, 8, 27, 64, 125, 216, (......)
    (*a*) 354   (*b*) 343   (*c*) 392   (*d*) 245

45. 11, 13, 17, 19, 23, 29, 31, 37, 41, (......)
    (*a*) 43   (*b*) 47   (*c*) 53   (*d*) 51

46. 16, 33, 65, 131, 261, (......)
    (*a*) 523   (*b*) 521   (*c*) 613   (*d*) 721

47. 3, 7, 6, 5, 9, 3, 12, 1, 15, (......)
    (*a*) 18   (*b*) 13   (*c*) − 1   (*d*) 3

48. 15. 31, 63, 127, 255, (......)
    (*a*) 513   (*b*) 511   (*c*) 517   (*d*) 523

49. 2, 6, 12, 20, 30, 42, 56, (......)

(a) 60   (b) 64   (c) 72   (d) 70

50. 8, 24, 12, 36, 18, 54, (......)

(a) 27   (b) 108   (c) 68   (d) 72

51. 165, 195, 255, 285, 345, (......)

(a) 375   (b) 420   (c) 435   (d) 390

52. 7, 26, 63, 124, 215, 342, (......)

(a) 481   (b) 511   (c) 391   (d) 421

53. 2, 4, 12, 48, 240, (......)

(a) 960   (b) 1440   (c) 1080   (d) 1920

54. 8, 7, 11, 12, 14, 17, 17, 22, (......)

(a) 27   (b) 20   (c) 22   (d) 24

55. 10, 5, 13, 10, 16, 20, 19, (......)

(a) 22   (b) 40   (c) 38   (d) 23

56. 1, 2, 4, 8, 16, 32, 64, (......), 256

(a) 148   (b) 128   (c) 154   (d) 164

57. 71, 76, 69, 74, 67, 72, (......)

(a) 77   (b) 65   (c) 80   (d) 76

58. 9, 12, 11, 14, 13, (......), 15

(a) 12   (b) 16   (c) 10   (d) 17

59. Complete the series

2, 5, 9, 19, 37, ...

(a) 76   (b) 74   (c) 75   (d) None of these

(Railways 1989)

60. Find the wrong number in the series :

3, 8, 15, 24, 34, 48, 63

(a) 15   (b) 24   (c) 34   (d) 48   (e) 63

(Bank P.O. 1988)

61. Find the wrong number in the series :

2, 9, 28, 65, 126, 216, 344

(a) 2   (b) 28   (c) 65   (d) 126   (e) 216

(Bank P.O. 1988)

62. Find out the wrong number in the series :

5, 15, 30, 135, 405, 1215, 3645

(a) 3645   (b) 1215   (c) 405   (d) 30   (e) 15

(Bank P.O. 1988)

63. Find out the wrong number in the series :

125, 106, 88, 76, 65, 58, 53

(a) 125   (b) 106   (c) 88   (d) 76   (e) 65

(Bank P.O. 1987)

Find out the wrong number in the series :

64. 190, 166, 145, 128, 112, 100, 91

      (a) 100   (b) 166   (c) 145   (d) 128   (e) 112

(Bank P.O. 1991)

65. 1, 1, 2, 6, 24, 96, 720

      (a) 720   (b) 96   (c) 24   (d) 6   (e) 2

(Bank P.O. 1991)

66. 40960, 10240, 2560, 640, 200, 40, 10

      (a) 640   (b) 40   (c) 200   (d) 2560   (e) 10240

(Bank P.O. 1991)

67. 64, 71, 80, 91, 104, 119, 135, 155

      (a) 71   (b) 80   (c) 104   (d) 119   (e) 135

(Bank P.O. 1991)

68. 7, 8, 18, 57, 228, 1165, 6996

      (a) 8   (b) 18   (c) 57   (d) 228   (e) 127

(Bank P.O. 1991)

69. 3, 7, 15, 27, 63, 127, 255

      (a) 7   (b) 15   (c) 27   (d) 63   (e) 127

(Bank P.O. 1991)

70. 19, 26, 33, 46, 59, 74, 91

      (a) 26   (b) 33   (c) 46   (d) 59   (e) 74

(Bank P.O. 1991)

71. 19, 26, 33, 46, 59, 74, 91

      (a) 26   (b) 33   (c) 46   (d) 59   (e) 74

(Bank P.O. 1991)

72. 445, 221, 109, 46, 25, 11, 4

      (a) 221   (b) 109   (c) 46   (d) 25   (e) 11

(Bank P.O. 1991)

73. 3, 7, 15, 39, 63, 127, 255, 511

      (a) 7   (b) 15   (c) 39   (d) 63   (e) 127

(Bank P.O. 1991)

74. 1, 3, 10, 21, 64, 129, 356, 777

      (a) 10   (b) 21   (c) 64   (d) 129   (e) 356

(Bank P.O. 1991)

75. 196, 169, 144, 121, 100, 80, 64

      (a) 169   (b) 144   (c) 121   (d) 100   (e) 80

(Bank P.O. 1991)

76. 6, 12, 48, 100, 384, 768, 3072

      (a) 768   (b) 384   (c) 100   (d) 48   (e) 12

(Bank P.O. 1993)

77. 10, 26, 74, 218, 654, 1946, 5834

      (a) 26   (b) 74   (c) 218   (d) 654   (e) 1946

(Bank P.O. 1993)

478   *Quantitative Aptitude*

78. 15, 16, 34, 105, 424, 2124, 12576
    (*a*) 16   (*b*) 34   (*c*) 105   (*d*) 424   (*e*) 2124
                                                      (Bank P.O. 1993)

79. 2807, 1400, 697, 347, 171, 84, 41, 20
    (*a*) 697   (*b*) 347   (*c*) 171   (*d*) 84   (*e*) 41
                                                        (Bank P.O. 1993)

80. 32, 36, 41, 61, 86, 122, 171, 235
    (*a*) 41   (*b*) 61   (*c*) 86   (*d*) 122   (*e*) 171
                                                        (Bank P.O. 1993)

81. 3, 4, 9, 22.5, 67.5, 202.5, 810
    (*a*) 4   (*b*) 9   (*c*) 22.5   (*d*) 67.5   (*e*) 202.5
                                                         (Bank P.O. 1993)

82. 1, 2, 8, 33, 148, 760, 4626
    (*a*) 2   (*b*) 8   (*c*) 33   (*d*) 148   (*e*) 760
                                                         (Bank P.O. 1993)

83. 3, 8, 18, 46, 100, 210, 432
    (*a*) 8   (*b*) 18   (*c*) 46   (*d*) 100   (*e*) 210
                                                        (Bank P.O. 1993)

84. 789, 645, 545, 481, 440, 429, 425
    (*a*) 645   (*b*) 545   (*c*) 481   (*d*) 440   (*e*) 429
                                                        (Bank P.O. 1994)

85. 1050, 510, 242, 106, 46, 16, 3
    (*a*) 510   (*b*) 242   (*c*) 106   (*d*) 46   (*e*) 16
                                                         (Bank P.O. 1994)

86. 5, 8, 20, 42, 124, 246, 736
    (*a*) 8   (*b*) 20   (*c*) 42   (*d*) 124   (*e*) 246
                                                        (Bank P.O. 1994)

87. 2, 3, 6, 15, 52.5, 157.5, 630
    (*a*) 3   (*b*) 6   (*c*) 15   (*d*) 52.5   (*e*) 157.5
                                                        (Bank P.O. 1994)

88. 888, 440, 216, 104, 48, 22, 6
    (*a*) 440   (*b*) 216   (*c*) 104   (*d*) 48   (*e*) 22

89. 4, 5, 15, 49, 201, 1011, 6073
    (*a*) 5   (*b*) 15   (*c*) 49   (*d*) 201   (*e*) 1011

ANSWERS

1. (d)	**2.** (c)	**3.** (c)	**4.** (b)	**5.** (a)	**6.** (d)	**7.** (b)	**8.** (c)	**9.** (c)
10. (b)	**11.** (b)	**12.** (b)	**13.** (a)	**14.** (b)	**15.** (d)	**16.** (b)	**17.** (b)	**18.** (d)
19. (c)	**20.** (c)	**21.** (b)	**22.** (a)	**23.** (c)	**24.** (d)	**25.** (a)	**26.** (d)	**27.** (d)
28. (a)	**29.** (a)	**30.** (b)	**31.** (b)	**32.** (a)	**33.** (b)	**34.** (d)	**35.** (c)	**36.** (c)
37. (b)	**38.** (b)	**39.** (c)	**40.** (d)	**41.** (b)	**42.** (a)	**43.** (c)	**44.** (b)	**45.** (a)
46. (a)	**47.** (c)	**48.** (b)	**49.** (c)	**50.** (a)	**51.** (c)	**52.** (b)	**53.** (b)	**54.** (b)
55. (b)	**56.** (b)	**57.** (b)	**58.** (b)	**59.** (c)	**60.** (c)	**61.** (e)	**62.** (d)	**63.** (c)
64. (d)	**65.** (b)	**66.** (c)	**67.** (e)	**68.** (d)	**69.** (c)	**70.** (b)	**71.** (c)	**72.** (c)
73. (c)	**74.** (e)	**75.** (e)	**76.** (c)	**77.** (d)	**78.** (e)	**79.** (b)	**80.** (a)	**81.** (a)
82. (e)	**83.** (b)	**84.** (d)	**85.** (c)	**86.** (b)	**87.** (d)	**88.** (e)	**89.** (a)	

SOLUTIONS

1. Each of the numbers except 12, is a prime number.

2. Each of the numbers except 21, is an even number.

3. Each of the numbers except 14, is an odd number.

4. Each of the given numbers except 23, is a perfect square.

5. Each of the numbers except 28, is a multiple of 3.

6. Each of the numbers except 81, is a prime number.

7. Each of the numbers except 72, is a perfect square.

8. Each of the numbers except 54, is a multiple of 5.

9. The pattern is $1^2, 2^2, 3^2, 4^2, 5^2, 6^2, 7^2$. But, instead of 5^2, it is 20, which is to be turned out.

10. The pattern is $2^3, 3^3, 4^3, 5^3, 6^3, 7^3$. But 100 is not a perfect cube.

11. The pattern is $1^2, 1^2, + 2^2, 1^2 + 2^2 + 3^2, 1^2 + 2^2 + 3^2 + 4^2,$ $1^2 + 2^2 + 3^2 + 4^2 + 5^2, 1^2 + 2^2 + 3^2 + 4^2 + 5^2 + 6^2$. But 50 is not of this pattern.

12. In each number except 427, the middle digit is sum of the other two.

13. In each number except 751, the difference of third and first digit is the middle one.

14. In each number except 383, the product of first and third digits is the middle one.

15. The pattern is $x^2 + 1$, where $x = 1, 2, 3, 4, 5, 6, 7, 8$ etc. But, 64 is out of pattern.

16. The pattern is $x^2 + 3$, where $x = 4, 5, 6, 7, 8, 9$ etc. But, 102 is out of pattern.

17. Sum of the digits in each number, except 324 is 10.

18. Pattern is 1st × 2nd = 3rd ; 2nd × 3rd = 4th ; 3rd × 4th = 5th.

But, 4th × 5th = 50 × 500 = 25000 ≠ 5000 = 6th.

19. 2nd = (1st + 1) ; 3rd = (2nd + 2) ; 4th = (3rd + 3) ; 5th = (4th + 4).
But, 18 = 6th ≠ 5th + 5 = 14 + 5 = 19.

20. Each number except 279 is a multiple of 11.

21. The terms are alternately multiplied by 1.5 and divided by 3. However 18.5 does not satisfy it.

22. Alternately 23 is added and 17 is subtracted from the terms.
So, 634 is wrong.

23. The terms are successively divided by 12, 10, 8, 6, ... etc.
So, 24 is wrong.

24. The numbers are $1^3, 2^3, 3^3, 4^3$ etc.

So, 124 is wrong ; it must have been 5^3 *i.e.* 125.

25. Terms at odd places are 5, 6, 7, 8 etc. and each term at even place is 16.
So, 9 is wrong.

26. The difference between two successive terms from the beginning are 7, 5, 7, 5, 7, 5.
So, 40 is wrong.

27. The numbers are $7 \times 8, 8 \times 9, 9 \times 10, 10 \times 11, 11 \times 12, 12 \times 13$.
So, 150 is wrong.

28. Go on adding 5, 8, 11, 14, 17, 20.
So, the number 47 is wrong and must be replaced by 46.

29. The numbers are squares of odd natural numbers, starting from 5 upto 15.
So, 36 is wrong.

30. Add $1^2, 2^2, 3^2, 4^2, 5^2, 6^2$.
So, 91 is wrong.

31. Subtract 1, 3, 5, 7, 9, 11 from successive numbers.
So, 34, is wrong.

32. Subtract 20, 25, 30, 35, 40, 45 from successive numbers.
So, 0 is wrong.

33. Each number is a composite number except 11.

34. Prime numbers 2, 3, 5, 7, 11, 13 are to be added successively.
So, 165 is wrong.

35. Each number is the square of a composite number except 190.

36. Prime numbers 2, 3, 5, 7, 11, 13 have successively been subtracted.
So, 100 is wrong. It must be (108 − 11) i.e. 97.

37. The pattern is $1 \times 3, 2 \times 5, 3 \times 7, 4 \times 9, 5 \times 11, 6 \times 13, 7 \times 15$ etc.

38. Double the number and add 1 to it, to get the next number.
So, 160 is wrong.

39. Alternately, we add 4 and double the next.
So, 132 is wrong.

It must be (68×2) i.e. 136.

40. The numbers are cubes of primes i.e. $2^3, 3^3, 5^3, 7^3, 11^3$.
Clearly, none is wrong.

41. Each number is the preceding number multiplied by -2.
So, the required number is -128.

42. Numbers are alternately multiplied by 2 and increased by 3.
So, the missing number $= 61 \times 2 = 122$.

43. Numbers are $1^2, 2^2, 3^2, 4^2, 5^2, 6^2, 7^2$.
So, the next number is $8^2 = 64$.

44. Numbers are $1^3, 2^3, 3^3, 4^3, 5^3, 6^3$. So, the missing number is $7^3 = 343$.

45. Numbers are all primes. The next prime is 43.

46. Each number is twice the preceding one with 1 added or subtracted alternately. So, the next number is $(2 \times 261 + 1) = 523$.

47. There are two series, beginning respectively with 3 and 7. In one 3 is added and in another 2 is subtracted. The next number is $1 - 2 = -1$.

48. Each number is double the preceding one plus 1. So, the next number is $(255 \times 2) + 1 = 511$.

49. The pattern is $1 \times 2, 2 \times 3, 3 \times 4, 4 \times 5, 5 \times 6, 6 \times 7, 7 \times 8$.
So, the next number is $8 \times 9 = 72$.

50. Numbers are alternately multipled by 3 and divided by 2.
So, next number $= 54 \div 2 = 27$.

51. Each number is 15 multiplied by a prime number i.e., $15 \times 11, 15 \times 13, 15 \times 17, 15 \times 19, 15 \times 23$.
So, the next number is $15 \times 29 = 435$.

52. Numbers are $(2^3 - 1), (3^3 - 1), (4^3 - 1), (5^3 - 1), (6^3 - 1), (7^3 - 1)$ etc.
So, the next number is $(8^3 - 1) = (512 - 1) = 511$.

53. Go on multiplying the given numbers by 2, 3, 4, 5, 6.
So, the correct next number is 1440.

54. There are two series (8, 11, 14, 17, 20) and (7, 12, 17, 22) increasing by 3 and 5 respectively.

55. There are two series (10, 13, 16, 19) and (5, 10, 20, 40) one increasing by 3 and the other multiplied by 2.

56. Each previous number is multiplied by 2.

57. Alternately, we add 5 and subtract 7.

58. Alternately, we add 3 and subtract 1.

59. Second number is one more than twice the first ; third number is one less than twice the second ; fourth number is one more than twice the third; fifth number is one less than the fourth.
Therefore, the sixth number is one more than twice the fifth.
So, the missing number is 75.

60. The difference between consecutive terms are respectively 5, 7, 9, 11 and 13.
    So, 34 is a wrong number.

61. $2 = (1^3 + 1)$; $9 = (2^3 + 1)$; $28 = (3^3 + 1)$; $65 = (4^3 + 1)$;
    $125 = (5^3 + 1)$; $216 \neq (6^3 + 1)$ & $344 = (7^3 + 1)$.
    $\therefore$ 216 is a wrong number.

62. Multiply each term by 3 to obtain the next term.
    Hence, 30 is a wrong number.

63. Go on subtracting prime numbers, 19, 17, 13, 11, 7, 5 from the numbers to get the next number. So, 88 is wrong.

64. Go on subtracting 24, 21, 18, 15, 12, 9 from the numbers to get the next number.
    Clearly, 128 is wrong.

65. Go on multiplying with 1, 2, 3, 4, 5, 6 to get the next number.
    So, 96 is wrong.

66. Go on dividing by 4 to get the next number.
    So, 200 is wrong.

67. Go on adding 7, 9, 11, 13, 15, 17, 19 respectively to obtain the next number.
    So, 135 is wrong.

68. Let the given numbers be A, B, C, D, E, F, G. Then,
    $A, A \times 1, B \times 2 + 2, C \times 3 + 3, D \times 4 + 4, E \times 5 + 5, F \times 6 + 6$ are the required numbers.
    Clearly, 228 is wrong.

69. Go on multiplying the number by 2 and adding 1 to it to get the next number.
    So, 27 is wrong.

70. Go on adding 7, 9, 11, 13, 15, 17 respectively to obtain the next number.
    So, 33 is wrong.

71. Go on dividing by 6, 5, 4, 3, 2, 1 respectively to obtain the next number.
    Clearly, 92 is wrong.

72. Go on subtracting 3 and dividing the result by 2 to obtain the next number.
    Clearly 46 is wrong.

73. Go on multiplying 2 and adding 1 to get the next number.
    So, 39 is wrong.

74. $A \times 2 + 1, B \times 3 + 1, C \times 2 + 1, D \times 3 + 1$ and so on.
    $\therefore$ 356 is wrong.

75. Numbers must be $(14)^2, (13)^2, (11)^2, (10)^2, (9)^2, (8)^2$.
    So, 80 is wrong.

76. Each even term of the series in obtained by multiplying the previous term by 2.

2nd term = (1st term) × 2 = 6 × 2 = 12,
4th term = (3rd term) × 2 = 48 × 2 = 96,
6th term = (5th term) × 2 = 384 × 2 = 768.
∴ 4th term should be 96 instead of 100.

77. 2nd term = (1st term) × 3 − 4 = 10 × 3 − 4 = 26,
3rd term = (2nd term) × 3 − 4 = 26 × 3 − 4 = 74,
4th term = (3rd term) × 3 − 4 = 74 × 3 − 4 = 218,
5th term = (4th term) × 3 − 4 = 654 − 4 = 650.
∴ 5th term must be 650 instead of 654.

78. 2nd term = (1st term) × 1 + 1 = 15 × 1 + 1 = 16,
3rd term = (2nd term) × 2 + 2 = 16 × 2 + 2 = 34,
4th term = (3rd term) × 3 + 3 = 34 × 3 + 3 = 105,
5th term = (4th term) × 4 + 4 = 105 × 4 + 4 = 424,
6th term = (5th term) × 5 + 5 = 425 × 5 + 5 = 2125.
∴ 6th term should be 2125 instead of 2124.

79. 7th term = (8th term) × 2 + 1 = 20 × 2 + 1 = 41,
6th term = (7th term) × 2 + 2 = 41 × 2 + 2 = 84,
5th term = (6th term) × 2 + 3 = 84 × 2 + 3 = 171,
4th term = (5th term) × 2 + 4 = 342 × 2 + 4 = 346.
∴ 4th term should be 346 instead of 347.

80. 2nd term = (1st term) + 2^2 = 32 + 4 = 36,

3rd term = (2nd term) + 3^2 = 36 + 9 = 45,

4th term = (3rd term) + 4^2 = 45 + 16 = 61,

5th term = (4th term) + 5^2 = 61 + 25 = 86.
∴ 3rd term should be 45 instead of 41.

81. There are two sequences (3, 9, 67.5, 810) and (4, 22.5, 202.5)
Pattern is : (1st term × 3), (2nd term × 7.5), (3rd term × 12) for the
first sequence and (1st term × 5), (2nd term × 9) and so on for the
second sequence.

82. 2nd term = (1st term × 1 + 1^2) = 1 × 1 + 1^2 = 2,

3rd term = (2nd term × 2 + 2^2) = 2 × 2 + 2^2 = 8,

4th term = (3rd term × 3 + 3^2) = 8 × 3 + 3^2 = 33,

5th term = (4th term × 4 + 4^2) = 33 × 4 + 4^2 = 148,

6th term = (5th term × 5 + 5^2) = 148 × 5 + 5^2 = 765.
∴ 760 is wrong.

83. 2nd term = (1st term × 2 + 2) = 3 × 2 + 2 = 8,
3rd term = (2nd term × 2 + 4) = 8 × 2 + 4 = 20,
4th term = (3rd term × 2 + 6) = 20 × 2 + 6 = 46,
5th term = (4th term × 2 + 8) = 46 × 2 + 8 = 100 and so on.
∴ 18 is wrong.

84.   2nd term = 1st term − $(12)^2 = 789 - 144 = 645$,

3rd term = (2nd term) − $(10)^2 = 645 - 100 = 545$,

4th term = (3rd term) − $(8)^2 = 545 - 64 = 481$,

5 th term = (4 th term) − $(6)^2 = 481 - 36 = 445$.

∴ 440 is wrong.

85.   2nd term = (1st term − 30) ÷ 2 = $\dfrac{(1050 - 30)}{2} = 510$,

3rd term = (2nd term − 26) ÷ 2 = $\left(\dfrac{510 - 26}{2}\right) = 242$,

4 th term = (3rd term − 22) ÷ 2 = $\left(\dfrac{242 - 22}{2}\right) = 110$.

∴ 106 is wrong.

86.   2nd term = (1st term × 2 − 2) = $(5 \times 2 - 2) = 8$,

3 rd term = (2nd term × 3 − 2) = $(8 \times 3 - 2) = 22$,

4 th term = (3rd term × 2 − 2) = $(22 \times 2 - 2) = 42$,

5 th term = (4 th term × 3 − 2) = $(42 \times 3 - 2) = 124$ and so on.

∴ 20 is wrong.

87.   2nd term = (1st term × 1.5) = $2 \times 1.5 = 3$,

3rd term = (2nd term × 2) = $3 \times 2 = 6$,

4th term = (3rd term × 2.5) = $6 \times 2.5 = 15$,

5th term = (4th term × 3) = $15 \times 3 = 45$.

∴ 52.5 is wrong.

88.   2nd term = $\left(\dfrac{1\text{st term} - 8}{2}\right) = \left(\dfrac{888 - 8}{2}\right) = 440$,

3rd term = $\left(\dfrac{2\text{nd term} - 8}{2}\right) = \left(\dfrac{440 - 8}{2}\right) = 216$,

4th term = $\left(\dfrac{3\text{rd term} - 8}{2}\right) = \left(\dfrac{216 - 8}{2}\right) = 104$,

5 th term = $\left(\dfrac{4\text{th term} - 8}{2}\right) = \left(\dfrac{104 - 8}{2}\right) = 48$,

6th term = $\left(\dfrac{5\text{ th term} - 8}{2}\right) = \left(\dfrac{48 - 8}{2}\right) = 20$.

∴ 22 is wrong.

89.   2nd term = (1st term × 1 + 2) = $(4 \times 1 + 2) = 6$,

3rd term = (2nd term × 2 + 3) = $(6 \times 2 + 3) = 15$,

4th term = (3rd term × 3 + 4) = $(15 \times 3 + 4) = 49$,

5th term = (4th term × 4 + 5) = $(49 \times 4 + 5) = 201$ and so on.

∴ 5 is wrong.

33. Data Interpretation

Tabulation : In studying problems on statistics, the data collected by the investigator are arranged in a systematic form, called the **tabular form.** In order to avoid same heads again and again, we make tables, consisting of horizontal lines, called **rows** and vertical lines, called **columns** with distinctive heads, known as **captions.** Units of measurements are given along with the captions.

Solved Problems

Ex. 1. *The table given below shows the population, literates and illiterates (in thousands) and the percentage of literacy in three states, in a year :*

State	Population	Literates	Illitrates	Percentage of Literacy
Madras	49342	6421	......	......
Bombay	......	4068	16790	......
Bengal	60314	......	......	16.1

After reading the table, mark a tick (√) against the correct answer in each question given below and hence complete the table.

1. Percentage of literacy in Madras is :
   (a) 14.9%   (b) 13.01%   (c) 12.61%   (d) 15.04%
2. Percentage of literacy in Bombay is :
   (a) 19.5%   (b) 16.7%   (c) 18.3%   (d) 14.6%
3. Number of literates in Bengal (in thousands) is :
   (a) 50599   (b) 9715   (c) 76865   (d) 9475

Answers & Solutions

1. (b) : Percentage of literacy in Madras
$$= \left(\frac{6421}{49342} \times 100 \right) \% = 13.01\%.$$

2. (a) : Population of Bombay = (4068 + 16790) thousands
$$= 20858 \text{ thousands.}$$
   ∴ Percentage of literacy in Bombay

$$= \left(\frac{4068}{20858} \times 100 \right) \% = 19.5\%.$$

3. (b) : Number of literates in Bengal $= \left(\frac{16.1}{100} \times 60314 \right) = 9715$ thousands.

emark : Number of illiterates in Bengal
$$= (60314 - 9715) \text{ thousands} = 50599 \text{ thousands}.$$
Filling these entries, the complete table is given below.

Table

State	Population (in thousands)	Literates (in thousands)	Illiterates (in thousands)	Percentage of Literacy
Madras	49342	6421	42921	13.01%
Bombay	20858	4068	16790	19.5%
Bengal	60314	9715	50599	16.1%

Ex. 2. *The following table shows the production of food grains (in nillion tonnes) in a state for the period from 1989–90 to 1993—94.*

Year	Production in Million Tonnes				Total
	Wheat	*Rice*	*Maize*	*Other cereals*	
1989 – 90	580	170	150	350	1350
1990 – 91	600	220	234	400	1474
1991 – 92	560	240	228	420	1538
1992 – 93	680	300	380	460	1660
1993 – 94	860	260	340	500	1910
Total	3280	1190	1332	2130	7932

Read the above table and mark ($\sqrt{}$) against the correct answer in each of the following questions :

1. During the period from 1989 – 90 to 1993 – 94, what percent of the total production is the wheat ?
   (a) 42.6%   (b) 43.1%   (c) 41.3%   (d) 40.8%
2. During the year 1993 – 94, the percentage increase in production of wheat over the previous year was :
   (a) 26.4%   (b) 20.9%   (c) 23.6%   (d) 18.7%
3. In the year 1992 – 93, the increase in production was maximum for :
   (a) wheat   (b) rice   (c) maize   (d) other cereals
4. During 1991 – 92, the percentage of decrease in the production of maize was :
   (a) 2.63%   (b) 2.56%   (c) 2.71%   (d) 2.47%
5. The increase in the production of other cereals was minimum during the year :
   (a) 1990 – 91   (b) 1991 – 92   (c) 1992 – 93   (d) 1993 – 94

Answers & Solutions

1. (c) : Total production = 7932 million tonnes.
Wheat production = 3280 million tonnes.
$$\text{Required percentage} = \left(\frac{3280}{7932} \times 100\right)\% = 41.3\%.$$

2. (a) : Production of wheat in 1993 – 94 = 860 million tonnes
Production of wheat in 1992 – 93 = 680 million tonnes
$$\therefore \text{ Increase } \% = \left[\frac{860 - 680}{680} \times 100\right]\% = \left(\frac{180}{680} \times 100\right)\% = 26.4\%.$$

3. (c) : It is clear from the table that during the year 1992 – 93, the increase in the production of wheat, rice, maize and other cereals is
(680 – 560) = 120, (300 – 240) = 60, (380 – 228) = 152
and (460 – 420) = 40 million tonnes respectively. Clearly, increase in maize production is maximum.

4. (b) : Production of maize in 1991 – 92 = 228 million tonnes
Production of maize in 1990 – 91 = 234 million tonnes
$$\text{Decrease in production} = \left(\frac{6}{234} \times 100\right)\% = 2.56\%.$$

5. (b) : Increase in production of other cereals over previous year was 50, 20, 40 and 40 million tonnes during 1990 – 91, 1991 – 92, 1992 – 93 & 1993 – 94 respectively.
So, it is minimum in 1991 – 92.

Ex. 3. *Study the table given below and answer the questions given below it :*
(Bank P.O. 1990)

Number of Employees Working In Various Departments of a Factory

Year	Departments (Number of employees)				
	Production	*Sales*	*Purchase*	*Accounts*	*Research*
1989	150	25	50	45	75
1990	225	40	45	62	70
1991	450	65	30	90	73
1992	470	73	32	105	70
1993	500	80	35	132	74
1994	505	75	36	130	75

1. In which year, the total number of employees reached approximately twice the total number of employees the factory had in the year 1989?
(a) 1994   (b) 1993   (c) 1992   (d) 1991

2. In which department the number of employees approximately remained the same during the years 1989 to 1994 ?

(a) Production   (b) Sales   (c) Research   (d) Accounts
3.   In which year the number of employees working in production department was less than 50% of the total employees ?
(a) 1989   (b) 1991   (c) 1992   (d) 1993
4.   In which of the following years each department had more number of employees than it had in the immediately preceding year ?
(a) 1993   (b) 1992   (c) 1991   (d) 1990
5.   Which department had less than 10% of the total employees all through the years 1989 to 1994 ?
(a) Purchase   (b) Sales   (c) Accounts   (d) Research

Answers & Solutions

1. (d) : Total number of employees in various years are :
1989 → 345, 1990 → 442, 1991 → 708, 1992 → 750,
1993 → 821, 1994 → 821.
Employees in 1989 = 345
∴ Number in 1991 is twice the number in 1989.
2. (c) : Clearly, the number of employees approximately remained the same in research department.
3. (a) : In 1989, th number of employees in production was 150 while the total
number of employees was 345.
Clearly, 150 < 50% of 345.
4. (a) : Clearly, in 1993 the factory had more number of employees in each department than it had in 1992.
5. (b) : Clearly, sales department had less than 10% of the total employees all through the years 1989 to 1994.

Ex. 4. *Study the following table carefully and answer the questions given below it.*   (S.B.I. P.O., 1988)

Number of boys of standard XI participating in different games

Games \ Class	XI A	XI B	XI C	XI D	XI E	TOTAL
Chess	8	8	8	4	4	32
Badminton	8	12	8	12	12	52
Table tennis	12	16	12	8	12	60
Hockey	8	4	8	4	8	32
Football	8	8	12	12	12	52
Total No. of Boys	44	48	48	40	48	228

Note : (i) Every student (boy or girl) of each class of standard XI partcipates in a game (*ii*) In each class, the number of girls participating in each game is 25% of the number of boys participating in each game.

(*iii*) Each student (boy or girl) participates in one and only one game.

1. All the boys of class XI *D* passed at the annual examination but a few girls failed. If all the boys and girls who passed and entered class XII *D* and if in class XII *D*, the ratio of boys to girls is 5 : 1, what would be the number of girls who failed in class XI *D* ?

   (*a*) 8   (*b*) 5   (*c*) 2   (*d*) 1
   (*e*) None of these

2. Girls playing which of the following games need to be combined to yield a ratio of boys to girls of 4 : 1, if all boys playing Chess and Badminton are combined ?

   (*a*) Table Tennis and Hockey   (*b*) Badminton and Table Tennis
   (*c*) Chess and Hockey   (*d*) Hockey and Football
   (*e*) None of these

3. What should be the total number of students in the school if all the boys of class XI *A* together with all the girls of class XI *B* and class XI *C* were to be equal to 25% of the total number of students ?

   (*a*) 272   (*b*) 560   (*c*) 656   (*d*) 340
   (*e*) None of these

4. Boys of which of the following classes need to be combined to equal to four times the number of girls in class XI *B* and XI *C* ?

   (*a*) XI *D* and XI *E*   (*b*) XI *A* and XI *B*
   (*c*) XI *A* and XI *E*   (*d*) XI *A* and XI *D*
   (*e*) None of these

5. If boys of class XI *E* participating in Chess together with girls of class XI *B* and XI *C* participating in Table tennis and Hockey respectively are selected for a course at the college of sports, what percent of the students will get this advantage approximately ?

   (*a*) 4.38   (*b*) 3.51   (*c*) 10.52   (*d*) 13.5
   (*e*) None of these

6. If for social work, every boy of class XI *D* and class XI *C* is paired with a girl of the same class, what percentage of the boys of these two classes cannot participate in social work ?

   (*a*) 88   (*b*) 66   (*c*) 60   (*d*) 75
   (*e*) None of these

Answers & Solutions

1. (*c*) : Number of boys in XI *D* = 40
   Number of girls in XI *D* = 25% of 40 = 10.
   As all boys in XI *D* passed, so number of boys in XII *D* = 40.
   Ratio of boys and girls in XII *D* is 5 : 1.

$\therefore$ Number of girls in XII $D = \left(\dfrac{1}{5} \times 40\right) = 8$.

Number of girls failed in XI $D = (10 - 8) = 2$.

2. (d) : Number of boys playing Chess & Badminton = $(32 + 52) = 84$.

Number of girls playing hockey & football

$$= 25\% \text{ of } 84 = \left(\dfrac{25}{100} \times 84\right) = 21.$$

Required ratio = $84 : 21 = 4 : 1$.

3. (a) : Number of boys in XI $A = 44$,

Number of girls in XI $B = 25\%$ of $48 = 12$,

Number of girls in XI $C = 25\%$ of $48 = 12$.

Let total number of students $= x$.

$\therefore$ 25% of $x = (44 + 12 + 12)$ or $\dfrac{25x}{100} = 68$ or $x = 272$.

$\therefore$ Total number of students in the school is 272.

4. (e) : 4 times the number of girls in XI B & XI $C = 4\,(12 + 12) = 96$.

But, none of the pairs of classes given through (a) to (d) has this as the number of boys.

5. (b) : Number of boys of XI E playing chess = 4 ;

Number of girls of XI B playing table tennis = 25% of $16 = 4$;

Number of girls of XI C playing hockey = 25% of $8 = 2$.

Number of those selected at the college of sports = $(4 + 4 + 2) = 10$.

Total number of students = $(228 + 25\% \text{ of } 228) = 285$.

Let $x\%$ of $285 = 10$. Then, $x = \left(\dfrac{10 \times 100}{285}\right) = 3.51$.

6. (d) : Number of girls = 25% of the number of boys.

$\therefore$ 25% of the boys can participate in social work.

$\therefore$ 75% of the boys cannot participate in social work.

Ex. 5. Study the following table carefully and answer the questions given below it :

(Bank P.O. 1994)

Number of candidates appeared (App.) and percentage of candidates qualified (Qual.) under different disciplines over the years.

Year	Arts		Commerce		Science		Engineering		Agriculture	
	App.	Qual%	App.	Qual%	App.	Qual%	App.	Qual%	App.	Qual%
1986	842	29	908	21	1928	40	579	45	843	42
1987	1019	27	878	28	2028	38	608	38	719	36
1988	985	31	1156	31	2536	42	492	42	645	41
1989	1215	28	1290	32	2113	45	714	55	720	39
1990	1429	34	1025	24	1725	36	801	48	586	48
1991	1128	24	1416	35	1820	39	726	51	620	35

1. Approximately, what was the percentage decrease in the number of candidates appeared under Arts discipline from 1990 to 1991.
   (*a*) 40   (*b*) 10   (*c*) 20   (*d*) 25   (*e*) 35

2. Approximately, how many candidates qualified under Science discipline in 1989 ?
   (*a*) 950   (*b*) 1050   (*c*) 650   (*d*) 1000   (*e*) 850

3. In which of the following pairs of years was approximately the number of candidates qualified under Agriculture discipline the same ?
   (*a*) 1986 and 1989   (*b*) 1987 and 1991
   (*c*) 1988 and 1990   (*d*) 1989 and 1991
   (*e*) 1989 and 1990

4. Approximately what was the percentage increase in the number of candidates qualified under Commerce discipline, from 1987 to 1991 ?
   (*a*) 80   (*b*) 200   (*c*) 150   (*d*) 100   (*e*) 50

5. In which of the following pairs of years was the total number of candidates appeared under Arts discipline exactly equal to the number of candidates appeared under Science discipline in 1989 ?
   (*a*) 1988 and 1990   (*b*) 1988 and 1991
   (*c*) 1989 and 1990   (*d*) 1987 and 1991
   (*e*) 1986 and 1990

Answers & Solutions

1. (*c*) : Candidates appeared in arts in 1990 = 1429
   Candidates appeared in arts in 1991 = 1128 .
   Decrease % $= \left(\dfrac{301}{1429} \times 100 \right) \% = 21.06 = 20 \%$ (approximately).

2. (*a*) : Candidates qualified in Science in 1989 $= \left(\dfrac{45}{100} \times 2113 \right) = 950$.

3. (*e*) : Candidates qualified in Agriculture in various years :
   In 1986 $\rightarrow \left(\dfrac{42}{100} \times 843 \right) = 354$;   In 1987 $\rightarrow \left(\dfrac{36}{100} \times 719 \right) = 258$;
   In 1988 $\rightarrow \left(\dfrac{41}{100} \times 645 \right) = 264$;   In 1989 $\rightarrow \left(\dfrac{39}{100} \times 720 \right) = 280$;
   In 1990 $\rightarrow \left(\dfrac{48}{100} \times 586 \right) = 281$; In 1991 $\rightarrow \left(\dfrac{35}{100} \times 620 \right) = 217$.
   Clearly, it is the same in 1989 and 1990.

4. (*d*) : Candidates qualified in Commerce in 1987 $= \left(\dfrac{28}{100} \times 878 \right) = 245$.

Candidates qualified in Commerce in 1991 $= \left(\dfrac{35}{100} \times 1416 \right) = 495$.

Increase $\% = \left(\dfrac{250}{245} \times 100 \right) \% = 100\%$ (nearly).

5. (b) : Candidates appeared in Science discipline in 1989 = 2113.

Total number of candidates appeared in arts in 1988 and 1991
$$= 2113.$$

EXERCISE 33A (Solved)

Directions (Questions 1 to 5) : *The following table shows the courier charges for sending 1 kg parcel from one city to another. Study the table carefully and answer the questions that follow.*   *(Assistant Grade 1993)*

Cities \ Cities	A	B	C	D	E
A	–	10	5	15	10
B	–	–	7	25	20
C	–	–	–	20	15
D	–	–	–	–	10
E	–	–	–	–	–

1. Among the following, the charges will be the least for sending parcel from :
   (*i*) A to E   (*ii*) B to D   (*iii*) E to D   (*iv*) C to B
   (*a*) (i)   (*b*) (ii)   (*c*) (iii)   (*d*) (iv)

2. For sending parcel from the city C, the least charges will be for city.
   (*a*) A   (*b*) B   (*c*) D   (*d*) E

3. For which one of the following will the charges be different from the other three ?
   (i) B to A   (ii) A to E   (iii) D to E   (iv) D to B
   (*a*) (i)   (*b*) (ii)   (*c*) (iii)   (*d*) (iv)

4. B city is nearest to :
   (*a*) A   (*b*) C   (*c*) C   (*d*) E

5. Cost of sending parcel from city B to A and then A to E is :
   (*a*) Rs 15   (*b*) Rs 17   (*c*) Rs 20   (*d*) Rs 25

Directions (Questions 6 to 10) : *A table showing the percentage of the total population of a state in different age groups is given below :*

(Assistant Grade 1992)

Age Group	Percent
Upto 15	30.00
16 – 25	17.75
26 – 35	17.25
36 – 45	14.50
46 – 55	14.25
56 – 65	05.12
66 and above	01.13
Total	100.00

Study the table and answer the questions given below :

6. Which one of the age groups listed below accounts for the maximum population in the state :
   (a) 16–25　　　　(b) 26–25　　　(c) 36–45　　　(d) 56–65
   (e) None of these

7. Out of every 4200, the number of persons below 25 years is :
   (a) 2005 (approx.)　　　　　　(b) 1260 (approx.)
   (c) 746　(approx.)　　　　　　(d) 515　(approx.)

8. There are 200 million people below 36 years. How many million people (approx.) are in the age group 56-65 ?
   (a) 30.07　　　　(b) 15.75　　　(c) 12.72　　　(d) 59.30

9. If there are 10 million people in the age group 56 and above, what is the difference between the total number of people in the age group 16–25 and 46–55 ?
   (a) 6.8 million (approx.)　　　　(b) 5.6 million (approx.)
   (c) 28.4 million (approx.)　　　　(d) 34.7 million (approx.)

10. If the difference between the number of people in the age groups 46–55 and 26–35 is 11.75 million, then the total population of the state is :
    (a) 400 million (approx.)　　　　(b) 391.67 million (approx.)
    (c) 360 million (approx.)　　　　(d) 460 million (approx.)

Directions (Questions 11 to 15) : *Study the following table and answer questions 11 to 15 given below it*　　　　*(Bank P.O. 1991)*

Source of income	Employees				
	K	L	M	N	O
Salary	12000	6000	21000	9000	12000
Bonus	2400	1200	4500	2400	3000

Overtime	5400	2100	6000	5100	6000
Arrears	6000	5400	12000	4200	7500
Miscellaneous	1200	300	1500	300	1500
Total	27000	15000	45000	21000	30000

11. Who among the following employees has minimum ratio of income from arrears to income from salary ?
    (a) K   (b) L   (c) M   (d) N   (e) O
12. Who among the following employees earns maximum bonus in comparison to his total income ?
    (a) K   (b) L   (c) M   (d) N   (e) O
13. Who among the following employees has maximum percentage of his salary out of the total income ?
    (a) K   (b) L   (c) M   (d) N   (e) O
14. How many employees have their salary less than four times the income from bonus ?
    (a) 0   (b) 1   (c) 2   (d) 3   (e) 4
15. The income from overtime is what percent of the income from arrears in case of employees in category O ?
    (a) 8   (b) 25   (c) 20   (d) 125   (e) None

    Directions (Questions 16 to 20) : *Study the following table carefully and answer the questions given below it.*

    Total Number (in thousands) of different types of toys produced and percentage defect under each type in a factory over the years.

                                                                    (Bank P.O. 1993)

year	A		B		C		D		E	
	Number Produced	Percentage Defect	Number Produced	Percentage Defect	Number Produced	Percentage Defect	Number Produced	Percentage Defect	Number produced	Percentage defect
1986	64	12	75	20	45	08	85	14	48	18
1987	80	08	90	12	30	09	95	16	94	14
1988	40	06	65	16	55	06	75	12	84	05
1989	95	09	80	18	25	05	70	10	78	09
1990	75	14	60	19	40	07	65	13	62	11
1991	112	16	55	15	60	04	80	15	37	10

16. What was the approximate number of E type toys without defect in the year 1988 ?
    (a) 60,000   (b) 80,000   (c) 82,000   (d) 76,000
    (e) 78,000

17. What was the difference in the production of D type toys without defect between 1989 and 1991 ?
    (*a*) 10,000   (*b*) 5000   (*c*) 6,000   (*d*) 8,000
    (*e*) None of these

18. What was the percentage increase in production of C type toys from 1989 to 1990 ?
    (*a*) 40   (*b*) 160   (*c*) 20   (*d*) 60
    (*e*) None of these

19. What was the approximate number of defective A type toys in the year 1991 ?
    (*a*) 18,000   (*b*) 12,000   (*c*) 15,000   (*d*) 24,000
    (*e*) 16,000

20. In the case of which of the following types of toys was the average percentage defect over the given years the minimum among all the types?
    (*a*) A   (*b*) B   (*c*) C   (*d*) D   (*e*) E

Directions (Questions 21 to 26) : *Study the following table carefully and answer the questions given below.*

Loan Disbursed By Five Banks
(Rupees in crores)

Banks	Year				
	1990	1991	1992	1993	1994
A	18	23	45	30	70
B	27	33	18	41	37
C	29	29	22	17	11
D	31	16	28	32	43
E	13	19	27	34	42
Total	118	120	140	154	203

21. In which year was the disbursement of loans of all the banks put together least compared to the average disbursement of loans over the years ?
    (*a*) 1990   (*b*) 1991   (*c*) 1992   (*d*) 1993
    (*e*) 1994

22. What was the percentage increase of disbursement of loans of all banks together from 1992 to 1993 ?
    (*a*) 110   (*b*) 14   (*c*) 10   (*d*) $90\frac{10}{11}$
    (*e*) None

23. In which year was the total disbursement of loans of the banks A and B exactly equal to the total disbursement of banks D and E ?

(a) 1991   (b) 1992   (c) 1990   (d) 1994
(e) None of these

24. In which of the following banks did the disbursement of loans continuously increase over the years ?
    (a) A   (b) B   (c) C   (d) D   (e) E

25. If the minimum target in the preceding years was 20% of the total disbursement of loans, how many banks reached the target in 1991 ?
    (a) 1   (b) 2   (c) 3   (d) 4   (e) None

26. In which bank was loan disbursement more than 25% of the disbursement of all bank together in 1994 ?
    (a) A   (b) B   (c) C   (d) D   (e) E

Solutions & Answers

1. (d) : Charges are :
   A to E = 10, B to D = 25, E to D = D to E = 10,
   C to B = B to C = 7.
   ∴ Charges from C to B are the least.

2. (a) : Charges from C to :
   A → 5, B = 7, D → 20, E → 15
   ∴ Least charges are for city A.

3. (d) : Charges are :
   B to A → 10, A to E → 10, D to E → 10, D to B → 25.
   So, they are different for D to B.

4. (b) : Charges from B to :
   A → 10, C → 7, D → 25, E → 20.
   ∴ B is nearest to C.

5. (c) : Required charges = Rs (10 + 10) = Rs 20 .

6. (e) : Clearly, the maximum population consists of persons in the age group upto 15 years.

7. (a) : Number of persons below 25 years out of 4200
   $$=\left[\frac{(30+17.75)}{100}\times 4200\right]=2005 \text{ (approx.)}$$

8. (b) : Let total population be x.
   Then, $\dfrac{30+17.75+17.25}{100}\times x = 200$ million.
   $$\Rightarrow x=\left(\frac{200\times 100}{65}\right)\text{million}=\left(\frac{4000}{13}\right)\text{million.}$$
   People in age group 56–65 $=\left(\dfrac{5.12}{100}\times\dfrac{4000}{13}\right)$ million = 15.75 million.

9. (b) : Let total population = x. Then,

$$\frac{5.12 + 1.13}{100} \times x = 10 \text{ million} \Rightarrow x = \left(\frac{10 \times 100}{6.25}\right) \text{ million}$$

$$= 160 \text{ million.}$$

Diff. in age groups 16–25 & 46–55 = $(17.75 - 14.25)$ % of 160

$$= \left(\frac{3.5}{100} \times 160\right) \text{million} = 5.6 \text{ million.}$$

10. (*b*) : Let total population = x.. Then,

$$\frac{17.25 - 14.25}{100} \times x = 11.75 \text{ million.}$$

or $x = \left(\dfrac{11.75 \times 100}{3}\right) = 391.67 \text{ million}$

11. (*d*) : Ratio of income from arrears to income from salary :

$$K \to \frac{6000}{12000} = \frac{1}{2} = 0.5, \ L \to \frac{5400}{6000} = \frac{9}{10} = 0.9 , \ M \to \frac{12000}{21000} = \frac{4}{7} = 0.57,$$

$$N \to \frac{4200}{9000} = \frac{7}{15} = 0.46, \ O \to \frac{7500}{12000} = \frac{5}{8} = 0.625$$

The ratio is clearly minimum in case of N.

12. (*d*) : The ratio of bonus and total income is :

$$K \to \frac{2400}{27000} = \frac{4}{45} = 0.08, \ L \to \frac{1200}{15000} = \frac{2}{25} = 0.08 ,$$

$$M \to \frac{4500}{45000} = \frac{1}{10} = 0.1 , \ N \to \frac{2400}{21000} = \frac{4}{35} = 0.11, \ O \to \frac{3000}{30000} = 0.1$$

Clearly, it is maximum in case of N.

13. (*c*) : Percentage of salary out of total income is :

$$K \to \left(\frac{12000}{27000} \times 100\right) = 44.4 \ \%, \ L \to \left(\frac{6000}{15000} \times 100\right) = 40 \ \%,$$

$$M \to \left(\frac{21000}{45000} \times 100\right) = 46.6 \ \%, \ N \to \left(\frac{9000}{21000} \times 100\right) = 42.8 \ \%,$$

$$O \to \left(\frac{12000}{30000} \times 100\right) = 40 \ \% .$$

Clearly, it is maximum for M.

14. (*b*) : [$(4 \times \text{Bonus})$ – salary] is equal to :

K $\to$ $(9600 - 12000) < 0$, L $\to$ $(4800 - 6000) < 0$,

M = $(18000 - 21000) < 0$

N $\to$ $(9600 - 9000) > 0$, O $\to$ $(12000 - 12000) = 0$.

∴ Salary is less than 4 times bonus in case of N.

15. (*e*) : For employee O :

$$\text{Required percentage} = \left(\frac{6000}{7500} \times 100\right) \% = 80 \ \% .$$

16. (*b*) : Required number = 95 % of 84000.

$$= \left(\frac{95}{100} \times 84000 \right) = 79800 = 80000 \quad (\text{App.})$$

17. (*b*) : D type toys without defect in 1989 = 90 % of 70000 = 63000.
D type toys without defect in 1991 = 85% of 80000 = 68000.
Difference = (68000 − 63000) = 5000.

18. (*d*) : Production of C type toys in 1989 = 25000
Production of C type toys in 1990 = 40000

$$\text{Increase } \% = \left(\frac{15000}{25000} \times 100 \right) = 60 \%.$$

19. (*a*) : Defective A type toys in 1991 $= \left(\frac{16}{100} \times 112000 \right) = 17920$

$$= 18000 \text{ (approximately).}$$

20. (*c*) : Average percentage defect :

$$A \to \left(\frac{65}{6} \right) = 10.8 , \quad B \to \left(\frac{100}{6} \right) = 16.6, \quad C \to \left(\frac{39}{6} \right) = 6.5$$

$$D \to \left(\frac{80}{6} \right) = 13.3 , \quad E \to \left(\frac{67}{6} \right) = 11.1.$$

Clearly, it is minimum for C.

21. (*a*) : Average disbursement of loans $= \frac{1}{5} (118 + 120 + 140 + 154 + 203)$

$$= 147 \text{ crores.}$$

Clearly, it is least in the year 1990.

22. (*c*) : Increase of loans from 1992 to 1993

$$= \left[\frac{(154 - 140)}{140} \times 100 \right] \% = 10 \%.$$

23. (*e*) : In none of the years, the sum of loans of A and B is equal to the sum of loans of D and E.

24. (*e*) : In bank E, the disbursement of loans continuously increase over the years.

25. (*b*) : 20% of total loans disbursed in 1990 = (20 % of 118) = 23.6 crores.
B and C reached the target in 1991.

26. (*a*) : In 1994, 25% of total disbursement = (25 % of 203) = 50.75 crores.
In Bank A, the loan disbursed is more than 25% of the total disbursement of all banks in 1994.

BAR GRAPHS & PIE DIAGRAMS

Ex. 1 (Questions 1 to 5) : *Study the graph carefully and answer the questions given below it :* **(Bank P.O. 1993)**

Percentages Of Villages Which Are Not Electrified

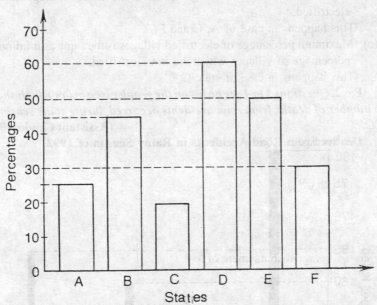

1. If the Central Government desires to give aid for speedy electrification starting from states with least electrification, which state will get fourth rank in the order of priority ?
   (a) C   (b) B   (c) A   (d) E   (e) F

2. Which state has twice the percentage of villages electrified in comparison to state D ?
   (a) C   (b) F   (c) A   (d) B   (e) E

3. In case of state B, what percent of villages are electrified ?
   (a) 65   (b) 25   (c) 45   (d) 55   (e) 75

4. How many states have at least 60% or more electrified villages ?
   (a) 5   (b) 3   (c) 4   (d) 2   (e) 1

5. Which state has the maximum percentage of electrified villages ?
   (a) A   (b) B   (c) C   (d) D   (e) E

Answers & Solutions

1. (e) : The states from least to greatest electrification are D, E, B, F, A and C.

∴ Fourth rank goes to F.

2. (*a*) : In state D, 40% of the villages are electrified. Clearly, 80% of the villages are electrified in state C.

3. (*d*) : In case of state B, 45% of villages are not electrified. So, 55% of the villages are electrified.

4. (*b*) : 60% or more electrified villages means less than 40% villages not electrified.

This happens in case of A, C and F.

5. (*c*) : Maximum percentage of electrified villages is the same as minimum percentage of villages which are not electrified.

This happens in case of state C.

Ex. 2. *Questions 1 to 4 are based on the graph given below which shows the number of deaths from road accidents occurred during rainy season of 1992.*   **(Assistant Grade, 1994)**

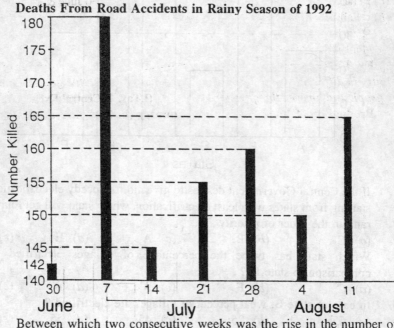

Deaths From Road Accidents in Rainy Season of 1992

1.   Between which two consecutive weeks was the rise in the number of deaths greatest ?

    (*a*) 30 June – 7 July   (*b*) 14 July – 21 July

    (*c*) 4 August – 11 August   (*d*) 21 July – 28 July

2.   In how many weeks were there more than 150 deaths ?

    (*a*) 1   (*b*) 2   (*c*) 3   (*d*) 4

3.   In how many weeks were there less than 150 deaths ?

    (*a*) 0   (*b*) 1   (*c*) 2   (*d*) 3

4. Between which two consecutive weeks was the fall in the number of deaths greatest ?
(a) 30 June – 7 July   (b) 7 July – 14 July
(c) 28 July – 4 August   (d) None of these

Answers & Solutions

1. (a) : Rise in deaths between (30 June – 7 July) = (180 – 142) = 38.
Rise in deaths between (14 July – 21 July) = (155 – 145) = 10 .
Rise in deaths between (21 July – 28 July) = (160 – 155) = 5 .
Rise in deaths between (4 August – 11 August) = (165 – 150) = 15 .
∴ Rise in deaths between (30 June – 7 July) is greatest.

2. (d) : During 4 weeks there were more than 150 deaths. These weeks end on 7 July, 21 July, 28 July and 11 August.

3. (c) : There are less than 150 deaths during weeks ending 30 June & 14 July.

4. (b) : Fall between (7 July – 14 July) = (180 – 145) = 35 .
Fall between (28 July – 4 August) = (160 – 150) = 10 .
Fall is greatest between (7 July – 14 July).

Ex. 3. *The graph, given here, shows the production of foodgrains of a country in different years . Questions 1 to 4 are based on this graph. Study the graph and answer the questions.* (I.Tax. & Central Excise 1993)

Production of Food Grains in a Country (in thousand tonnes)

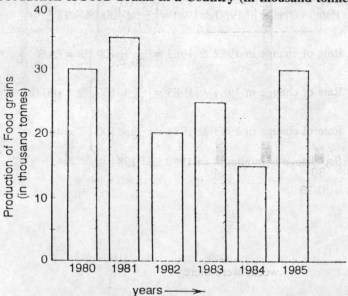

1. The sum of the production of foodgrains in the year 1982 and 1984 is equal to that in the year :
(a) 1980   (b) 1981   (c) 1983   (d) 1985

2. The difference of the production of foodgrains for the years 1981 and 1985 is

   (a) 500 tonnes   (b) 1000 tonnes (c) 5000 tonnes (d) 10000 tonnes

3. The percentage increase in production from 1984 to 1985 was :

   (a) 15   (b) 30   (c) 50   (d) 100

4. The two consecutive years in which rate of change of production of foodgrains is minimum are :

   (a) 1980 and 1981   (b) 1982 and 1983

   (c) 1984 and 1985   (d) 1983 and 1984

Answers & Solutions

1. (b) : Sum of production in 1982 and 1984 = (20 + 15) = 35 thousand tonnes
= Production in the year 1981.

2. (c) : Difference of production in 1981 & 1985 = (35 − 30) thousand tonnes
= 5000 tonnes.

3. (d) : Production in 1984 = 15000 tonnes.
Production in 1985 = 30000 tonnes.

Increase % $= \left(\dfrac{15000}{15000} \times 100 \right) \% = 100 \%$.

4. (a) : Rate of change in 1980 & 1981 $= \left(\dfrac{5}{30} \times 100 \right) \% = 16 \dfrac{2}{3} \%$.

Rate of change in 1982 & 1983 $= \left(\dfrac{5}{20} \times 100 \right) \% = 25 \%$.

Rate of change in 1984 & 1985 $= \left(\dfrac{15}{15} \times 100 \right) \% = 100 \%$.

Rate of change in 1983 & 1984 $= \left(\dfrac{10}{25} \times 100 \right) \% = 40 \%$.

So, change is minimum in 1980 and 1981.

Ex. 4. *Study the figure given below and answer questions 1 to 3.*

(Hotel Management 1991)

Foreign Exchange Reserves

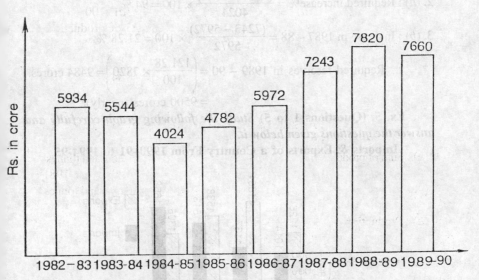

1. The maximum percentage change in the foreign exchange reserves took place during the year :

    (*a*) 1985 – 86   (*b*) 1986 – 87   (*c*) 1988 – 89   (*d*) 1984 – 85

2. Compared to the lowest foreign exchange reserves in any one year, the foreign exchange reserves in 1988 – 89 increased by nearly :

    (*a*) 47%   (*b*) 82 %   (*c*) 94 %   (*d*) 97 %

3. If the reserves had increased in the full 1989 – 90 year at the rates at which they increased in 1987 – 88, it would have been nearly :

    (*a*) Rs 10,500 crore   (*b*) Rs. 9,500 crore

    (*c*) Rs 8,700 crore   (*d*) Rs. 12,000 croe

Answers & Solutions

1. (*d*) : Percentage change in :

$$1985 - 1986 = \frac{(4782 - 4024)}{4024} \times 100 = 18.84 \% .$$

$$1986 - 1987 = \frac{(5972 - 4782)}{4782} \times 100 = 24.88 \% .$$

$$1988 - 1989 = \frac{(7820 - 7243)}{7243} \times 100 = 7.97 \% .$$

$$1984 - 1985 = \frac{(5544 - 4024)}{5544} \times 100 = 27.42 \%.$$

So, maximum percentage change took place in 1984 – 85.

2. (*a*) : Required increase% $= \dfrac{(7820 - 4024)}{4024} \times 100 = 94 \%.$

3. (*b*) : Increase in 1987 – 88 $= \dfrac{(7243 - 5972)}{5972} \times 100 = 21.28 \%.$

$\therefore$ Required reserves in 1989 – 90 $= \left(\dfrac{121.28}{100} \times 7820 \right) = 9484$ crores.

$= 9500$ crores (nearly).

Ex. 5. (Questions 1 to 5) *Study the following graph carefully and answer the questions given below it.*

Imports & Exports of a Country From 1990–91 to 1994-95

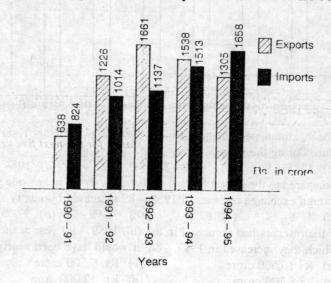

1. The exports in 1993–94 was approximately how many times that of the year 1990 – 91 ?

    (*a*) 0.41   (*b*) 2.41   (*c*) 0.55   (*d*) 1.84

2. In which of the following years was the gap in the imports and exports the least ?

    (*a*) 1990 – 91   (*b*) 1992 – 93   (*c*) 1993 – 94   (*d*) 1994 – 95

3. What is the ratio of years having above average exports to those having below average exports in the given period ?

    (*a*) 3 : 2   (*b*) 4 : 1   (*c*) 2 : 3   (*d*) 1 : 4

4. Which of the following statements is not true about the graph ?

    (*a*) There is a continuous rise in imports.

(b) From 1992 – 93, the export is above average.

(c) Till 1992 – 93, imports is below average.

(d) Total imports in the given period is more than the total exports.

5. The imports in 1994 – 95 is approximately how many percent more than the imports of 1990 – 91 ?

    (a) 49   (b) 50   (c) 201   (d) None of these

Answers & Solutions

1. (b) : Let export in 1993 – 94 = $k \times$ export in 1990 – 91.

$$\therefore k = \frac{\text{Export in 1993–94}}{\text{Export in 1990–91}} = \frac{1538}{638} = 2.41 .$$

2. (c) : Distance between two adjacent bars is minimum in the year 1993 – 94.

3. (a) : Average export $= \left(\frac{638 + 1226 + 1661 + 1538 + 1305}{5} \right) = 1273.6 .$

4. (a) : Clearly, there is a continuous rise in imports.

5. (d) : Import in 1994 – 95 = 1658 crores.

    Import in 1990 – 91 = 824 crores. Excess $= \left(\frac{834}{824} \times 100 \right) \% = 101.2 \%.$

Ex. 6. *The following bar diagram represents the percentages of total expenditure incurred by a state during the years 1981 – 90 for different items. In each bar, the dotted portion stands for the expenditure during the first five years and the remaining portion stands for the next five years.*

Study the above graph and answer questions 1 to 5 (Assistant Grade 1992)

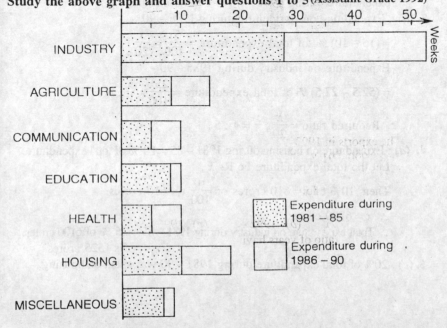

1.   Which of the items listed below accounts for the maximum expenditure during the year 1981 to 1985 ?
     (*a*) Communication (*b*) Education   (*c*) Health   (*d*) Housing
2.   Which of the items listed below accounts for the maximum expenditure during 1986 to 1990 ?
     (*a*) Agriculture (*b*) Communication (*c*) Education (*d*) Health
3.   The amount of expenditure on Agriculture is approximately what proportion of that on industry during the year 1986 – 90 ?
     (*a*) $\dfrac{1}{5}$ (*b*) $\dfrac{1}{4}$ (*c*) $\dfrac{1}{3}$ (*d*) Data inadequate
4.   If the total expenditure on housing is Rs 610 crores during 1981 – 85, the total expenditure on industry during the same period would be (approximately)
     (*a*) Rs 2,440 crores   (*b*) Rs 1,220 crores
     (*c*) Rs 4,620 crores   (*d*) None of these
5.   Out of every 10,000 rupees spent during 1981 – 90 approximately, how much was spent during the years 1981 – 85 on Housing ?
     (*a*) Rs 1,400   (*b*) Rs 700   (*c*) Rs 1000   (*d*) Rs 2,800

Answers & Solutions

1. (*d*) : Out of the items listed in the question, clearly maximum expenditure during 1981 – 85 is on Housing.

2. (*a*) : Out of the items listed in the question, clearly the maximum expenditure during 1986 – 90 is on Agriculture.

3. (*a*) : Expenditure on Agriculture during 1986 – 90
     $= (15 - 10)\ \%$ of total expenditure $= \dfrac{5x}{100} = \dfrac{x}{20}$.

     Expenditure on Industry during 1986 – 90
     $= (52.5 - 27.5)\ \%$ of total expenditure $= \dfrac{25x}{100} = \dfrac{x}{4}$.

     ∴ Required ratio $= \dfrac{x}{20} : \dfrac{x}{4} = 1 : 5$.

4. (*d*) : Expenditure on housing during 1981 – 85 = 10 % of total expenditure.
     Let the total expenditure be Rs x.

     Then, 10% of $x = 610$ crores or $\dfrac{10}{100} x = 610$ crores.

     ∴ $x = 6100$ crores.
     ∴ Total expenditure on industry during 1981 – 85 = 25 % of 6100 crores.
                                                              = Rs 1525 crores.

5. (*c*) : 20% of total expenditure during 1981 – 90 was spent on housing.

∴ Expenditure on housing during 1981 – 90 for a total expenditure

of Rs 10000 $= \left(\dfrac{20}{100} \times 10000 \right) = $ Rs 2000 .

Ratio of expenditure on housing during 1981 – 85.

and that during 1986 – 90 $= \dfrac{10 \%}{(20 - 10) \%} = \dfrac{1}{1}$.

∴ Expenditure on housing during 1981 – 85 = Rs 1000 .

PIE CHARTS or CIRCLE GRAPHS

Ex. 7. *The following pie-diagram shows the expenditure incurred on the preparation of a book by a publisher, under various heads.*

A : Paper 20%   B : Printing 25%

C : Binding, Canvassing, Designing etc 30%

D : Miscellaneous 10%   E : Royalty 15%

Study the diagram carefully and answer questions 1 to 5 :

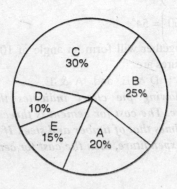

1. What is the angle of pie-diagram showing the expenditure incurred on paying the royalty ?

    (a) 15°   (b) 24°   (c) 48°   (d) 54°

2. The marked price of a book is 20% more than the C.P. If the marked price of the book be Rs 30, what is the cost of paper used in a single copy of the book ?

    (a) Rs 6   (b) Rs 5   (c) Rs 4.50   (d) Rs 6.50

3. Which two expenditures together will form an angle of 108° at the centre of the pie-diagram :

    (a) A and E   (b) B and E   (c) A and D   (d) D and E

4. If the difference between two expenditures be represented by 18° in the pie-diagrm, these expenditures are :

    (*a*) B and E   (*b*) A and C   (*c*) B and D   (*d*) None of these

Answers & Solutions

1. (*d*) Angle representing royalty D= $\left(\dfrac{15}{100} \times 360\right)^{\circ} = 54°$

2. (*b*) : C.P. of a book = Rs $\left(\dfrac{100}{120} \times 30\right)$ = Rs 25 .

    Cost of paper = Rs $\left(\dfrac{20}{100} \times 25\right)$ = Rs 5 .

3. (*c*) : $\angle A = \left(\dfrac{20}{100} \times 360\right)^{\circ} = 72°$, $\angle B = \left(\dfrac{25}{100} \times 360\right)^{\circ} = 90°$,

    $\angle C = \left(\dfrac{30}{100} \times 360\right)^{\circ} = 108°$, $\angle D = \left(\dfrac{10}{100} \times 360\right)^{\circ} = 36°$,

    $\angle E = \left(\dfrac{15}{100} \times 360\right) = 54°$.

Thus, A and D together will form an angle of 108°.

4. (*d*) : These expenditures are :

    A & B ; B & C ; D & E and A & E.

Ex. 8. *The following pie chart indicates the expenditure for construction of a house. The cost for cement is three times that of bricks and for labour is two times that of timber and steel. If the timber and steel cost 20% of the total expenditure, then the cost for cement and labour are respectively :*

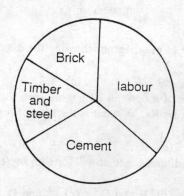

(a) 18% and 24 %   (b) 24 % and 32 %
(c) 30% and 40 %   (d) 45 % and 60 %

Sol. Let total cost be Rs 100.

Cement = 3 × Bricks ; Labour = 2 × (Timber + Steel) .

(Timber + Steel) = Rs 20 .

∴ Labour = (2 × 20) = Rs 40 .

Bricks + Cement = Rs [100 – (20 + 40)] = Rs 40.

∴ Bricks + 3 × Bricks = 40   or   Bricks = Rs 10 .

∴ Cement = (3 × 10) = Rs 30 .

Ex. 9. *The circle graph, drawn here shows the spendings of a country on various sports during a particular year. Study the graph and answer questions 1 to 5.*   **(Assistant Grade 1993)**

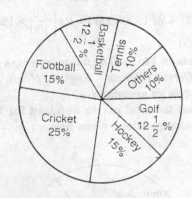

1. The ratio of the total amount spent on football to that spent on hockey is :

(a) 1 : 15   (b) 1 : 1   (c) 15 : 1   (d) 3 : 20

2. If the total amount spent on sports during the year was Rs 1,20,000,00 how much was spent on basketball ?

(a) Rs 9,50,000   (b) Rs 10,00,000
(c) Rs 12,00,000   (d) Rs 15,00,000

3. Graph shows that the most popular game of the country is :

(a) Hockey   (b) Football   (c) Cricket   (d) Tennis

4. Out of the following, the country spent the same amount on :

(a) Hockey and Tennis   (b) Golf and Basketball
(c) Cricket and Football   (d) Hockey and Golf

5. If the total amount spent on sports during the year was Rs 1,50,00,000, the amount spent on cricket and hockey together was :

(a) Rs 60,00,000   (b) Rs 50,00,000
(c) Rs 37,50,000   (d) Rs 25,00,000

Answers & Solutions

1. (b) : Let the total amount spent be Rs 100.

Ratio of amount spent on football and that on hockey = $15 : 15 = 1 : 1$.

2. (d) Money spent on basket ball $= \left(\dfrac{25}{2 \times 100} \times 12000000 \right) = $ Rs 1500000.

3. (c) : Since maximum percentage is spent on cricket, so it is the most popular game.

4. (b) : Since $12\frac{1}{2}$ % of the total spendings are on each one of Golf and Baskeball, so equal amount is spent on these two games.

5. (a) : Amount spent on Cricket and Hockey

$$= [(25 + 15) \text{ \% of } 15000000] = \text{Rs} \left(\dfrac{40}{100} \times 15000000 \right)$$

$$= \text{Rs } 6000000.$$

Ex. 10. (Questions 1 to 5) : *The following graph gives the marks scored by a student in different subjects – English, Hindi, Mathematics, Science and Social Science in an examination.*

Assuming that the total marks obtained for the examination are 540, answer the questions given below :

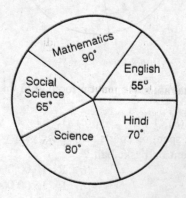

1.   The marks scored in English, Science and Social Science exceed the marks scored in Hindi and Mathematics by :

(a) 10%   (b) $10\frac{1}{9}$%   (c) 11%   (d) $11\frac{1}{9}$%

2. The marks scored in Hindi and Mathematics exceed the marks scored in English and Social Science By :
   (a) 30   (b) 40   (c) 60   (d) 75

3. The subject in which the student scored 105 marks is :
   (a) English   (b) Hindi   (c) Mathematics   (d) Science

4. The subject in which marks obtained are 22.2%, is . ·
   (a) English   (b) Hindi   (c) Science   (d) Mathematics

5. The difference of marks between English and Science is the same as between
   (a) Science and English   (b) Hindi and Social Science
   (c) English and Hindi   (d) Mathematics and Social Science

Answers & Solutions

1. (d) : Total angle representing $[(E + S + S.Sc) - (H + M)]$
$$= [(55 + 80 + 65) - (70 + 90)]° = 40° .$$
$\therefore$ Required percentage $= \left(\dfrac{40}{360} \times 100 \right) \% = 11\dfrac{1}{9} \% .$

2. (c) : Angle representing $[(H + M) - (E + S. Sc.)]$
$$= [(70 + 90) - (55 + 65)]° = 40° .$$
$\therefore$ Required marks $= \left(\dfrac{40}{360} \times 540 \right) = 60 .$

3. (b) : For 540 marks, angle made $= 360°$.
For 105 marks, angle made $= \left(\dfrac{360}{540} \times 105 \right)° = 70°$

Clearly, the concerned subject is Hindi.

4. (c) : For 100% marks, angle made $= 360°$.
For 22.2% marks, angle made $= \left(\dfrac{360}{100} \times 22.2 \right)° = (79.92)° = 80°.$
$\therefore$ The required subject is Science.

5. (d) : Angle made by $(S - E) = (80 - 55)° = 25°.$
Also, $25° = (90° - 65°) =$ Angle made by $(M - S.Sc.)$

EXERCISE 33B

Directions (Questions 1 to 5) : *Study the given graph and answer the following questions :*

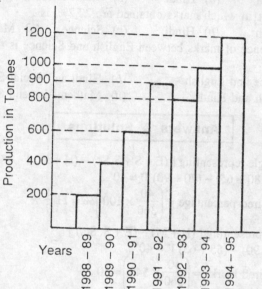

1. During which year the percent increase in production was lowest as compared to previous year ?
   (a) 1990-91   (b) 1991-92   (c) 1993-94   (d) 1994-95
2. The percent decrease in the production from 1991-92 to 1992-93 is :
   (a) 10%   (b) $11\frac{1}{9}\%$ (c) $88\frac{8}{9}\%$ (d) 90%
3. During which year, the percent increase in production was highest as compared to the previous year ?
   (a) 1989-90   (b) 1990-91   (c) 1991-92   (d) 1993-94
4. The production in 1989-90 in comparison to the production in 1988-89 was :
   (a) 100% more   (b) 75% more   (c) 50% more   (d) None of these
5. The percent increase in production from 1988-89 to 1994-95 is :
   (a) 1000%   (b) 600%   (c) 500%   (d) 300%

Directions (Questions 6 to 10) : *Study the given graph and answer the questions given below it.*

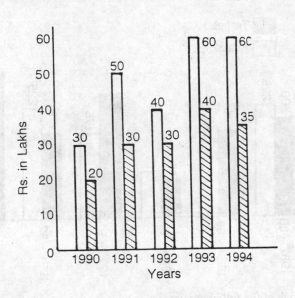

6. What was the difference in profit between 1991 and 1992 ?
   (a) Rs. 10 lakh (b) Rs. 5 lakh (c) Rs. 15 lakh (d) No profit
7. In the case of how many years was the income more than the average income of the given years ?
   (a) One (b) Two (c) Three (d) Four
8. What was the percentage increase in expenditure from 1992 to 1993 ?

   (a) 10% (b) $33\frac{1}{3}\%$ (c) $66\frac{2}{3}\%$ (d) 20%

9. The income in 1992 was equal to the expenditure of which of the following years ?
   (a) 1990 (b) 1991 (c) 1993 (d) 1994
10. In which of the following years was the profit maximum ?
    (a) 1990 (b) 1994 (c) 1992 (d) 1993

514   *Quantitative Aptitude*

Directions (Questions 11 to 15) : *Study the following graph carefully and answer the questions given below it.*   **(Bank P.O. 1993)**

Target and Actual Production of cement of a Factory (in thousand gunny bags)

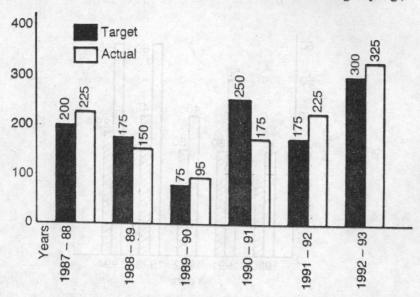

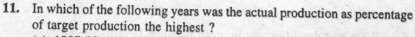

11. In which of the following years was the actual production as percentage of target production the highest ?

    (*a*) 1987-88   (*b*) 1989-90   (*c*) 1992-93   (*d*) 1991-92

12. If the combined trageted production of two adjacent years is compared to the combined actual production of these two years, then in which of the following pairs of years will it have a complete match ?

    (*a*) 1989-90, 1990-91   (*b*) 1990-91, 1991-92
    (*c*) 1987-88, 1988-89   (*d*) 1988-89, 1989-90

13. The actual production of cement for 1987-88 was how many times that of the targeted production set for that year ?

    (*a*) 0.88   (*b*) 1.025   (*c*) 1.25   (*d*) 1.125

14. What is the ratio of years in which actual production was above average to those below it ?

    (*a*) 1 : 2   (*b*) 3 : 2   (*c*) 1 : 1   (*d*) 2 : 1

15. What was the difference between the target set and the actual production for the year 1990-91 ?

    (*a*) 75000   (*b*) 25000   (*c*) 12500   (*d*) 7500

Directions (Questions 16 to 20) : *Study the following graph carefully and answer the questions given below it.*

Registration of New Vehicles in Delhi

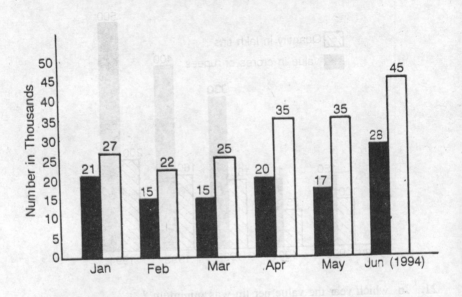

16. What was the increase in registration of vehicles other than cars from January to April 1994 ?
    (*a*) 5000   (*b*) 9000   (*c*) 15000   (*d*) 10000

17. What was the difference between the number of cars registered in January to those registered in June ?
    (*a*) 2000   (*b*) 5000   (*c*) 6000   (*d*) None of these

18. In which of the following months was the registration of vehicles other than cars maximum ?
    (*a*) April   (*b*) May   (*c*) June   (*d*) January

19. What was the percentage increase in registration of cars from March to June, 1994 ?
    (*a*) 80%   (*b*) 74.8%   (*c*) 86.6%   (*d*) 82.5%

20. What was the number of vehicles other than cars registered in March 1994 ?
    (*a*) 5000   (*b*) 10000   (*c*) 37000   (*d*) 40000

Directions (Questions 21 to 25) : *Study the following graph carefully and answer the questions given below it.*

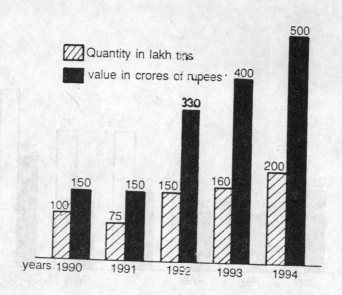

21. In which year the value per tin was minimum ?
    (*a*) 1990   (*b*) 1991   (*c*) 1993   (*d*) 1994
22. What was the difference between the tins exported in 1992 and 1993 ?
    (*a*) 10   (*b*) 1000   (*c*) 100000   (*d*) 1000000
23. What was the approximate percent increase in export value from 1990 to 1994 ?
    (*a*) 350   (*b*) 330.3   (*c*) 433.3   (*d*) None of thses
24. What was the percentage drop in export quantity from 1990 to 1991 ?
    (*a*) 75   (*b*) 50   (*c*) 25   (*d*) None of these
25. If in 1993, the tins were exported at the same rate per tin as that in 1992, what would be the value (in crores of rupess) of export in 1993 ?
    (*a*) 400   (*b*) 375   (*c*) 352   (*d*) 330

Directions (Questions 26 to 29) : *Study the following graph carefully and answer the questions given below it.*

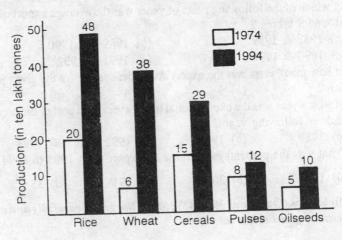

26. During the period 1974-94, the minimum rate of increase in production is in the case of :
    (a) Wheat   (b) Cereals   (c) Pulses   (d) Oil seeds

27. The production has doubled during the period 1974-94 in the case of :
    (a) Rice   (b) Pulses   (c) Cereals   (d) Oil seeds

28. The production has increased by 50% during the period 1974-94 in the case of :
    (a) Rice   (b) Pulses   (c) Cereals   (d) Oil seeds

29. The production has increased by nearly 93% during 1974-94 in the case of :
    (a) Cereals   (b) Rice   (c) Oil seeds   (d) Rice

Directions (Questions 34 to 38) : *Study the following graph carefully and answer the questions given below it.*

Export in crore Rs.

	5.2	6.5	7.8	9.9	10.8	9.5	11.4
	1988	1989	1990	1991	1992	1993	1994
	89	90	91	92	93	94	95

34. In which year there was maximum percentage increase in export of pearls to that in the previous year ?

    (*a*) 1989   (*b*) 1993   (*c*) 1991   (*d*) 1990

35. In which of the following pairs of years was the average export of pearls around 9 crores ?

    (*a*) 1988 & 1989   (*b*) 1989 and 1990

    (*c*) 1990 & 1991   (*d*) 1991 & 1992

36. In how many years was the export above the average for the given period ?

    (*a*) 2   (*b*) 3   (*c*) 4   (*d*) 5

37. In which year was the export equal to the average export of the preceding and the following year ?

    (*a*) 1989   (*b*) 1990   (*c*) 1992   (*d*) 1993

38. What was the percentage increase in export from 1993 to 1994 ?

    (*a*) $16\frac{2}{3}\%$ (*b*) 20%   (*c*) 19%   (*d*) $33\frac{1}{3}\%$

Directions (Questions 39 to 43) : *Study the graph carefully and answer the questions given below it.*

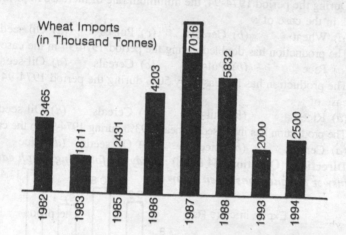

Wheat Imports
(in Thousand Tonnes)

39. In which year did the imports register highest increase over its preceding year ?

    (*a*) 1985   (*b*) 1986   (*c*) 1997   (*d*) 1994

40. The imports in 1983 was approximately how many times that of the year 1988 ?

    (*a*) 0.31   (*b*) 1.68   (*c*) 2.41   (*d*) 3.22

41. What is the ratio of the years which have above average imports to those which have below average imports ?

    (*a*) 3 : 5   (*b*) 5 : 3   (*c*) 8 : 3   (*d*) 3 : 8

42. The increase in imports in 1994 was what percent of the imports in 1993 ?

    (*a*) 25%   (*b*) 5%   (*c*) 125%   (*d*) 80%

43. The imports in 1986 is approximately what percent of average imports for the given years ?

    (*a*) 125   (*b*) 115   (*c*) 85   (*d*) 190

Directions (Questions 44 to 48) : *Study the graph carefully and answer the questions given below it.*

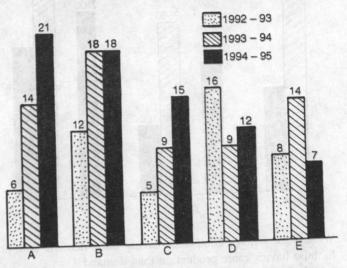

44. The production of state D in 1993-94 is how many times its production in 1994-95 ?

    (*a*) 1.33   (*b*) 0.75   (*c*) 0.56   (*d*) 1.77

45. In which of the states there is a steady increase in the production of cotton during the given period ?

    (*a*) A & B   (*b*) A & C   (*c*) B only   (*d*) D & E

46. How may tonnes of cotton was produced by state E during the given period ?

    (*a*) 2900   (*b*) 29000   (*c*) 290000   (*d*) 2900000

47. How many states showing below average production in 1992-93 showed above average production in 1993-94 ?

    (*a*) 4   (*b*) 2   (*c*) 3   (*d*) 1

48. Which of the following statements in false ?

    (*a*) States A and E showed the same production is 1993-94

(b) There was no improvement in the production of cotton in state B during 1994-95.

(c) State A has produced maximum cotton during the given period.

(d) Products of states C and D together is equal to that of state B during 1993-94.

Directions (Questions 49 to 53) : *Study the graph carefully and answer the questions given below it.*

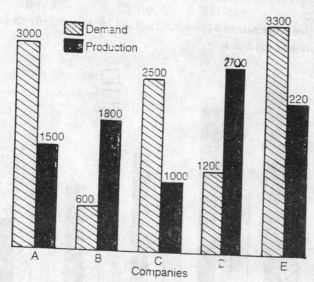

49. What is the ratio of companies having more demand than production to those having more production than demand ?

    (a) 2 : 3   (b) 4 : 1   (c) 2 : 2   (d) 3 : 2

50. What is the difference between average demand and average production of the five companies taken together ?

    (a) 1400   (b) 400   (c) 280   (d) 138

51. The production of company D is how many times that of the production of the company A ?

    (a) 1.8   (b) 1.5   (c) 2.5   (d) 1.11

52. The demand for company B is approximately what percent of the demand for company C ?

    (a) 4   (b) 24   (c) 20   (d) 60

53. If company A desires to meet the demand by purchasing T.V. sets from a single company, which one of the following companies can meet the need adequately ?

    (a) B   (b) C   (c) D   (d) None of these

Data Interpretation

Directions (Qestions 54 to 59) : *The subdivided bar diagram given below depicts the result of B.com. students of a college for three years.*

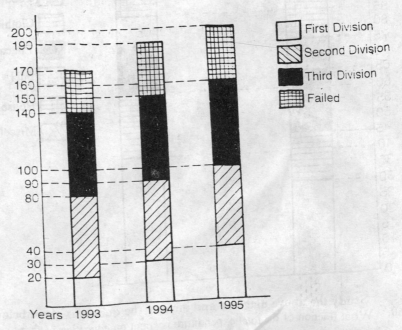

Study the above diagram and answer the questions given below.

54. How many percent passed in first division in 1993 ?
    (a) 20%   (b) 34%   (c) 14.28%   (d) 11.76%
    the pass percentage in 1993 ?
    (a) 65%   (b) 70%   (c) 74.6%   (d) 82.3%

56. In which year, the college had the best result for B.Com. ?
    (a) 1993   (b) 1994   (c) 1995   (d) Can't be determined

57. What is the number of third divisioners in 1995 ?
    (a) 160   (b) 70   (c) 60   (d) 65

58. What is the percentage of students in 1995 over 1993 ?
    (a) 30%   (b) 17.6%   (c) 117.6%   (d) 85%

59. What is the aggregate pass percentage during three years ?
    (a) 51.6%   (b) 80.3%   (c) 82.5%   (d) 77.6%

Directions (Questions 60 to 64) : *Following bar diagram shows the monthly expenditure of two families A & B on food, clothing, education, fuel, house rent and miscellaneous* (in percentage).

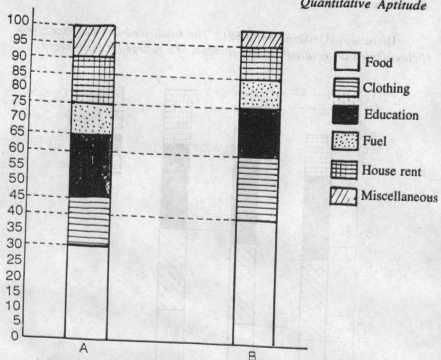

Study the above diagram and answer the questions given below.

60. What fraction of the total expenditure is spent on education in family A ?

(a) $\dfrac{13}{20}$ (b) $\dfrac{2}{3}$ (c) $\dfrac{9}{13}$ (d) None of these

61. If the total expenditure on family B is Rs. 10000, then money spent on clothes by this family during the year is :

(a) Rs. 200   (b) Rs. 666   (c) Rs. 2000   (d) Rs.

62. If the total annual expenditure of family A is Rs. 30000, then money spent on food, clothes and house rent is :

(a) Rs. 18500   (b) Rs. 18000   (c) Rs. 21000   (d) Rs. 15000

63. If both the families have same expenditure, which one spends more on education and miscellaneous together ?

(a) A   (b) B   (c) Both spend equal amounts

64. What percentage is B's expenditure on food over A's expenditure on food, taking equal total expenditure ?

(a) 10%   (b) 70%   (c) 133.33%   (d) 75%

Directions (Questions 65 to 69) : *Circle graph given below shows the expenditure incurred in bringing out a book by a publisher.*

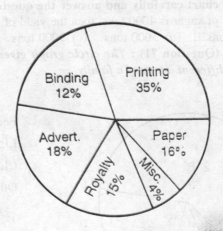

Study the graph carefully and answer the questions given below.

65. What is the central angle of the sector for the cost of the paper ?
    (a) 22.5°   (b) 16°   (c) 54.8°   (d) 57.6°

66. If the cost of printing is Rs. 17500, the royalty is :
    (a) Rs. 8750   (b) Rs. 7500   (c) Rs. 3150   (d) Rs. 6300

67. If the miscellaneous charges are Rs. 9000, the advertisement charges are :
    (a) Rs. 13500   (b) Rs. 20000   (c) Rs. 40500   (d) Rs. 18000

68. If 5500 copies are published and miscellaneous expenditure on them amounts to Rs. 5544 and the publisher earns a profit of 25%, then marked price of each copy is :
    (a) Rs. 25.20   (b) Rs. 37.50   (c) Rs. 31.50   (d) Rs. 30

69. Royalty on the book is less than the advertisement charges by :
    (a) 3%   (b) $16\frac{2}{3}$%   (c) 20%   (d) None of these

Directions (Question 70) : *The following pie chart shows the annual agricultural yield of a certain place.*

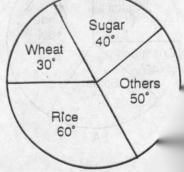

Study the chart carefully and answer the questions given below.

70. If the yield of sugar is 4000 tons, then the yield of rice and wheat is :
    (*a*) 4000 tons   (*b*) 5000 tons   (*c*) 9000 tons   (*d*) 10000 tons

Directions (Question 71) : *The circle graph given below shows the expenditure on different items, of a family.*

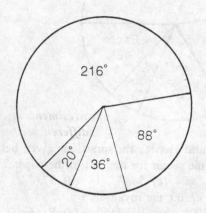

Food → 60%

Light & Fuel → 5%

Cloth → 10%

Other items → 25%

Study the graph carefully and answer the questions given below.

71. Which one of the following statements is not correct ?
    (*a*) 60% on food is represented by 216° in the circle graph.
    (*b*) One fourth of the money is spent on other items.
    (*c*) 5% on light and fuel is represented by 20° in the circle graph.
    (*d*) 10% on cloth is not correctly represented in the circle graph.

Directions (Questions 72 to 75) : *The following circle graph shows the distribution of workers of two industries A and B.*

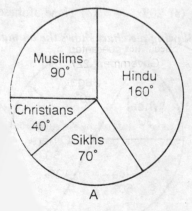

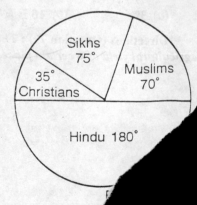

Study the graphs carefully and answer the questions given below.

72. Hindu workers in A are :
    (a) 50%   (b) more than 50%
    (c) less than 50%   (d) unknown

73. Christian workers in *A* are how many percent of christian workers in *B* ?
    (a) 114.3%   (b) 87.5%   (c) 12.5%   (d) 112.5%

74. If there are 1500 Sikh workers in *B*, then the total number of workers in *B* is :
    (a) 3600   (b) 4800   (c) 8000   (d) 7200

75. If there are 7200 workers in each one of *A* and *B*, then how many Muslim workers are more in *A*, then those in *B* ?
    (a) 22.22%   (b) 28.57%   (c) 23.47%   (d) 33.61%

Directions (Questions 76 to 80) : *The gross investments of Life Insurance Corporation of India (in crores of rupees) in different sectors are shown in the pie chart given below.*

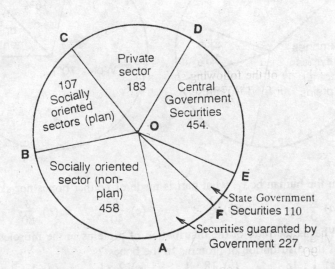

On the basis of the above information answer the following questions.

76. The percentage of gross investments in State Goverment Securities nearly :
    (a) 7.1%   (b) 7.8%   (c) 8.6%   (d) 9.2%

77. The magnitude of ∠ *AOC* is nearly :
    (a) 123°   (b) 132°   (c) 126°   (d) 115°

78. The investment in socially oriented sectors (plan and non plan) is
    ......than the investment in Government securities (Central and State) by
    .....
    (a) more, 4 crore   (b) more, 1 crore
    (c) more, 111 crore   (d) less, 106 crore
79. The investment in private sectors is nearly ....percent higher than the
    investment in State Government Securities ?
    (a) 66   (b) 54   (c) 46   (d) 40
80. The ratio of the area of the circle above COF to the area of the circle
    below it is, nearly :
    (a) 1   (b) 0.966   (c) 0.94   (d) 0.92

    Directions (Questions 81 to 85) : *Study the following graphs carefully
    and answer the questions that follow :*

81. In the human body, what part is made of neither bones nor skin ?
    (a) $\frac{2}{5}$ (b) $\frac{3}{5}$ (c) $\frac{1}{40}$ (d) $\frac{3}{80}$
82. What is the ratio of the distribution of proteins in the muscles to that
    of the distribution of proteins in the bones ?
    (a) 1 : 18   (b) 18 : 1   (c) 2 : 1   (d) 1 : 2
83. What will be the quantity of water in the body of a person weighing
    50 kg ?
    (a) 20 kg   (b) 35 kg   (c) 71.42 kg   (d) 120 kg
4. What percent of the total weight of human body is equivalent to the
   weight of the skin in human body ?
    (a) .016   (b) 1.6   (c) 0.16   (d) Data inadequate
   To show the distribution of proteins and other dry elements in the hum
   dy, the arc of the circle should subtend at the centre an angle
        54°   (b) 126°   (c) 108°   (d) 252

$$\boxed{\textbf{ANSWERS \& SOLUTIONS}}$$

1. (*d*) : Increase in 1989 – 90 = $\left[\dfrac{(400-200)}{200} \times 100\right]\% = 100\%$;

Increase in 1990 – 91 = $\left[\dfrac{(600-400)}{400} \times 100\right]\% = 50\%$;

Increase in 1991 – 92 = $\left[\dfrac{(900-600)}{600} \times 100\right]\% = 50\%$;

There is a decrease in production in 1992 – 93 ;

Increase in 1993 – 94 = $\left[\dfrac{(1000-800)}{800} \times 100\right]\% = 25\%$;

Increase in 1994 – 95 = $\left[\dfrac{(1200-1000)}{1000} \times 100\right]\% = 20\%.$

So, the increase percent is lowest in 1994 – 95.

2. (*b*) : Percent Decrease from 1991 – 92 to 1992 – 93

$$= \left[\dfrac{(900-800)}{900} \times 100\right]\% = 11\dfrac{1}{9}\%.$$

3. (*a*) : From Q. 1, it is obvious that the percentage increase in the production was highest in 1989 – 90.

4. (*a*) : Production in 1988 – 89 = 200 tonnes.

Production in 1989 – 90 = 400 tonnes.

$\therefore$ Increase % = $\left(\dfrac{200}{200} \times 100\right)\% = 100\%.$

So, the production in 1989 – 90 is 100% more than that in 1988 – 89.

5. (*c*) : Increase in production from 1988 – 89 to 1994 – 95

$$= \left[\dfrac{(1200-200)}{200} \times 100\right]\% = 500\%.$$

6. (*a*) : Profit in 1991 = (50 lakh – 30 lakh) = 20 lakh.

Profit in 1992 = (40 lakh – 30 lakh) = 10 lakh.

$\therefore$ Difference in profit = (20 – 10) lakh = 10 lakh.

7. (*c*) : Average income = $\dfrac{1}{4}$ (30 + 50 + 40 + 60 + 60) lakh = 48 lakh

Clearly, the income more than the average income is in the years 1991, 1993 and 1994, i.e. during 3 years.

8. (*b*) : Expenditure in 1992 = 30 lakh.

Expenditure in 1993 = 40 lakh.

Percentage increase = $\left(\dfrac{10 \text{ lakh}}{30 \text{ lakh}} \times 100\right)\% = 33\dfrac{1}{3}\%.$

9. (*c*) : Income in 1992 = 40 lakh = Expenditure in 1993.

10. (*b*) : Profits in various years are :

1990 → (30 – 20) lakh = 10 lakh,
1991 → (50 – 30) lakh = 20 lakh,
1992 → (40 – 30) lakh = 10 lakh,
1993 → (60 – 40) lakh = 20 lakh,
1994 → (60 – 35) lakh = 25 lakh.

∴ Profit is maximum in the year 1994.

11. (*d*) : Actual production as percentage of target production

in 1987 – 88 $= \left(\dfrac{225}{200} \times 100\right)\% = 112.5\%$

in 1988 – 89 $= \left(\dfrac{150}{175} \times 100\right)\% = 85.7\%$

in 1989 – 90 $= \left(\dfrac{95}{75} \times 100\right)\% = 126.6\%$

in 1990 – 91 $= \left(\dfrac{175}{250} \times 100\right)\% = 70\%$

in 1991 – 92 $= \left(\dfrac{225}{175} \times 100\right)\% = 128.5\%$

in 1992 – 93 $= \left(\dfrac{325}{300} \times 100\right)\% = 108.3\%$

Clearly, it is highest in the year 1991 – 92.

12. (*c*) :

Years	Combined targeted production	Combined actual production
1987 – 88, 1988 – 89	200 + 175 = 375	225 + 150 = 375
1988 – 89, 1989 – 90	175 + 75 = 250	150 + 95 = 245
1989 – 90, 1990 – 91	75 + 250 = 325	95 + 175 = 270
1990 – 91, 1991 – 92	250 + 175 = 425	175 + 225 = 400
1991 – 92, 1992 – 93	175 + 300 = 475	225 + 325 = 550

Clearly, it has a complete match in the years 1987 – 88 and 1988 – 89.

13. (*d*) : Let actual production in 1987 – 88 be *x* times targeted production.

Then, $225 = x \times 200$ or $x = \dfrac{225}{200} = 1.125$.

14. (*c*) : Average of actual production over the years.

$$= \frac{1}{6}(200 + 150 + 95 + 175 + 225 + 325) = 195.$$

Ratio of number of years having actual production above average and those having below average $= \frac{3}{3} = 1 : 1$.

15. (*b*) : Difference between target set and the actual production in
1990 – 91 = (250 – 175) thousand gunny bags
$\qquad$ = 25000 gunny bags.

16. (*b*) : Number of other vehicles in Jan 1994 = (27000 – 21000) = 6000.
Number of other vehicles in April 1994
= (35000 – 20000) = 15000.
∴ Increase = (15000 – 6000) = 9000.

17. (*d*) : Number of cars registered in January = 21000.
Number of cars registered in June = 28000.
Difference = (28000 – 21000) = 7000.

18. (*b*) : Other vehicles registered in various months are :
January → (27000 – 21000) = 6000,
February → (22000 – 15000) = 7000,
March → (25000 – 15000) = 10000,
April → (35000 – 20000) = 15000,
May → (35000 – 17000) = 18000,
June → (45000 – 28000) = 17000.
Clearly, the maximum registration of other vehicles was in May.

19. (*c*) : Registration of cars in March = 15000.
Registration of cars in June = 28000.

$$\text{Increase } \% = \left(\frac{13000}{15000} \times 100 \right) \% = 86.6\%.$$

20. (*b*) : Number of vehicles other than cars registered in March 1994
$$= (25000 - 15000) = 10000.$$

21. (*a*) : Values of 1 tin in various years :

$$1990 \to \text{Rs} \left(\frac{150 \text{ crores}}{100 \text{ lakhs}} \right) = \text{Rs.} \left(\frac{150}{1.00} \right) = \text{Rs. } 150.$$

$$1991 \to \text{Rs.} \left(\frac{150}{.75} \right) = \text{Rs. } 200, \; 1992 \to \text{Rs.} \left(\frac{330}{1.50} \right) = \text{Rs. } 220.$$

$$1993 \to \text{Rs.} \left(\frac{400}{1.60} \right) = \text{Rs. } 250, \; 1994 \to \text{Rs.} \left(\frac{500}{2.00} \right) = \text{Rs. } 250.$$

So, the value per tin was minimum in 1990.

22. (*d*) : Difference between the number of tins exported in 1992 and 1993
$$= (160 \text{ lakh}) - (150 \text{ lakh}) = 1000000.$$

23. (*d*) : Percentage increase in export value from 1990 to 1994

$$= \left[\frac{500 \text{ crores} - 150 \text{ crores}}{150 \text{ crores}} \times 100 \right] \%$$

$$= \left(\frac{350}{150} \times 100 \right) \% = 233.3\%.$$

24. (c) : Percentage drop in export quantity from 1990 to 1991

$$= \left[\frac{(100 \text{ lakh}) - (75 \text{ lakh})}{100 \text{ lakh}} \times 100 \right] \% = 25\%.$$

25. (c) : In 1992, cost of 1 tin = Rs $\left(\frac{330 \text{ crores}}{150 \text{ lakhs}} \right)$ = Rs. $\left(\frac{330}{1.50} \right)$ = Rs. 220.

In 1993, export value = Rs. (160 lakh × 220)

                                     = Rs. (1.60 × 220) crores = Rs. 352 crores.

26. (c) : Increase in production of :

Rice → $\left(\frac{28}{20} \times 100 \right) \% = 140\%$; Wheat → $\left(\frac{32}{6} \times 100 \right) \% = 533.3\%$;

Cereals → $\left(\frac{14}{15} \times 100 \right) \% = 93.3\%$; Pulses → $\left(\frac{4}{8} \times 100 \right) \% = 50\%$;

Oilseeds → $\left(\frac{5}{5} \times 100 \right) \% = 100\%$.

Clearly, rate of increase is minimum in case of pulses.

27. (d) : In case of oilseeds :

Production in 1974 = (5 × 10) = 50 lakh tonnes.

Production in 1994 = (10 × 10) = 100 lakh tonnes.

∴ Production has doubled in case of oil seeds.

28. (b) : Clearly, the production has increased by 50% in case of pulses (as shown above).

29. (a) : Clearly, the production has increased by 93% (approximately) in case of cereals (as calculated above).

34. (c) : Increase percent in export of pearls in various years :

1989 → $\left(\frac{1.3 \text{ crores}}{6.2 \text{ crores}} \times 100 \right) = \left(\frac{1.3}{6.2} \times 100 \right) \% = 20.9\%$,

1990 → $\left(\frac{1.3}{6.5} \times 100 \right) = 20\%$, 1991 → $\left(\frac{2.1}{7.8} \times 100 \right) \% = 26.9\%$,

1992 → $\left(\frac{0.9}{9.9} \times 100 \right) \% = 9.09\%$, 1993 → No increase,

1994 → $\left(\frac{1.9}{9.5} \times 100 \right) \% = 20\%$.

So, **maximum percentage increase in export was in the year 1991.**

35. (c) : Average export :

$$\text{in 1988 \& 1989} = \left(\frac{5.2 + 6.5}{2}\right) \text{ crores} = 5.85 \text{ crores,}$$

$$\text{in 1989 \& 1990} = \left(\frac{6.5 + 7.8}{2}\right) \text{ crores} = 7.15 \text{ crores,}$$

$$\text{in 1990 \& 1991} = \left(\frac{7.8 + 9.9}{2}\right) \text{ crores} = 8.85 \text{ crores.}$$

So, the required average is in 1990 & 1991.

36. (c) : Average export $= \frac{1}{7} (5.2 + 6.5 + 7.8 + 9.9 + 10.8 + 9.5 + 11.4)$

$$= \frac{61.1}{7} = 8.73.$$

So, the export above the average was in the years 1991, 1992, 1993 and 1994.

37. (a) : Average of export in 1988 & 1990 $= \left(\frac{5.2 + 7.8}{2}\right) = 6.5$

$$= \text{Export in 1989.}$$

38. (b) : Increase percent in export from 1993 to 1994

$$= \frac{(11.4 - 9.5)}{9.5} \times 100 = \left(\frac{1.9}{9.5} \times 100\right) \% = 20\%.$$

39. (b) : Increase percent :

$$\text{in 1985} \rightarrow \left(\frac{2413 - 1811}{1811} \times 100\right) \% = 33.2\%;$$

$$\text{in 1986} \rightarrow \left(\frac{4203 - 2413}{2413} \times 100\right) \% = 74.18\%;$$

$$\text{in 1987} \rightarrow \left(\frac{7016 - 4203}{4203} \times 100\right) \% = 66.9\%;$$

$$\text{in 1994} \rightarrow \left(\frac{2500 - 2000}{2000} \times 100\right) \% = 25\%.$$

∴ Highest increase is in 1986.

40. (a) : Let import in 1983 $= k \times$ (import in 1988)

∴ $1811000 = k \times 5832000$ or $k = \frac{1811000}{5832000} = 0.31.$

41. (a) : Average import

$$= \frac{1}{8} (3465 + 1811 + 2413 + 4203 + 7016 + 5832 + 2000 + 2500)$$

$$= \left(\frac{29240}{8}\right) = 3655.$$

Years having imports above average are 1986, 1987, 1988.

Their number is 3.

Number of years having imports below average = 5.

∴ Required ratio = 3 : 5.

42. (*a*) : Required percentage = $\left[\dfrac{(2500-2000)}{2000} \times 100\right]\% = 25\%$.

43. (*b*) : Required percentage = $\left(\dfrac{4203}{3655} \times 100\right)\% = 115\%$.

44. (*b*) : Let production of *D* in 1993 – 94 = $k \times$ (production of *D* in 1994 – 95).

Then, 9 lakhs = k × 12 lakhs or $k = \dfrac{9}{12} = \dfrac{3}{4} = 0.75$.

45. (*b*) : Clearly, there is a steady increase in the production of cotton during the given period in case of states *A* and *C*.

46. (*b*) : Total number of bales produced by *E* = (8 + 14 + 7) lakhs = 29 lakhs.

∴ Its weight = $\left(\dfrac{29 \times 100000 \times 100}{1000}\right)$ tonnes = 29000 tonnes.

47. (*c*) : Average production of :

$$A \to \left(\frac{6+14+21}{3}\right) = 13.66, \quad B \to \left(\frac{12+18+18}{3}\right) = 16,$$

$$C \to \left(\frac{5+9+15}{3}\right) = 9.66, \quad D \to \left(\frac{16+9+12}{3}\right) = 12.3,$$

$$E \to \left(\frac{8+14+7}{3}\right) = 9.66.$$

Clearly, states *A*, *B*, *E* showed below average production in 1992-93 and above average production in 1993 – 94.

48. (*c*) : During the given period, state *B* has produced 48 lakhs of bales while state *A* has produced only 41 lakhs.

So, statement (*c*) is false.

49. (*d*) : The companies having more demand than production are $\bar{A}, \bar{C}, E$. Their number is 3. The companies having more production than demand are *B* and *D*. Their number is 2.

∴ Required ratio = 3 : 2.

50. (*c*) : Average demand = $\left(\dfrac{3000+600+2500+1200+3300}{5}\right) = 2120$.

Average production = $\left(\dfrac{1500+1800+1000+2700+2200}{5}\right) = 1840$.

∴ Difference in average demand & average production

$$= (2120 - 1840) = 280.$$

51. (*a*) : Let production of *D* = $k \times$ production of A

Then, 2700 = k × 1500 or $k = \dfrac{2700}{1500} = 1.8$.

52. (*b*) : Let *x*% of demand for *C* = Demand for B.

Then, $\dfrac{x}{100} \times 2500 = 600$ or $x = \left(\dfrac{600 \times 100}{2500}\right) = 24\%$.

53. (*c*) : Since *D* produces highest number of sets and *A* desires to meet the demand by purchasing surplus sets from a single company,

So, *D* can meet the demand of *A*.

54. (*d*) : Percentage of first divisioners in 1993

$= \left(\dfrac{20}{170} \times 100\right)\% = 11.76\,\%.$

55. (*d*) : pass percentage in 1993 $= \left(\dfrac{140}{170} \times 100\right)\% = 82.3\,\%.$

56. (*c*) : Pass percentage in 1993 = 82.3 %.

Pass percentage in 1994 $= \left(\dfrac{150}{190} \times 100\right)\% = 78.9\,\%.$

Pass percentage in 1995 $= \left(\dfrac{170}{200} \times 100\right)\% = 85\,\%.$

∴ The college had best result for B.Com in 1995.

57. (*c*) : Number of third divisioners in 1995

$= (160 - 100) = 60.$

58. (*c*) : Percentage of students in 1995 over 1993

$= \left(\dfrac{200}{170} \times 100\right)\% = 117.6\,\%.$

59. (*b*) : Number of students who passed = (140 + 150 + 160) = 450.

Number of students who appeared = (170 + 190 + 200) = 560.

∴ Aggregate pass percentage $= \left(\dfrac{450}{560} \times 100\right)\% = 80.3\,\%.$

60. (*d*) : Money spent on education in family *A*

$= (65 - 45)$ *i.e.* 20 % of total expenditure

$= \dfrac{20}{100}$ of total expenditure $= \dfrac{1}{5}$ of total expenditure.

61. (*c*) : Money spent on clothes by family *B*

$= (60 - 40)$ % of total expenditure

$= $ Rs. $\left(\dfrac{20}{100} \times 10000\right) = $ Rs. 2000.

62. (*b*) : Money spent by *A* on food, clothes and house rent

$= [30 + (45 - 30) + (90 - 75)]$ % of total expenditure

$= (60 \% \text{ of Rs } 30000) = $ Rs. $\left(\dfrac{60}{100} \times 30000\right) = $ Rs. 18000.

63. (*a*) : Money spent by *A* on eductaion & miscellaneous

$= [(65 - 45) + (100 - 90)]\% = 30\,\%.$

Money spent by *B* on education & miscellaneous
= [(75 − 60) + (100 − 95)] % = 20 %.

∴ Family *A* spends more on these heads.

64. (*c*) : *B*'s expenditure on food = 40 %

A's expenditure on food = 30 %.

B's percentage over *A*'s = $\left(\dfrac{40}{30} \times 100\right)\% = 133.33\,\%$.

65. (*d*) : Central angle for the cost of the paper = $\left(\dfrac{16}{100} \times 360\right)^{\circ} = 57.6^{\circ}$.

66. (*b*) : Let the royalty be Rs. *x*. Then,

$35 : 15 :: 17500 : x =$ or $x = \left(\dfrac{15 \times 17500}{35}\right) = $ Rs. 7500.

67. (*c*) : Let the advertisement charges be Rs. *x*.

Then, $4 : 18 :: 9000 : x$ or $x = \left(\dfrac{18 \times 9000}{4}\right) = $ Rs. 40500.

68. (*c*) : Let the total charges be Rs. *x*.

Then, $4 : 100 :: 5544 : x$ or $x = \left(\dfrac{100 \times 5544}{4}\right) = $ Rs. 138600.

∴ Total cost = Rs. 138600.

∴ Cost price of each copy = Rs. $\left(\dfrac{138600}{5500}\right) = $ Rs. 25.20.

∴ Marked price = 125% of Rs. 25.20

$= $ Rs. $\left(\dfrac{125}{100} \times 25.20\right) = $ Rs. 31.50.

69. (*b*) : Let royalty be Rs. 15. Then, advertisement charges = Rs. 18.

∴ Required percentage $= \left(\dfrac{3}{18} \times 100\right)\% = 16\dfrac{2}{3}\,\%$.

70. (*c*) : Sugar : (Wheat + Rice) = 4000 : *x*

$40 : (30 + 60) = 4000 : x$ or $x = \left(\dfrac{90 \times 4000}{40}\right) = 9000$.

∴ Yield of wheat and Rice is 9000 tons.

71. (*c*) : (*a*) 60% on food $\equiv \left(\dfrac{60}{100} \times 360\right)^{\circ} = 216^{\circ}$, which is correct.

(*b*) $\dfrac{1}{4}$ th of money = 25% on other items, which is correct.

(*c*) 5% on light and fuel $\equiv \left(\dfrac{5}{100} \times 360\right)^{\circ} = 18^{\circ}$.

So, 20° is incorrect.

(*d*) 10% on cloth $\equiv \left(\dfrac{10}{100} \times 360\right)^{\circ} = 36^{\circ}$, which is there on the graph.

72. (c) : Hindu workers in $A = \left(\dfrac{160}{360} \times 100\right)\% = 44.44\% < 50\%.$

73. (a) : Christian Workers in $A = \left(\dfrac{40}{360} \times 100\right)\% = \dfrac{100}{9}\%$.

Christian workers in $B = \left(\dfrac{35}{360} \times 100\right)\% = \dfrac{175}{18}\%.$

Required percentage $= \left(\dfrac{100}{9} \times \dfrac{18}{175} \times 100\right)\% = 114.3\%.$

74. (d) : Percentage of Sikh workers in $B = \left(\dfrac{75}{360} \times 100\right)\% = \dfrac{125}{6}\%.$

$\dfrac{125}{6} : 100 = 1500 : x$ or $x = \left(100 \times 1500 \times \dfrac{6}{125}\right) = 7200.$

$\therefore$ Total number of workers in $B = 7200.$

75. (b) : Muslim workers in $A = \left(\dfrac{90}{360} \times 7200\right) = 1800.$

Muslim workers in $B = \left(\dfrac{7}{360} \times 7200\right) = 1400.$

$\therefore$ Excess of Muslim workers in A over those of B
$$= \left(\dfrac{400}{1400} \times 100\right)\% = 28.57\%.$$

76. (a) : Total investment $= (458 + 107 + 183 + 454 + 110 + 227)$ crores
$$= 1539 \text{ crores}$$
Investment in State Government securities $= 110$ crores.

$\therefore$ Required percentage $= \left(\dfrac{110}{1539} \times 100\right)\% = 7.1\%.$

77. (b) : $\angle AOC = \left[\dfrac{(458 + 107) \text{ crores}}{1539 \text{ crores}} \times 360\right]^{\circ} = \left(\dfrac{565}{1539} \times 360\right)^{\circ} = 132^{\circ}.$

78. (b) : Investment in socially oriented sectors
$$= (458 + 107) \text{ crores} = 565 \text{ crores.}$$
Investment in Government Securities
$$= (454 + 110) \text{ crores} = 564 \text{ crores.}$$
$\therefore$ Investment in socially oriented sectors is more than investment in Government securities by 1 crore.

79. (a) : Investment in Private Sector $= 183$ crores.
Investment in State Government Securities $= 110$ crores.

$\therefore$ Required excess $= \left(\dfrac{73}{110} \times 100\right)\% = 66\%.$

80. (c) : Angle $\angle COF = \left(\dfrac{107 + 458 + 227}{1539} \times 360\right)^{\circ} = \left(\dfrac{792}{1539} \times 360\right)^{\circ} = 185.2^{\circ}$.

Angle above COF $= (360^{\circ} - 185^{\circ}) = 175^{\circ}$.

$\therefore \quad \dfrac{\text{Area above COF}}{\text{Area below COF}} = \left(\dfrac{\pi r^2 \times 175}{360} \times \dfrac{360}{\pi r^2 \times 185}\right) = \dfrac{175}{185} = 0.94$.

81. (a) : Part of body made of neither bones nor Skin

$= 1 - \left(\dfrac{1}{3} + \dfrac{1}{10} + \dfrac{1}{6}\right) = \left(1 - \dfrac{6}{10}\right) = \dfrac{4}{10} = \dfrac{2}{5}$.

82. (c) : Required ratio $= \dfrac{1}{3} : \dfrac{1}{6} = 2 : 1$.

83. (b) : Quantity of water in the body of a person weighing 50 kg

$= 70\ \%\ \text{of}\ 50\ \text{kg} = \left(\dfrac{70}{100} \times 50\right) \text{kg} = 35\ \text{kg}$.

84. (b) : Weight of Skin $= \dfrac{1}{10}$ parts of 16 % of proteins

$= \left(\dfrac{1}{10} \times \dfrac{16}{100} \times 100\right) \%\ \text{of proteins} = 1.6\%\ \text{of proteins}$.

85. (c) : Percentage of proteins & other dry elements = 30 %.

$\therefore \quad$ Required angle $= \left(\dfrac{30}{100} \times 360\right)^{\circ} = 108^{\circ}$.

PROBLEMS RELATED TO GRAPHS

Example 1 : *Study the following graph carefully and answer the questions given below it :*   (Bank P.O. 1993)

Income And Expenditure of a Company over the years (Rs. in crores)

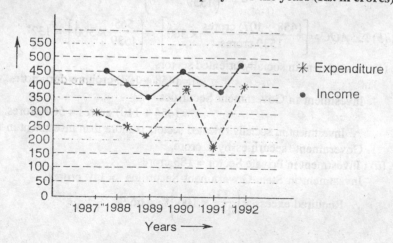

1. The total expenditure of which of the following pairs of years was equal to the income in 1992 ?
    (*a*) 1987 and 1988   (*b*) 1987 and 1989
    (*c*) 1988 and 1989   (*d*) 1988 and 1990
    (*e*) None of these
2. What was the percentage decrease in expenditure from 1988 to 1989?
    (*a*) 80   (*b*) 50   (*c*) 40   (*d*) 10
    (*e*) None of these
3. In how many of the given years was the expenditure more than the average expenditure of the given years ?
    (*a*) 4   (*b*) 3   (*c*) 1   (*d*) 5
    (*e*) None of these
4. In which of the following years was the percentage of expenditure to income, the highest ?
    (*a*) 1987   (*b*) 1988   (*c*) 1989   (*d*) 1991
    (*e*) None of these
5. What was the approximate percentage increase in income from 1991 to 1992 ?
    (*a*) 35   (*b*) 40   (*c*) 20   (*d*) 15   (*e*) 25

Solutions

1. (*c*) : Income in 1992 = 475 crores.
    Total Expenditure in 1988 & 1989 = Rs. (250 + 225) crores
                                = Rs. 475 crores.

2. (*d*) : Expenditure in 1988 = Rs. 250 crores.
    Expenditure in 1989 = Rs. 225 crores.
    Decrease % $= \left(\dfrac{25 \text{ crores}}{250 \text{ crores}} \times 100 \right) \% = 10\%$.

3. (*b*) : Average expenditure = Rs. $\left(\dfrac{300 + 250 + 225 + 375 + 175 + 400}{6} \right)$

    = Rs. 287.5.

The expenditure is greater than the average expenditure during the years 1987, 1990 and 1992.
    ∴ Required number of years = 3.

4. (*e*) : The required percentage :
    In 1987 is $\left(\dfrac{300}{450} \times 100 \right) \% = 66.66\%$.

    In 1988 is $\left(\dfrac{250}{400} \times 100 \right) \% = 62.5\%$.

    In 1989 is $\left(\dfrac{225}{350} \times 100 \right) \% = 64.29\%$.

In 1990 is $\left(\dfrac{375}{425} \times 100\right) \% = 88.24\%.$

In 1991 is $\left(\dfrac{175}{375} \times 100\right) \% = 46.6\%.$

In 1992 is $\left(\dfrac{400}{475} \times 100\right) \% = 84.21\%.$

Clearly, the percentage is highest in 1990.

5. (e) : Income in 1991 = 375 crores.
Income in 1992 = 475 crores.

$\therefore$ Increase $\% = \left(\dfrac{100}{375} \times 100\right) \% = 26.6\% = 25\%$ nearly.

Example 2 : *Study the following graph carefully and answer the questions given below it.*

Production of three types of vehicles by a company over the years (in thousands)

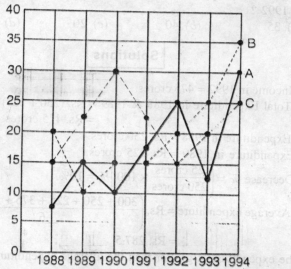

1. The number of A type vehicles produced in 1990 was what percent of the number of C type vehicles produced in 1992 ?

   (a) $33\dfrac{1}{3}$ (b) 40   (c) 50   (d) 15   (e) $66\dfrac{2}{3}$

2. In how many years was the production of A type vehicles less than its average production over the given years ?

   (a) 2   (b) 4   (c) 3   (d) 1

   (e) None of these

3. What was the average number of *B* type vehicles produced by the company over the years ?
   (*a*) 20,000   (*b*) 25,000   (*c*) 15,000   (*d*) 30,000
   (*e*) None of these

4. In which of the following years was the total production of all the three types of vehicles 60,000 ?
   (*a*) 1988   (*b*) 1990   (*c*) 1991   (*d*) 1992
   (*e*) 1994

5. What was the percentage increase in the production of *C* type vehicles from 1989 to 1990 ?
   (*a*) 10   (*b*) 5   (*c*) 20   (*d*) 25
   (*e*) None of these

Solutions

1. (*e*) : Number of Type *A* vehicles in 1990 = 10000.
Number of Type *C* vehicles in 1992 = 15000.
Required percentage $= \left(\dfrac{10000}{15000} \times 100 \right) \% = 66\dfrac{2}{3}\%.$

2. (*b*) : Average production of
$$A = \left(\frac{7.5 + 15 + 10 + 17.5 + 25 + 12.5 + 30}{7} \right) \text{thousand}$$
= 16.8 thousand.
During 4 years the production of *A* was less than the average production.

3. (*a*) : Average of *B* type vehicles
$$= \left(\frac{20 + 10 + 15 + 15 + 20 + 25 + 35}{7} \right) \text{thousand} = 20 \text{ thousand}.$$

4. (*d*) : In 1992, the total production of all the three types of vehicles was 60 thousand.

5. (*e*) : Number of *C* type vehicles in 1989 = 22500
Number of *C* type vehicles in 1990 = 30000
Increase percent $= \left(\dfrac{7500}{22500} \times 100 \right) \% = 33\dfrac{1}{3}\%.$

EXERCISE 33C

Directions (Questions 1 to 5) : *Study the following graph carefully and answer questions 1 to 5.*

Imports and Exports Between Two Countries A and B (in million dollars)

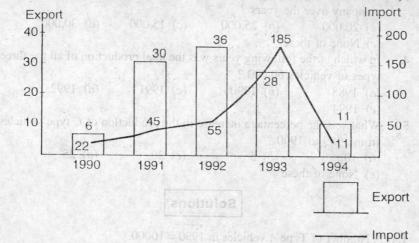

1. The percent increase in exports from 1990 to 1991 is :
    (a) 400   (b) 40   (c) 200   (d) 4
2. The exports in which year was 50% of the average exports during the given years ?
    (a) 1991   (b) 1992   (c) 1993   (d) 1994
3. What was the approximate percent increase in imports from 1990 to 1991 ?
    (a) 44   (b) 100   (c) 200   (d) 400
4. The imports in which year was nearer to the total value of imports and exports in 1994 ?
    (a) 1990   (b) 1990 & 1991   (c) 1992   (d) 1991 & 1992
5. The approximate percent decrease in exports from 1992 to 1993 is
    (a) 20   (b) 8   (c) 40   (d) 80

Directions (Questions 6 to 10) : *The following graph shows the quarterly price index of a textile company during 1993-94. Examine it carefully and answer the questions given below :*

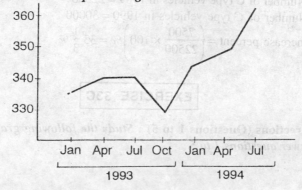

6. During which quarter the rate of increase of price index was the maximum ?

   (a) October 1993 - December 1993 (b) January 1993 - April 1993
   (c) April 1994 - June 1994   (d) January 1994 - March 1994

7. In which of the following months, the price index was maximum ?

   (a) April 1993   (b) July 1993   (c) April 1994 (d) July 1994

8. During which of the following quarters, the price index remained same throughout ?

   (a) April 1994 - June 1994   (b) April 1993 - June 1993
   (c) July 1993 - September 1993   (d) January 1993 - April 1993

9. The increase in price index was approximately same during periods

   (a) October - December 1993 and April - June 1994
   (b) January - March 1994 and April - June 1994
   (c) January - March 1993 and October - December 1993
   (d) April - June 1993 and January - March 1994

10. Approximately, what is the percentage of increase in index during the period January 1993 - June 1994 ?

    (a) 7%   (b) 8%   (c) 10%   (d) 7.5%

Directions (Questions 11 to 15) : *Study the following graph and answer the questions given below it.*

Sales Of Three Brands Of Cycles Over The Years
(in thousands)   **(Bank P.O. 1992)**

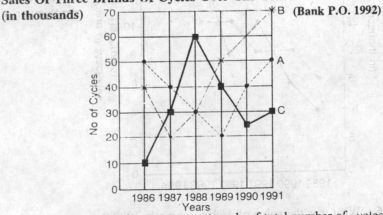

11. In which of the following years was the sale of total number of cycles of three brands taken together the lowest ?

    (a) 1986   (b) 1987   (c) 1989   (d) 1990
    (e) None of these

12. In which of the following years was the sale of cyles of brand *A* and brand *B* exactly the same ?

    (a) 1987   (b) 1990   (c) 1988   (d) 1989
    (e) None of these

13. In which of the following years was the sale of cycles of brand *C* exactly one-fourth of the sale of cycles of brand *B* ?

   (*a*) 1990   (*b*) 1989   (*c*) 1988   (*d*) 1986

   (*e*) None of these

14. The sale of cycles of brand *A* in 1988 was what percent of sale of cycles of brand *B* in 1990 ?

   (*a*) 25   (*b*) 50   (*c*) 100   (*d*) 150

   (*e*) None of these

15. What was the percentage decrease in sale of number of cycles of brand *C* from 1989 to 1990 ?

   (*a*) 50   (*b*) 125   (*c*) 70   (*d*) 20

   (*e*) None of these

Directions (Questions 16 to 20) : *Study the following graphs and answer the questions given below it :*

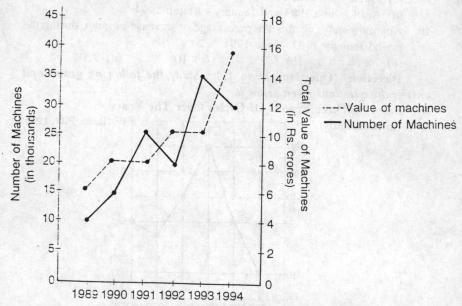

16. What was the value of each machine in 1990 ?

   (*a*) Rs. 3 thousand   (*b*) Rs. 50 thousand

   (*c*) Rs. 5,103   (*d*) Rs. $5\frac{1}{3}$ thousand

   (*e*) None of these

17. What was the percentage drop in production of number of machines from 1991 to 1992 ?

   (*a*) 5   (*b*) 20   (*c*) 25   (*d*) 30

   (*e*) None of these

18. What was the difference in revenue from the machines sold in 1992 and 1994 ?
    (*a*) Rs. 10 lakhs (*b*) Rs. 1 crore (*c*) Rs. 4 crores   (*d*) Rs. 6 crores
    (*e*) None of these

19. If the price per machine was increased by 25% in the year 1993, what would have been the total value of the machines produced in that year ?
    (*a*) Rs. 35 crores   (*b*) Rs. 20 crores
    (*c*) Rs. 17.5 crores   (*d*) Rs. 15.5 crores
    (*e*) None of these

20. What was the difference in the value per machine between the years 1991 and 1992 ?
    (*a*) Rs. 1,500   (*b*) Rs. 2,500   (*c*) Rs. 2,800   (*d*) Rs. 3,200
    (*e*) None of these

Directions (Questions 21 to 25) : *Study the following graph carefully and answer the questions given below it :*   **(Bank P.O., 1993)**

Income and Expenditure of a company over the years (Rs. in crore)

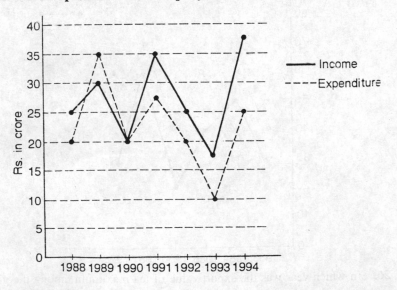

21. In which of the following years was the difference between the income and the expenditure the maximum ?
    (*a*) 1991.   (*b*) 1994   (*c*) 1989   (*d*) 1990
    (*e*) None of these

22. The income in 1990 was equal to the expenditure in which of the following years ?
    (*a*) 1988 only   (*b*) 1993 only
    (*c*) 1988 and 1992   (*d*) 1991 and 1992

(e) None of these

23. What was the approximate percentage drop in expenditure from 1991 to 1992 ?
    (a) 25　　　　　(b) 35　　　　　(c) 75　　　　　(d) 40　　　　(e) 60
24. What was the percentage increase in income from 1990 to 1991 ?
    (a) 75　　　　　(b) 25　　　　　(c) 125　　　　　(d) 60
    (e) None of these
25. In how many of the given years was the expenditure more than the income ?
    (a) 1　　　　　(b) 3　　　　　(c) 4　　　　　(d) 2
    (e) None of these

Directions : *Study the following graph carefully and answer questions 26 to 30 given below it*　　　　　　　　　(Bank P.O. 1990)

Total value of exports of Rice, Sugar and Tea over the years (in Rs. hundred crores)

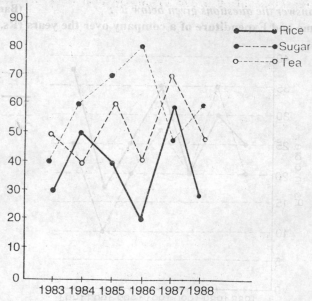

26. In which year was the export value of tea maximum among the given years ?
    (a) 1983　　　　(b) 1985　　　　(c) 1986　　　　(d) 1987
    (e) 1988
27. What was the difference in the export value of rice and tea in the year 1986 ?
    (a) Rs. 20 crore　　　　　　(b) Rs. 2000 crore
    (c) Rs. 200 lakh　　　　　　(d) Rs. 200 crore
    (e) None of these

28. What was the percent decrease in export value of sugar from 1986 to 1987 ?

    (a) 37.5 (b) 63.5 (c) $266\frac{2}{3}$ (d) 30

    (e) None of these

29. What was the percent increase in the export value of tea from 1986 to 1987 ?

    (a) 75 (b) 25 (c) 125 (d) 50

    (e) None of these

30. In which of the following years was the total export value of rice, tea and sugar together the minimum among the given years ?

    (a) 1984 (b) 1986 (c) 1983 (d) 1988

    (e) None of these

Directions (Questions 31 to 35) : *Study the following graph carefully and answer the questions given below it.* (Bank P.O. 1994)

Ratio of Imports and Exports of Two Companies Over the Years

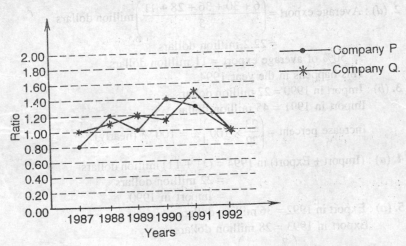

31. If the total exports of company Q in 1989 and 1990 and together was 24 crores, what was the total imports of the same company in these two years together ?

    (a) 20 crore (b) 32 crore (c) 16 crore (d) Data inadequate

    (e) None of these

32. In how many of the given years were the imports more than the exports of company Q ?

    (a) 2 (b) 4 (c) 3 (d) 1

    (e) None of these

33. If the exports for company P in 1990 were 60 crore, what were the imports of this company in the same year ?

(a) 62 crore   (b) 88 crore   (c) 68 crore   (d) 84 crore
(e) None of these

34. What were the average exports of company Q over the given years ?
   (a) 60 crore   (b) 70 crore   (c) 100 crore (d) Data inadequate
   (e) None of these

35. The exports of company P with relation to imports were maximum in which of the following years among the given years ?
   (a) 1988   (b) 1991   (c) 1992   (d) 1989
   (e) None of these

Answers & Solutions

1. (a) : Export in 1990 = 6 million dollars
   Export in 1991 = 30 million dollars
   Increase % = $\left(\dfrac{24}{6} \times 100\right)$ % = 400%.

2. (d) : Average export = $\left(\dfrac{6 + 30 + 36 + 28 + 11}{5}\right)$ million dollars

   = 22.2 million dollars
   ∴ 50% of average export = 11 million dollars.
   This happens in the year 1994.

3. (b) : Import in 1990 = 22 million dollars.
   Import in 1991 = 45 million dollars.
   Increase percent = $\left(\dfrac{23}{22} \times 100\right)$ % = 100 % (nearly)

4. (a) : (Import + Export) in 1994 = (11 + 11) million dollars
                                    = 22 million dollars
                                    = Import in 1990.

5. (a) : Export in 1992 = 36 million dollars.
   Export in 1993 = 28 million dollars.
   Decrease % = $\left(\dfrac{7}{36} \times 100\right)$ % = 20% (nearly).

6. (c) : Clearly, the rate of increase of price index was maximum during April 94 to June 94.

7. (d) : Price index was maximum in July 1994.

8. (b) : Since the graph is a straight line for the period from April 1993 to June 1993, it follows that during this period price index was same.

9. (a) : Since the graph lines for the period October - December 1993 and for the period April - June 1994 are parallel, so the increase in price index was Approximately same during these periods.

10. (d) : Price index in Jan 1993 = 335

Price index in June 1994 = 360.

Increase % $= \left(\dfrac{25}{335} \times 100 \right) \% = 7.5\%$ (Approx.)

11. (b) : Total sale (in thousands of rupees) in various years was :

1986 → $(10 + 40 + 50) = 100$; 1987 → $(20 + 30 + 40) = 90$;
1988 → $(30 + 30 + 60) = 120$; 1989 → $(20 + 40 + 50) = 110$;
1990 → $(25 + 40 + 60) = 125$; 1991 → $(30 + 50 + 70) = 150$.

∴ Sale is lowest in the year 1987.

12. (c) : In 1988, the graphs of A and B intersect at the sale point.
Thus in 1988, the sale of A and B was same.

13. (d) : In 1986, sale of brand B = 40 thousands and, sale of brand C = 10 thousands

∴ In 1986, sale of $C = \dfrac{1}{4}$ (sale of B).

14. (b) : Sale of A in 1988 = 30 thousands
Sale of B in 1990 = 60 thousands.

Required percentage $= \left(\dfrac{30}{60} \times 100 \right) \% = 50\%$.

15. (e) : Sale of C in 1989 = 40 thousands.
Sale of C in 1990 = 25 thousands.

Decrease % $= \left(\dfrac{15}{40} \times 100 \right) \% = 37.5\%$.

16. (d) : Value of each machine $= \dfrac{\text{Total value}}{\text{Number of machines}}$

$= \text{Rs.} \left(\dfrac{80000000}{15000} \right)$

$= \text{Rs. } 5\dfrac{1}{3}$ thousands.

17. (b) : Production in 1991 = 25000
Production in 1992 = 20000

Decrease % $= \left(\dfrac{5000}{25000} \times 100 \right) \% = 20\%$.

18. (d) : Total value of machines sold in 1992 = 10 crores.
Total value of machines sold in 1994 = 16 crores
Difference in revenue = Rs. 6 crores.

19. (e) : After increasing the value by 25%, the total value of machines sold in 1993 = 125% of 10 crores = 12.5 crores.

20. (e) : Value of each machine in 1991 = Rs. $\left(\dfrac{80000000}{25000} \right)$ = Rs. 3200.

Value of each machine in 1992 = Rs. $\left(\dfrac{100000000}{20000} \right)$ = Rs. 5000.

∴ Difference in values = Rs. (5000 − 3200) = Rs. 1800.

21. (b) : It is clear from the graphs that the distance between the graphs is maximum for the year 1994.

So, difference between the income and expenditure is maximum in 1994.

22. (e) : Income in 1990 was equal to the expenditure in 1988, 1990 and 1992.

23. (a) : Expenditure in 1991 = 27.5 crores

Expenditure in 1992 = 20 crores

Decrease % = $\left(\dfrac{7.5}{27.5} \times 100\right)$ % = 27.3% = 25% (approx)

24. (a) : Income in 1990 = 20 crores

Income in 1991 = 35 crores

Increase in income = $\left(\dfrac{15}{20} \times 100\right)$ % = 75%.

25. (a) : Expenditure graph lies above income graph in the year 1989 only.

26. (d) : The highest peak of graph concerning the export value of tea is in the year 1987. So, it is maximum in 1987.

27. (b) : Export value of rice in 1986 = 20 hundred crores.

Export value of tea in 1986 = 40 hundred crores.

Difference = 2000 crores.

28. (a) : Export value of sugar in 1986 = 8000 crores.

Export value of sugar in 1987 = 5000 crores.

Decrease % = $\left(\dfrac{3000}{8000} \times 100\right)$ % = 37.5%.

29. (a) : Export value of tea in 1986 = 4000 crores

Export value of tea in 1987 = 7000 crores

Increase % = $\left(\dfrac{3000}{4000} \times 100\right)$ % = 75%.

30. (e) : Export (in Rupees hundred crores) in various years was :

1983 → (30 + 40 + 50) = 120,

1984 → (40 + 50 + 60) = 150,

1985 → (40 + 60 + 70) = 170,

1986 → (20 + 40 + 80) = 140,

1987 → (50 + 60 + 70) = 180,

1988 → (30 + 50 + 60) = 140.

So, it is minimum in 1983.

31. (e) : For company Q, we have :

In 1989, $\dfrac{I_1}{E_1} = 1.2 \Rightarrow I_1 = 1.2\,E_1$

In 1990, $\dfrac{I_2}{E_2} = 1.2 \Rightarrow I_2 = 1.2\,E_2.$

$\therefore \ I_1 + I_2 = 1.2\,(E_1 + E_2) = (1.2 \times 24) = 28.8$ crores.

32. (*b*) : The ratio of imports to exports for company Q is greater than 1 in the years 1988, 89, 90 & 91 i.e. for 4 years.

33. (*d*) : For company P, we have :

In 1990, $\dfrac{I}{E} = 1.4 \Rightarrow I = 1.4\,E = (1.4 \times 60) = 84$ crores.

34. (*d*) : Average export of company Q cannot be obtained as data is inadequate.

35. (*e*) : Export of company P will be maximum, when the ratio $\left(\dfrac{\text{Import}}{\text{Export}}\right)$ is minimum and it is clearly minimum in 1987.

SELECTED BOOKS FOR COMPETITIVE EXAMINATIONS

GENERAL KNOWLEDGE/SCIENCE/STUDIES

Mani Ram Aggarwal's

GENERAL KNOWLEDGE DIGEST AND GENERAL STUDIES

This book on General Knowledge will provide relevant and appropriate guidance to the students appearing in the various competitive examinations.

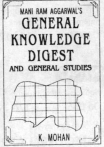

CONTENT: Abbreviations * Multiple Choice Questions * Books and Authors * History of Freedom Movement and Indian Polity * The Constitution of India * Foreign Words and Phrases in Common Use * Inventions and Discoveries * World Personalities-Who is Who ? * Science * Scientific and Geographical Phenomena * Hygiene and Physiology * Geography * Terminology * Pacts, Plans Treaties, Alliances, Conference etc. * United Nations Organization * Gandhi, Nehru and Tagore * Sports * Miscellaneous Facts * Facts about India * * International Political Scene * Model Test Papers* Current G.K.

| 60 001 | 56/e | pp.xvi+708 |

Girish Chandra

GENERAL SCIENCE
(For Competitive Examinations)

The present book will be useful to those preparing for various competitive examinations and particularly to those who have not studied science as a subject.

CONTENTS : Branches of Knowledge * The Origin of the Universe * About Calendars * Astronomy and Space Science * Biosphere * Physics * Elements and their Discoveries * Chemistry * Biology * Human Diet * Human Genetics * Micro-biology Virus and Toxicology * Human Physiology * Hygiene * Inventions and Discoveries * Laws of Science * Abbreviations of Terms * Units of Measurement * Science Quiz * Computer * Noted Men of Science * Objective Questions.

| 06 042 | 7/e 1994 | pp.vi+277 |

ENGLISH

Vinod Kumar

I.C.S. GENERAL ENGLISH

This book will prove useful to the students of Civil Services Examination and other competitive examinations.

CONTENTS : The Art and Science of Precis Writing * Comprehension * The Art of Essay Writing * Idioms and Phrases * Words often Confused * Grammar.

| 11 080 | 1/e 1987 | pp.viii+240 |

T. Saran

PRECIS WRITING & DRAFTING

This book will teach the candidates how to write precis and drafting letters, so that 'English' portion of the competitive examinations won't be tough to them.

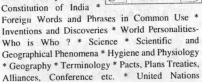

CONTENTS : PRECIS WRITING : Rules for Precis Writing * Some Hints for Precis Writing * Indexing * Solved Exercises * Exercises. DRAFTING : General Procedure * Some Set Official Phrases * Forms of Official Communications * Specimens of Official Communications * Solved Exercises * Exercises.

| 11 103 | 30/e 1995 | pp.viii+214 |

MATHEMATICS

R.S. Aggarwal

I.I.T. – J.E.E. MATHEMATICS

This book will help those students who wish to opt engineering as carrer and seek admissions to I.I.T. and other engineering colleges through entrance examinations.

CONTENTS : ALGEBRA : Determinants * Complex Numbers * Logarithms * Progressions * Binomial Theorem * Inequalities * Mathematical

1

Induction * Quadratic Equations * Equations * Surds and Indices * Permutations and Combinations * Exponential & Logarithmic Series * PROBABILITY * VECTOR ALGEBRA.

06 050   1/e 1995   pp.iv+804

R.S. Aggarwal

MATHEMATICS FOR N.D.A. & C.D.S. ENTRANCE EXAMINATIONS (Fully Solved)

This book on Mathematics is really an asset to those who plan to appear in the competitive examination conducted by N.D.A. & C.D.S.

CONTENTS : ARITHMETIC : Numbers * H.C.F. & L.C.M. * Decimal Fractions * Square Roots * Percentage * Average * Ratio & Proportion * Partnership * Profit and Loss * Chain Rule * Time &

Work * Time & Distance * Problems on Ages * Simple Interest * Compound Interest * Logarithms * Miscellaneous Exercise. **MENSURATION** : Area & Field Work * Volume and Surface Area. **ALGEBRA** . Basic Operations and Factorization * H.C.F. & L.C.M. of Polynomials * Linear Equations in Two Variables * Quadratic Equations * Rational Expressions * Surds and Indices * Set Theory. **TRIGONOMETRY**: Identities and T-Ratios * Heights and Distances. **GEOMETRY**: Lines and Angles * Polygons * Triangles * Quadrilaterals and Parallelograms * Circles * Lochi. **CO-ORDINATE GEOMETRY**: Co-ordinate Geometry. **STATISTICS** : Statistical Data (Frequency Distribution, Mean, Mode, Median and S.D.) * Data Interpretation.

06031   1/e 1995   pp. viii+672

REASONING

R.S. Aggarwal

A MODERN APPROACH TO VERBAL & NON-VERBAL REASONING

A MODERN APPROACH TO VERBAL & NON VERBAL **REASONING**

R.S. AGGARWAL

This book has been written in such a way, so that the candidates can prepare themselves for the various competitive examinations (Bank Clerical, Bank P.O., L.I.C., G.I.C., M.B.A., Assistant Grade, Excise and Income Tax, IAS, IFS, AAO, Railways, Hotel Management and others) in a comprehensive and methodical way.

CONTENTS : PART I : VERBAL REASONING * **Section I** : GENERAL MENTAL ABILITY : Analogy * Classification * Series Completion * Coding Decoding * Blood Relations * Puzzle Test * Direction Sense Test * Logical Venn Diagrams * Alphabet Test * Number Ranking & Time Sequence * Decision Making * Assertion & Reason * Situation Reaction Test * Verification of Truth of the Statements * Mathematical Operations * Inserting the Missing one. **Section II** : LOGICAL DEDUCTION : Logic * Statement Arguments * Statements and Assumption * Statements and Courses of Action * Statements and Conclusions * Deriving Conclusions from Passages * Questions and Statements. **Section III** : LATEST PAPER SCENARIO : PART II NON-VERBAL : Mirror-Images * Water-Images * Spotting out the Embeded Figure * Completion of Incomplete Pattern * Paper Folding * Paper Cutting * Analytical Reasoning * Problems on Cubes & Dice * Series * Analogy * Classification * Construction of

Squares * Dot Situation * Miscellaneous Exercise.

06 055   1/e 1994   pp.viii+720

R.S. Aggarwal

A MODERN APPROACH TO VERBAL REASONING

This book will help the students to prepare for the competitive examinations viz., Bank Clerical, Bank P.O., LIC, GIC, MBA, Assistant Grade, Excise and Income Tax, IAS, IFS, AAO, Railways, Hotel Management and others.

CONTENTS : GENERAL MENTAL ABILITY : Analogy * Classification * Series Completion * Coding Decoding * Blood Relations * Puzzle Test * Direction Sense Test * Logical Venn Diagrams * Alphabet Test * Number Ranking & Time Sequence * Decision Making * Assertion & Reason * Situation Reaction Test * Verification of Truth of the Statements * Mathematical Operations * Inserting the Missing one. **LOGICAL DEDUCTION** : Logic * Statement Arguments * Statements and Assumption * Statements and Courses of Action * Statements and Conclusions * Deriving Conclusions from Passages * Questions and Statements.

06 053   1/e 1994   pp. viii+464

R.S. Aggarwal

A MODERN APPROACH TO NON-VERBAL REASONING

CONTENTS : Mirror Images * Water Images * Spotting out the Embedded Figure * Completion of Incomplete Pattern * Paper Folding * Paper Cutting * Analytical Reasoning * Problems on Cubes & Dice * Series * Analogy * Classification * Construction of Squares * Dot-Situation * Miscellaneous Exercise.

06 054   1/e 1994   pp. viii+256